1970

Calculus and Linear Algebra

A Series of Books in Mathematics

EDITORS *R. A. Rosenbaum, G. Philip Johnson*

Calculus and
Linear Algebra

BURROWES HUNT *Reed College*

W. H. FREEMAN AND COMPANY *San Francisco and London*

Preface

Some proposed curricula for today's grade schools seem more sophisticated than yesterday's college courses for a mathematics major, which makes it difficult to define exactly the level of any textbook. This textbook, throughout its development, has been intended for the freshmen at a liberal arts college with a strongly intellectual orientation. The emphasis throughout is on concepts rather than techniques. To profit from a course based on the book a student need not be either brilliant or unusually well prepared, but he should be well motivated and able to think logically.

I have included considerably more material than can be covered adequately in a one-year course. Ignoring the introductory Chapter I, which affords an opportunity for students and instructor to get used to each other and to the text, the remaining ten chapters group themselves into three parts, not so identified in the text. The first part, Chapters II through IV, is a discussion of the real number system, including basic theory of convergence of sequences. The second part, Chapters V and VI, treats elementary analytic geometry by the methods of linear algebra. The last five chapters develop the elements of calculus, almost entirely restricted to functions of one real variable, in this order: continuity, integration, differentiation, the Fundamental Theorem, and related matters. I think that to cover any two of these parts reasonably adequately in a year one must prune the third drastically.

Given a class of students with a good background in high school algebra, who were aware that many theorems can be proved from a few algebraic axioms about numbers, one could omit all the algebraic material in Chapters II and III. This would cut the first part to the following. From Chapter II, some discussion of mathematical induction, especially as it applies to the simplest sorts of recursive definitions. From Chapter III the recursive embedding of $\mathfrak{N}$ into $\mathfrak{R}$, and some consequences of the Least Upper Bound Axiom, especially the existence of square roots of positive numbers. Most of Chapter IV, which begins the algebra of functions and covers basic theory of convergence of real sequences. (The last section of Chapter IV establishes the Cauchy Completeness of $\mathcal{R}$, but this is not used later except in the last section of the last chapter, in exercises on complex power series.)

Much of the second part can be omitted. In particular, none of the material on determinants, oriented areas, and volumes in $\mathcal{R}^2$ or $\mathcal{R}^3$, or rotations in $\mathcal{R}^3$ is used later. Also, an instructor wanting to concentrate on high school algebra and on calculus could replace chapters V and VI by the usual intuitive argument that a line in the plane should have an equation of the form $ax + by + c = 0$, and by some sort of treatment of analytic trigonometry.

Although Chapters V and VI can be deleted or cut, I don't think one can compromise with them. The basic idea is that $\mathcal{R}^1$ and $\mathcal{R}^2$ are intuitively satisfactory models of the real line and the Euclidean plane, and that if a subset of $\mathcal{R}^n$ is to be a line, or plane, it must be congruent to $\mathcal{R}^1$, or $\mathcal{R}^2$. Here a congruence is a distance-preserving mapping.

This approach immediately gives parametric equations to a line, and in particular makes it easy to prove that, if **a** is a point different from the origin, then the set of all scalar multiples of **a** is a line through **o** and **a**. It also makes a difficult theorem of the statement that two distinct points determine a unique line. Essentially the same algebraic manipulations that prove this will prove that, if S is a similarity of $\mathcal{R}^n$ into $\mathcal{R}^m$ and maps the origin in the domain to the origin in the range, then S is a linear transformation. This is the key theorem in Chapter V, and the motivation for introducing linear algebra.

In the first half of Chapter VI linear transformations in $\mathcal{R}^2$ are presented in some detail, and proper linear similarities in great detail. This of course gives the algebra of the complex field and the addition theorems for the circular functions. The second half of the chapter can be omitted.

The motivating idea for Chapter VII is that the graph of a real function f over a bounded interval is a curve *iff* it can be uniformly well approximated by polygonal arcs. This is equivalent to the uniform continuity of f on the interval. The chapter gives the principal theorems about continuity, and includes a brief discussion of curves given parametrically.

The first of the two chapters on integration consists of ad hoc treatments of several problems with the common feature that in each the answer is squeezed between lower and upper sums. Chapter IX gives a common definition of the Riemann-Darboux integral over a bounded interval, and establishes the integrability of functions that are continuous or monotone. The ostensible purpose of much of the rest of the chapter is to evaluate some integrals. The real purpose is to help the student develop a feeling for integrals. For example, I think he should know that

$$\int_0^1 \sin\,(5x + 7)\,dx = \int_7^{12} \frac{\sin t}{5}\,dt$$

because the two sets of underlying sums are identical.

The chapter on differentiation is reasonably standard, and includes a discussion of tangents to curves given parametrically. The material can be covered quickly if the students have had a course in the techniques of calculus. Otherwise it will require perhaps two more weeks.

The last chapter gives the Mean Value Theorem, the Fundamental Theorem, and some applications: integration by substitution and by parts, second-order linear equations with constant coefficients, and Taylor expansions. If one objective of a course is that the student should master the usual routine manipulations, then the chapter will need to be supplemented by some treatment, perhaps programmed, of techniques of integration, including methods for finding particular solutions of inhomogeneous linear equations.

In brief summary, I think the following remarks are true. A selected group of well-prepared freshmen could use the book for a one-year course covering a good deal of linear algebra in $\mathcal{R}^2$ and $\mathcal{R}^3$ and a good deal of elementary calculus. If the students' background includes some rough-and-ready calculus, they will be able to cover somewhat more. An ill-prepared but reasonably able class could spend most of a semester on the first part of the book; Section 9 of Chapter III covers many of the high spots of high school algebra. They could then cover a good sampling of the basic ideas of calculus during the rest of the year; or most of the book could be covered in three semesters.

In the back of the book are answers to a few selected exercises.

Acknowledgements

This book has grown in a usual way, starting in the form of lecture notes for a freshman course for which no completely suitable text seemed to exist. I owe thanks to a good many students, sometimes for specific suggestions for improvements, more often for conveying a general class reaction that a topic was or was not being presented in a satisfactory way.

Some of my colleagues have taught all or part of preliminary versions, and have made valuable comments. In particular, I want to thank John Leadley and Lloyd Williams for their advice and encouragement.

Dudley S. Hunt has read the entire manuscript in detail, corrected many errors, and suggested many clarifications. I especially want to thank her; and also Prof. G. Philip Johnson for his perceptive criticism and suggestions for improvements. It should not be necessary to add that the remaining errors and flaws are mine, not theirs.

BURROWES HUNT

Reed College
November 1966

Contents

11

The Central Theorems of Calculus and Some Applications

1
Introduction

"When I use a word," Humpty Dumpty said, in rather a scornful tone, "it means just what I choose it to mean—neither more nor less."

The object of this book is to develop some basic properties of the real number system and to illustrate their principal applications, especially those considered in calculus. The content of the book is mathematical and can be expounded adequately only in the language of mathematics. This language includes some ordinary words used in their ordinary meaning, some familiar words with special meanings, and some words peculiar to mathematics and closely related subjects. Examples of the latter are the verbs "$>$" and "$\subset$" or the nouns "$[3, 5]$" and "homomorphism."

Most people agree that it is desirable for terms basic in a certain context to have the same meaning to all concerned. Humpty Dumpty's precision is useless unless his words mean to Alice just what they mean to him. The object of this chapter is to help the reader understand just what certain words mean to mathematicians. Some of the examples used rely on the reader's familiarity with certain properties of numbers. Later chapters will be concerned with such properties stated formally as axioms or theorems. In this chapter the treatment is informal and assertions are made with no evidence given for their validity.

Here are two examples of admirably precise and concise definitions, in dictionary style:

messeoir   v.i.   N'être pas convenable.
constant   n.   A function whose range has just one element.

Each is clear to anyone who knows what the words used in the definition mean, and useless to anyone who doesn't. We shall shortly be in a position to define new words in terms of words already familiar; for the present we shall illustrate and discuss the mathematical meaning of a few basic words. [For an instructive and entertaining discussion of the impossibility of defining all words in terms of previously defined words see the first few pages of *Synge* [1].]*

§ 1. *Sets*

Webster [2nd ed.] gives 59 meanings to the noun *set*, most of them irrelevant to mathematics. The one closest to the meaning we employ says that a set is the totality of points or numbers that satisfy given conditions. Many of the sets occurring in mathematics are of this sort, but we do not want to insist that elements or members of a set *be* points or numbers. We want to allow sets of people, or fish, or any things whatsoever. Furthermore, there is no insistence on homogeneity. We can speak of a set whose members are George Washington, the Hudson River, and the number 5.

We shall make no attempt at a formal definition of *set*. If S is a set and x a "thing" (in the broadest possible sense of the word), then the statements

x is in S,

x is an element of S,

x is a member of S,

$x \in S$,

all have the same meaning, but this meaning is left undefined.

To specify a particular set we must specify what the members or elements of the set are.

Examples

1. Let P be the set of positive integers. Then 2 is in P, as are 117 and 2000, but $\frac{3}{2}$ is not in P, nor is any horse. Let $S = \{3, 7, 5\}$. [The braces are a conventional notation.] The members of S are the numbers 3, 5, and 7. Nothing else is an element of S.
2. Let $T = \{x \mid x$ is an integer larger than 17$\}$. [The arrangement of material between the braces is another conventional notation.] The elements of T are those integers that are larger than 17. The scheme is that $\{x \mid$ (statement about x)$\}$ denotes the set whose members are all those things x for which the statement is true.
3. Let $Q = \{y \mid y$ is a number and $y^2 = y\}$. A little reflection shows that $Q = \{0, 1\}$.

* This and other instances of *name* [*number*] are references to books listed in the Selected References at the end of this book.

§ 2. = *and* ⇒

These are two basic verbs with very different syntactical properties. The objects with which mathematics is concerned can seldom be seen or put on paper. One can print a numeral, but not the number it names. In this book the sentence $A = B$ will always mean that the symbols A and B denote the same thing. Since each of the symbols $2 + 3$ and $1 + 4$ denotes the same thing, the number often denoted by 5, we can write $2 + 3 = 1 + 4$.

In Example 3 we asserted that the symbols $\{y | y$ is a number and $y^2 = y\}$ and $\{0, 1\}$ denoted the same object: the set whose only members are the numbers 0 and 1. [More precisely, the numbers denoted by the symbols 0 and 1.] We also used Q as a temporary name for the same set.

The relation $=$ is *reflexive, symmetric,* and *transitive.* It is *reflexive* because, for every A which denotes a thing, $A = A$. It is *symmetric* because, if $A = B$, then $B = A$. It is *transitive* because, if $A = B$ and $B = C$, then $A = C$.

The verb ⇒ is pronounced *implies* and means something like *implies with absolute certainty.* There are several folk sayings which assert that a red sky in the evening is ground for optimism about the next day's weather. In the unlikely event that a mathematician or logician asserted that the existence of a red sky in the evening implies good weather the next day, he would be asserting that there never has been and never will be an instance of a red sky in the evening that wasn't or wouldn't be followed by good weather the next day.

The assertion "If a number is larger than 5, then its square is larger than 7" is valid. There is no number larger than 5 whose square fails to be larger than 7. We can make this look more mathematical by agreeing that the symbol $>$ is an abbreviation for *is larger than* if it appears between two symbols denoting numbers. Our assertion may then be restated as

If $x > 5$, then $x^2 > 7$.

This means exactly the same as

$$x > 5 \Rightarrow x^2 > 7,$$

which has the typical form of an implication. Let U be a temporary *universe,* the set of all things we are interested in at the moment. Let $p(x)$ and $q(x)$ be sentence forms, which become meaningful statements if x is an element of U. Each of the statements

$$p(x) \Rightarrow q(x)$$

If $p(x)$, then $q(x)$

means that there is no x in U for which $p(x)$ is true but $q(x)$ is false.

Examples

In these three examples U is the set of all nonnegative integers.

1. $x > 5 \Rightarrow 2x > 10$. If x is replaced by a nonnegative integer, both $x > 5$ and $2x > 10$ become meaningful—that is, either true or false. For instance, $1 > 5$ is false and so is $2 > 10$; $6 > 5$ is true and so is $12 > 10$.
2. If $x > 47$, then there are nonnegative integers a and b such that $x = 5a + 13b$. This statement asserts that there is no integer larger than 47 which cannot be written as $5a + 13b$ for appropriate nonnegative integers a and b. We leave it to the reader to find out why this is so.
3. $x^2 > 7 \nRightarrow x > 5$. [Read $\nRightarrow$ as *does not imply*.] This is easily proved: $3^2 > 7$ but 3 is not larger than 5.

The last example, together with the truth of $x > 5 \Rightarrow x^2 > 7$, shows that $\Rightarrow$ is not symmetric. The converse of a valid implication may not be a valid implication.

§ 3. *Ordered Pairs*

Given a set S and a set T, not necessarily different from S, we shall frequently deal with sets of *ordered pairs* (a, b), where a is an element of S and b is an element of T. The word *ordered* is intended to suggest that it may matter which element is a and which is b—that (a, b) may be different from (b, a). We can enforce this by the following definition.

> **Definition 1.1.** Let (a, b) and (c, d) be ordered pairs. Then $(a, b) = (c, d)$ iff* $a = c$ and $b = d$.

Thus $(3, 5 + 7) = (1 + 2, 12)$ because $3 = 1 + 2$ and $5 + 7 = 12$. But $(3, 2) \neq (2, 3)$ because $3 \neq 2$. It is clear that $(a, b) = (b, a)$ if and only if $a = b$. For example, $(2, 2) = (2, 2)$.

§ 4. *Subsets*

Let S be the set of positive integers. Two familiar subsets are E, the set of all even positive integers, and Q, the set of all odd positive integers. Another is the set of all primes, say $P = \{2, 3, 5, 7, 11, 13, \ldots\}$.

A less familiar subset is the set of all *perfect* numbers. The Greeks noticed that the proper divisors of 6 are 1, 2, and 3, and $6 = 1 + 2 + 3$. Similarly, $28 = 1 + 2 + 4 + 7 + 14$; 28 is the sum of all its proper divisors. The next number with this property of *perfection* is 496.

Let V be the set of all odd perfect numbers. This is a well-defined set. A thing is a member of V if and only if it is a positive integer, odd, and

---

* The abbreviation *iff* will be used throughout for the phrase *if and only if*.

perfect. Given a positive integer, we can readily find out whether it is odd; with enough time and effort we can find all its proper divisors and add them up to discover whether the number is perfect. Not much is known about this set V. In particular, it is not known whether there are any odd perfect numbers. Thus V may, or may not, be the *empty set* or *null set*, usually symbolized as $\varnothing$. The point of this example is that we want V to be a subset of the set of positive integers, whether or not V is empty.

Definition 1.2 [*Subset*]. If S and T are sets, then S is a *subset* of T iff

$$x \in S \Rightarrow x \in T.$$

We have finally achieved a concise definition! The definition says that S is a subset of T if there is no object which is in S but not in T. If S is the empty set, then there is no object in S; so the empty set is a subset of every set.

If T is any set, then there is no object which is in T but not in T, so T is a subset of T. Our definition has settled the only two questions left in doubt by a commonsense interpretation of *sub*. It also lets us settle the question of equality.

Definition 1.3 [*Equality of Sets*]. If S and T are sets, then $S = T$ iff S is a subset of T and T is a subset of S.

Question: Does $\{2, 3, 7\} = \{7, 3, 2\}$?

§ 5. *Unions and Intersections*

If A and B are sets, their *union*, $A \cup B$, is defined to be the set S such that x is in S iff x is in A or in B or both.

Their *intersection*, $A \cap B$, is the set T such that x is in T iff x is in A and also in B.

Examples

1. If $A = \{2, 3, 4, 5\}$ and $B = \{2, 4, 6, 8\}$, then
   $$A \cup B = \{2, 3, 4, 5, 6, 8\}, \quad A \cap B = \{2, 4\}.$$
2. If A is any set, then $A \cup A = A \cap A = A$.
3. If A is any set, then the union of A and the empty set is A, and the intersection of A and the empty set is the empty set.

§ 6. *Functions*

This topic has an interesting history. Mathematicians have been vitally concerned with functions since the 17th century. During the 18th century there arose a long-lasting dispute, not settled until well into the 19th century, about the nature of functions. This was not a quibble over terms, but a real substantive disagreement over whether certain functionlike things were or were not functions.

In about 1840 the German mathematician Dirichlet gave a definition that soon gained universal acceptance. Curiously enough, his definition did not say what a function *is*, but merely what a function *does*. We shall eventually complete the sentence "A function is . . ." in a satisfactory way— discovered rather recently—but experience shows that it is much more important to know what a function does than what it is. The substance of Dirichlet's definition is as follows.

Definition 1.4. Let D be a set. A function whose domain is D assigns to each element of D a unique element in some set R.

Examples

The following will illustrate the meaning of *function, domain, range*.

1. On some January 15 let D be the set of all living people who were not born in any January. It seems reasonable to assume that each person in D has an age in years which is unambiguously some integer. Under this assumption there is a function we might call *age* which assigns to each member of D an integer.

2. The function of Example 1 induces another function whose domain is the set of nonnegative integers. To each nonnegative integer n, assign the set of people in D whose age is n. Thus to each nonnegative integer we have assigned a subset of D.

3. Consider a classroom with some students, properly seated in chairs. Let D be the set of students and R the set of all chairs in the room. There is a function, say C, which assigns to each student the chair he is sitting in. The domain of C is the set D. The range of C is the set of chairs that are actually occupied. Thus the range of C is a subset of R.

4. Let D be the set of positive integers. Each positive integer x has a unique square x^2. There is a function, say S, mapping x to x^2. One partial picture of the function S is

   $1 \longrightarrow 1$
   $2 \longrightarrow 4$
   $3 \longrightarrow 9$
   $4 \longrightarrow 16$
   $\cdots$

5. For each positive integer n, let $f(n)$ be the set of all positive divisors of n. Thus

   $f(1) = \{1\}$
   $f(2) = \{1, 2\}$
   $f(3) = \{1, 3\}$
   $f(4) = \{1, 2, 4\}$

$f(5) = \{1, 5\}$
$f(6) = \{1, 2, 3, 6\}$
. . .

This function f assigns to each positive integer a set of positive integers.

6. Let $D = \{(1, 1), (1, 2), (2, 1), (2, 2)\}$, and let F be the function

(1, 1) $\longrightarrow$ 1
(1, 2) $\longrightarrow$ 1
(2, 1) $\longrightarrow$ 2
(2, 2) $\longrightarrow$ 4

Then F is a function whose domain is D and whose range is $\{1, 2, 4\}$.

7. If $D = \{0, 1\}$ and $R = \{5, 7\}$, there are exactly four functions whose domain is D and whose range is a subset of R:

F_1	F_2	F_3	F_4
0 $\longrightarrow$ 5	0 $\longrightarrow$ 5	0 $\longrightarrow$ 7	0 $\longrightarrow$ 7
1 $\longrightarrow$ 5	1 $\longrightarrow$ 7	1 $\longrightarrow$ 5	1 $\longrightarrow$ 7

Two of these functions, F_2 and F_3, are one-to-one correspondences of D to R; the others are two-to-one mappings of D into R.

8. The diagram below does not define a function.

It does not assign to 1 a unique image in $\{4, 5\}$. The diagram below does define a function.

9. Let C be the set of all circles and S the set of all spheres. If a circle is rotated around one of its diameters it generates a sphere—the same sphere no matter which diameter is used. Thus there is a function which assigns to each circle a unique sphere. The range of the function is S because any sphere can be generated by rotating one of its equators.

To define a function F we must specify the domain of F, say D, and, for each x in D, the *image* F assigns to x. It is usual to denote the thing F assigns to x by $F(x)$. The range of F is the set of all images $F(x)$.

As one more example we define a function G as follows. The domain of G is the set of positive integers. If n is a positive integer and odd, $G(n) = n^2$; if n is a positive integer and even, $G(n) = n/2$. Thus $G(7) = 49$, $G(20) = 10$.

However, G is not a one-to-one correspondence of its domain to its range because $G(7) = 49$ and also $G(98) = 49$. The range of G is the set of all positive integers, because if n is any positive integer, then $2n$ is in the domain of G and $G(2n) = n$.

In the preceding Example 8 there is a diagram of a function, say H, such that $H(1) = 5$, $H(2) = 4$, and $H(3) = 5$. This tells us all there is to be known about the function H. The domain of H is $\{1, 2, 3\}$, and the range of H is $\{4, 5\}$. We also know what $H(x)$ is for each x in the domain of H.

We now ask a question which is perhaps unnecessary, but interesting. What *is* H? A first answer might be "H is the function described above." A second answer, the currently usual one, is

$$H = \{(1, 5), (2, 4), (3, 5)\}.$$

This exhibits H as a thing, a set of ordered pairs, which contains all the relevant information.

> **Definition 1.5** [*Function*].   A *function* is any set of ordered pairs such that no two different pairs have the same first element. Stated perhaps more clearly, if pairs (a, b) and (c, d) are in a function and $a = c$, then $b = d$.

If F is a function, then $F(a) = b$ means that the pair (a, b) is in F. The requirement that "if also (c, d) is in F and $c = a$, then $d = b$" can be stated as "if $a = c$, then $F(a) = F(c)$." This makes sure that F assigns a unique image to each element of its domain.

> **Definition 1.6** [*Domain and Range*].   Let F be a function, a set of ordered pairs such that no two different pairs have the same first element. The **domain** of F is the set of all first elements of pairs in F. The **range** of F is the set of all second elements of pairs in F.

Remark: The nouns *map* and *mapping* are synonyms for *function*. The participle *mapping* is also used, as in "a function *mapping* each integer to its square."

> **Definition 1.7** [*One-to-one Correspondence*].   Let F be a function and F^* be the set obtained from F by reversing all the pairs in F; that is,
>
> $$F^* = \{(a, b) \mid (b, a) \text{ is in } F\}.$$
>
> Then F is a **one-to-one correspondence** of its domain to its range iff F^* is a function.

Examples

1. Let $F = \{(1, 2), (2, 3), (3, 2)\}$ and $F^* = \{(2, 1), (3, 2), (2, 3)\}$; F^* is not a function because $(2, 1)$ and $(2, 3)$ are in F^* and $1 \neq 3$. So F is not a one-to-one correspondence of $\{1, 2, 3\}$ to $\{2, 3\}$.

2. Let F be the function mapping each positive integer n to $n + 1$:

$$F = \{(n, n + 1) \mid n \text{ is a positive integer}\}.$$

The domain of F is the set of all positive integers. The range of F is the set of all positive integers except 1.

$$F^* = \{(n + 1, n) \mid n \text{ is a positive integer}\}.$$

If the pairs $(a + 1, a)$ and $(b + 1, b)$ are in F^* and $a + 1 = b + 1$, then $a = b$. So F^* is a function and F is a one-to-one correspondence of $\{1, 2, 3, 4, \ldots\}$ to $\{2, 3, 4, \ldots\}$.

Remarks: If F is a function and F^* as defined above is also a function, then F^* is called the *inverse* of F. If x is in the domain of F and $F(x) = y$, then $F^*(y) = x$: the mapping F followed by the mapping F^* maps each object in the domain of F onto itself.

The criterion for a function F to be a one-to-one correspondence can be expressed directly in terms of F. By Definition 1.5, F^* is a function iff no two different pairs in F^* have the same first element. Since the pairs in F^* are just the reverses of the pairs in F, the criterion becomes: no two different pairs in F have the same second element. Equivalently, *a function F is a one-to-one correspondence of its domain to its range iff*

$$F(x) = F(y) \Rightarrow x = y.$$

We apply the criterion in this form to the function F in the preceding Example 2. If a and b are positive integers, then

$$F(a) = F(b) \Rightarrow a + 1 = b + 1 \Rightarrow a = b.$$

Therefore F is a one-to-one correspondence.

§ 7. *Operations*

The most familiar operations [in the mathematical sense] are addition, subtraction, multiplication, and division. Given a pair of numbers, they have a sum and a product. Depending on what sort of numbers we are using, they may or may not have a difference or a quotient. Given the numbers 4 and 8 they have a sum, 12, and a product 32. Have they a quotient? Evidently this is not a clear question. Are we talking about $4 \div 8$ or $8 \div 4$?

Let us start again. Suppose that—like young children or Archimedes—we have never heard of any numbers other than positive integers. Let (a, b) be an *ordered* pair of numbers. To this pair we can assign a sum, $a + b$, and a product, ab. If a is larger than b, we can assign a difference, $a - b$. If a is a multiple of b, we can assign a quotient, $a \div b$.

If we also allow negative numbers, then we can assign to (a, b) the number $a - b$, and to (b, a) the number $b - a$. But $a - b \neq b - a$ unless $a = b$. The order is essential.

Definition 1.8. Let S be a set. An **operation in S** is a function whose domain is a set of ordered pairs of elements of S and whose range is a subset of S. If the domain of the operation is the set of *all* ordered pairs of elements of S, then S is **closed** under the operation, or the operation is an **operation on S.**

Notation: The set of positive integers is closed under both addition and multiplication. Both operations are functions, as defined above. If we call one of them S for sum and the other P for product, the usual functional notation would call for $S((3, 5)) = 8$, $P((3, 5)) = 15$, and so on. But instead, we usually write $3 + 5 = 8$ and $3 \cdot 5 = 15$. It may be partly habit, but the usual notation looks better. Certainly $(3 + 5) + 7 = 15$ looks simpler than $S((S((3, 5)), 7)) = 15$.

It is customary to abandon the usual function notation for functions which are operations. We shall use $*$ as a generic symbol for operations, not reserved for any particular operation. For the image of the pair (a, b) under the operation $*$ we write $a * b$ instead of $*((a, b))$.

Remarks: In high school the reader probably had some experience with very formal proofs, in which a justification is given for each step. For example, he might have justified going from $2 + 3 = 5$ to $(2 + 3) + 7 = 5 + 7$ by citing Euclid's axiom that if equals are added to equals the results are equal.

No such axiom appears in this book, but its content is built into the definition of an operation as a function. The axioms of the next chapter assert that the set of natural numbers is closed under the operation $+$. From $2 + 3 = 5$ follows $(2 + 3, 7) = (5, 7)$. Since $+$ is a function, it assigns the same image to $(2 + 3, 7)$ as to $(5, 7)$. In other words, $(2 + 3) + 7 = 5 + 7$ because $2 + 3 = 5$ and $+$ is an operation on the set of natural numbers.

More generally, if the set S is closed under an operation $*$ and in S we have $a = b$ and $c = d$, then $(a, c) = (b, d)$ and $*$ assigns the same image to (a, c) as to (b, d). From $a = b$ and $c = d$ it follows automatically that $a * c = b * d$ because $*$ is an operation on S.

§ 8. *Quantifiers*

Consider

    When the moon $AB = BA$

The first does not look very different from "Watch the moon!" and perhaps might seem to some foreigners to be an English sentence. There are several technical reasons why it fails to be a sentence, but its real fault is that it fails to have any meaning: it does not say anything. Although "When the moon rises" perhaps fails to meet the technical specification for a sentence, it can be meaningful in an appropriate context. For example, it could be an appropriate answer to a question as to when a trip should start.

The second has the form of a sentence but fails to be meaningful because the apparent subject and predicate have no meaning. Presumably A and B are mathematical objects of some sort and the juxtaposition is shorthand for some sort of operation. The four sentences below *are* sentences because they incorporate properly used *quantifiers*. The first two are true, the others false.

If A and B are numbers, then $AB = BA$.

There exist matrices A and B such that $AB = BA$.

For all matrices A and B, $AB = BA$.

If $AB = BA$, then A and B are numbers.

Below are several more examples of properly quantified sentences containing *dummies*. A dummy is a symbol, usually a letter of some alphabet, which has no particular permanent meaning. A statement containing dummies can be meaningful only if it incorporates, or acquires from the context, sufficient quantification to make it unambiguously meaningful.

If x is a number, there exists a number y such that $x + y = 0$.
[True.]

If x is a number, there exists a number y such that $xy = 1$.
[False: for every number y, $0y = 0 \neq 1$.]

There exists an integer n such that $n^2 = n + 1$.
[False.]

There exists an integer n such that $n(n + 1)$ is a multiple of 10.
[True: for example, $n = 10$ or 9 or -11.]

For every integer n, $n(n + 1)$ is a multiple of 10.
[False.]

Find every number x such that $x^2 = x + 1$.
[Clear.]

In the first few chapters of this book we shall try to be very careful to quantify dummies explicitly. In later chapters we shall sometimes rely partly on the context. The student should be extremely self-conscious about this point whenever he writes out a proof or the solution of an exercise. To be readable, his statements must have an unambiguous meaning, and should, furthermore, mean what he intends them to mean. For example, if he wants to convey the information that he wishes his breakfasts to consist entirely of oranges, he should not simply say "Orange, breakfast," and he should not write that he wants oranges only for breakfast nor that only he wants oranges for breakfast. The use of unquantified dummies produces gibberish with a superficial resemblance to mathematics; quantifiers that are wrong or wrongly placed may produce meaningful but wrong statements.

Exercises

1. List all subsets of $\{2, 4, 6\}$.

2. Which of the following sets are functions?
$$A = \{(5, 1), (6, 1), (7, 1)\},$$
$$B = \{(1, 5), (1, 6), (1, 7)\},$$
$$C = \{(1, 1), (2, 7), (3, 11), (4, 1)\},$$
$$D = \{(a, b) \mid a \text{ is an integer and } b = a^2 + 5\},$$
$$E = \{((1, 2), 2), ((2, 3), 6), ((3, 2), 6)\}.$$

3. For each function in Exercise 2 give its domain and range.

4. Let $D = \{0, 1, 2, 3, 4\}$ and let F be the function with domain D such that, for each x in D, $F(x) = x^2$. What is the range of F? Is F a one-to-one correspondence of D to the range of F?

5. Let $D' = \{-4, -3, -2, -1, 0, 1, 2, 3, 4\}$ and let G be the function mapping each number in D' to its square. What is the range of G? Is G a one-to-one correspondence of D' to the range of G?

6. Let $S = \{a, b\}$. An operation under which S is closed is a function assigning to each of the four pairs (a, a), (a, b), (b, a), (b, b) some image in S. For example,
$$(a, a) \longrightarrow a$$
$$(a, b) \longrightarrow b$$
$$(b, a) \longrightarrow a$$
$$(b, b) \longrightarrow b$$
defines an operation under which S is closed. List all possible operations under which S is closed.

7. If T is a set of three elements, how many operations are there under which T is closed?

8. Let P be the set of all positive integers. Define a function H with domain P as follows. To begin with, $H(1) = 3$. Second, for each positive integer n, $H(n + 1) = 2H(n)$; for example, $H(2) = H(1 + 1) = 2H(1) = 6$. Find $H(5)$.

9. Let the universe be the set of positive integers; that is, agree that symbols a and b represent positive integers. Form a sentence by connecting the left and right sides of each line below with either $\Rightarrow$ or $\nRightarrow$, whichever is appropriate.

a. $a^2 + b^2 = 13$ $(a, b) = (3, 2)$.
b. $a^2 + b^2 = 13$ $\{a, b\} = \{3, 2\}$.
c. $a^2 + b^2 = 85$ $\{a, b\} = \{9, 2\}$.
d. $a > b$ $a^2 > b^2 + 1$.
e. $(a, b) = (b, a)$ $a = b$.
f. $a + ab = 5a$ $b = 4$.

10. Make up an example of a clearly defined set such that you don't know whether or not it is the empty set.

11. Find all positive integers x and y such that $xy + 1 = 2x + 2y$.

12. Let F be the function mapping each positive integer n to $2n$; that is, $F(1) = 2$, $F(2) = 4$, $F(3) = 6$, and so on. Is F a one-to-one correspondence of the set of all positive integers to the set of all even positive integers?

13. For any two nonnegative integers a and b, let $a * b$ denote the remainder on dividing ab by $2a + 1$. For example, $3 * 5 = 1$, the remainder on dividing 15 by 7. Fill in the rest of the table below, putting $a * b$ to the right of a and under b.

*	0	1	2	3
0	0			
1				
2				
3	3			

Is $*$ an operation in $\{0, 1, 2, 3\}$? Is $*$ an operation in the set of all nonnegative integers? Find numbers a, b, and c such that $a * b = a * c$, but $b \neq c$.

14. Let $A = \{1, 2, 3, 4, 5\}$ and $B = \{3, 4, 5, 6, 7\}$, and let C be the set of all positive integers. Describe each set below.

a. $A \cap B$.

b. $A \cup B$.

c. $B \cup C$.

d. $B \cap C$.

e. $A \cap (B \cup C)$.

f. $(A \cap B) \cup (A \cap C)$.

15. If A, B, and C are any three sets, is the following statement true?
$$A \cap (B \cup C) = (A \cap B) \cup (A \cap C).$$
[*Hint:* There are two standard ways of establishing the equality of two sets. One is to assert that the equality is obvious; the second is to prove that each set is a subset of the other.]

16. Is the following statement true for any three sets A, B, C?
$$A \cup (B \cap C) = (A \cup B) \cap (A \cup C).$$

§ 9. *A Problem About Polynomials*

We begin now on an interesting topic, to which we shall return in a later chapter. Let $\Re$ be the set of all real numbers. A *polynomial over* $\Re$ is a special sort of function with domain $\Re$ and range a subset of $\Re$. First, let a be any number in $\Re$ except 0. The function P_a: $P_a(x) = a$, for all real x, is a *polynomial of degree* 0.

If a and b are any two real numbers, with $a \neq 0$, the function

$$P_{ab}: P_{ab}(x) = ax + b,$$

for all real x, is a *polynomial of degree* 1.

If a, b, and c are any three real numbers, with $a \neq 0$, then the function

$$P_{abc}: P_{abc}(x) = ax^2 + bx + c,$$

for all real x, is a *polynomial of degree* 2.

Polynomials of higher degree are defined similarly, but 2 is the largest degree we need for the time being. The numbers a; a, b; a, b, c above are the *coefficients* of the displayed polynomials.

Now consider the polynomial P of degree 2, defined by: for all x in $\Re$, $P(x) = \frac{1}{2}x^2 + \frac{3}{2}x + 1$. Then P [which we should call $P_{1/2,3/2,1}$] has the interesting property that, even though the coefficients are not all integers, $P(x)$ is an integer for every integer x. For example,

$P(0) = 1,$

$P(1) = \frac{1}{2} + \frac{3}{2} + 1 = 3,$

$P(2) = \frac{4}{2} + 3 + 1 = 6.$

A separate consideration of $P(x)$ for x an odd integer and x an even integer makes our assertion quite plausible.

We would now like to make two *claims*. Each is actually a theorem, but in the context of our informal assumption of some familiarity with numbers we can't give any formal proofs. We shall simply try to establish the plausibility of the claims.

Claim 1. If P is a polynomial of degree 1 and $P(0)$ and $P(1)$ are integers, then the coefficients of P are integers, and consequently, for every integer x, $P(x)$ is an integer.

Claim 2. If P is a polynomial of degree 2 and $P(0)$, $P(1)$, and $P(2)$ are integers, then $P(x)$ is an integer for every integer x.

The argument for the first claim is quite straightforward. Let $P(x) = ax + b$ for all x. Then $P(0) = b$ and $P(1) = a + b$. If $P(0)$ and $P(1)$ are integers, then b is an integer and $a + b$ is an integer, which makes a an integer.

Our argument for the second claim is not straightforward. Let the polynomial P of degree 2 have coefficients $a \neq 0$, b, and c. For all x,

$P(x) = ax^2 + bx + c.$

Also, for all x,

$$P(x + 1) = a(x + 1)^2 + b(x + 1) + c$$
$$= ax^2 + 2ax + a + bx + b + c.$$

By subtraction we have, for all x,

$P(x + 1) - P(x) = 2ax + a + b.$

Let Q be the function defined by

for all real x, $Q(x) = 2ax + a + b.$

Since $2a \neq 0$, Q is a polynomial of degree 1. Therefore, for all x,

(1) $P(x + 1) - P(x) = Q(x),$

where Q is a polynomial of degree 1.

Now assume that $P(0)$, $P(1)$, and $P(2)$ are integers. Putting $x = 0$ in (1) above gives

$P(1) - P(0) = Q(0),$

and putting $x = 1$ in (1) gives

$$P(2) - P(1) = Q(1).$$

Since the difference of two integers is an integer, both $Q(0)$ and $Q(1)$ are integers. Therefore, by Claim 1, $Q(x)$ is an integer for every integer x. Now rewrite Equation (1) as

(2)   for all x, $P(x + 1) = P(x) + Q(x)$.

By hypothesis, $P(2)$ is an integer, and $Q(2)$ is an integer because 2 is an integer. Statement (2) now says that $P(3) = P(2) + Q(2)$ is an integer.

Now, since $P(3)$ is an integer by the paragraph above, and $Q(3)$ is an integer, from (2) we deduce that $P(4)$ is an integer. From this deduction, and knowing that $Q(4)$ is an integer, we can now use (2) to deduce that

$$P(5) = P(4) + Q(4) \text{ and is an integer.}$$

As an exercise, deduce that $P(7)$ is an integer. Deduce that $P(-1)$ and $P(-2)$ are integers.

2
The Natural Numbers

Informally the natural numbers are either the numbers 1, 2, 3, . . . or the numbers 0, 1, 2, 3, ... Some texts include 0, some do not. The Greeks were not familiar with 0, and there is a historical reason for excluding it. On the other hand, 0, like each of the positive natural numbers, is a possible reasonable answer to questions such as "How many fish did you catch?" "How many stars are visible?" "How many electrons are there in the solar system?"

There are also both technical and esthetic arguments for each choice. Without going into these arguments we shall in this book regard 0 as a natural number. Thus we insist from the beginning that the symbol 0 denotes a number and therefore does not denote nothing.

This chapter presents the natural number system—the set of natural numbers along with the operations addition and multiplication—as an example of a deductive system. This means that we shall state some axioms, or postulates, and examine some of their logical consequences. On the formal level, *natural numbers* is an undefined term, and at the outset we know nothing about them except what the axioms say.

The student should read the chapter on two levels. Informally he should make sure that the axioms and theorems agree with his intuitions about the familiar natural numbers. On the formal level he should check carefully whether the theorems really are logical consequences of axioms, definitions, and previous theorems. The theorems will not be very astounding. For example, one of them says that there is no natural number between 0 and 1. Such a theorem should be regarded this way: it is certainly [on the informal level] true; therefore, if it can't be formally proved from our axioms, we have not stated enough axioms. The fact that it can be proved is a bit of evidence that perhaps we have enough axioms.

As a matter of fact we have more axioms than are necessary. Later sections of the chapter indicate rather briefly how the number of axioms can be considerably reduced. These sections are not used in the rest of the book, but any reader who has or acquires a taste for mathematical induction should find them interesting.

§ 1. *Some Algebraic Axioms*

The axioms given just below are not quite enough to let us deduce all the properties we want. Later we shall state a few more. Our final set of axioms will not by any means be the only reasonable or logical choice; one has considerable freedom in deciding what to assume and what to prove. The axioms in this section are given because they express basic properties of a great many algebraic systems. Later axioms will be more restrictive.

Axiom 2.1 [*Existence*]. We assume the existence of a set $\mathfrak{N}$ having the properties postulated below. Furthermore, we assume there are some a and b in $\mathfrak{N}$ with $a \neq b$.

Note: We are ruling out a set with only one element. If, however, the reader considers a set containing just one element, say q, and defines addition and multiplication by $q + q = q$ and $qq = q$, he will see that all the axioms below are true in the system.

Addition Axioms

Axiom 2.2. The set $\mathfrak{N}$ is closed under an operation called addition. To each ordered pair (a, b) of elements of $\mathfrak{N}$ corresponds a unique element of $\mathfrak{N}$ denoted by $a + b$.

Axiom 2.3. Addition is *associative*. For all a, b, and c in $\mathfrak{N}$,

$$a + (b + c) = (a + b) + c.$$

Axiom 2.4. Addition is *commutative*. For all a and b in $\mathfrak{N}$,

$$a + b = b + a.$$

Axiom 2.5. There is an *additive identity* called 0 in $\mathfrak{N}$. For all a in $\mathfrak{N}$,

$$a + 0 = 0 + a = a.$$

Axiom 2.6 [*Cancellation Law for Addition*]. If a, b, and c are in $\mathfrak{N}$ and $a + b = a + c$, then $b = c$.

Multiplication Axioms

Axiom 2.7. The set $\mathfrak{N}$ is closed under an operation called multiplication. To each ordered pair (a, b) of elements of $\mathfrak{N}$ corresponds a unique element of $\mathfrak{N}$ called $a \cdot b$ [or simply ab].

Axiom 2.8. Multiplication is *associative*. For all a, b, and c in $\mathfrak{N}$,

$$a(bc) = (ab)c.$$

Axiom 2.9. Multiplication is *commutative*. For all a and b in $\mathfrak{N}$,

$$ab = ba.$$

Axiom 2.10. There is a *multiplicative identity* called 1 in $\mathfrak{N}$. For all a in $\mathfrak{N}$,

$$a1 = 1a = a.$$

Axiom 2.11 [*Cancellation Law for Multiplication*]. If a, b, and c are in $\mathfrak{N}$, and $ab = ac$, and $a \neq 0$, then $b = c$.

Axiom 2.12 Multiplication is *distributive over addition*. For all a, b, and c in $\mathfrak{N}$,

$$a(b + c) = ab + ac.$$

This completes our strictly algebraic axioms. We now give a sampling of their logical consequences.

Theorem 2.1. For all a in $\mathfrak{N}$, $a0 = 0 = 0a$.

PROOF: Let a be in $\mathfrak{N}$. Since $\mathfrak{N}$ is closed under multiplication, $a0$ is in $\mathfrak{N}$. By the distributive law,

$$a0 + a0 = a(0 + 0),$$

and, since $0 + 0 = 0$ by Axiom 2.5,

$$a0 + a0 = a0,$$

and also by Axiom 2.5,

$$a0 + a0 = a0 + 0.$$

The last three steps give

$$a0 + a0 = a0 + 0.$$

By the cancellation law for addition,

$$a0 = 0,$$

and by the commutative law for multiplication, also

$$0a = 0. \qquad \blacksquare$$

Theorem 2.2. $1 \neq 0$.

PROOF: The proof will consist in showing that the assumption that $1 = 0$ leads to a contradiction of Axiom 2.1. From the postulate there are a and b in $\mathfrak{N}$ with $a \neq b$. If

$$1 = 0,$$

then, by Theorem 2.1,

$$1a = 0a = 0,$$

and, also by Theorem 2.1,

$$1b = 0b = 0.$$

But as 1 is the multiplicative identity, $1a = a$ and $1b = b$. So the assumption that $1 = 0$ leads to $a = 0$ and $b = 0$, contradicting $a \neq b$. ∎

Exercises

1. Prove that if a and b are in $\mathfrak{N}$ and $a + b = a$, then $b = 0$. [*Hint:* $a = a + 0$.]
2. Prove that if a and b are in $\mathfrak{N}$ and $ab = a$, then either $a = 0$ or $b = 1$.
3. Prove that if a and b are in $\mathfrak{N}$ and $ab = 0$, then either $a = 0$ or $b = 0$ or both. [*Hint:* If $ab = 0$, then, from Theorem 2.1, $ab = a0$, and if $a \neq 0$, what results?]
4. Prove that for all a, b, and c in $\mathfrak{N}$, $(b + c)a = ba + ca$. [*Hint:* Start by observing that if b and c are in $\mathfrak{N}$, then, by the closure under addition, $b + c$ is in $\mathfrak{N}$.]
5. Prove that for all a, b, c, and d in $\mathfrak{N}$,
   $$(a + b) + (c + d) = (a + d) + (b + c).$$
6. Let $S = \{a, b, c\}$ and define "addition" and "multiplication" in S by the tables below. Which of our axioms are true in the system $(S; +, \cdot)$?

+	a	b	c
a	a	b	c
b	b	c	a
c	c	a	b

·	a	b	c
a	a	a	a
b	a	b	c
c	a	c	b

7. With the definitions $2 = 1 + 1$, $3 = 2 + 1$, $4 = 3 + 1$, and $5 = 4 + 1$, prove that $2 + 3 = 5$.
8. For a, b, and c in $\mathfrak{N}$, investigate the equality of all expressions of the type $a + (b + c)$, $(b + c) + a$, $(c + a) + b$, and so on.
9. For a and b in $\mathfrak{N}$, prove that if the equation $a + x = b$ has any solution, it has only one. [*Hint:* If $a + x_1 = b$ and $a + x_2 = b$, then $a + x_1 = a + x_2$.]
10. For a and b in $\mathfrak{N}$ and $a \neq 0$, prove that if the equation $ax = b$ has any solution, it has only one.

§ 2. *Special Axioms*

Experience shows that the axioms of the previous section apply to many algebraic systems. In this section we give two axioms that do not apply to some of these systems; also, they will enable us to define a *linear ordering* of $\mathfrak{N}$.

Axiom 2.13. If a and b are in $\mathfrak{N}$ and $a + b = 0$, then $a = 0$ and $b = 0$.

Axiom 2.14.   If a and b are in $\mathfrak{N}$ and $a \neq b$, then either there is some p in $\mathfrak{N}$ such that $a + p = b$, or else there is some q in $\mathfrak{N}$ such that $b + q = a$.

Note on Axiom 2.14: The p and q of Axiom 2.14 are $\neq 0$, since $a \neq b$. We cannot have both $a + p = b$ and $b + q = a$, since this gives

$$(a + p) + q = b + q = a,$$

or

$$a + (p + q) = a.$$

From the last equation and Exercise 1 above follows $p + q = 0$. But Axiom 2.13 excludes this result unless $p = q = 0$, which contradicts the hypothesis $a \neq b$.

Definition 2.1.   Let a and b be in $\mathfrak{N}$. We define $a < b$ [read a *is less than* b] to mean *There is some* p *in* $\mathfrak{N}$, $p \neq 0$, *such that* $a + p = b$. We also define $b > a$ [read b *is greater than* a] to mean $a < b$.

Note that whether we write $a < b$ or $b > a$, the pointed end of $<$ or $>$ points at the smaller number. The statement $a \leq b$ is true iff either $a < b$ or $a = b$.

Theorem 2.3.   If a is in $\mathfrak{N}$ and $a \neq 0$, then $a > 0$.

PROOF:

$$a = 0 + a \quad \text{and} \quad a \neq 0. \qquad \blacksquare$$

Lemma for Theorem 2.4.   If a and b are in $\mathfrak{N}$ and either $a < b$ or $b < a$, then $a \neq b$.

PROOF: If $a < b$, then $b = a + p$, where $p \neq 0$. By Exercise 1 above, $b \neq a$. Similarly, if $b < a$, then $a = b + q$ for $q \neq 0$, and $b \neq a$. $\blacksquare$

[The German word for "lemma" is "Hilfsatz," which literally means "helptheorem." There are some famous lemmas in the literature, each having many applications and helping to establish many theorems. The lemma above is simply one part of the proof of Theorem 2.4 below. We shall occasionally make the structure of a proof clearer by breaking it up into several parts, each called a lemma.]

Theorem 2.4 [*The Trichotomy Law*].   For a and b in $\mathfrak{N}$, one and only one of the following statements holds:

$$a = b, \qquad a < b, \qquad a > b.$$

PROOF: The proof consists of Axiom 2.14, the Lemma for Theorem 2.4, and the Note on Axiom 2.14, which says that we can't have both $a + p = b$ and $b + q = a$ if $a \neq b$. $\blacksquare$

Theorem 2.5 [*Transitivity of* <]. If a, b, and c are in $\mathfrak{N}$ and $a < b$ and $b < c$, then $a < c$.

PROOF: Left to reader.

Because < has the properties asserted by Theorems 2.4 and 2.5, it is a *linear order relation* in $\mathfrak{N}$.

Theorem 2.3 and the Lemma for Theorem 2.4 say that in the natural number system the statements $a \neq 0$ and $a > 0$ are equivalent. In statements about inequalities, if we need either we shall generally choose $a > 0$.

As an informal exercise prove the following theorems.

Theorem 2.6. If a, b, and c are in $\mathfrak{N}$ and $a < b$, then $a + c < b + c$. [*Hint:* Use the definition of <.]

Theorem 2.7. If a, b, and c are in $\mathfrak{N}$ and $a + c < b + c$, then $a < b$.

Theorem 2.8. If a, b, and c are in $\mathfrak{N}$, with $a > 0$ and $b < c$, then $ab < ac$.

Theorem 2.9. If a, b, c are in $\mathfrak{N}$ and $ab < ac$, then $b < c$.

Theorem 2.10. $0 < 1$.

Theorem 2.11. If a is in $\mathfrak{N}$ and $a > 1$, then $a^2 > a$. [Of course, a^2 means aa.]

Theorem 2.12. If a is in $\mathfrak{N}$ and $0 < a < 1$ [that is, $0 < a$ and also $a < 1$], then $0 < a^2 < a$.

Theorem 2.12 is interesting. On the informal level we are thinking of $\mathfrak{N}$ as the set of natural numbers and we know that there is no natural number between 0 and 1. From this point of view Theorem 2.12 seems rather silly. However, all our postulates so far stated are also true of the set of all nonnegative real numbers or all nonnegative rational numbers. And there are many rational numbers between the rational number 0 and the rational number 1.

§ 3. *A Final Axiom*

Axiom 2.15 [*The Least Integer Principle*]. Every nonempty subset of $\mathfrak{N}$ has a smallest member. That is, if S is a subset of $\mathfrak{N}$ having at least one number in it, then there is some s_0 in S with the property that if s is in S, then either $s = s_0$ or $s > s_0$.

We shall see that this axiom, together with those we have already stated, will let us prove the rest of what we want to prove about the natural number system. The following five theorems seem in accord with our basic intuitions about the natural numbers.

Theorem 2.13.   There is no n in $\mathfrak{N}$ with $0 < n < 1$.

PROOF: Let S be the set of all natural numbers between 0 and 1. By the least integer principle either S is empty or S has a smallest member. By Theorem 2.12, if a is any member of S, then a^2 is a smaller member of S. Thus S can't have a smallest member, and must be empty.   ∎

Theorem 2.14.   If n is in $\mathfrak{N}$, there is no x in $\mathfrak{N}$ with $n < x < n + 1$.

PROOF: If $n < x$, then there is some $p \neq 0$ in $\mathfrak{N}$ such that $x = n + p$. Then the statement $n < x < n + 1$ can be replaced by $n + 0 < n + p < n + 1$. Theorem 2.7 gives $0 < p$ and $p < 1$, which is impossible by Theorem 2.13.   ∎

Theorem 2.15.   If n is in $\mathfrak{N}$ and $n \neq 0$, then there is one and only one k in $\mathfrak{N}$ such that $n = k + 1$.

PROOF: First, $1 = 1 + 0$. Second, if $n \neq 0$ and $n \neq 1$, then by Theorem 2.13, $n > 1$. By definition of $>$, there is some k in $\mathfrak{N}$ such that $n = 1 + k = k + 1$. Finally, if $n = k + 1$ and $n = m + 1$, then

$$k + 1 = m + 1,$$

and, by the cancellation law,

$$k = m.   \quad ∎$$

Definition 2.2.   If n is in $\mathfrak{N}$ and $n \neq 0$, let $n - 1$ denote the unique number in $\mathfrak{N}$ such that $n = n - 1 + 1$.

Theorem 2.16.   If M is a subset of $\mathfrak{N}$ such that (a) 0 is in M, and (b) for each n in M, also $n + 1$ is in M, then $M = \mathfrak{N}$.

PROOF: Theorem 2.16 will be proved in proving Theorem 2.17.

Theorem 2.17.   If M is a subset of $\mathfrak{N}$ such that (a) some number s is in M, and (b) for each n in M, also $n + 1$ is in M, then s and every natural number $> s$ are in M.

Remark: To begin with, let us say that a subset of $\mathfrak{N}$, say S, is an *inductive set* in case x in $S \Rightarrow x + 1$ in S.

Theorem 2.16 says that if M is an inductive set containing 0, then M is the set of all natural numbers. Theorem 2.17 says that if an inductive set contains some number s, then it also contains all larger numbers. Clearly Theorem 2.16 is a special case of Theorem 2.17. Either may be called the *principle of mathematical induction* or the *principle of finite induction*.

Before proving Theorem 2.17 we illustrate its compelling plausibility. Suppose that S is an inductive set and 3 is in S. Then $3 + 1$ must be in S, so 4 is in S. But if 4 is in S, then $4 + 1$ has to be in S, and so 5 is in S. From this, and the fact that S is an inductive set, 6 is in S. Next, 7 has to be in S. In three more steps we get 10 in S.

Can there be any natural numbers larger than 3 but not in S? Intuition says not. The least integer principle also says not. To show this, let E be the set of natural numbers which are larger than 3 but not in S. If E is not empty, E has a smallest member, say e. From our observations above, $e > 7$. By Theorem 2.15 there is some k in $\mathfrak{N}$ such that $e = k + 1$. But $k < e$, and e is the *smallest* member of E, so k is not in E. Also, $k > 3$ (since $k \geq 7$), so k must be in S. But then $k + 1 = e$ has to be in S, as S is an inductive set. Assuming E to be nonempty leads to a contradiction: some number e is both in S and not in S. Thus E must be empty and every number > 3 in S.

This example contains all the essentials of a proof of Theorems 2.17 and 2.16 based on the least integer principle. Before giving a formal proof we make two remarks.

1. The statement "$\mathfrak{N}$ is *well-ordered* by $<$" means that every nonempty subset of $\mathfrak{N}$ has a least element. That is, to say that $\mathfrak{N}$ is well-ordered by $<$ is another way of asserting the least integer principle.

2. We could take Theorem 2.16 as an axiom and deduce the least integer principle. This is done in the last section of the chapter.

PROOF OF THEOREM 2.17: Let M be an inductive set containing the number s. For any k in $\mathfrak{N}$, either k and $k + 1$ are both in M or else neither is in M. This follows from hypothesis (b), that M is an inductive set: if k is in M, so is $k + 1$; if $k + 1$ is not in M, neither is k, because if k were in M, so would $k + 1$.

Let E be the set of numbers x such that $x > s$ but x is not in M. If E is not empty, let e be the smallest member of E. Then $e > s$, so $e \neq 0$, and there is a natural number $e - 1$.

Since s is in M and M is inductive, $s + 1$ is in M, and $e \neq s + 1$. From $e - 1 \neq s$ and $e > s$ follows $e - 1 > s$.

We now have a contradiction. Because $e - 1$ is less than the smallest member of E, $e - 1$ is not in E. So, as $e - 1 > s$, $e - 1$ is in M. But then e has to be in M, contradicting the supposition that e is in E.

Conclusion: E is empty and Theorem 2.17 is proved. ∎

§ 4. *Applications of Theorem 2.17*

It is intuitively clear that every alternate natural number is a multiple of 2, and hence that the product of two consecutive numbers is always a multiple of 2. We shall give a formal statement and proof as an example of a typical argument based on mathematical induction.

Theorem 2.18. For every n in $\mathfrak{N}$, $n(n + 1)$ is a multiple of 2.

PROOF: Let M be the set of those natural numbers n for which it is true that $n(n + 1)$ is a multiple of 2.

1. Since $0 \cdot 1 = 0 = 0 \cdot 2$, 0 is in M.
2. Let n be in M. Then there is a natural number m such that
$$n(n + 1) = 2m.$$

We now have

$$
\begin{aligned}
(n + 1)(n + 2) &= (n + 1)n + (n + 1)2 \\
&= n(n + 1) + 2(n + 1) \\
&= 2m + 2(n + 1) \\
&= 2(m + (n + 1)).
\end{aligned}
$$

We have shown that 0 is in M and that if some n is in M, then so is $n + 1$. By Theorem 2.17, 0 and every natural number > 0 is in M [or, by Theorem 2.16, $M = \mathfrak{N}$]. This shows that every natural number is in M, and proves the theorem. ∎

Remarks: In connection with this proof we can formulate three questions, each containing "$n(n + 1)$ is a multiple of 2."

Question 1. How do we know there are natural numbers n such that $n(n + 1)$ is a multiple of 2? *Answer:* 0 is such a number; so are 1, 2, and 3.

Question 2. How do we prove that if n is a natural number and $n(n + 1)$ is a multiple of 2, then also $(n + 1)((n + 1) + 1)$ is a multiple of 2? *Answer:* As shown above, this follows from our axioms in several steps. [How do you know that $n(n + 1)$ is a multiple of 2? This contains an unquantified dummy and isn't a true question. So there isn't any answer.]

Question 3. How do you know that for every natural number n, $n(n + 1)$ is a multiple of 2? *Answer:* We have shown that the set of n with this property is an inductive subset of $\mathfrak{N}$ containing 0, so by the principle of mathematical induction every natural number has the property.

As an exercise, show that if some natural number k has the property that $k(k + 1)(k + 2)$ is a multiple of 6, then also $(k + 1)(k + 2)(k + 3)$ is a multiple of 6.

The Sum of the First n Squares

This is an example of a *recursion formula* for a function from $\mathfrak{N}$ to $\mathfrak{N}$. Assume that there is a function S_2 such that (a) $S_2(1) = 1^2$, and (b) for each $k > 0$ in $\mathfrak{N}$,

$$S_2(k + 1) = S_2(k) + (k + 1)^2.$$

Some examples of the use of this formula are the following:

$$S_2(2) = S_2(1 + 1) = S_2(1) + 2^2 = 1^2 + 2^2 = 5,$$
$$S_2(3) = S_2(2 + 1) = S_2(2) + 3^2 = 5 + 9 = 14,$$

$$S_2(4) = S_2(3 + 1) = S_2(3) + 4^2 = 14 + 16 = 30,$$
$$S_2(5) = S_2(4 + 1) = S_2(4) + 5^2 = 30 + 25 = 55.$$

Observation:

$$6S_2(1) = 6 = 1 \cdot 2 \cdot 3,$$
$$6S_2(2) = 30 = 2 \cdot 3 \cdot 5,$$
$$6S_2(3) = 84 = 3 \cdot 4 \cdot 7,$$
$$6S_2(4) = 180 = 4 \cdot 5 \cdot 9,$$
$$6S_2(5) = 330 = 5 \cdot 6 \cdot 11.$$

As an exercise, try to find a formula giving $6S_2(n)$, for each n in $\mathfrak{N}$. Make sure your formula is correct at least for $1 \leq n \leq 5$. See whether the assumed correctness of your formula for a particular number k implies its correctness for $k + 1$.

Exercises

1. Investigate $2S_1(n)$, where (a) $S_1(1) = 1$, (b) for each $k > 0$, $S_1(k + 1) = S_1(k) + (k + 1)$.
2. Say what you can about numbers such as $1, 1 + 3, 1 + 3 + 5, \ldots$.
3. Assume there is a mapping F such that (a) $F(0) = 1$, (b) for each n in $\mathfrak{N}$
   $$F(n + 1) = (n + 1)F(n).$$
   Can you find a formula for F? [*Hint:* For this and all similar problems, the first thing to do is to compute enough special cases—$F(1)$, $F(2)$, $F(3)$, and so on—to get a feeling for what you are doing.]
4. Define G by (a) $G(0) = 1$, (b) if n is in the domain of G, $G(n + 1) = G(n)$. Find and prove a simple formula for G.
5. Find a function f with domain $\mathfrak{N}$ such that
   $$f(0) = 0;$$
   if n is in the domain of f, then
   $$f(n + 1) = f(n) + 2n + 1.$$
6. Assume for this and the next four problems that there is an operation $*$ such that (a) for all x in $\mathfrak{N}$, $x * 0 = x$, (b) for all x and y in $\mathfrak{N}$,
   $$x * (y + 1) = (x * y) + (1 + x).$$
   Find $3 * 0, 3 * 1, 3 * 2, 3 * 3$.
   Find $17 * 0, 17 * 1, 17 * 2$.
   Find $5 * 5$.
7. Let S_5 be the set of n in $\mathfrak{N}$ such that Exercise 6 fails to determine $5 * n$. If S_5 is not empty, find the smallest number in S_5.
8. Let M_0 be the set of y in $\mathfrak{N}$ such that
   $$0 * y = y.$$
   Prove that 0 is in M_0 and that M_0 is an inductive set.
9. Prove that, for every y in $\mathfrak{N}$, $1 * y = 2y + 1$.
10. Let $M = \{x \mid x * 1 = 2x + 1\}$. What can you say about M?

11. Prove that if we define an operation $*'$ by "for all x and y in $\mathfrak{N}$, $x *' y = xy + (x + y)$," then $*'$ has the properties assumed in Exercise 6. Can any other operation have these properties?

12. Let H be a function such that (a) $H(0) = 1$, (b) if n is in the domain of H, then $H(n + 1) = 2H(n)$. Let x be a natural number and prove that, for every natural number y,

$$H(x + y) = H(x) \cdot H(y).$$

[*Hint:* Let M_x be the set of all y such that the equation holds. Prove that 0 is in M_x and, that if some y is in M_x, then so is $y + 1$. Note that $x + (y + 1) = (x + y) + 1$.] Finally, put the displayed equation in a more familiar form.

13. If $f_0 = 0$, $f_1 = 1$, and, for every n in $\mathfrak{N}$, $f_{n+2} = f_{n+1} + f_n$, what are f_5, f_6, f_{10}? The number f_n determined from this formula is the nth *Fibonacci number*, named for Leonardo of Pisa [the son of Bonacci], who first discovered some of the interesting properties of this sequence around the year 1200.

14. Let $S = \{a, b, c, d\}$ be the set of the first four letters of the alphabet, and let G be the function with domain S such that

$$G(a) = b, \qquad G(b) = c, \qquad G(c) = G(d) = d.$$

Let g be a function with domain $\mathfrak{N}$ such that $g(0) = a$, and, for every n in $\mathfrak{N}$, $g(n + 1) = G(g(n))$. For example, $g(1) = g(0 + 1) = G(g(0)) = G(a) = b$. Prove that, for every $n > 2$,

$$g(n) = d.$$

Several of the exercises above raise the question of whether a function g with domain $\mathfrak{N}$ can be defined by specifying $g(0)$ [or, as in Exercise 13, perhaps $g(0)$ and $g(1)$] and giving a way of determining, for every n, $g(n + 1)$ from $g(n)$. We shall return to this question after a brief discussion of bounded subsets of $\mathfrak{N}$.

§ 5. *Bounded Subsets of* $\mathfrak{N}$

Definition 2.3. Let S be a subset of $\mathfrak{N}$. Then S is **bounded** if there is some b in $\mathfrak{N}$ such that x in $S \Rightarrow x \leq b$; any such b is an **upper bound** of S.

For example, if $S = \{1, 2, 4\}$, S is bounded because x in $S \Rightarrow x \leq 6$. Also, x in $S \Rightarrow x \leq 4$, and clearly 4 is the *least* upper bound of S.

The empty set is bounded because, for example, x in the empty set $\Rightarrow x \leq 1$.

Remark: If S is a bounded subset of $\mathfrak{N}$, then the set of upper bounds of S is not empty and hence has a least member.

Theorem 2.19. If S is a bounded nonempty subset of $\mathfrak{N}$, then the least upper bound of S is in S and is the largest member of S.

PROOF: 1. The set $\{0\}$ has 0 as its least upper bound and largest member.

2. If $S \neq \{0\}$ is a nonempty subset of $\mathfrak{N}$, then S contains some n in $\mathfrak{N}$

with $n \neq 0$. Let b be the least upper bound of S. Clearly $b \neq 0$, because S contains some $n > 0$. Because b is an upper bound of S, for each s in S, $s \leq b$. If b is not in S, then for each s in S, $s < b$, making $b - 1$ an upper bound of S and contradicting our choice of b as the least upper bound of S. So b must be in S.

3. Finally, no member of S can be larger than b, because b is an upper bound of S. ∎

Definition 2.4. For each k in $\mathfrak{N}$, let $\mathfrak{N}_k = \{n \mid n \leq k\}$.

For example, $\mathfrak{N}_0 = \{0\}$ and $\mathfrak{N}_2 = \{0, 1, 2\}$.

To introduce an intuitively clear idea into our formal language we shall call $\mathfrak{N}_k$ *the set of the first* $k + 1$ *natural numbers*. We shall also say that a set S, not necessarily a subset of $\mathfrak{N}$, *has exactly* $k + 1$ *elements* in case there is some k in $\mathfrak{N}$ such that there is a one-to-one correspondence of $\mathfrak{N}_k$ to S. This is just the familiar notion of counting, slightly distorted by starting with 0 rather than 1.

The spirit of the chapter now demands the formal assertion of three statements, each of which is intuitively obvious.

Theorem 2.20. If S is a nonempty bounded subset of $\mathfrak{N}$, then there is some k in $\mathfrak{N}$ such that S has exactly $k + 1$ elements.

Theorem 2.21. If k and j are in $\mathfrak{N}$ and $k \neq j$, then there is no one-to-one correspondence of $\mathfrak{N}_k$ to $\mathfrak{N}_j$.

Theorem 2.22. If S is a nonempty bounded subset of $\mathfrak{N}$, then there is only one k in $\mathfrak{N}$ such that S has exactly $k + 1$ elements. In other words, if two people count the elements of S and get different answers, then at least one of them is wrong.

We shall prove the first of these and leave the other two to the reader.

PROOF OF THEOREM 2.20: If S is a nonempty bounded subset of $\mathfrak{N}$ whose least upper bound is 0, then $S = \{0\} = \mathfrak{N}_0$.

If the least upper bound of S is 1, then S is either $\{1\}$ or $\{0, 1\}$. There is a one-to-one correspondence of $\mathfrak{N}_0$ to $\{1\}$: the function f with domain $\{0\}$ such that $f(0) = 1$.

There are two one-to-one correspondences of $\mathfrak{N}_1$ to $\{0, 1\}$: the functions $\{(0, 0), (1, 1)\}$ and $\{(0, 1), (1, 0)\}$.

Let B be the set of all b in $\mathfrak{N}$ such that if S is a subset of $\mathfrak{N}$ with least upper bound $\leq b$, then, for some $k \leq b$, there is a one-to-one correspondence of $\mathfrak{N}_k$ to S.

We have established that 0 and 1 are in B. Let b be in B and let S be a subset of $\mathfrak{N}$ whose least upper bound is $b + 1$. If $b + 1$ is the only element of S, then the function mapping 0 to $b + 1$ is a one-to-one correspondence of $\mathfrak{N}_0$ to S.

If $b + 1$ is not the only element of S, let S' be the set whose elements are all the elements of S except $b + 1$. Then S' is nonempty and the least upper bound of S' is $\leq b$. Since b is in B, there is some $k \leq b$ such that there is a one-to-one correspondence of $\mathfrak{N}_k$ to S'. Call this function g, and define a function f with domain $\mathfrak{N}_{k+1}$ as follows:

for $n \leq k$, $f(n) = g(n)$,

$f(k + 1) = b + 1$.

By hypothesis, g is a one-to-one correspondence of $\mathfrak{N}_k$ to S'. Since $k + 1$ is not in $\mathfrak{N}_k$ and $b + 1$ is not in S', f as defined above maps $\mathfrak{N}_k$ one-to-one onto S' and $\mathfrak{N}_{k+1}$ one-to-one onto S.

We have shown that B is an inductive set containing 0, so that $B = \mathfrak{N}$ and Theorem 2.20 is established.   ∎

As an example of the inductive step above, let

$S = \{5,\ 7,\ 56,\ 70\}$,

$S' = \{5,\ 7,\ 56\}$.

A suitable function g is $\{(0, 7),\ (1, 56),\ (2, 5)\}$, which is a one-to-one correspondence of $\mathfrak{N}_2$ to S'. Therefore

$f = \{(0, 7),\ (1, 56),\ (2, 5),\ (3, 70)\}$

is a one-to-one correspondence of $\mathfrak{N}_3$ to S.

§ 6. *Recursive Definitions*

On the informal level we can easily define 3^n for each n in $\mathfrak{N}$ by stipulating that $3^0 = 1$ and that, for $n \neq 0$, 3^n is a product of n factors, each of which is 3. It is then clear that for all n and m in $\mathfrak{N}$, $3^n \cdot 3^m = 3^{n+m}$. In particular, $3^n \cdot 3 = 3^{n+1}$.

Formally we want to establish that there is one and only one function f with domain $\mathfrak{N}$ such that

$f(0) = 1$,

and that, for all n in $\mathfrak{N}$,

$f(n + 1) = 3f(n)$.

Perhaps another example will make the one difficulty clearer. Is there a function g with domain $\mathfrak{N}$ such that $g(0) = 2$, and, for all n in $\mathfrak{N}$,

$g(n + 1) = ng(n) + 5$?

If there is such a function, then

$g(1) = 0g(0) + 5 = 5$,

$$g(2) = 1g(1) + 5 = 10,$$
$$g(3) = 2g(2) + 5 = 25,$$
$$g(4) = 3g(3) + 5 = 80,$$
$$g(5) = 4g(4) + 5 = 325.$$

No simple explicit formula for g is apparent.

We do have above, however, the makings of explicit formulas for several functions. For example, let g_2 be the function with domain $\mathfrak{N}_2$ such that $g_2(0) = 0$, $g_2(1) = 5$, and $g_2(2) = 10$. Then g_2 is a function with the properties

$$g_2(0) = 0,$$

and, if $n < 2$,

$$g_2(n + 1) = ng_2(n) + 5.$$

There is also a function we might call g_5, with domain $\mathfrak{N}_5$:

$$g_5 = \{(0, 2), (1, 5), (2, 10), (3, 25), (4, 80), (5, 325)\}.$$

Of g_5 we can assert that

$$g_5(0) = 2,$$

and, for $n < 5$,

$$g_5(n + 1) = ng_5(n) + 5.$$

If we now define g_6 by

for $n \leq 5$, $g_6(n) = g_5(n)$,

and

$$g_6(6) = 5g_5(5) + 5,$$

we see that g_6 is a function with domain $\mathfrak{N}_6$: it assigns a unique image to each n in $\mathfrak{N}_5$ because g_5 is a function on $\mathfrak{N}_5$, and it assigns a unique image to 6 because 6 is not in the domain of g_5; the formula $g_6(6) = 5g_5(5) + 5$ does assign an image to 6. Also, g_6 is such that

$$g_6(0) = 2,$$

and, for $n < 6$,

$$g_6(n + 1) = ng_6(n) + 5.$$

It is clear that mathematical induction will establish that, for every k in $\mathfrak{N}$, there is a function g_k with domain $\mathfrak{N}_k$ such that

$$g_k(0) = 2,$$

and, for $n < k$,

$$g_k(n + 1) = ng_k(n) + 5.$$

That is, for every k in $\mathfrak{N}$ there is a function which behaves the way we want on the set of the first $k + 1$ natural numbers. Furthermore, if $k < j$, then

$g_k(n) = g_j(n)$ for all $n \leq k$. Any two of these functions agree on the intersection of their domains.

We can now produce a formula for a function g with domain $\mathfrak{N}$ that has the properties we want. For each k in $\mathfrak{N}$, let $g(k) = g_k(k)$. Then

$$g(0) = g_0(0) = 2,$$

and, for each n in $\mathfrak{N}$,

$$g(n+1) = g_{n+1}(n+1) = ng_{n+1}(n) + 5$$
$$= ng_n(n) + 5$$
$$= ng(n) + 5.$$

The theorem below will not apply to the example we have just looked at, nor to the Fibonacci numbers, but it has a great many other applications.

Theorem 2.23.   Let G be any function such that the range of G is a subset of the domain of G. Let a be an element of the domain of G. Then there is one and only one function g with domain $\mathfrak{N}$ such that

$$g(0) = a,$$

and, for all n in $\mathfrak{N}$,

$$g(n+1) = G(g(n)).$$

As an example, for all x in $\mathfrak{N}$, let G be given by

$$G(x) = 3x.$$

The range of G is a subset of its domain, and 1 is in the domain. The theorem asserts that there is one and only one function g with domain $\mathfrak{N}$ such that

$$g(0) = 1,$$

and, for all n in $\mathfrak{N}$,

$$g(n+1) = G(g(n)) = 3g(n).$$

PROOF OF THEOREM 2.23:   First, the uniqueness. Let g and g' be functions with domain $\mathfrak{N}$ and having the properties specified. Then $g(0) = a$ and $g'(0) = a$, so $g(0) = g'(0)$. If, for some n in $\mathfrak{N}$, $g(n) = g'(n)$, then

$$g(n+1) = G(g(n))$$
$$= G(g'(n))$$
$$= g'(n+1).$$

By the induction principle, $g(n) = g'(n)$ for all n in $\mathfrak{N}$; that is, $g = g'$. To prove the existence of such a function g, we proceed as in the example above.

Let g_0 be the function with domain $\{0\}$ such that $g_0(0) = a$. Also, let g_1 be the function with domain $\mathfrak{N}_1$ such that $g_1(0) = a$ and $g_1(1) = G(a)$. Assume that for some $k \geq 1$ in $\mathfrak{N}$ there is a function g_k such that the domain of g_k is $\mathfrak{N}_k$, and for all n in $\mathfrak{N}$, with $n < k$, $g_k(n + 1) = G(g_k(n))$. Then there is also the following function h, which we shall rename g_{k+1}. For $n \leq k$,

$$h(n) = g_k(n),$$

and

$$h(k + 1) = G(g_k(k)).$$

This h assigns a unique image to each $n \leq k$ because g_k is a function on $\mathfrak{N}_k$, and explicitly maps $k + 1$ to $G(g_k(k))$. By our assumption about the function g_k, $g_k(k) = G(g_k(k - 1))$. Thus $g_k(k)$ is in the range of G. But the range of G is a subset of the domain of G, and G is a function, so $G(g_k(k))$ is a well-defined object and h does assign a unique image to $k + 1$.

By the induction principle there is, for each k in $\mathfrak{N}$, a function g_k such that

$$g_k(0) = a,$$

and, for $n < k$,

$$g_k(n + 1) = G(g_k(n)).$$

By another application of the induction principle, if $j > k$, then $g_j(n) = g_k(n)$ for all $n \leq k$.

We are now able, as in the example above, to define g, for each n in $\mathfrak{N}$, by

$$g(n) = g_n(n). \quad \blacksquare$$

§ 7. *Multiplication Defined in Terms of Addition*

As an application of Theorem 2.23 and the induction principle we shall indicate how all our axioms about multiplication can be proved as theorems if we start from an appropriate definition.

For an informal start, some of what we know about multiplication is that, for all x in $\mathfrak{N}$,

$$x \cdot 0 = 0,$$

and, for all x and y in $\mathfrak{N}$,

$$x(y + 1) = xy + x.$$

This is, in fact, enough to determine all products, assuming that we know all about addition. For example, what is $4 \cdot 3$? Let us multiply 4 by 0, 1, 2, and 3:

$$4 \cdot 0 = 0,$$
$$4 \cdot 1 = 4(0 + 1) = 4 \cdot 0 + 4 = 4,$$
$$4 \cdot 2 = 4(1 + 1) = 4 \cdot 1 + 4 = 4 + 4,$$
$$4 \cdot 3 = 4(2 + 1) = 4 \cdot 2 + 4 = (4 + 4) + 4.$$

For a formal start we define, for each x in $\mathfrak{N}$, a function G_x: for all y in $\mathfrak{N}$, $G_x(y) = y + x$. Thus G_x is a function with domain $\mathfrak{N}$ and range a subset of $\mathfrak{N}$, and 0 is in the domain of G_x.

By Theorem 2.23 there is a unique function g_x with domain $\mathfrak{N}$ such that

$$g_x(0) = 0,$$

and, for all y in $\mathfrak{N}$,

$$g_x(y + 1) = G_x(g_x(y)) = g_x(y) + x.$$

Now, given any ordered pair (x, y) with x and y in $\mathfrak{N}$, there is a function g_x [defined above] and y is in the domain of g_x, and $g_x(y)$ is in $\mathfrak{N}$.

Definition 2.5 [*The Operation* *].   For all x and y in $\mathfrak{N}$, $x * y = g_x(y)$.

By the paragraph just above Definition 2.5, * is an operation and $\mathfrak{N}$ is closed under *. Also, * has the following two properties.
1. For all x in $\mathfrak{N}$, $x * 0 = 0$.
2. For all x and y in $\mathfrak{N}$, $x * (y + 1) = (x * y) + x$.

Exercises

1. Prove that if ** is an operation in $\mathfrak{N}$ having properties (1) and (2) above, then ** = *. [*Hint:* For x in $\mathfrak{N}$ let M_x be the set of y in $\mathfrak{N}$ such that $x * y = x ** y$. Prove that M_x is an inductive set containing 0.]
2. Prove that, for all x in $\mathfrak{N}$, $x * 1 = x$.
3. Prove that, for all x in $\mathfrak{N}$, $1 * x = x$.
4. Prove that, for all x and y in $\mathfrak{N}$,
   $$(y + 1) * x = (y * x) + x.$$
5. Prove that * is commutative.
6. Prove that * is distributive over +.
7. Prove that * is associative.
   [*Hints:* In Exercise 4 one might, for x a number in $\mathfrak{N}$, consider the set M_x of all y such that
   $$(y + 1) * x = (y * x) + x.$$
   Or one might, for y in $\mathfrak{N}$, consider the set M_y of all x in $\mathfrak{N}$ such that
   $$(y + 1) * x = (y * x) + x.$$
   Each of these should be an inductive set containing 0. This fact may well be easier to demonstrate for one set than for the other. Similar remarks apply to Exercises 6 and 7.]

§ 8. *Some Familiar Theorems*

The first of our familiar theorems has a resounding name, but is completely obvious. We include it here partly because we shall see it again in a context where its truth is not quite so clear.

Theorem 2.24 [*The Archimedean Property*]. If a and b are any two positive natural numbers, there is a natural number n such that $nb > a$.

For example, $(a + 1)b > a$.

Theorem 2.25 [*Euclid's Basic Arithmetic Theorem*]. If a and b are natural numbers, with $b \neq 0$, then there are unique natural numbers q and r, with $0 \leq r < b$, such that $a = qb + r$.

The obviousness of this is probably connected with the fact that we all spent so much time in grade school learning how to find the quotient q and remainder r.

One proof runs as follows. First, if $a < b$,

$$a = 0b + a, \qquad \text{and} \qquad a < b.$$

Second, if $a \geq b$, there are, by the Archimedean property, numbers n such that $nb > a$. The smallest such n is at least 1; call it $q + 1$. Then

$$qb \leq a \qquad \text{but} \qquad (q + 1)b > a.$$

Either $a = qb = qb + 0$ or $a > qb$, and there is some $r > 0$ such that $a = qb + r$. In this case,

$$qb + r < (q + 1)b,$$
$$r < b.$$

We have proved that the fifth-grade problem has an answer. Now we must establish that there is only one answer—that if two people get different quotients and remainders, at least one of them is wrong. To prove this we need a lemma, which will also be useful in the exercises below.

Lemma on Divisibility. If $a = b + c$ and any two of a, b, c are divisible by a number d, then the third is divisible by d.

PROOF: 1. If b and c are divisible by d—that is, if there are m and n such that $b = md$ and $c = nd$—then

$$a = md + nd = (m + n)d,$$

which shows that a is also divisible by d.

2. Suppose $a = kd$ and $b = jd$. If $c = 0$, then, since $0 = 0d$, c is a multiple of d. Otherwise, the equation

$$kd = jd + c$$

implies $kd > jd$.

By Theorem 2.9, $k > j$ and there is some q such that $k = j + q$. From $(j + q)d = jd + c$ follow

$$jd + qd = jd + c,$$

or

$$c = qd.$$

Because addition is commutative it is not necessary to consider also the case in which a and c are divisible by d.   ∎

Now, to finish the theorem, suppose $a = qb + r$, $0 \leq r < b$, and $a = q'b + r'$, $0 \leq r' < b$. If $r \neq r'$, one is larger than the other; without loss of generality suppose that $r' = r + p$, where perhaps $p = 0$. Then

$$qb + r = q'b + r + p,$$

and

$$qb = q'b + p.$$

From the lemma, p is a multiple of b. But

$$r' = r + p < b,$$

and

$$p < b.$$

The only multiple of b which is less than b is $0 = 0b$. Thus $p = 0$ and $r' = r$. From this, $qb = q'b$, and $q = q'$.

The Euclidean Algorithm

An *algorithm* is a systematic method of computation such as long division or one of the standard methods of approximating square roots of positive real numbers. If we start with natural numbers a and b and find the q and r of Euclid's theorem, we can, if $r \neq 0$, apply the theorem again to b and r instead of a and b, and obtain:

$$a = qb + r, \qquad 0 < r < b,$$
$$b = q_1 r + r_1, \qquad 0 \leq r_1 < r.$$

If now $r_1 \neq 0$, we can continue to

$$r = q_2 r_1 + r_2, \qquad 0 \leq r_2 < r_1.$$

If $r_2 \neq 0$, we can continue to find q_3 and r_3, with $r_3 < r_2$. But evidently, as the remainders keep decreasing, we must eventually get a 0 remainder and the game is over. As the examples below indicate, the last positive remainder is the greatest common divisor of a and b.

Examples

1. Here $a = 72$ and $b = 51$; the quotients, the q, are in parentheses.
$$72 = (1)51 + 21,$$
$$51 = (2)21 + 9,$$
$$21 = (2)9 + 3,$$
$$9 = (3)3 + 0.$$
2. $3841 = (3)1081 + 598.$

Why must any common divisor of 3841 and 1081 also be a divisor of 598?
$$1081 = (1)598 + 483.$$
Why must any common divisor of 1081 and 598 be a divisor of 483? Why must any common divisor of 3841 and 1081 be a divisor of 483?
$$598 = (1)483 + 115,$$
$$483 = (4)115 + 23,$$
$$115 = (5)23 + 0.$$
Why must any common divisor of 3841 and 1081 be a divisor of 23? Is 23 a common divisor of 115 and 483? Of 483 and 598? Of 1081 and 3841?

Exercises

1. Use the Euclidean algorithm to find the greatest common divisor of 57 and 779; 10672 and 2378; 1111 and 537; 13 and 8.
2. Find a and b, with $10 < b < 20$, such that the algorithm takes as many steps as possible.
3. Show that, whatever a and b are, $2r_1 < b$. [*Hint:* Consider the two cases $2r \leq b$ and $2r > b$.]
4. Show that $4r_3 < b$ and $8r_5 < b$.
5. If $b < 1000$, how many steps at the most can the algorithm take?

§ 9. *Names for Numbers*

We are so accustomed to the base-ten scheme for naming natural numbers that it seems surprising that one of the great mathematicians of all time, Archimedes, devoted a paper, *The Sand Reckoner*, to working out a scheme to provide a name for a number larger than the number of poppy seeds that could be packed into the universe of his time. His scheme lacked the simplicity of the one that strikes us as so obvious.

First we take arbitrary symbols such as 0, 1, . . . , 9, as many as we have fingers [digits], and make them names for the first ten natural numbers. Next let t be a temporary name for $9 + 1$.

Now we have a name, a digit, for every number from 0 to 9; and a special name, t, for $9 + 1$. Consider now any number a with $t \leq a < t^2$. There are q and r, with $0 \leq r < t$, such that $a = qt + r$. Since $a < t^2$, $q < t$; that is, q is a digit and a is given the standard name qr as an abbreviation for $qt + r$. Thus every number $< t^2$ now has a standard name, with t renamed 10 as an abbreviation for $1t + 0$. For t^2 we write 100, again as an abbreviation.

Exercises

1. Make the recursive definition $t^0 = 1$; if t^n is in $\mathfrak{N}$, then $t^{n+1} = t^n \cdot t$. Prove that, for all n in $\mathfrak{N}$, $t^n > n$. [All you need know about t is $t > 1$.]
2. Prove that for any natural number a there are natural numbers k such that $t^k > a$.

3. Prove that, for any natural number a, there is one and only one natural number n such that $t^n \leq a < t^{n+1}$.

4. Suppose that, for some n, each natural number x such that $x < t^{n+1}$ has a unique representation:

$$x = a_0 + a_1 t + \cdots + a_n t^n,$$

where each a_i is a digit. Then prove that each y such that $t^{n+1} \leq y < t^{n+2}$ has a unique representation:

$$y = b_0 + b_1 t + \cdots + b_n t^n + b_{n+1} t^{n+1},$$

where each b_i is a digit: $0 \leq b_i < t$.

This puts you well ahead of Archimedes.

§ 10. *The Peano Postulates*

The Italian mathematician Peano (1858–1932) formulated the five postulates below to express some of our most basic intuitions about the natural numbers. The function S should, for intuition's sake, be thought of as *successor*.

Postulate 1. There exists a set $\mathfrak{N}$ containing an element 0.

Postulate 2. There exists a function S, with domain $\mathfrak{N}$ and range a subset of $\mathfrak{N}$.

Postulate 3. For all n in $\mathfrak{N}$, $S(n) \neq 0$.

Postulate 4. For all n and m in $\mathfrak{N}$, if $S(n) = S(m)$, then $n = m$. That is, S is a one-to-one correspondence of $\mathfrak{N}$ to the range of S.

Postulate 5. If M is a subset of $\mathfrak{N}$ such that (1) 0 is in M, and (2) n in $M \Rightarrow S(n)$ in M, then $M = \mathfrak{N}$.

Theorem 2.26. The only member of $\mathfrak{N}$ which is not in the range of S is 0. In other words, if n is in $\mathfrak{N}$ and $n \neq 0$, there is some k in $\mathfrak{N}$ such that $S(k) = n$.

PROOF: Let M be the set containing 0 and each element of the range of S. Then 0 is in M. And if n is in M, then $S(n)$ is in M because $S(n)$ is in the range of S. By Postulate 5, $M = \mathfrak{N}$. ∎

Theorem 2.27. There exists an operation, $+$, such that (a) for all x in $\mathfrak{N}$, $x + 0 = x$, and (b) for all x and y in $\mathfrak{N}$, $x + S(y) = S(x + y)$.

The proof of Theorem 2.27 is the difficult part of establishing that one can, starting with the Peano Postulates, define addition in accord with Theorem 2.27 and prove that $+$ has the properties we have assumed it to have. For a straightforward proof see *Thurston* [7, Chapter A].

Another approach is first to establish the following, essentially equivalent to Theorem 2.23.

A Statement Equivalent to Theorem 2.23: If G is a function such that the range of G is a subset of the domain of G, and if a is in the domain of G, then there is one and only one function g with domain $\mathfrak{N}$ such that (a) $g(0) = a$, and (b) for all n in $\mathfrak{N}$, $g(S(n)) = G(g(n))$.

For a good discussion of how one can use the Peano Postulates to prove such a statement, see *Henkin* [3].

To make it clearer that the Statement is essentially Theorem 2.23, and to give more intuitive flavor to the rest of this section, we make the following definition: $1 = S(0)$.

Setting $y = 0$ in Theorem 2.27, and using part (a) and this definition of 1, we can rewrite part (b) as

for all x in $\mathfrak{N}$, $x + 1 = S(x)$.

Assuming that the Statement equivalent to Theorem 2.23 is proved, Theorem 2.27 is readily proved as follows. For each x in $\mathfrak{N}$ let G_x be the function S. By Postulate 2 the range of G_x is a subset of the domain of G_x, and x is in the domain of G_x. Then by the Statement, for each x in $\mathfrak{N}$, there is a unique function g_x with domain $\mathfrak{N}$ such that

$$g_x(0) = x,$$

and, for all y in $\mathfrak{N}$,

$$g_x(S(y)) = S(g_x(y)).$$

We now define $+$ by: for all x and y in $\mathfrak{N}$,

$$x + y = g_x(y).$$

Since, for each x in $\mathfrak{N}$, g_x is a function with domain $\mathfrak{N}$, $+$ is an operation under which $\mathfrak{N}$ is closed; and g_x was constructed to make $+$ have properties (a) and (b) of Theorem 2.27.

Once Theorem 2.27 is established, either directly or via the Statement equivalent to Theorem 2.23, it is clear that Theorem 2.27 implies that $\mathfrak{N}$ is closed under $+$: otherwise, $S(x + y)$ wouldn't make sense for all x and y in $\mathfrak{N}$.

The uniqueness of $+$ is easy. Suppose $+'$ also has the properties of Theorem 2.27. For x in $\mathfrak{N}$ let M_x be the set of y in $\mathfrak{N}$ such that $x + y = x +' y$. Then 0 is in M_x because $x + 0 = x = x +' 0$. If y is in M_x, then $S(y)$ is in M_x because

$$x + S(y) = S(x + y)$$
$$= S(x +' y)$$
$$= x +' S(y).$$

By Postulate 5, $M_x = \mathfrak{N}$.

Now we make use of the fact that, for all z in $\mathfrak{N}$, $S(z) = z + 1$, to rewrite property (b) of $+$ as for all x and y in $\mathfrak{N}$, $x + (y + 1) = (x + y) + 1$.

Also, by property (a) of $+$,

for all x and y in $\mathfrak{N}$, $x + (y + 0) = (x + y) + 0$.

These two special cases of the associative law suggest trying to prove this law. For x and y in $\mathfrak{N}$, let M_{xy} be the set of z in $\mathfrak{N}$ such that

$$x + (y + z) = (x + y) + z.$$

Both 0 and $S(0) = 1$ are in M_{xy}. The reader should be able to establish that if z is in M_{xy}, so is $z + 1$. Since $\mathfrak{N}$ is closed under $+$ and the associative law works if 1 is on the right, then, for all x, y, z in $\mathfrak{N}$,

$$x + (y + [z + 1]) = x + ([y + z] + 1)$$
$$= (x + [y + z]) + 1.$$

A method of making further progress is to use mathematical induction to establish, in turn, each of these statements:

for all x in $\mathfrak{N}$, $0 + x = x$.

for all x in $\mathfrak{N}$, $x + 1 = 1 + x$.

$+$ is commutative.

Next, let M be the set of a in $\mathfrak{N}$ such that if b and c are in $\mathfrak{N}$ and $b + a = c + a$, then $b = c$.

If $b + 0 = c + 0$, then $b = c$. So 0 is in M. Let a be in M and suppose there are b and c in $\mathfrak{N}$ such that $b + S(a) = c + S(a)$. By a defining property of $+$, $S(b + a) = S(c + a)$. By Postulate 4, $b + a = c + a$, and since a is in M, $b = c$. Thus the set of the cancellable a contains 0 and is an inductive set, and the cancellation law for addition is proved. This concludes an outline of the derivability of our algebraic axioms about $+$ from the Peano Postulates.

We also assumed early in the chapter two special axioms and the least integer principle. If a and b are in $\mathfrak{N}$ and $b \neq 0$, then by Theorem 2.26 there is some k in $\mathfrak{N}$ such that $b = S(k)$. Then $a + b = a + S(k) = S(a + k) \neq 0$, by Postulate 3. Hence, if $a + b = 0$, $b = 0$. By the commutativity of $+$, also, if $a + b = 0$, then $a = 0$.

The second special axiom, essential to the definition of $<$, was more complicated: given two different natural numbers, some number can be added to one of them to get the other.

Let M be the set of those numbers a in $\mathfrak{N}$ having the following property.

If b is in $\mathfrak{N}$ and, for all x in $\mathfrak{N}$, $b + x \neq a$, then there is some y in $\mathfrak{N}$ such that $a + y = b$. Then 0 is in this set M because, if b is in $\mathfrak{N}$, then $0 + b = b$.

Suppose a is in M and there is some b in $\mathfrak{N}$ such that, for all x in $\mathfrak{N}$, $b + x \neq a + 1$. Then also, for all x in $\mathfrak{N}$, $b + (x + 1) \neq a + 1$, or, for all x in $\mathfrak{N}$, $b + x \neq a$. Since a is in M, there is some y in $\mathfrak{N}$ such that $a + y = b$. This y cannot be 0 because then $a = b$ and $b + 0 = a$. So there is some z in $\mathfrak{N}$

such that $y = z + 1$. This gives $a + (z + 1) = b$ or, finally, $(a + 1) + z = b$.

To conclude the chapter we give a way of using mathematical induction to establish the least integer principle. Clearly any subset of $\mathfrak{N}$ containing 0 has 0 as its smallest member. Suppose S is a subset of $\mathfrak{N}$ containing 1. If 0 is in S, 0 is the smallest member of S. If 0 is not in S, then 1 is the smallest member of S. In either case S has a smallest member.

Let n be a natural number with the property that every subset of $\mathfrak{N}$ containing n has a smallest member. Let S be a subset of $\mathfrak{N}$ containing $n + 1$. If 0 is in S, 0 is the smallest member of S. If 0 is not in S, we can form a set S' by subtracting 1 from each member of S. That is, if 0 is not in S, let

$$S' = \{x \mid x + 1 \text{ is in } S\}.$$

Then S' contains n and must have a smallest member, say s. It follows now that $s + 1$ is the smallest member of S.

3
The Real Numbers

In the first section of this chapter we give a set of axioms for the real number system. In the rest of the chapter—indeed, in the rest of the book—we examine consequences of these axioms. Some of these consequences are difficult for the intuition to accept and during the 19th century it became intellectually necessary to explore the question of whether there really is a real number system. The answer, due primarily to the German mathematicians Cantor (1845–1918), Dedekind (1831–1916), and Weierstrass (1815–1897), is that if there is a natural number system satisfying the axioms of the last chapter, then there is a real number system satisfying the axioms of this chapter.

For sketches of the lives and mathematical work of Cantor and Weierstrass, see *Bell* [2]. A construction of a real number system from the natural number system is carried out in each of the books [4] through [7] in the bibliography. Less systematic is *Dedekind* [8], which has, nevertheless, the distinction of being a mathematical classic. Reading one of these five books with understanding takes perhaps two days for a mathematically sophisticated reader, and perhaps three months for an intelligent but unsophisticated one.

Our set of axioms is split into three subsets, the first of which can be summarized by saying that the system $(\Re; +, \cdot)$ is a *field*. There are many fields, and several of them are considered in this book. The second section of the chapter is concerned with some basic theorems true of all fields.

The second subset of axioms is concerned with a linear order relation $<$, and makes the system $(\Re; +, \cdot; <)$ an *ordered field*. We shall be concerned with more than one ordered field, and § 3 of the chapter establishes some theorems true in all ordered fields.

The third subset contains only one axiom, the least upper bound axiom.

§ 1. *Axioms*

Field Axioms

Axiom 3.1. The set $\mathcal{R}$ contains at least two different elements, called O and I.

Axiom 3.2. Addition and multiplication are operations in $\mathcal{R}$.

Axiom 3.3. The set $\mathcal{R}$ is closed under both addition and multiplication. That is, for all a and b in $\mathcal{R}$, both $a + b$ and $a \cdot b$ [or simply ab] are uniquely determined elements of $\mathcal{R}$.

Axiom 3.4. Both addition and multiplication are commutative. For all a and b in $\mathcal{R}$, $a + b = b + a$ and $ab = ba$.

Axiom 3.5. Both operations are associative. For all a, b, c in $\mathcal{R}$, $a + (b + c) = (a + b) + c$ and $a(bc) = (ab)c$.

Axiom 3.6. The element O is an additive identity and I is a multiplicative identity. For all a in $\mathcal{R}$, $a + O = O + a = a$ and $aI = Ia = a$.

Axiom 3.7. Each member of $\mathcal{R}$ has an **additive inverse;** each member of $\mathcal{R}$ except O has a **multiplicative inverse.** More explicitly, (1) for each a in $\mathcal{R}$ there is some $-a$ in $\mathcal{R}$ such that $a + -a = -a + a = O$; and (2) for each $a \neq O$ in $\mathcal{R}$ there is some a^{-1} in $\mathcal{R}$ such that $aa^{-1} = a^{-1}a = I$.

Axiom 3.8. Multiplication is distributive over addition. For all a, b, c in $\mathcal{R}$, $a(b + c) = ab + ac$.

Order Axioms

Axiom 3.9. The set $\mathcal{R}$ admits a linear order relation $<$, with the properties given in the next four axioms.

Axiom 3.10 [*Trichotomy*]. If a and b are in $\mathcal{R}$, then exactly one of $a = b$, $a < b$, $b < a$ is true.

Axiom 3.11 [*Transitivity*]. If a, b, c are in $\mathcal{R}$ and $a < b$ and $b < c$, then $a < c$.

Axiom 3.12. If a and b are in $\mathcal{R}$ and $a < b$, then, for each c in $\mathcal{R}$, $a + c < b + c$.

Axiom 3.13. If a and b are in $\mathfrak{R}$ and $a < b$, then, for any c in $\mathfrak{R}$ with $0 < c$, $ac < bc$.

Definitions: For a and b in $\mathfrak{R}$ we define $b > a$ to mean $a < b$. Also we say that a is *positive* iff $a > 0$. The statement $a \leq b$ is true iff $a > b$ is false.

The Least Upper Bound Axiom

Definition 3.1. Let S be a subset of $\mathfrak{R}$. Then S has an **upper bound,** b, in case b is an element of $\mathfrak{R}$ such that x in $S \Rightarrow x \leq b$.

Axiom 3.14 [*Least Upper Bound Axiom*]. Each nonempty subset of $\mathfrak{R}$ that has an upper bound has a least upper bound. Explicitly this means the following. If S is a nonempty subset of $\mathfrak{R}$ and has an upper bound, then there is some b in $\mathfrak{R}$ such that

$$x \text{ in } S \Rightarrow x \leq b,$$

and, if $a < b$, then there is some s in S with $s > a$.

§ 2. *Field Theorems*

Below are stated some theorems. None has a complete proof supplied, and it is up to the reader to establish that the theorems do follow from the field axioms 3.1 through 3.8. In some cases there are hints; in others all that is missing is a justification, by reference to axioms or previous theorems, for each step.

We have asserted that there are many fields. Later we shall discuss some subfields of the real number system. The reader can readily verify that the following system is a field with just two elements. Let $S = \{0, I\}$ and define $+*$ and $\cdot*$ in S by the tables below.

$+*$	0	I		$\cdot*$	0	I
0	0	I		0	0	0
I	I	0		I	0	I

We can give a reasonable interpretation to these operations. Let 0 be the set of all even natural numbers and I the set of all odd natural numbers. The sum of any two odd numbers is even, which is an interpretation of $I +* I = 0$.

Exercise 6 on page 19 also gave an example of a field, the *residue class field modulo 3*. We get a reasonable interpretation of the operations $+$ and by taking a to be the set of all multiples of 3, b the set of all natural numbers of the form $3q + 1$, and c the set of all $3q + 2$. The sum of any number in b and any number in c is a number in a.

Theorem 3.1. If a and b are in $\Re$ and $a + b = a$, then $b = O$.

Start of Proof: By Axiom 3.7, there is some $-a$ in $\Re$ such that $O = -a + a$. If $a + b = a$, then, since $+$ is an operation and $\Re$ is closed under $+$, also $O = -a + (a + b)$.

Theorem 3.2. For all a in $\Re$ $aO = Oa = O$.

Skeleton of Proof:

$$a + aO = aI + aO$$
$$= a(I + O)$$
$$= aI$$
$$= a.$$

Theorem 3.3. Additive inverses are unique. That is, if a and b are in $\Re$ and $a + b = O$, then $b = -a$ and $a = -b$.

Axiom 3.7 states that each a in $\Re$ has an additive inverse in $\Re$: there is some $-a$ such that $a + -a = O$. This theorem states that there is only one element of $\Re$ that can be added to a to give O. In order to prove the theorem, add $-a$ to $a + b$ and to O.

Theorem 3.4. For each a in $\Re$, $-(-a) = a$.

[*Hint:* By Theorem 3.3, the additive inverse of $-a$ is the unique element you can add to $-a$ to get O.]

Theorem 3.5. If a and b are in $\Re$ and $ab = I$, then $b = a^{-1}$ and $a = b^{-1}$.

Note that since $ab = I$ and $I \neq O$, Theorem 3.2 establishes that $a \neq O$ and $b \neq O$.

Theorem 3.6. For each $a \neq O$ in $\Re$, $(a^{-1})^{-1} = a$.

Theorem 3.7. If a, b, c are in $\Re$ and $a + c = b + c$, then $a = b$.

Skeleton Proof 1:

$$a = a + O$$
$$= a + (c + -c)$$
$$= (a + c) + -c$$
$$= (b + c) + -c$$
$$= b + (c + -c)$$
$$= b.$$

Skeleton Proof 2:

$$a + c = b + c \Rightarrow (a + c) + -c = (b + c) + -c$$
$$\Rightarrow a + (c + -c) = b + (c + -c)$$
$$\Rightarrow a + 0 = b + 0$$
$$\Rightarrow a = b.$$

Theorem 3.8.   If a, b, c are in $\Re$ and $ac = bc$ and $c \neq 0$, then $a = b$.

Theorem 3.9.   For all a and b in $\Re$, $a(-b) = -(ab)$.

Because of Theorem 3.3, we need only prove that $ab + a(-b) = 0$.

Theorem 3.10.   For each a in $\Re$, $(-a)(-a) = aa$.

Skeleton Proof:

$$(-a)(-a) = -[(-a)a]$$
$$= -[a(-a)]$$
$$= -[-(aa)]$$
$$= aa.$$

Theorem 3.11.   If a and b are in $\Re$ and $ab = 0$, then $a = 0$ or $b = 0$. [*Hint:* If $b \neq 0$, b has a multiplicative inverse.]

Theorem 3.12.   For a and b in $\Re$, there is one and only one x in $\Re$ such that $a + x = b$.

Definition 3.2 [*Subtraction*].   For a and b in $\Re$, $a - b = a + -b$.

Theorem 3.13.   For all a, b, c, in $\Re$,

$$a(b - c) = ab - ac.$$

Outline of Proof:

$$ab - ac = ab + -(ac)$$
$$= ab + a(-c)$$
$$= a(b + -c)$$
$$= a(b - c).$$

Theorem 3.14.   If a and b, $b \neq 0$, are in $\Re$, then there is one and only one x in $\Re$ such that $a = bx$.

Definition 3.3 [*Division*].   If a and b, $b \neq 0$, are in $\Re$, then

$$\frac{a}{b} = ab^{-1}.$$

Theorem 3.15. If $a \neq 0$ and $b \neq 0$ are in $\mathfrak{R}$, then

$(ab)^{-1} = b^{-1}a^{-1}$.

To prove this, multiply ab by $b^{-1}a^{-1}$.

Theorem 3.16. If a, b, c, d are in $\mathfrak{R}$ and $b \neq 0$ and $d \neq 0$, then

(1) $\quad \dfrac{a}{b} \cdot \dfrac{c}{d} = \dfrac{ac}{bd}$

and

(2) $\quad \dfrac{a}{b} + \dfrac{c}{d} = \dfrac{ad + bc}{bd}$.

Outline of Proof of Equation (2):

$$\frac{ad + bc}{bd} = (ad + bc)(bd)^{-1}$$

$$= (ad + bc)(d^{-1}b^{-1})$$

$$= (ad)(d^{-1}b^{-1}) + (bc)(d^{-1}b^{-1})$$

$$= ab^{-1} + cd^{-1}$$

$$= \frac{a}{b} + \frac{c}{d}.$$

Theorem 3.17. If a, b, c, d are in $\mathfrak{R}$ and $b \neq 0$ and $d \neq 0$, then

$$\frac{a}{b} - \frac{c}{d} = \frac{ad - bc}{bd}.$$

Theorem 3.18. If a and b are in $\mathfrak{R}$ and $a \neq 0$ and $b \neq 0$, then

$$\left(\frac{a}{b}\right)^{-1} = \frac{b}{a}.$$

Theorem 3.19. If a and b are in $\mathfrak{R}$ and $b \neq 0$, then

$$-\left(\frac{a}{b}\right) = \frac{-a}{b} = \frac{a}{-b}.$$

Outline of a Proof:

$$\frac{a}{b} + \frac{-a}{b} = 0 = \frac{a}{b} + \frac{a}{-b}.$$

Theorem 3.20. For each a in $\mathfrak{R}$, $(-I)a = -a$.

Theorem 3.21. For each $a \neq 0$ in $\mathfrak{R}$,

$$\frac{I}{a} = a^{-1}.$$

Theorem 3.22. For each $a \neq 0$ in $\mathfrak{R}$, $(-a)^{-1} = -(a^{-1})$.

§ 3. *Theorems Involving Order*

Some preliminary remarks are in order. We have already said that a real number x is positive iff $x > O$. We now define *negative:* x in $\mathfrak{R}$ is *negative* iff $x < O$. A consequence of the theorems to follow is that there are some positive real numbers, for example I and $I + I$. And there are some negative real numbers, for examples $-I$ and $-(I + I)$. Some real numbers, relatively few, have *numerals*, or standard names.

Anticipating for the moment later sections, each of the symbols 3, -5, π, $\sqrt{7}$, $-\sqrt[3]{11}$ is a numeral, the standard name of a specific real number. A numeral that starts with $-$ usually denotes a negative number. Unfortunately the same symbol $-$ is the standard way of denoting the additive inverse of a real number. The number $-\sqrt{7}$ has an additive inverse, $-(-\sqrt{7})$, which is positive. In fact, since $-\sqrt{7}$ is the additive inverse of $\sqrt{7}$,

$$-(-\sqrt{7}) = \sqrt{7}$$

by Theorem 3.4.

The theorem "If x and y are in $\mathfrak{R}$, then $(-x)y = -(xy)$" has no numerals in it, only dummies. Each of x and y may be positive, or negative, or O. This is a theorem about additive inverses, not about the product of a negative number by a positive number.

Theorems

The proofs of these theorems are left entirely to the reader. Each can be proved by use of the field and order axioms, the field theorems, and perhaps previous theorems in the present section.

Theorem 3.23. If a is in $\mathfrak{R}$, then $-a$ is positive iff a is negative. Put otherwise, $-a > O$ iff $a < O$.

Theorem 3.24. If a is in $\mathfrak{R}$ and $a \neq O$, then $aa > O$.

Theorem 3.25. $I > O$.

Theorem 3.26. If $a \neq O$ is in $\mathfrak{R}$, then $a^{-1} > O$ iff $a > O$.

Theorem 3.27. If a, b, c are in $\mathfrak{R}$ and $a + c < b + c$, then $a < b$.

Theorem 3.28. If a and b are in $\mathfrak{R}$, then $a < b$ iff $-a > -b$.

Theorem 3.29. If a, b, c are in $\mathfrak{R}$ and $c > O$ and $ac < bc$, then $a < b$.

Theorem 3.30. If a, b, c are in $\mathfrak{R}$ and $c < O$ and $a < b$, then $ac > bc$.

Theorem 3.31. If a, b, c are in $\mathfrak{R}$ and $c < O$ and $ac < bc$, then $a > b$.

Remarks: Setting $b = 0$ in Theorem 3.30 gives the result that, if a and c are negative, then ac is positive. This usually seems to be something of a mystery in high school courses. By appealing to examples involving temperatures, bank accounts, or journeys back and forth on a line, it can be made highly plausible, for example, that, $-3 + 2$ should be -1, and $2(-3)$ should be -6. Some feeling for commutativity then suggests that $(-3)2 = -6$.

In these applications no natural reasons for multiplying -2 by -3 seem to occur. But there are algebraic motives. To have closure we want $(-2)(-3)$ to be a number, say $(-2)(-3) = q$; also, $(-2)3 = -6$. Therefore, $(-2)(-3) + (-2)(3) = q + -6$.

Now we also want to preserve the distributive law, so we want $-2(-3 + 3) = q + -6$, or $-2 \cdot 0 = q + -6$.

Since (again by the distributive law [see Theorem 3.2]) $-2 \cdot 0 = 0$, we must have $q = 6$.

§ 4. *The Real Integers*

So far we have standard names for only a few real numbers: 0, I, and $-I$. By Theorem 3.25, $I > 0$, and from this and Axiom 3.12,

$$I + I > I + 0 = I.$$

Therefore, $I + I > 0$ and $I + I \neq 0$, or $-I \neq I$. We couldn't have established this without some use of order axioms because in the field with only two elements the multiplicative identity is its own additive inverse.

We want to establish a one-to-one correspondence, the natural one, of the set $\mathfrak{N}$ of natural numbers to the set of real numbers consisting of 0, I, $I + I$, $I + I + I$, ... To do this we shall undertake a little temporary renaming. We have, for example, two different operations named $+$, one in $\mathfrak{N}$ the other in $\mathfrak{R}$. In order to avoid confusion we shall rename the natural number system $(\mathfrak{N}; \oplus, \odot; \otimes)$. The circled symbols are simply the familiar operations and order relation renamed. For example,

$$2 \oplus 3 = 5, \quad 4 \otimes 7, \quad 2 \odot 4 = 8.$$

The circled symbols go between natural numbers. The uncircled symbols $+$, $\cdot$, $<$ go between real numbers.

The tool for establishing the one-to-one correspondence we want will be Theorem 2.23. Let G be the function with domain $\mathfrak{R}$ such that, for each x in $\mathfrak{R}$, $G(x) = x + I$.

Since $\mathfrak{R}$ is closed under $+$, G is indeed a function with domain $\mathfrak{R}$, and the range of G is a subset of $\mathfrak{R}$. By Theorem 2.23 there is one and only one function g with domain $\mathfrak{N}$ such that $g(0) = 0$, and, for each n in $\mathfrak{N}$, $g(n \oplus 1) = G(g(n))$. For example,

$$g(1) = g(0 \oplus 1) = G(g(0)) = G(O) = O + I = I,$$
$$g(2) = g(1 \oplus 1) = G(g(1)) = G(I) = I + I.$$

Definition 3.4. The **nonnegative integers** are the real numbers in the range of the function g above. Then $\mathfrak{GN}$ will denote the set of all nonnegative integers; that is, $\mathfrak{GN}$ is the range of g.

Theorem 3.32, below, is the formal statement of the fact that the set of nonnegative integers, along with the operations $+$ and $\cdot$ and the order relation $<$, behaves just like the set $\mathfrak{N}$ with its operations and order relation. Technically, the two systems are *isomorphic*, and the function g is not only a one-to-one mapping of $\mathfrak{N}$ onto $\mathfrak{GN}$, but also an *isomorphism* of one system to the other. The content of the theorem can be summarized as follows: g is a one-to-one mapping of $\mathfrak{N}$ onto $\mathfrak{GN}$ which preserves addition, multiplication, and order.

For a simpler informal example of an isomorphism, let

$$T = \{1, 2, 4, 8, \ldots\}$$

be the set of all 2^k, for $k = 0, 1, 2, \ldots$. The function f: for n in $\mathfrak{N}$, $f(n) = 2^n$, is a one-to-one mapping of $\mathfrak{N}$ onto T. For n and m in $\mathfrak{N}$, $f(n \oplus m) = 2^{n \oplus m} = 2^n \odot 2^m = f(n) \odot f(m)$. This function f is an isomorphism of $(\mathfrak{N}; \oplus)$ to $(T; \odot)$.

Theorem 3.32. The function g is an isomorphism of $(\mathfrak{N}; \oplus, \odot ; <)$ to $(\mathfrak{GN}; +, \cdot; <)$. For all n and m in $\mathfrak{N}$: (1) $g(n \oplus m) = g(n) + g(m)$; (2) $g(n \odot m) = g(n) \cdot g(m)$; (3) $n < m$ iff $g(n) < g(m)$; (4) $n \neq m \Rightarrow g(n) \neq g(m)$: that is, g is one-to-one.

PROOF: 1. Let $M = \{m$ in $\mathfrak{N} \mid$ for all n in $\mathfrak{N}$, $g(n \oplus m) = g(n) + g(m).\}$ Then 0 is in M because, for all n in $\mathfrak{N}$,

$$g(n \oplus 0) = g(n) = g(n) + O = g(n) + g(0).$$

Let m be in M. Then, for all n in $\mathfrak{N}$,

$$
\begin{aligned}
g(n \oplus [m \oplus 1]) &= g([n \oplus m] \oplus 1) \\
&= G(g(n \oplus m)) \\
&= g(n \oplus m) + I \\
&= [g(n) + g(m)] + I \\
&= g(n) + [g(m) + I] \\
&= g(n) + G(g(m)) \\
&= g(n) + g(m \oplus 1).
\end{aligned}
$$

Thus M is an inductive set containing 0, and (1) is proved.

2. Let $Q = \{m$ in $\mathfrak{N} \mid$ for all n in $\mathfrak{N}$, $g(n \odot m) = g(n) \cdot g(m).\}$ Then 0 is in Q because, for each n in $\mathfrak{N}$,

$g(n \odot 0) = g(0) = 0 = g(n) \cdot 0.$

Let m be in Q. Then, for any n in $\mathfrak{N}$,

$$g(n \odot [m \oplus 1]) = g([n \odot m] \oplus n)$$
$$= g(n \odot m) + g(n), \qquad \text{by (1),}$$
$$= g(n) \cdot g(m) + g(n) \cdot I$$
$$= g(n) \cdot [g(m) + I]$$
$$= g(n) \cdot G(g(m))$$
$$= g(n) \cdot g(m \oplus 1).$$

Thus Q is an inductive set containing 0, and (2) is proved.

3. First note that $g(1) = I > 0$. And if, for some n in $\mathfrak{N}$, $g(n) > 0$, then $g(n \oplus 1) = G(g(n)) = g(n) + I > g(n) > 0$. Hence, for each n in $\mathfrak{N}$, with $n \neq 0$, $g(n) > 0$.

If $n < m$, then there is some p in $\mathfrak{N}$, $p \neq 0$, such that $m = n \oplus p$. By (1), $g(m) = g(n) + g(p)$. Since $p \neq 0$, $g(p) > 0$ and $g(m) > g(n)$. We have established that

(a) $n < m \Rightarrow g(n) < g(m)$.

The converse follows by trichotomy. Suppose n and m are in $\mathfrak{N}$ and $g(n) < g(m)$. Since g is a function, $n \neq m$. If $m < n$, then by (a) $g(m) < g(n)$; so m is not less than n. By trichotomy, $n < m$.

4. That g is a one-one correspondence of $\mathfrak{N}$ to $\mathfrak{GN}$ is immediate from the discussion above. ∎

Exercise

We have seen before that there is a field with three elements. The set S of elements was $\{a, b, c\}$ and the operations were defined in such a way that a is the 0 element and b the I element. Let h be the function with domain $\mathfrak{N}$ such that

$h(0) = a.$

For all n in $\mathfrak{N}$, $h(n \oplus 1) = h(n) + b$. Compute $h(n)$ for $n \leq 10$. How much of Theorem 3.32 applies to h?

Consequences of the Isomorphic Embedding of $\mathfrak{N}$ into $\mathfrak{R}$.

One consequence, since we already have a name for each natural number, is that we now automatically have names for the nonnegative integers—names such as $g(14)$, $g(53)$, $g(2017)$. Another is that anyone who can compute with natural numbers can compute with nonnegative integers. Because

$14 \oplus 53 = 67,$

$g(14) + g(53) = g(67).$

Also, since we have additive inverses for each real number, and have defined a/b for $b \neq 0$, we have names for real numbers such as $-g(15)$ or $g(2)/g(7)$.

As an exercise, compute $\dfrac{g(2)}{g(7)} + \dfrac{g(3)}{g(5)}$.

There is an alternative possibility: simplify the notation by simply dropping the g. That is, speak of real numbers 0, 1, 2, 14, and so on; use n as an abbreviation for $g(n)$. Since it is undesirable to have a symbol, say 14, denote two different things—the natural number 14 and the real number $g(14)$—we shall discard the system $(\mathfrak{N}; \oplus, \odot; \lessdot)$ and use in its place the system $(\mathfrak{R}\mathfrak{N}; +, \cdot; <)$.

Before doing this we make sure that some essential properties of the natural number system carry over to the system of nonnegative integers.

Theorem 3.33. Let S be a subset of $\mathfrak{R}$ such that (1) some nonnegative integer a is in S, and (2) x in $S \Rightarrow x + I$ in S. Then S contains every nonnegative integer b such that $a \leq b$.

PROOF: Since a is a nonnegative integer, there is some natural number k such that $g(k) = a$. Let M be the set of all n in $\mathfrak{N}$ such that $g(n)$ is in S. In particular, k is in M.

If n is in M, then $g(n)$ is in S. By (2), $g(n) + I$ is also in S. But

$$g(n) + I = g(n) + g(1) = g(n \oplus 1).$$

Thus n in $M \Rightarrow n \oplus 1$ in M.

Thus k and each $n > k$ are in M. By definition of M, $g(n)$ is in S for every $n \geqslant k$. But a nonnegative integer b is greater than a iff $b = g(n)$ for some $n \geqslant k = g(a)$. Thus the theorem is proved. In particular, if S is a set of real numbers containing O and with the property that x in $S \Rightarrow x + I$ in S, then S contains every nonnegative integer. ∎

Theorem 3.34. The set $\mathfrak{R}\mathfrak{N}$ is closed under addition and multiplication. If a is in $\mathfrak{R}\mathfrak{N}$ and $a \neq O$, then $-a$ is not in $\mathfrak{R}\mathfrak{N}$. If a is in $\mathfrak{R}\mathfrak{N}$ and $a \neq I$, then a^{-1} is not in $\mathfrak{R}\mathfrak{N}$.

PROOF: If a and b are in $\mathfrak{R}\mathfrak{N}$, the range of g, there are natural numbers m and n such that $g(m) = a$ and $g(n) = b$. By the isomorphism theorem, $a + b = g(m \oplus n)$ and $ab = g(m \odot n)$, so $a + b$ and ab are in $\mathfrak{R}\mathfrak{N}$.

If a and b are in $\mathfrak{R}\mathfrak{N}$ and $a + b = O = g(0)$, then, with m and n as above, $g(m \oplus n) = O$ and, since g is one-to-one, $m \oplus n = 0$. From this, $m = n = 0$ and $a = b = O$. Similarly, if $ab = I$, then $mn = 1$ and

$$m = n = 1. \qquad \blacksquare$$

As an informal exercise, prove that every nonempty subset of $\mathfrak{R}\mathfrak{N}$ has a smallest member.

Notational Changes

We now abandon $\mathfrak{N}$ and replace the natural number system by the system $(\mathfrak{RN}; +, \cdot; <)$.

Old Names	New Names
O	0
I	1
$I + I$	2
$I + I + I$	3
$\cdots$	$\cdots$
$g(n)$	n
$\cdots$	$\cdots$

Definition 3.5 [*The Real Integers*]. Let $\mathbb{Z}$ be the set which is the union of $\mathfrak{RN}$ and the set of all additive inverses of members of $\mathfrak{RN}$. The members of $\mathbb{Z}$ are **integers.** If x is in $\mathbb{Z}$ but not in $\mathfrak{RN}$, then x is **a negative integer.**

Exercises

1. Show that the system $(\mathbb{Z}; +, \cdot)$ satisfies all the field axioms except the axiom about multiplicative inverses, but that the only elements of $\mathbb{Z}$ which have multiplicative inverses in $\mathbb{Z}$ are 1 and -1. [Because $a + b = b + a$ for all a and b in $\mathfrak{R}$, then in particular $a + b = b + a$ if a and b are in $\mathbb{Z}$. This is so trivial that there is no point in doing it. Both operations are commutative and associative, and the distributive law holds. Also, 0 and 1 are in $\mathbb{Z}$ because they are in $\mathfrak{RN}$. The interesting questions are closure and inverses.]
2. Prove that if a, b, c are in $\mathbb{Z}$ and $ac = bc$ and $c \neq 0$, then $a = b$. [*Hint:* c has a multiplicative inverse in $\mathfrak{R}$.]
3. Prove that $(\mathbb{Z}, +, \cdot, <)$ satisfies all the order axioms and the least upper bound axiom (Axioms 3.9 through 3.14). [For this last axiom, show that a subset of $\mathbb{Z}$ which has an upper bound in $\mathbb{Z}$ has a least upper bound in $\mathbb{Z}$.]

Theorem 3.35 [*The Archimedian Property* of the Real Numbers]. If x and y are positive real numbers, then there is a real integer n, necessarily positive, such that $nx > y$.

PROOF: If the theorem is false, then there are positive x and y such that the set $\{nx \mid n$ in $\mathbb{Z}\}$ has y as an upper bound. By the least upper bound axiom the set has a least upper bound, say b. We shall prove that this is impossible. Let b be the least upper bound of the set. Then, since $x > 0$, $b - x < b$, and $b - x$ is not an upper bound of the set. So there is some member of the set larger than $b - x$.

That is, for some n in $\mathbb{Z}$, $nx > b - x$. From this, $nx + x > b - x + x$, or $(n + 1)x > b$. But $(n + 1)x$ is in our set, so that our hypothetical least upper bound b is seen not to be an upper bound. Hence the set $\{nx \mid n$ in $\mathbb{Z}\}$ has no upper bound. In particular, y isn't one. ∎

Corollary to Theorem 3.35. If ϵ is a positive real number, then there are positive integers n such that $1/n < \epsilon$.

PROOF: If $\epsilon > 0$, then $1/\epsilon > 0$; also $1 > 0$. By Theorem 3.35 there is a positive integer n such that $n \cdot 1 > 1/\epsilon$, which implies $1/n < \epsilon$. If m is any integer larger than n, then also $1/m < \epsilon$. ∎

§ 5. *The Rational Real Numbers*

Definition 3.6. A real number r is **rational** iff there are integers a and b, $b \neq 0$, such that $r = a/b = ab^{-1}$.

For example, $0 = 0/1$, $5/2$, $10/4$, $-6/3$ are rational numbers.

Theorem 3.36. If a, b, c, d are integers and $b \neq 0$ and $d \neq 0$, then $a/b = c/d$ iff $ad = bc$. Furthermore, if $b > 0$ and $d > 0$, then $a/b < c/d$ iff $ad < bc$.

PROOF: The proof is left to the reader.

As an example of this theorem,

$$\frac{-3}{5} < \frac{-4}{7} \quad \text{because} \quad -21 < -20.$$

Consider a rational number $a/b = ab^{-1}$, where a and b are integers and $b \neq 0$. Since $(-b)^{-1} = -(b^{-1})$ [Theorem 3.22], $(-a)(-b)^{-1} = ab^{-1} = a/b$. That is, $-a/-b = a/b$. Either b or $-b$ is positive and consequently each rational number can be represented as a quotient of integers with a positive denominator.

Definition 3.7. Let r be a rational number. The *standard name* of r or **reduced form** of r is the quotient a/b, where b is the smallest positive integer such that, for an appropriate integer a, $r = a/b$.

For example,

$$r = \frac{-17}{-51} = \frac{17}{51} = \frac{1}{3} = \frac{-2}{-6} = \frac{100}{300}.$$

The reduced form of r is $\frac{1}{3}$.

Each integer is also a rational number. Its reduced form has the denominator 1.

We shall write $\mathbb{Q}$ for the set of all rational numbers.

Exercises

1. Prove that the system $(Q; +, \cdot)$ is a field. Don't bother with obvious statements, such as that $+$ is commutative in Q, but make sure you establish the crucial properties.
2. Prove that $(Q; +, \cdot; <)$ is an ordered field. We shall show later that this rational field does not satisfy the least upper bound axiom, but that statement does not make a suitable exercise.

§ **6.** *Pictures and Diagrams*

The *real line* is simply the set of real numbers, called points and thought of in the context of the two definitions below.

Definition 3.8. If a and b are real numbers, the **directed distance** from a to b is $b - a$.

Definition 3.9 [*Preliminary*]. For any real number a, the distance between a and a is 0. If a and b are real numbers, with $a \neq b$, the **distance between** a and b is $a - b$ or $b - a$, whichever is positive.

This definition of *distance between* is awkward, but is easily smoothed out by the definition of the *absolute value* function on the real numbers. This function assigns to each real number x a nonnegative real number, written $|x|$ and called *the absolute value of x*.

Definition 3.10. For x real,

if $x \geq 0,$ $|x| = x,$

if $x < 0,$ $|x| = -x.$

From this definition follows immediately

Theorem 3.37.

$|0| = 0.$

If $x \neq 0$ is a real number, then $|x| = x$ or $-x$, whichever is positive.

We can now redefine *distance between* more briefly.

Definition 3.11. If a and b are real numbers, the **distance between** a and b is $|a - b|$.

Along with this formal definition goes an informal picture. We draw, mentally or on paper, a segment of a straight line. That is, we draw with pencil and ruler a streak which suggests a piece of our mental image of a straight line.

On this segment of line, which we imagine extendable as far as we please in both directions, we select a point and call it 0 and select a point to the right of 0 and call it 1.

Now, in imagination, we mark each integer on the line in such a way that the distance [psychophysical distance] from n to $n + 1$ is, for each n in Z, the same as the distance from 0 to 1.

Thus part of the picture is the following.

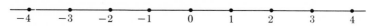

Eventually we want to think, informally, of a one-to-one correspondence of $\Re$ to the points of the line. In this chapter we shall only be concerned with a one-to-one correspondence of Q to a subset of the points on the line.

We are not stating any geometric axioms about our line. It is simply a picture that we find helpful. None of our pictures or diagrams will prove anything, but generations of experience have shown that such pictures are extremely helpful. They suggest proofs, conjectures, theorems, and counter-examples.

Exercises

Each of the first four exercises below simply states a theorem; the exercise is to prove it. The most direct proof may be by an inelegant but convincing examination of cases.

For example, consider the statement

$$|x + y| \leq |x| + |y|.$$

If $x = 0$ or $y = 0$, this is true with $=$ for $\leq$. If both numbers are positive, or both are negative, the statement is true with $=$ for $\leq$. If one is positive and the other negative, then $|x + y| < |x| + |y|$. [Why?] This completes an outline of a proof that, for all x, y in $\Re$,

$$|x + y| \leq |x| + |y|.$$

For any real number x, $|x| = |x - 0|$ is by definition the distance between the point x and the point 0. It is then clear in our intuitive model that if x and y are real numbers such that $|x| = |y|$ [that is, if x and y are equally distant from 0], then necessarily either $x = y$ or $x = -y$. The fact that this intuitively clear statement can be proved as a theorem is a confirmation that our definition of *distance between* is appropriate: we can use $\Re$ and the absolute value function to get a formal model of the intuitive line.

Theorem 3.38.   If x and y are in $\Re$, then $|x| = |y|$ iff $x = y$ or $x = -y$.

Theorem 3.39.   For all x and y in $\Re$, $|xy| = |x|\,|y|$.

Theorem 3.40. For all x and y in $\mathfrak{R}$, $|x + y| \leq |x| + |y|$.

Theorem 3.41. For all x and y in $\mathfrak{R}$, $|x - y| \leq |x| + |y|$. [*Hint:* $x - y = x + (-y)$.]

The following exercises should now present no difficulties.

1. Prove that $|x - 3| < 0.2$ iff $2.8 < x < 3.2$. [*Hint:* If $x - 3 \geq 0$, then $|x - 3| = x - 3$, and to satisfy the inequality $|x - 3| < 0.2$, $3 \leq x < 3.2$.]
2. Prove that $|x - 7| < 2$ iff $5 < x < 9$.
3. On a diagram of part of the real line, mark the points 3, 4, 5, and all points x such that $|x - 4| < \frac{1}{10}$.
4. If a is a real number and ϵ is a positive real number, prove that $|x - a| < \epsilon$ iff $a - \epsilon < x < a + \epsilon$.

Intervals

Definition 3.12. Let a and b be any real numbers such that $a < b$. The **open interval** (a, b) and **closed interval** $[a, b]$ are defined as

$$(a, b) = \{x \mid a < x < b\},$$
$$[a, b] = \{x \mid a \leq x \leq b\}.$$

$$a \qquad b$$

To picture the open interval (a, b) one must erase the points a and b, but no other points in the diagram above.

Definition 3.13 [*Neighborhood*]. Let c be a real number and ϵ a positive number. The open interval $(c - \epsilon, c + \epsilon)$ is called a **neighborhood** of c.

Thus a neighborhood of c is any open interval centered on c.

Exercises

1. Prove that if (a, b) is an open interval and c is in (a, b), then some neighborhood of c is a subinterval [that is, an interval and a subset] of (a, b). In other words, prove that there is a positive number ϵ such that $|x - c| < \epsilon \Rightarrow x$ is in (a, b). A diagram will suggest an appropriate ϵ.
2. Prove that the intersection of two closed intervals is either empty, or a one-point set, or a closed interval. What can you say about the intersection of two open intervals?
3. Let $[a, b]$ be a closed interval and n a positive integer. Prove that $[a, b]$ is the union of n subintervals where, for each integer k such that $1 \leq k \leq n$, the kth subinterval is

$$\left[a + (k - 1)\frac{b - a}{n}, a + k\frac{b - a}{n}\right].$$

Definition 3.14. For any real a and b, with $a < b$, the **length** of $[a, b]$ is $b - a$, and so is the length of (a, b).

Exercise 3 above says that, for any positive integer n, an interval $[a, b]$ can be partitioned into n subintervals each of length $(b - a)/n$.

Farey Sections

The English geologist John Farey (1776–1826) once set out, in connection with a study of crystals, to write down in the proper linear order the set of all rational numbers between 0 and 1 with reasonably small denominator.* He made a discovery so interesting that we now, for each positive integer n, call the set of all rational numbers with denominator $\leq n$ the *Farey section of order n, F_n*. Thus F_1 is just the set of all integers, all rational numbers with denominator 1. F_2 is the union of F_1 with the set of all numbers $n + \frac{1}{2}$, n in $\mathbb{Z}$.

We can think of F_1 as partitioning the real line into subintervals of length 1, and we shall speak of the intervals $[n, n + 1]$, n in $\mathbb{Z}$, as the intervals of F_1. Similarly, the intervals of F_2 are the intervals $[n, n + \frac{1}{2}]$ and $[n + \frac{1}{2}, n + 1]$, n in $\mathbb{Z}$. Clearly, each real number is in at least one and at most two of the intervals of F_1 or of F_2.

Below are diagrams of the restrictions of F_3, F_4, and F_5 to the interval $[0, 1]$.

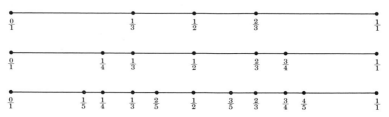

Farey's discovery was that F_5, for example, is obtained from F_4 by putting numbers with denominator 5 only between adjacent numbers a/b and c/d in F_4, where $b + d = 5$. Furthermore, if $[a/b, c/d]$ is an interval in a Farey section, then its length is $1/bd$.

In order to establish what we want to about Farey sections it will be convenient to have a preliminary definition and a lemma.

Suppose b and d are positive integers and that a/b and c/d are rational numbers such that $a/b < c/d$. Then the length of the interval $[a/b, c/d]$ is $(c/d) - (a/b) = (bc - ad)/bd$. By hypothesis, $bc - ad$ is a positive integer, and the length of $[a/b, c/d]$ is at least $1/bd$.

---

* In this section rational numbers are assumed to be in reduced form.

Definition 3.15. If a/b and c/d are rational numbers, with b and d positive integers and $a/b < c/d$, then the interval $[a/b, c/d]$ is **minimal** in case its length is $1/bd$ [that is, in case $bc - ad = 1$].

Lemma About Minimal Intervals. If $[a/b, c/d]$ is a minimal interval, then

(1)
$$\frac{a}{b} < \frac{a+c}{b+d} < \frac{c}{d},$$

(2) each of
$$\left[\frac{a}{b}, \frac{a+c}{b+d}\right] \quad \text{and} \quad \left[\frac{a+c}{b+d}, \frac{c}{d}\right]$$

is a minimal interval,

(3) if p/q is a rational number, with q a positive integer, and $a/b < p/q < c/d$, then $q \geq b + d$.

PROOF: To establish both (1) and (2), observe that
$$\frac{a+c}{b+d} - \frac{a}{b} = \frac{ab + cb - ab - ad}{(b+d)b} = \frac{1}{(b+d)b},$$

and
$$\frac{c}{d} - \frac{a+c}{b+d} = \frac{1}{d(b+d)}.$$

To establish (3), observe that if
$$\frac{a}{b} < \frac{p}{q} < \frac{c}{d},$$

then
$$\frac{c}{d} - \frac{a}{b} = \left(\frac{c}{d} - \frac{p}{q}\right) + \left(\frac{p}{q} - \frac{a}{b}\right),$$

or
$$\frac{1}{bd} = \frac{cq - pd}{dq} + \frac{pb - aq}{qb}.$$

Since each of the fractions on the right side of the last equation is positive and has a positive denominator, each has a positive numerator, an integer ≥ 1. Thus,
$$\frac{1}{bd} \geq \frac{1}{dq} + \frac{1}{qb}.$$

Multiplying this inequality by the positive number bdq gives
$$q \geq b + d. \quad \blacksquare$$

If $[a/b, c/d]$ is a minimal interval we shall call $(a + c)/(b + d)$ the *mediant* of the interval. The mediant of a minimal interval is located geometrically by (2) of the lemma. The original interval has length $1/bd$, the sub-intervals $[a/b, (a + c)/(b + d)]$ and $[(a + c)/(b + d), c/d]$ have lengths $1/b(b + d)$ and $1/(b + d)d$, respectively. To locate the mediant, partition the original interval into $b + d$ subintervals each of length $1/bd(b + d)$ and locate the mediant at the right end point of the dth subinterval. This merely means that, if $bc - ad = 1$, then

$$\frac{a}{b} + d \cdot \frac{1}{bd(b + d)} = \frac{a + c}{b + d},$$

which is an algebraic fact.

Suppose now that for some positive integer n the Farey section F_n has the following properties.

1. For each a/b in F_n, the smallest number in F_n larger than a/b is a number c/d such that the interval $[a/b, c/d]$ is minimal.

2. The real line is the union of all the intervals of F_n, no two of which intersect in more than one point.

Let $[a/b, c/d]$ be an interval of F_n. Since the mediant $(a + c)/(b + d)$ is between the end points but not in F_n, $b + d > n$. If $b + d > n + 1$, then $[a/b, c/d]$ is also an interval of F_{n+1}. If $b + d = n + 1$, then each of $[a/b, (a + c)/(b + d)]$ and $[(a + c)/(b + d), c/d]$ is a minimal interval of F_{n+1}.

Finally, let $p/(n + 1)$ be any reduced fraction with denominator $n + 1$. By property 2 of F_n, this member of F_{n+1} is in some interval of F_n, and by the lemma must be the mediant of the interval.

This establishes

Theorem 3.42. For each positive integer n, F_n partitions the real line into a union of minimal intervals, no two of which intersect in more than one point; F_{n+1} is obtained from F_n by inserting all mediants with denominator $n + 1$.

Exercises

1. Mark on a line the points of F_1, F_2, F_3, and F_4 in the interval $[-2, 2]$.
2. Starting with the diagram on page 56 of the restriction of F_5 to the unit interval, insert the points of F_6 and F_7, locating them geometrically in accord with the discussion on page 57.
3. Verify that $[37/29, 23/18]$ is a minimal interval. Find all rational numbers in this interval with denominator less than 100.
4. Let f be the function assigning to each positive real number t the number $(2 + 5t)/(3 + 7t)$. Prove that f is a one-to-one correspondence of the set of positive real numbers to the open interval $(2/3, 5/7)$.
5. The fraction $23/17$ is reduced and between $4/3$ and $3/2$. Find it as the mediant of a minimal interval. Then find at least five pairs of integers x and y such that $23x + 17y = 1$.

§ 7. *Basic Arithmetic Theorems*

The theorems of this section are concerned with integers only and form a small but essential part of the subject known as "elementary theory of numbers." The essential content could be stated, sometimes a little awkwardly, in terms of positive integers only, and is to be found in *Euclid*.

If a and d are integers, then d is a divisor of a in case a is a multiple of d—that is, in case there is some integer q such that $a = qd$. Since $0 = 0d$ for every integer d, every integer is a divisor of 0. If $a \neq 0$ and d is a divisor of a, then $|d| \leq |a|$, so that for $a \neq 0$ the set of positive divisors of a is a bounded set of positive integers, nonempty because it contains 1 and $|a|$.

It follows that if a and b are integers, not both 0, then the set of positive common divisors of a and b has a largest member, the *greatest common divisor* (gcd) of a and b. For any integer $b \neq 0$, the gcd of 0 and b is $|b|$. Integers a and b are *relatively prime* if the gcd of a and b is 1. For example, 35 and 12 are relatively prime.

As an exercise, prove that if d is the gcd of a and b, and if $a = a'd$ and $b = b'd$, then a' and b' are relatively prime.

The paragraphs above summarize informally some very familiar definitions and easy theorems. Before stating any theorems formally, we might add that an integer p is a *prime* if p has exactly two positive divisors, 1 and $|p|$. Thus 2 is the smallest positive prime.

Theorem 3.43. If a is an integer and b an integer $\neq 0$, then there are unique integers q and r such that

$$a = qb + r, \qquad 0 \leq r < |b|.$$

PROOF: If $b > 0$ and $a \geq 0$, this follows by isomorphism from the corresponding theorem about the natural numbers.

If $b > 0$ and $a < 0$, then there are unique q and r, with $0 \leq r < b$, such that

$$-a = qb + r,$$

$$a = (-q)b - r.$$

If $r = 0$, the last equation is what we want. If $0 < r < b$, then

$$a = (-q - 1)b + (b - r), \qquad 0 < b - r < b.$$

Thus the theorem is proved for a any integer, if $b > 0$. For $b < 0$, there are, for any a, unique q and r such that

$$a = q|b| + r, \qquad 0 \leq r < |b|.$$

Then

$$a = (-q)b + r, \qquad 0 \leq r < |b|. \qquad \blacksquare$$

Theorem 3.44.   If a is an integer and b is a positive integer, then the fraction a/b is reduced if and only if a and b are relatively prime.

Recall that the definition of *reduced* was that a/b is the reduced form of a rational number r iff b is the smallest positive integer such that, for some integer a, $r = a/b$.

PROOF OF *only if*:   Let d be the gcd of a and b and let $a = a'd, b = b'd$. Then $a/b = a'd/b'd = a'/b'$, and a/b is reduced only if $d = 1$ and $b' = b$.

PROOF OF *if*:   This is not quite so easy. For example, since $272 \cdot 65 - 83 \cdot 213 = 1$, any positive common divisor of 272 and 213 is a positive divisor of 1, and has to be 1. Thus 272 and 213 are relatively prime. Why does it follow that $272/213$ is reduced? that there are no positive integers c and d, $d < 213$, such that $272d = 213c$?

Our argument will be that if $272/213 = 1 + (59/213)$ is not reduced, then neither $59/213$ or $213/59$ is reduced. But 213 and 59 are relatively prime; so if we already had the theorem for all denominators < 213, then also $272/213$ is reduced.

To proceed with a proof, first suppose $b = 1$. For any integer a, a and 1 are relatively prime and $a/1$ is reduced.

For $b > 1$ and a relatively prime to b, there are q and r, $0 \le r < b$, such that

$$a = qb + r.$$

Since the gcd of a and b is $1 \neq b$, b is not a divisor of a, and $r > 0$. Thus $a/b = q + (r/b)$ where $0 < r/b < 1$. If a/b is not reduced, then there are integers c and d, with $0 < d < b$, such that $a/b = c/d$. Then $r/b = (a/b) - q = (c/d) - q = (c - dq)/d$, and r/b is not reduced because $0 < d < b$.

Since $a = qb + r$, any common divisor of b and r is a divisor of a; so r and b are relatively prime.

We have shown that if for some integer $b > 1$ there is an integer a such that a and b are relatively prime but a/b is not reduced, then also there is an integer r, $0 < r < b$, such that r and b are relatively prime, but r/b is not reduced.

From this it follows that there are integers e and f, $0 < f < b$, such that $r/b = e/f$. This implies that $0 < e < r$ and that $b/r = f/e$, and b/r is not reduced.

The set of positive integers b such that, for some a, a and b are relatively prime, but a/b is not reduced, is a set of positive integers which, by the argument above, has no smallest member. Thus the set is empty, and the theorem is proved.   ∎

Theorem 3.45.   If a and b are relatively prime integers, there are integers x and y such that

$$ax + by = 1.$$

First, two trivial cases. If a and 0 are relatively prime, then $a = 1$ or -1, and $aa + 0y = 1$ for any y. If $|b| = 1$, then $0a + bb = 1$ for any a.

For $b > 1$ and a relatively prime to b, a/b is reduced and appears as a mediant in the Farey section F_b. Say a/b is the mediant of the interval $[c/d, e/f]$. Then $da - cb = 1$, and $(-f)a + eb = 1$.

If $b < -1$ and a is relatively prime to b, then a and $-b$ are also relatively prime and there are x and y such that

$$1 = ax + (-b)y = ax + b(-y).$$

Theorem 3.46. If a, b, c are integers, a is a divisor of bc, and a and b are relatively prime, then a is a divisor of c.

PROOF: Since a divides bc, there is some integer k such that $bc = ka$. Since a and b are relatively prime, there are integers x and y such that

$$ax + by = 1.$$

Then $acx + bcy = c$, or $acx + kay = c$, and

$$a(cx + ky) = c. \qquad ∎$$

Theorem 3.47. If n is a positive integer and there is a rational number r such that $r^2 = n$, then r is an integer.

PROOF: Suppose $r^2 = n$ and let a/b be the reduced form of r. Then $a^2/b^2 = n$, or $a^2 = nb^2$. Then b is a factor of the product $a^2 = aa$.

But b and the first factor of the product, a, are relatively prime; by Theorem 3.46 then, b divides the second factor, a. Since b is relatively prime to a and also a positive divisor of a, $b = 1$ and r is an integer. ∎

Exercises

1. Prove that 55 has no rational square root.
2. Find the smallest positive integers x and y such that $29x - 17y = 1$.
3. Find positive integers x and y such that $87x - 51y = 3$.
4. Observing that, for any integer t, $29(17t) - 17(29t) = 0$, find a formula for infinitely many pairs of integers x and y such that $29x - 17y = 1$.
5. Prove that, if d is the gcd of a and b, there are integers x and y such that $ax + by = d$. [*Hint:* Let $a = a'd$, $b = b'd$ and apply Theorem 3.46 to a' and b'.]
6. Verify that 101 and 103 are primes. If p is a positive prime, the only possible common divisors of p and 101 are 1 and p. Prove that if p is a positive prime and $pq = (101)(103)$, then $p = 101$ or 103.
7. Prove that if p, q, r, s, t are positive primes, then $pq \neq rst$.
8. Prove that if the equation $x^3 - x - 2 = 0$ has a rational root a/b, then $a/b = 1$ or 2 or -1 or -2. [*Hint:* If a and b are relatively prime and $a^3 - ab^2 - 2b^3 = 0$, then by Theorem 3.47 a is a divisor of 2 and b is a divisor of 1.]
9. Are there any rational numbers x such that $x^3 = x + 1$?

§ 8.   *Square Roots*

Let D be a positive real number. If x is a positive real and $x^2 < D$, it seems intuitively clear that there should be numbers y a "little bigger" than x such that $y > x$ but $y^2 < D$. Also, if $x^2 > D$, we should be able to find y such that $y < x$ but $y^2 > D$.

Dedekind [8, page 14] gives an elegant formula. Given $D > 0$, to each positive x let correspond the positive number y given by the formula

$$(1) \quad y = \frac{x(x^2 + 3D)}{3x^2 + D}.$$

A little computation shows that (1) implies both (2) and (3):

$$(2) \quad y = x + \frac{2x}{3x^2 + D}(D - x^2),$$

$$(3) \quad y^2 = D + \frac{(x^2 - D)^2}{(3x^2 + D)^2}(x^2 - D).$$

Inspection of (2) and (3) shows that if $x^2 < D$ (with $x > 0$), then $y > x$ but $y^2 < D$. Also, if $x^2 > D$, then $y < x$ but $y^2 > D$.

Now choose D to be a rational number with no rational square root. Specifically, let $D = 5$. Since 5 is not the square of an integer, 5 is not, by Theorem 3.48, the square of any rational number.

Let S be the set of positive *rational* x such that $x^2 < 5$, and let T be the set of positive rational x such that $x^2 > 5$. A glance at equation (1), with $D = 5$, shows that to each rational x corresponds a rational y. Hence, for each x in S, formula (1) produces a rational number y with $y > x$ but $y^2 < 5$, so that y is also in S. That is, S has no largest element.

Similarly, if x is in T, then (1) produces y in T with $y < x$; T has no smallest element.

The set S is bounded. In fact each t in T is an upper bound of S because, if $t^2 > 5$ and $x^2 < 5$, it follows easily, for positive x and t, that $x < t$. Also, since S has no largest member, no member of S is an upper bound of S. Thus the set of rational upper bounds of S is exactly the set T. But T has no smallest element.

Thus S is an example of a set of rational numbers with a rational upper bound, but no *rational* least upper bound. This shows that the rational field does not satisfy the least upper bound axiom and that there must be real numbers which are not rational.

[Let S' be the union of S with the set of all nonpositive rational numbers. Then each rational number is in S' or in T, and each number in S' is less than any number in T. The ordered pair (S', T) is an example of what Dedekind called a *cut*. With an appropriate definition of multiplication of cuts we get $(S', T)(S', T) = (A, B)$, where A is the set of all rational r such that $r \leq 5$ and B is the set of all rational numbers > 5. Then (A, B) is the Dedekind cut which defines the real number 5. Of course Dedekind's construction of the real numbers assumes the rational field as a known object.]

Now, let D be any positive real number. Let U be the set of positive real x such that $x^2 < D$, and let V be the set of positive real x such that $x^2 > D$.

As shown above, from (1), (2), and (3), U has no largest member and V has no smallest member. Also, U has an upper bound: any member of V is an upper bound of U, and V is not empty because, for example, $D + \frac{1}{2}$ is in V since $(D + \frac{1}{2})^2 > D$.

By the least upper bound axiom, U has a least upper bound, say L. There are positive numbers in U: for example, if m is the smallest positive integer such that $1/m < D$, then $(1/m)^2 \leq 1/m < D$, and $1/m$ is in U. So $L > 0$.

Finally, L is a positive number which is not in U, because no member of U is an upper bound of U, and is not in V, because for each x in V there is some y in V such that y is an upper bound for U but $y < x$. Because L is not in U, $L^2 \not< D$. Because L is not in V, $L^2 \not> D$. By trichotomy, $L^2 = D$.

It is clear that if $0 < x < L$, then $x^2 < L^2$, and that if $x > L$, then $x^2 > L^2$. Thus we have proved

Theorem 3.48. If D is a positive real number, then there is one and only one positive real number L such that $L^2 = D$.

Definition 3.16.

$$\sqrt{0} = 0.$$

If $D > 0$, then $\sqrt{D}$ is the positive real number such that $(\sqrt{D})^2 = D$.

Corollary to Definition 3.16. For every real number x, $\sqrt{x^2} = |x|$.

To conclude, we point out that in any field F the equation $x^2 = a$, for a in F, can have at most two solutions. For suppose there is some x_1 in F such that $x_1^2 = a$. Then, if x is in F and $x^2 = a$, we have $x^2 = x_1^2$ and $(x - x_1)(x + x_1) = 0$. If $x \neq x_1$, then $x - x_1 \neq 0$ and, by the cancellation law, $x + x_1 = 0$, or $x = -x_1$.

Exercises on Bounds

These exercises are an essential prat of the text. They establish results which are crucial whenever needed. All are easy, perhaps especially when considered abstractly rather than in a particular context. A usual way of proving that the number L is the least upper bound of a set S is to prove that L is an upper bound of S and that for each $\epsilon > 0$ there is some s in S larger than $L - \epsilon$.

A set of real numbers is *bounded* iff it is a subset of some closed interval $[a, b]$.

1. Let S be a nonempty bounded set of real numbers, r a positive real number, and rS the set of all numbers rs for s in S. Prove that lub $rS = r$ lub S.

2. Let S and T be nonempty bounded sets of real numbers, and $S + T$ be the set of all numbers $s + t$, s in S and t in T. Prove that lub $(S + T) =$ lub $S +$ lub T.

3. Let T be a nonempty bounded set of real numbers and S a nonempty subset of T. Prove that lub $S \leq$ lub T.

4. Let T be a nonempty bounded set of real numbers and S a bounded set of real numbers such that for each t in T there is an s in S with $s > t$. Prove that lub $S \geq$ lub T.

5. Let T be a nonempty bounded set of real numbers and S a subset of T such that for each t in T there is an s in S with $s > t$. Prove that lub $S =$ lub T. [Example: T is the open interval $(0, 1)$ and S the set of rational numbers in T. See Exercise 6.]

6. A set S, a subset of $\Re$, is *dense in* $\Re$, or *dense on the real line*, iff each open interval (a, b) contains a point of S. Prove that Q is dense in $\Re$. [*Hint:* If $a < b$, then by the Corollary to Theorem 3.35 (page 52), there is a positive integer n with $1/n < b - a$. For such n prove that there is at least one integer m such that $a < m/n < b$.]

7. The set $\sqrt{2}Q$ is the set of all rational multiples of $\sqrt{2}$. Prove that every member of this set except 0 is irrational [not rational] and that the set is dense in $\Re$.

8. Prove that if α is any irrational real number, then the set αQ is dense in $\Re$.

§ 9. *Views and Reviews*

Mathematical induction is essential for most of the proofs, and much of this section can be regarded as an extended exercise in the use of this basic tool. The section is concerned with topics covered in high school algebra, which are included here primarily because the results will be used when needed in the rest of this book.

Integer Exponents

Here 0 is a special case. For each positive integer n, $0^n = 0$. But 0^0 is a symbol without a meaning, and so is 0^n for any negative integer n.

For x a real number different from 0, and n an integer, the symbol x^n denotes a real number. There are two usual ways of making the definition. The most familiar is probably this three-part definition.

1. $x^0 = 1$.
2. For each nonnegative integer n, $x^{n+1} = x^n x$.
3. For each positive integer n, $x^{-n} = (x^{-1})^n$.

The following two-part definition allows a less tedious proof of the principal theorem—the *laws of exponents* for integer exponents.

4. $x^0 = 1$.
5. For every integer n, $x^{n+1} = x^n x$.

Under either scheme of definition, x^{-1} is redefined, but in a way consistent with its original definition as the multiplicative inverse of x. For example, from 4 and 5,

$$1 = x^0 = x^{-1+1} = x^{-1}x.$$

This defines x^{-1} as being the number such that $x^{-1}x = 1$.

The effectiveness of 5 for negative integers rests on the following

Lemma. If S is a set of real numbers such that 0 is in S, and, for each x in S, both $x + 1$ and $x - 1$ are in S, then S contains all the integers.

The proof is simple. First, each nonnegative integer is in S by the mathematical induction principle. Now let M be the set of positive integers m such that $-m$ is in S. Since 0 is in S, $0 - 1 = -1$ is in S, and 1 is in M. If m is in M, then $-m$ is in S; by an assumed property of S, $-m - 1$ is in S, which puts $m + 1$ in M. Therefore M is an inductive set containing 1, and hence all positive integers.

Theorem 3.49 [*Laws of Exponents*]. If $x \neq 0$, then, for any integers n and m,

$$x^n x^m = x^{n+m} \quad \text{and} \quad (x^n)^m = x^{nm}.$$

Combinations and Binomial Coefficients

If n is a nonnegative integer and r an integer [especially if $0 \leq r \leq n$], the symbol $\binom{n}{r}$ is read as *the number of combinations of n things taken r at a time*, or as *the binomial coefficient n above r*, or just as *n above r*.

We shall define $\binom{n}{r}$ from the combinatorial viewpoint and postpone the binomial theorem to an exercise below. There are two standard definitions. We give the one which allows r to be any integer, but admit that our definition is trivial except for $0 \leq r \leq n$.

Definition 3.17. For each integer r, $\binom{0}{r}$ is the number of r-element subsets of the null set.

For n a positive integer and r any integer, $\binom{n}{r}$ is the number of r-element subsets of the set of positive integers from 1 to n inclusive.

The trivial consequences of the definition are clear. Since no set has a negative number of elements, $r < 0 \Rightarrow \binom{n}{r} = 0$.

Since a set with n elements has no subset with more than n elements, $r > n \Rightarrow \binom{n}{r} = 0$.

Here are some nontrivial but easy consequences. The null set has just one 0-element subset, itself: $\binom{0}{0} = 1$. For each positive integer n, the set $\{1, \ldots, n\}$ has one 0-element subset, the null set, and one n-element subset, itself. Thus for n any nonnegative integer, $\binom{n}{0} = 1$ and $\binom{n}{n} = 1$.

Theorem 3.50 [*The Basic Identity for Binomial Coefficients*]. If n is a nonnegative integer and r an integer, then

$$\binom{n}{r} + \binom{n}{r+1} = \binom{n+1}{r+1}.$$

Suggestions for a Proof: First dispose of the trivial cases: $r < -1$ and $r > n$.

Next consider the borderline cases: $r = -1$ and $r = n$.

Finally, consider the interesting case: $0 \le r < n$. Count the $(r+1)$-element subsets of the set $\{1, \ldots, n, n+1\}$ by counting separately those which contain $n+1$ and those which do not.

Pascal's triangle, partly shown below, displays Theorem 3.50 in a pleasing form.

Pascal's Triangle

```
              1
           1     1
        1     2     1
     1     3     3     1
  1     4     6     4     1
1     5    10    10     5     1
              . . .
```

The Summation Notation

The symbol $1^2 + 2^2 + \cdots + 11^2$ presumably means the sum of the squares of the first eleven positive integers, rather than $1^2 + 2^2 + 4^2 + 7^2 + 11^2$.

The symbol $\sum_{k=1}^{11} k^2$ *definitely* means the sum of the squares of the first eleven positive integers. Similarly, $\sum_{j=3}^{5} j^4 = 3^4 + 4^4 + 5^4$.

Suppose we have somehow assigned to each positive integer k a real number u_k. Then formally,

$$\sum_{k=1}^{1} u_k = u_1.$$

For each positive integer n,

$$\sum_{k=1}^{n+1} u_k = \sum_{k=1}^{n} u_k + u_{n+1}.$$

Also formally, if n and m are positive integers and $1 < n < m$, then

$$\sum_{k=n}^{m} u_k = \sum_{k=1}^{m} u_k - \sum_{k=1}^{n-1} u_k.$$

Exercises

Verify the following.

1. $\displaystyle\sum_{k=1}^{5} (k^2 + 1) = 60.$

2. $\displaystyle\sum_{j=3}^{11} j = 63.$

3. $\displaystyle\sum_{k=2}^{7} (k - 1)^2 = \sum_{j=1}^{6} j^2 = \sum_{j=1}^{5} j^2 + 36 = 60 - 5 + 36.$

4. For $n \geq 1$,

$$\sum_{k=1}^{n} k = \frac{n(n + 1)}{2}.$$

5. If f is a real-valued function whose domain includes all the positive integers, then, for every positive integer n,

$$\sum_{k=1}^{n} 3f(k) = 3\sum_{k=1}^{n} f(k).$$

6. If f and g are real-valued functions whose domains include all the positive integers, then, for every positive integer n,

$$\sum_{k=1}^{n} (f(k) + g(k)) = \sum_{k=1}^{n} f(k) + \sum_{k=1}^{n} g(k).$$

7. If m is a positive integer and n an integer larger than m, then

$$\sum_{k=m}^{n} 2k = (n + m)(n + 1 - m).$$

8. Give a formal definition of $\displaystyle\sum_{k=0}^{n} f(k)$ in such a way that

$$\sum_{k=0}^{n} f(k) = f(0) + f(1) + \cdots + f(n).$$

Theorem 3.51 [*The Binomial Theorem*]. If a and b are real numbers and n a nonnegative integer, then

$$(a + b)^n = \sum_{r=0}^{n} \binom{n}{r} a^{n-r} b^r.$$

Hints:

$$(a + b)^{n+1} = (a + b)^n (a + b)$$
$$= (a + b)^n a + (a + b)^n b.$$

The relevance of the basic identity for binomial coefficients will be clearer if $(a + b)^n$ is written out as

$$\binom{n}{0} a^n + \binom{n}{1} a^{n-1}b + \binom{n}{2} a^{n-2}b^2 + \cdots + \binom{n}{n-1} ab^{n-1} + \binom{n}{n} b^n.$$

Calculation of $\binom{n}{r}$

The *factorial function* is defined on the nonnegative integers by $0! = 1$; for every nonnegative integer n, $(n + 1)! = (n + 1)(n!)$.

For n a nonnegative integer and r an integer such that $0 \le r \le n$, show that

$$\binom{n}{r} = \frac{n!}{r!(n - r)!}.$$

Hint: For every n the formula is true for $\binom{n}{0}$ and $\binom{n}{n}$. Assume it true for some positive n and all r such that $0 \le r \le n$. The basic identity will help establish its truth for $n + 1$ and all r such that $0 \le r \le n + 1$.

Arithmetic Progressions

Given real numbers a and d, consider the *arithmetic progression* a, $a + d$, $a + 2d$, $a + 3d$, ... For each positive integer k, the kth term of the progression is $a + (k - 1)d$.

Prove that, for every positive integer n,

$$\sum_{k=1}^{n} [a + (k - 1)d] = na + d \frac{(n - 1)n}{2}$$

$$= \frac{n\,(\text{1st term} + n\text{th term})}{2}.$$

Geometric Progressions

Given real numbers a and r, consider the *geometric progression* a, ar, ar^2, ar^3, ... For each positive integer k, the kth term is ar^{k-1}. Prove that, for any positive integer n, if $r \ne 0$,

$$(1 - r) \sum_{k=1}^{n} r^{k-1} = 1 - r^n.$$

Hence, if $r \neq 0$ and $r \neq 1$,

$$\sum_{k=1}^{n} r^{k-1} = \frac{1 - r^n}{1 - r}.$$

Also, if $r \neq 0$ and $r \neq 1$,

$$\sum_{k=1}^{n} ar^{k-1} = a\frac{1 - r^n}{1 - r}.$$

Exercises

1. Simplify $\sum_{k=0}^{100} \binom{100}{2k}$.

$$\left[\text{A more modest problem is to simplify } \binom{4}{0} + \binom{4}{2} + \binom{4}{4}.\right]$$

2. Prove that, if $0 \leq r \leq 499$, then $\binom{1000}{r} < \binom{1000}{r+1}$.

3. Simplify $\sum_{k=1}^{100} \left(\frac{1}{2}\right)^k \left[= \frac{1}{2} \sum_{k=1}^{100} \left(\frac{1}{2}\right)^{k-1}\right]$.

4. Simplify $\sum_{k=1}^{1000} \frac{3}{10^k}$.

5. Prove that $\sum_{r=0}^{101} (-1)^r \binom{101}{r} = 0$.

6. Prove that, for every positive integer n, the sum of the Fibonacci numbers from f_1 to f_n is $f_{n+2} - 1$.

7. Prove that $\binom{2}{2} + \binom{3}{2} + \binom{4}{2} + \binom{5}{2} = \binom{6}{3}$, and generalize. [*Hint:* Looking at Pascal's triangle will help.]

Polynomials

Let $(F; +, \cdot)$ be any field, with the identity elements called O and I. The constant function O—the function mapping x to O for all x in F—is a polynomial without a degree. If a is in F and $a \neq O$, the constant function a—the function mapping x to a for all x in F—is a polynomial of degree 0.

For each positive integer n, let $a_0 \neq O$ be in F and let $a_1, \ldots, a_n$ be any n elements of F. Associated with these $n + 1$ elements of F is a function P, a *polynomial of degree* n, defined, for all x in F, by

$$P(x) = a_0 x^n + a_1 x^{n-1} + \cdots + a_{n-1} x + a_n$$

$$= \sum_{k=0}^{n} a_k x^{n-k}.$$

We have defined a set of *polynomials over* F consisting of the degreeless O function, the nonzero constant functions [polynomials of degree 0], and, for each positive integer n, many polynomials of degree n.

This set of polynomials has an arithmetic quite similar to that of $\mathfrak{N}$ or Z. The cornerstone theorem is that if A is any polynomial over F and B

is any polynomial over F except O, there are unique Q and R, polynomials over F, such that

$A = QB + R,$

and either

$R = O$

or

the degree of $R <$ the degree of B.

It is an important theorem that if A and B are polynomials over F not both O, and if D is any greatest common divisor of A and B, then there are X and Y, polynomials over F, such that

$D = AX + BY.$

For this exercise we need only a fragment of the arithmetic. For each c in F let P_c be the polynomial of degree 1 defined, for all x in F, by

$P_c(x) = x - c.$

Theorem 3.52 [*The Remainder Theorem*].   Let P be a polynomial over F of degree $n \geq 1$. For each c in F there is a polynomial Q_c, of degree $n - 1$, such that

$P = P_c Q_c + R_c,$

where either $R_c = O$ or R_c is a polynomial of degree 0.

In other words, there is a polynomial Q_c of degree $n - 1$, and an element r_c of F such that, for all x in F,

$P(x) = (x - c)Q_c(x) + r_c.$

PROOF: The usual proof is by induction on the degree of P. If P is of degree 1, there are $a_0 \neq O$ and a_1 such that, for all x in F, $P(x) = a_0 x + a_1$. But, for all x in F and c in F,

$a_0 x + a_1 = (x - c)a_0 + ca_0 + a_1$

$\qquad\qquad = (x - c)Q_c(x) + r_c,$

where Q_c is of degree 0 and r_c is in F.

The induction is valid because a polynomial of degree $n + 1$ has the formula

$a_0 x^{n+1} + P_1(x),$

where either $P_1(x) = 0$ for all x, or P_1 is a polynomial of degree $\leq n$. ∎

If, in the conclusion of the Remainder Theorem, for all x in F, $P(x) = (x - c)Q_c(x) + r_c$, we set $x = c$, we obtain

$P(c) = (c - c)Q_c(c) + r_c$

$\qquad = r_c.$

This gives us an immediate corollary to the Remainder Theorem.

Theorem 3.53 [*The Factor Theorem*].   If P is a polynomial of degree $n \geq 1$ over F, then, for c in F, $P(c) = O$ iff there is a polynomial Q_c of degree $n - 1$ such that, for all x in F,

$$P(x) = (x - c)Q_c(x).$$

The Factor Theorem also has an immediate corollary.

Corollary to Theorem 3.53.   If n is a nonnegative integer and P is a polynomial of degree n over F, then there are at most n elements c in F such that $P(c) = O$.

For $n = 0$, the corollary says that if $a \neq O$ is in F, there are at most 0 elements c of F such that $a = O$. For $n = 1$, it says that if $a_0 \neq O$ and a_1 are in F, there is at most one c in F such that $a_0c = -a_1$. This is true by Theorem 3.14. Since $(x - c)Q_c(x) = 0$ implies that either $x = c$ or $Q_c(x) = 0$, the step from n to $n + 1$ is immediate.

Exercises

1. In the rational field find the polynomial Q_1 and rational number r_1 such that, for all x in $\mathbb{Q}$,
$$x^3 - 3x^2 + 7x - 10 = (x - 1)Q_1(x) + r_1.$$
2. Find Q_3 and r_3 such that, for all x in $\mathbb{Q}$,
$$x^3 - 3x^2 + 7x - 10 = (x - 3)Q_3(x) + r_3.$$
3. Find Q_2 and r_2 such that, for all x in $\mathbb{Q}$,
$$x^3 - 3x^2 + 7x - 10 = (x - 2)Q_2(x) + r_2.$$
4. Find all x in $\mathbb{R}$ such that
$$x^3 - 3x^2 + 7x - 10 = 0.$$

§ 10.   *Approaches to Square Roots*

These approaches are to $\sqrt{7}$, but considerable generalization is possible. The end of the section gives a standard construction of the field $\mathbb{C}$ of complex numbers, in which the complex number -1 has two square roots. In Chapter 6 we give a very different construction of $\mathbb{C}$.

The Geometric Approach

This is essentially Greek. Given a square of area 7, one wants to find a slightly smaller square with a side of rational length. In the diagram on page 72 numbers inside rectangles give their areas. The big square has area 7.

Define x by $\sqrt{7} = 2 + x$. [The Greeks couldn't really write this; they resorted to circumlocutions.] Then $7 = 4 + 4x + x^2$, as in the diagram. Since $\sqrt{7} < 3$, $0 < x < 1$ and $0 < x^2 < 1$. Using this estimate for x^2 in the equation above gives

$$7 > 4 + 4x > 6,$$

or

$$3 > 4x > 2$$

and

$$\tfrac{3}{4} > x > \tfrac{1}{2}.$$

To get a better approximation, notice that from $\sqrt{7} = 2 + x$, where $\tfrac{1}{2} < x < \tfrac{3}{4}$, follows

$$\sqrt{700} = 20 + 10x,$$

where $5 < 10x < 7.5$. One trial gives

$$26^2 < 700 < 27^2.$$

Thus $\sqrt{700} = 26 + y$, where $0 < y < 1$, and $700 = 676 + 52y + y^2$, where $0 < y^2 < 1$.

As an exercise, deduce that $24/52 > y > 23/52$. Then find the integer k such that $100\sqrt{7} = 260 + k + z$, where $0 < z < 1$.

Approach Through Farey Sections

In F_1, $\sqrt{7}$ is in the interval $[2, 3]$. This interval is split into two subintervals in F_2, and since $(5/2)^2 < 7$, $\sqrt{7}$ is in $[5/2, 3/1]$.

With $\sqrt{7}$ located in a minimal interval $[a/b, c/d]$, we can insert the mediant $(a + c)/(b + d)$ and determine which subinterval $\sqrt{7}$ is in. The decision is whether $(a + c)^2 < 7(b + d)^2$ or not.

1. Starting with $\sqrt{7}$ in $[2, 3]$ and in $[5/2, 3/1]$, establish that also $\sqrt{7}$ is in $[5/2, 8/3]$. Continue step by step until you find that $\sqrt{7}$ is in $[82/31, 127/48]$, an interval of length $1/1488$.

2. At step 1, $\sqrt{7}$ is between $2/1$ and $3/1$. Arbitrarily, take $2/1$ as the first approximation. At each other step $\sqrt{7}$ is in an interval whose end

points have different denominators; take the one with the smaller denominator as the approximation at that step. You should have, in succession,

$$\tfrac{2}{1}, \tfrac{3}{1}, \tfrac{5}{2}, \tfrac{8}{3}, \tfrac{8}{3}, \tfrac{8}{3}, \tfrac{8}{3}, \tfrac{37}{14}, \tfrac{45}{17}, \tfrac{82}{31}.$$

The next four approximations will be $127/48$.

3. Observe that $8^2 - 7 \cdot 3^2 = 1$. Hence $(8 + 3\sqrt{7})(8 - 3\sqrt{7}) = 1$, and

$$\frac{8}{3} - \sqrt{7} = \frac{1}{3(8 + 3\sqrt{7})}.$$

Observe also that $(8 + 3\sqrt{7})^2(8 - 3\sqrt{7})^2 = 1^2 = 1$, or $(127 + 48\sqrt{7})(127 - 48\sqrt{7}) = 1$. Further observe that, for every positive integer n,

$$(8 + 3\sqrt{7})^n(8 - 3\sqrt{7})^n = 1.$$

Setting $(8 + 3\sqrt{7})^3 = x_3 + y_3\sqrt{7}$, where x_3 and y_3 are integers, about how big is $\left|\dfrac{x_3}{y_3} - \sqrt{7}\right|$?

4. Simplify each of the following:

$$2 + \frac{1}{1}, \qquad 2 + \frac{1}{1 + \frac{1}{1}}, \qquad 2 + \frac{1}{1 + \frac{1}{1 + \frac{1}{1}}}, \qquad 2 + \frac{1}{1 + \frac{1}{1 + \frac{1}{1 + \frac{1}{4}}}}.$$

The Machine Approach

Except for one detail this is a standard program for a machine for finding approximations to a square root. The detail is that the machine can only use rational numbers with denominators a power of 2 or 8 or 10 or whatever the nature of the circuits dictates. Hence the machine must replace $45/17$, for example, by a many-digit approximation in the binary or octal or decimal system.

The integer nearest to $\sqrt{7}$ is 3 and we take $x_1 = 3$ as a first approximation. Since $3 > \sqrt{7}$ and $3 \cdot \tfrac{7}{3} = 7$, it is clear that $\tfrac{7}{3} < \sqrt{7}$, and $\tfrac{7}{3} < \sqrt{7} < 3$. Not knowing where $\sqrt{7}$ is located in the interval $(\tfrac{7}{3}, 3)$ we choose as our next approximation, x_2, its midpoint:

$$x_2 = \tfrac{1}{2}(3 + \tfrac{7}{3}) = \tfrac{16}{6} = \tfrac{8}{3}.$$

This x_2 is an improvement on x_1 because $x_1{}^2 - 7 = 2$, but $x_2{}^2 - 7 = \tfrac{1}{9}$.

The algorithm now proceeds in a strictly mechanical way. Having an approximation x_n we define x_{n+1} by

$$x_{n+1} = \frac{1}{2}\left(x_n + \frac{7}{x_n}\right) = \frac{x_n{}^2 + 7}{2x_n}.$$

To see that x_{n+1} is an improvement on x_n observe that

$$x_{n+1}^2 - 7 = \left(\frac{x_n^2 + 7}{2x_n}\right)^2 - 7$$

$$= \frac{x_n^4 + 14x_n^2 + 49 - 28x_n^2}{4x_n^2}$$

$$= \frac{(x_n^2 - 7)^2}{4x_n^2}.$$

If $x_n^2 > 7$, then

$$0 < x_{n+1}^2 - 7 < \frac{(x_n^2 - 7)^2}{28}.$$

Exercises

1. Compute x_3 and $x_3^2 - 7$; x_4 and $x_4^2 - 7$.
2. Observing that, for all x, $x^2 - 7 = (x - \sqrt{7})(x + \sqrt{7})$, deduce that, for all $n \geq 1$,
$$|x_n - \sqrt{7}| < \frac{x_n^2 - 7}{4}.$$
3. Find a positive integer n such that
$$|x_n - \sqrt{7}| < 10^{-80}.$$
4. Find a rational number which differs from $\sqrt{11}$ by less than 10^{-10}.

Exercises in an Algebraic Number Field

Let $\mathbb{Q}(\sqrt{7})$ denote the set of all real numbers of the form $a + b\sqrt{7}$ for rational a and b.

1. Prove that $(\mathbb{Q}(\sqrt{7}); +, \cdot)$ is a field.
2. Define three functions, *conjugate*, *trace*, and *norm* on $\mathbb{Q}(\sqrt{7})$ as follows. Let $\alpha = a + b\sqrt{7}$ be any number in $\mathbb{Q}(\sqrt{7})$. Then $\bar{\alpha}$, the *conjugate* of α, is $a - b\sqrt{7}$; $\mathrm{Tr}(\alpha)$, the *trace* of α, is $\alpha + \bar{\alpha} = 2a$; $N(\alpha)$, the *norm* of α, is $\alpha\bar{\alpha} = a^2 - 7b^2$.
   a. Prove that α and $\bar{\alpha}$ are roots of the equation: $x^2 - \mathrm{Tr}(\alpha)x + N(\alpha) = 0$.
   b. Prove that the conjugate function is an isomorphism of $(\mathbb{Q}(\sqrt{7}); +, \cdot)$ to itself. It is called an *automorphism* of the system.
   c. Prove that for all α and β in $\mathbb{Q}(\sqrt{7})$, $N(\alpha\beta) = N(\alpha)N(\beta)$.
3. Let $\mathbb{Z}(\sqrt{7})$ be the set of all numbers $a + b\sqrt{7}$ for integers a and b. It is clear that, if α is in $\mathbb{Z}(\sqrt{7})$, then both $T(\alpha)$ and $N(\alpha)$ are integers. It is also clear that $(\mathbb{Z}(\sqrt{7}); +, \cdot)$ has most of the algebraic properties of $(\mathbb{Q}(\sqrt{7}); +, \cdot)$.
   a. Find a number α in $\mathbb{Z}(\sqrt{7})$, $\alpha \neq 0$, such that α^{-1} is not in $\mathbb{Z}(\sqrt{7})$. Also find a number β in $\mathbb{Z}(\sqrt{7})$, $\beta \neq 1$ or -1, such that β^{-1} is in $\mathbb{Z}(\sqrt{7})$. [See paragraph 3 in Approach Through Farey Sections, page 72.] A number in $\mathbb{Z}(\sqrt{7})$ whose multiplicative inverse is also in $\mathbb{Z}(\sqrt{7})$ is called a *unit* in $\mathbb{Z}(\sqrt{7})$.
   b. Prove that β is a unit in $\mathbb{Z}(\sqrt{7})$ iff $N(\beta) = 1$ or -1.
   c. Prove that if β is a unit, then so is β^n for every integer n.

    d. Prove that, if ϵ is any positive real number, there are members of $Z(\sqrt{7})$ in the open interval $(0, \epsilon)$. The set $Z(\sqrt{7})$ is *dense at 0*.

    e. Is $Z(\sqrt{7})$ dense on the real line? That is, is it true that, for any real x and positive ϵ, there are members of $Z(\sqrt{7})$ in the open interval $(x, x + \epsilon)$?

    f. Prove that no unit in $Z(\sqrt{7})$ has norm -1: for all integers a and b, $a^2 - 7b^2 \neq -1$.

Square Roots of (-1)

In a later chapter we will present a geometrical interpretation of the operations defined below. This exercise is a straightforward unmotivated construction of the field of complex numbers.

    Let $\mathcal{C} = \mathcal{R} \times \mathcal{R}$, the set of all ordered pairs of real numbers. Define addition and multiplication by: for all (a, b) and (c, d) in $\mathcal{C}$,

$$(a, b) \oplus (c, d) = (a + c, b + d),$$
$$(a, b) \odot (c, d) = (ac - bd, ad + bc).$$

    1. Prove that $(\mathcal{C}; \oplus, \odot)$ is a field.

    2. Let $\mathcal{CR} = \{(x, 0) | x \text{ in } \mathcal{R}\}$. Prove that $(\mathcal{CR}; \oplus, \odot)$ is a field.

    3. For each x in $\mathcal{R}$, let x' denote $(x, 0)$ in $\mathcal{CR}$. Prove that the nameless function mapping each x in $\mathcal{R}$ to x' in $\mathcal{CR}$ is an isomorphism of the real field to $(\mathcal{CR}; \oplus, \odot)$.

    4. Prove that, for all (x, y) in $\mathcal{C}$,

$$(x, y) = x' \oplus [(0, 1) \odot y'],$$

or, if we use i as an abbreviation for $(0, 1)$,

$$(x, y) = x' \oplus (i \odot y').$$

    5. Prove that $i \odot i = (-1)' = (-i) \odot (-i)$.

    If one is going to work seriously with $\mathcal{C}$, one soon sheds the primes and the circles around the operations and writes $x + iy$ for $x' \oplus (i \odot y')$. Then $i \odot i = (-1, 0)$ turns into $i^2 = -1$. This last makes sense if one remembers that "real number" now really means "element of $\mathcal{CR}$" and that "-1" no longer really denotes a real number.

    6. Prove that every complex number except $(0, 0)$ has exactly two complex square roots. This can be done in a fairly straightforward way. Given (a, b) in $\mathcal{C}$, the problem is to find all (x, y) in $\mathcal{C}$ such that $(x, y) \odot (x, y) = (a, b)$. Thus the problem is, given real numbers a and b, to find real x and y such that

$$x^2 - y^2 = a$$

and

$$2xy = b.$$

By squaring both sides of both these equations and adding, we obtain

$$(x^2 + y^2)^2 = a^2 + b^2.$$

From here on all is clear.

7. Let A, B, C be any three complex numbers except $A \neq (0, 0)$. Prove that there is at least one z in $\mathfrak{C}$ such that $Az^2 \oplus Bz \oplus C = (0, 0)$. [*Hint:* Since $A \neq (0, 0)$, the equation is equivalent to

$$z^2 \oplus \frac{B}{A} z \oplus \frac{B^2}{4'A^2} = -\frac{C}{A} \oplus \frac{B^2}{4'A^2}.$$

Here z^2 means $z \odot z$ and $4'A^2$ means $4' \odot A \odot A$.]

8. Find all z in $\mathfrak{C}$ such that

$$z^3 \ominus 3'z^2 \oplus 7'z \ominus 10' = 0'.$$

Historical Remarks

Carl Friedrich Gauss (1777–1855), generally regarded as the greatest of mathematicians except possibly for Archimedes or Newton, gave in his doctoral dissertation the first valid proof that, if P is any polynomial over the complex field of degree ≥ 1, then there is some z in $\mathfrak{C}$ such that $P(z) = O$. This theorem, now often called "the so-called fundamental theorem of algebra," is beyond the scope of this book. It and the factor theorem give the result that a polynomial of degree n over $\mathfrak{C}$ can be factored into n linear factors: $a_0(z - z_1)(z - z_2) \cdots (z - z_n)$, where $z_1, z_2, \ldots, z_n$ are complex numbers not necessarily all distinct.

    The current pejorative "so-called" reflects the growth of algebra. The theorem *was* the fundamental theorem of algebra so long as algebra dealt only with subsystems of the complex field. Today it is seen as *merely* a theorem about a particular algebra. Also, if *algebraic* is defined narrowly, every proof of the theorem [known to me] involves a crucial nonalgebraic step, using some notion from analysis or topology.

4
Sequences and Real Functions

§ 1. *Preliminary Definitions*

A *sequence* is any function whose domain is an unbounded subset of the set of nonnegative integers. Most of the sequences considered here have as domain either the set of all nonnegative integers or the set of all positive integers. We shall let Z^+ denote the set of positive integers, and let *sequence on* Z^+ mean a sequence whose domain includes Z^+.

The above definition says nothing about the range of a sequence. If the range is a set of intervals we have a sequence of intervals: we may, for example, assign to each positive integer n the interval $[n, 2n]$. If the range is a set of complex numbers we have a sequence of complex numbers, or a complex-valued sequence. Similarly, we can have sequences of sets or sequences of matrices or sequences of functions. For example, for each positive integer n, let f_n be the function with domain $\Re$ mapping x to $x^n + n^2$: for all x in $\Re$,

$$f_1(x) = x + 1 \qquad \text{and} \qquad f_2(x) = x^2 + 4.$$

We shall be primarily concerned with *real sequences*—sequences whose ranges are sets of real numbers. Thus real sequences are special sorts of *real functions*, where we define *real function* to mean a function whose domain and range are both sets of real numbers. The classical label is *real-valued function of a real variable*.

Let F be a real function and S a subset of the domain of F. Then F may have one or more of the following properties.

F is **bounded on** S if there are real numbers m and M such that, for all x in S, $m \le F(x) \le M$.

F is **monotone increasing on** S if, for all x and t in S, $x < t$ $\Rightarrow F(x) \le F(t)$.

F is **strictly monotone increasing on** S if, for all x and t in S, $x < t \Rightarrow F(x) < F(t)$.

F is **monotone decreasing on** S if, for all x and t in S, $x < t \Rightarrow F(x) \geq F(t)$.

F is **strictly monotone decreasing on** S if, for all x and t in S, $x < t \Rightarrow F(x) > F(t)$.

F is **(strictly) monotone on** S if either F is (strictly) monotone increasing on S or else F is (strictly) monotone decreasing on S.

Exercises

[The results of most of these will be used later.]

1. Let T be a nonempty bounded set of real numbers. Let $-T$ denote the set of additive inverses of members of T. Prove that a number x is an upper bound of T if and only if $-x$ is a lower bound of $-T$.
2. Prove the following theorem.

> **Theorem 4.1.**   Every nonempty set of real numbers with a lower bound has a greatest lower bound.

3. For each positive integer n, let g_n be the function defined by: for all real x,

   $$g_n(x) = x^n.$$

   Prove that, for every positive integer n, the function g_n is strictly monotone increasing on the set of all nonnegative real numbers.
4. With g_n defined as in Exercise 3, prove that g_n is strictly monotone increasing on $\Re$ if n is odd, and strictly monotone decreasing on the set of all nonpositive real numbers if n is even.
5. Define the *greatest integer function* or *square bracket function*, for each real x, by

   $$[x] \text{ is the integer with the property that } [x] \leq x < [x] + 1.$$

   For example, $[2.5] = 2$, $[\sqrt{11}] = 3$, $[-2] = -2$, $[-2.6] = -3$. Prove that this function is monotone increasing on $\Re$, but not strictly.
6. Let g be a real function strictly monotone on its domain. Prove that g is a one-to-one correspondence of its domain to its range.

§ 2. *Operations in Sets of Real Functions*

Definition 4.1.   Let f and g be real functions, and let D be the intersection of the domains of f and g. We define $f + g$, $f - g$, fg, and f/g as follows.

For each x in D,

$$[f + g](x) = f(x) + g(x),$$
$$[f - g](x) = f(x) - g(x),$$
$$[fg](x) = f(x)g(x).$$

For x in D and $g(x) \neq 0$,

$$\left[\frac{f}{g}\right](x) = \frac{f(x)}{g(x)}.$$

In case the intersection of the domains of f and g is the empty set, none of the four functions defined above assigns any image to any number. We could restrict the definitions to the only interesting situations, where the intersection is not empty. But it is in some ways preferable to admit the existence of an *empty function*, the empty set regarded as the set of no ordered pairs. However, we somewhat arbitrarily refuse to dignify the empty function with the title "real function"; thus the set of all real functions is not closed under any of these four operations.

Exercises

1. Let S be a nonempty set of real numbers and let FS be the set of all real functions with domain S. Prove that FS is closed under addition, subtraction, and multiplication, but not under division.
2. With S and FS as in Exercise 1, satisfy yourself that addition and multiplication in FS are commutative and associative, that for all f, g, h in $FS, f(g + h) = fg + fh$, that the constant functions 0 and 1 on S are additive and multiplicative identities in the system, and that each f in FS has an additive inverse in FS.
3. Let S be the closed interval $[0, 1]$ and let FS be as in Exercise 1. Find three functions f, g, h in FS such that

   f is not the constant function 0 on S,

   $fg = fh$,

   $g \neq h$.

   [*Note:* $fg = fh$ means that for each x in $[0, 1]$, $f(x)g(x) = f(x)h(x)$; $g \neq h$ means that for some x in $[0, 1]$, $g(x) \neq h(x)$.]

§ 3. *Composition of Functions*

In this section we admit the empty function so that Definition 4.2 will assign a composition to any two functions.

Definition 4.2. Let f and g be any two functions. Then $f \circ g$ is the function defined by (1) the domain of $f \circ g$ is the set of all x such that x is in the domain of g and $g(x)$ is in the domain of f, and (2) for each x in the domain of $f \circ g$,

$$[f \circ g](x) = f(g(x)).$$

Examples

1. Let $g(x) = x^2$ and $f(x) = x + 1$, for all real x. Then, for all real x,

   $$[f \circ g](x) = f(x^2) = x^2 + 1,$$

and

$$[g \circ f](x) = g(x + 1) = x^2 + 2x + 1.$$

2. Let $g(x) = x^2 + 10$ for all real x, and $f(x) = \sqrt{1 - x^2}$ for $-1 \leq x \leq 1$. Then

$$[g \circ f](x) = g\left(\sqrt{1 - x^2}\right) = 11 - x^2,$$

for $-1 \leq x \leq 1$, and $f \circ g$ is the empty function.

3. For each real x, let $g(x)$ be the ordered pair $(x + 3, x^2)$. Let f be the function which assigns to each ordered pair (x, y) of real numbers the ordered triple $(xy, x + y, x)$; that is,

$$f(x, y) = (xy, x + y, x).$$

Then, for each real x,

$$[f \circ g](x) = f(x + 3, x^2) = (x^3 + 3x^2, x^2 + x + 3, x + 3).$$

Thus $f \circ g$ is a function whose domain is $\mathcal{R}$ and whose range is a set of ordered triples of real numbers.

If we interpret ordered pairs and triples of real numbers as points in two-dimensional or three-dimensional Euclidean spaces, then [using the language of later chapters] the range of g is a curve in the plane. Also, the domain of f is the plane and the range of f is a surface in three-space. The composition $f \circ g$ has the real line as domain, and its range is a curve in three-space. But $g \circ f$ is the empty function.

4. With g as above, let h be the function mapping each ordered pair (x, y) to the number xy. Then, for all real x,

$$[h \circ g](x) = x^3 + 3x^2.$$

Thus $h \circ g$ is a real function, a polynomial over $\mathcal{R}$, although neither h nor g is such a function.

We can construct a symbolic picture of a composition of two functions. Let the domain of g be a set S and the range of g be a set T. Let f be a function whose domain includes T and whose range is a set U. Then $f \circ g$ is a function with domain S and with range a subset of U.

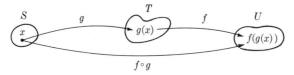

The picture shows the composition $f \circ g$ bypassing T. This is correct in principle, although in many examples S and U may be subsets of T and the bypassing may be obscured.

Exercises

1. Define f, g, and h as follows: for $x \geq 0$, $f(x) = x$, for all real x, $g(x) = x^2$, for $x \geq 1$, $h(x) = \sqrt{x^2 - 1}$. Give the domain of and the rule for

$$f \circ g, \qquad g \circ f, \qquad g \circ h, \qquad h \circ g, \qquad f \circ h.$$

2. With f, g, h as in Exercise 1, does $f \circ [g + h] = f \circ g + f \circ h$? Does $f \circ [g \circ h] = [f \circ g] \circ h$?

3. Let F be the function mapping each real $x \neq 0$ to $1/x$. What are the domain and the rule for $F \circ F$?

Theorem 4.2. Composition is associative. If $f, g,$ and h are functions, then

$$f \circ [g \circ h] = [f \circ g] \circ h.$$

PROOF: As is clear from examples above, the composition of arbitrary functions is very likely to be the empty function. The proof of the theorem will show that $f \circ [g \circ h]$ is empty iff $[f \circ g] \circ h$ is empty.

The proof is by a straightforward computation. The domain of $f \circ [g \circ h]$ is the set of all x such that (1) x is in the domain of $g \circ h$; (2) $[g \circ h](x)$ is in the domain of f. For x satisfying (1) and (2),

$$(f \circ [g \circ h])(x) = f([g \circ h](x)) = f(g(h(x))).$$

The domain of $[f \circ g] \circ h$ is the set of all x such that (3) x is in the domain of h, (4) $h(x)$ is in the domain of $f \circ g$. For x satisfying (3) and (4),

$$([f \circ g] \circ h)(x) = [f \circ g](h(x)) = f(g(h(x))).$$

As an exercise, finish the proof by establishing that conditions (1) and (2) determine the same domain as do conditions (3) and (4). ∎

Identity Functions and Composition Inverses

For each set S, let I_s be the *identity function* on S. That is, I_s has domain S and, for all x in S, $I_s(x) = x$.

Let f be a function with domain D and range R. For all x in D,

$$[f \circ I_D](x) = f(I_D(x)) = f(x).$$

Thus $f \circ I_D = f$. But unless some subset of R is a subset of D, the composition $I_D \circ f$ is empty: $f(x)$ is not in the domain of I_D unless $f(x)$ is in D.

However, consider the composition $I_R \circ f$. For each x in D, $f(x)$ is in R and $I_R(f(x)) = f(x)$. Thus $I_R \circ f = f$.

In Chapter 1 we defined one-to-one correspondence as follows. Think of a function f as a set of ordered pairs and let f^* be the set of reversed pairs: (b, a) is in f^* iff (a, b) is in f. Then f is a one-to-one correspondence of the domain of f to the range of f iff f^* is a function.

Let f be a one-to-one correspondence of D to R. Then f^* is a function with domain R and range D. And since $f^{**} = f$, f^* is a one-to-one correspondence of R to D. Let f map a in D to b in R. Then f^* maps b to a, and thus $f^* \circ f = I_D$, the identity function on D. Similarly, $f \circ f^* = I_R$.

Even though, except in the special case $D = R$, $f^* \circ f \neq f \circ f^*$, we want to consider f^* as the composition inverse of f.

We recapitulate this discussion in

Definition 4.3.   If the function f is a one-to-one correspondence of its domain to its range, we define f^{-1} by $f^{-1}(b) = a$ iff $f(a) = b$. Then $f^{-1} \circ f$ is the identity function on the domain of f, and $f \circ f^{-1}$ is the identity function on the range of f. The range of f is the domain of f^{-1}; the domain of f is the range of f^{-1}.

Examples

1. Since the function mapping x to x^2 for all real x is not a one-to-one correspondence, it has no composition inverse.
2. Since the function g: for $x \geq 0$, $g(x) = x^2$, is a one-to-one correspondence of the nonnegative real numbers to the nonnegative real numbers, g has a composition inverse. For $x \geq 0$, $g^{-1}(x) = \sqrt{x}$. Indeed, for $x \geq 0$, $\sqrt{x^2} = |x| = x$, and $(\sqrt{x})^2 = x$.
3. Let $h(x) = x^3$ for all real x. By Exercises 4 and 6 in the last section, h is a one-to-one correspondence of $\mathcal{R}$ to range of h. [By a very general theorem in a later chapter, the range of h is $\mathcal{R}$, but we don't need this here.] Define the cube root function by $\sqrt[3]{x} = a$ means $a^3 = x$. Then, for all real t, $\sqrt[3]{t^3} = t$, and, for all t in the range of h, $(\sqrt[3]{t})^3 = t$.
4. Let $G(x) = 1/(x-1)$ for all real $x \neq 1$. Then $G^{-1}(x) = (x+1)/x$ for all real $x \neq 0$. For $x \neq 1$, $[G^{-1} \circ G](x) = x$, and for $x \neq 0$, $[G \circ G^{-1}](x) = x$.

We conclude the section with a theorem which generalizes Example 3.

Theorem 4.3.   If f is a real function and strictly monotone on its domain, then f^{-1} is strictly monotone in the same sense on *its* domain, the range of f.

PROOF: By Exercise 6 (page 78), f is one-to-one and f^{-1} exists. Suppose f is strictly monotone increasing on its domain, and let a and b, with $a < b$, be in the domain of f^{-1}. Then a and b are in the range of f, and there are c and d in the domain of f such that $f(c) = a$ and $f(d) = b$. Since f is strictly increasing and $a < b$, it must be that $c < d$. But $c = f^{-1}(a)$ and $d = f^{-1}(b)$. Thus if a and b are in the domain of f^{-1} and $a < b$, then $f^{-1}(a) < f^{-1}(b)$.   ∎

The proof for strictly decreasing functions is not essentially different.

§ 4. *Graphs of Real Functions*

The next chapter gives a formal definition of the Euclidean plane, but this definition won't affect the intuitive picture of it as an infinite blackboard with the real line running horizontally across the middle. The point (a, b) is marked vertically above the real number a [the point $(a, 0)$] if b is positive, and vertically below if b is negative. Unless it is too inconvenient, we use the same scale for vertical distances as for horizontal.

A real function is, formally, a set of ordered pairs of real numbers. Its *graph* is the set of these same ordered pairs regarded as points in the plane. If, as we shall do, one says that a point in the plane *is* an ordered pair of real numbers, then there is no way of distinguishing a real function from its graph.

To draw reasonably correct graphs of complicated real functions we need as a tool the calculus of derivatives. The word *calculus* is from Latin and literally means "pebble." The root meaning of *calculation* seems to be "reckoning using pebbles." The functions considered in this section are extremely simple, and it wouldn't give a grossly bad picture if sufficiently many small pebbles were placed on points.

Exercises

1. Define g on the interval $[0, 1]$ by: for x in $[0, \frac{1}{2}]$,

   $$g(x) = 2x,$$

   for x in $(\frac{1}{2}, 1]$,

   $$g(x) = 2 - 2x.$$

   Draw a graph of g. [It should resemble an upsidedown **V**.]
2. Define four functions as below. For all real x,

   $$f_1(x) = 2x,$$
   $$f_2(x) = x + 3,$$
   $$f_3(x) = \frac{x}{5},$$
   $$f_4(x) = 3x - 7.$$

   With g as in Exercise 1, for each of the functions f_k work out the domain of $g \circ f_k$, a formula for $g \circ f_k$, and the graph of $g \circ f_k$.
3. Let S be the set of all functions having the closed interval $[0, 1]$ for domain and range. Below are a few examples of such functions:

   g_1: for $0 \leq x \leq 1$, $g_1(x) = 1 - x$.
   g_2: for $0 \leq x \leq 1$, $g_2(x) = x^2$.
   g_3: for $0 \leq x \leq 1$, $g_3(x) = \sqrt{x}$.
   g_4: for $0 \leq x \leq \frac{1}{3}$, $g_4(x) = 3x$, for $\frac{1}{3} < x \leq 1$, $g_4(x) = 0$.
   g_5: for $0 \leq x < \frac{9}{10}$, $g_5(x) = \frac{1}{2}$, for $\frac{9}{10} \leq x \leq 1$, $g_5(x) = 10x - 9$.

   a. Draw graphs of the five functions above. [*Hints:* No part of g_2 is a line segment; if you choose to make your graph of g_2 resemble a curve rather than a collection of pebbles, it should appear tangent to the horizontal axis at 0; g_3 should appear congruent to g_2.]
   b. Show by examples that the set S is not closed under addition or multiplication.
   c. Prove that S is closed under composition. This requires proving that, if f and g are in S, then the domain of $f \circ g$ is $[0, 1]$ and the range of $f \circ g$ is $[0, 1]$. For the latter you must establish that (i) $0 \leq x \leq 1 \Rightarrow 0 \leq [f \circ g](x) \leq 1$, and (ii) if $0 \leq y \leq 1$, then there is some x in $[0, 1]$ such that $[f \circ g](x) = y$.

4. Let T be the set of all functions which are one-to-one correspondences of $[0, 1]$ to $[0, 1]$. The functions g_1, g_2, g_3 in Exercise 3 are in T; g_4 and g_5 are not. Prove that T is closed under composition and that, for each f in T, f^{-1} is in T and $f \circ f^{-1} = f^{-1} \circ f = I_{[0, 1]}$.

5. If all the assertions made in Exercise 4 are correct, then each of the equations below should be solvable for some f in T. Solve them.

$$g_1 \circ f = g_2.$$
$$f \circ g_1 = g_2.$$
$$f \circ g_3 = g_1.$$

§ 5. *Examples of Real Sequences*

There are many examples in the exercises at the end of the last chapter. Every arithmetic or geometric progression is a sequence. We may prefer to think of an arithmetic progression as a string of numbers: $a, a + d, a + 2d, \ldots$ rather than as a function. However, we must be clear, whether explicitly or not, that the kth term is $a + (k - 1)d$. Underlying the concept of the string is a function assigning an image to each positive integer.

If we think of a sequence as a function, we picture a collection of isolated points in the plane: points (n, u_n) for each integer n in the domain of the sequence u. If we think of a string $u_1, u_2, u_3, \ldots$ of real numbers, we picture a collection of labeled points along the real line.

In § 10 of Chapter 3 we gave several ways of constructing sequences of rational approximations to $\sqrt{7}$. One such sequence had the property that each approximation was less than $\sqrt{7}$. In another, each approximation was larger than $\sqrt{7}$. In a third, the approximations were alternately too small and too large.

However, each sequence had the following property, which justifies our calling it a sequence of approximations to $\sqrt{7}$. Let u be any one of the sequences, and consider a neighborhood of $\sqrt{7}$:

No matter how small ϵ is, only "a few" of the numbers u_n are outside the neighborhood corresponding to ϵ. More precisely, for each $\epsilon > 0$ there exists some real number N_ϵ such that

$$n > N_\epsilon \Rightarrow |u_n - \sqrt{7}| < \epsilon.$$

If we think of the string $u_1, u_2, u_3, \ldots$, then these numbers are stacked up around the number $\sqrt{7}$ in the sense that only a few of them, those with $n \leq N_\epsilon$, are outside an ϵ-neighborhood of $\sqrt{7}$.

If we think of the set of points (n, u_n) in the plane, then for each $\epsilon > 0$ our picture will be like this:

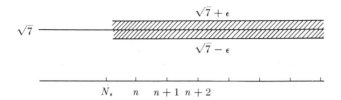

points (n, u_n) inside the shaded strip, if $n > N_\epsilon$

Think of it this way. There is an ideal line, of 0 thickness, parallel to the real line and at height $\sqrt{7}$ above it. For each $\epsilon > 0$, take a pencil with a point of width 2ϵ and draw a line centered on the ideal line. A sequence u is a sequence of approximations to $\sqrt{7}$ iff, for each $\epsilon > 0$, all except perhaps the first few of the points (n, u_n) [considered as ideal points] are hidden by the line of width 2ϵ.

If we define an ϵ-practical purpose as a purpose for which we don't bother distinguishing between numbers that differ by less than ϵ, then for every ϵ-practical purpose there is a number N_ϵ such that, for all $n > N_\epsilon$, u_n is ϵ-undistinguishable from $\sqrt{7}$.

These remarks about practical purposes should not be taken completely seriously, but they are not merely frivolous. For a hypothetical example, consider a physicist working with a system of n particles, where n is "large." Suppose he comes up with a formula which involves the term $(n^3 + n^2 + 100)/(3n^3 + 1000)$. It is obvious that if n is "very large" this term is close to $1/3$.

Exercises

An exercise will be helpful at this point. For each positive integer n, let

$$D_n = \frac{n^3 + n^2 + 100}{3n^3 + 1000} - \frac{1}{3}.$$

Then

$$D_n = \frac{3n^2 - 700}{9n^3 + 3000}.$$

1. Show that for $n \geq 16$, $|D_n| < 3n^2/(9n^3 + 3000)$.
2. Show that for $n \geq 16$, $|D_n| < 1/3n$.
3. Find a number N such that $n > N \Rightarrow |D_n| < 10^{-6}$.

An Obviously Convergent Sequence

Start with the interval $[\frac{1}{2}, \frac{2}{3}]$ and let M_1 be the mediant, $\frac{3}{5}$. Then let M_2 be the mediant of $[\frac{3}{5}, \frac{2}{3}]$: $M_2 = \frac{5}{8}$. For each positive integer n, let $M_n = (1 + 2n)/(2 + 3n)$. Then

$$\left|M_n - \frac{2}{3}\right| = \left|\frac{1+2n}{2+3n} - \frac{2}{3}\right| = \frac{1}{6+9n} < \frac{1}{9n}.$$

Given $\epsilon > 0$, let n be any integer larger than $1/9\epsilon$; then $|M_n - \frac{2}{3}| < 1/9n < \epsilon$. By the definition to be given presently, the sequence converges to $\frac{2}{3}$.

A Wildly Divergent Sequence

We define a sequence of rational numbers starting as follows:

$$r_1 = 1 = \tfrac{1}{1},$$
$$r_2 = \tfrac{1}{2}, r_3 = \tfrac{2}{1},$$
$$r_4 = \tfrac{1}{3}, r_5 = \tfrac{2}{2}, r_6 = \tfrac{3}{1},$$
$$r_7 = \tfrac{1}{4}, r_8 = \tfrac{2}{3}, r_9 = \tfrac{3}{2}, r_{10} = \tfrac{4}{1}.$$

The object is to have every positive rational number appear in the range of the sequence infinitely often. The following scheme to accomplish this is based on the sequence $1, 3, 6, 10, 15, \ldots$ of *triangular* numbers: for each n in $\mathbb{Z}^+$, $T_{n+1} - T_n = n + 1$.

Now let k be any positive integer. If k is a triangular number T_n we define r_k to be $n/1$. If k is not triangular, let T_n be the largest triangular number less than k, and write $k = T_n + j$. Then

$$r_k = \frac{j}{n+2-j}.$$

For example, since

$$5 = 3 + 2 = T_2 + 2, \qquad r_5 = \frac{2}{4-2} = 1,$$

$$40 = 36 + 4 = \frac{8 \cdot 9}{2} + 4 = T_8 + 4, \qquad r_{40} = \frac{4}{10-4} = \frac{4}{6}.$$

As a problem, find two distinct integers k and l such that $r_k = r_l = \frac{3}{4}$.

From the sequence r above, it is easy to construct a sequence such that every rational number appears in the range infinitely often. For example, for each positive integer n, let

$$u_{3n-2} = r_n,$$
$$u_{3n-1} = -r_n,$$
$$u_{3n} = 0.$$

The sequence u starts out as

$$1, -1, 0, \tfrac{1}{2}, -\tfrac{1}{2}, 0, 2, -2, 0, \tfrac{1}{3}, -\tfrac{1}{3}, 0, \ldots.$$

By deleting from this sequence all repetitions, we get a one-to-one correspondence of $\mathbb{Z}^+$ to $\mathbb{Q}$. Deleting the extra zeros is easy, but the other deletions are irregular. None of r_7, r_8, r_9, r_{10}, or their negatives are deleted, but the numbers from r_{11} to r_{15} are—$\frac{1}{5}$, $\frac{2}{4}$, $\frac{3}{3}$, $\frac{4}{2}$, $\frac{5}{1}$—and three of them are repetitions.

§ 6. *Convergence*

Definition 4.4. Let u be a real sequence on $\mathbf{Z}^+$ and L be a real number. Each of the statements **The limit of the sequence u is L** and **The sequence u converges to L** means that, for each $\epsilon > 0$, there exists a number N_ϵ such that

$$n \text{ in } \mathbf{Z}^+ \text{ and } n > N_\epsilon \Rightarrow |u_n - L| < \epsilon.$$

If the domain of a sequence does not include all positive integers, then the definition has to be modified by replacing "n in $\mathbf{Z}^+$ and $n > N_\epsilon$" by "n in the domain of u and $n > N_\epsilon$." To gain some simplicity in stating and proving theorems, we shall consider only sequences on $\mathbf{Z}^+$.

Definition 4.5. The statement that a sequence **converges** or **is convergent** or **has a limit** means that there is some number L such that the sequence converges to L.

Theorem 4.4. [*The First Principal Convergence Criterion*]. Every monotone bounded real sequence converges.

PROOF: We give the proof for a monotone decreasing sequence on $\mathbf{Z}^+$. Let u be such a sequence and be bounded. Because u is monotone decreasing, u_1 is automatically an upper bound. Thus the real force of the assumption of boundedness is the existence of a lower bound, and consequently a greatest lower bound, say B. We shall prove that u converges to B.

For $\epsilon > 0$, $B + \epsilon$ is not a lower bound because B is the greatest lower bound. Thus there is some positive integer N_ϵ such that $u_{N_\epsilon} < B + \epsilon$. Because the sequence is monotone decreasing, $n > N_\epsilon \Rightarrow u_n \le u_{N_\epsilon} < B + \epsilon$. However, B is a lower bound, and therefore

$$n > N_\epsilon \Rightarrow B \le u_n < B + \epsilon,$$

and $|u_n - B| < \epsilon$. ∎

Exercises

1. Picture the proof of the theorem for monotone increasing sequences.

For the rest of these exercises, and in other places, we use a common abbreviation. For example $\{n^2 + 1\}$ is understood to mean the sequence assigning to each positive integer n the number $n^2 + 1$. Similarly $\{(n + 1)/n\}$ means the sequence u such that for each positive integer n, $u_n = (n + 1)/n$.

2. Which of these sequences are convergent by Theorem 4.4?

a. $\left\{\dfrac{n+1}{n}\right\}$.

b. $\left\{\dfrac{n^2+1}{n^3}\right\}$.

c. $\{2\}$ $[u_n = 2$ for all n in $\mathbf{Z}^+]$.

d. $\left\{\dfrac{(-1)^n}{n}\right\}$.

e. $\left\{\dfrac{1}{n}\right\}$.

f. $\left\{\dfrac{n^2+1}{n}\right\}$.

3. Prove that $\left\{\dfrac{(-1)^n}{n}\right\}$ converges to 0. That is, find a way of producing, for each $\epsilon > 0$, a real number N_ϵ such that

$$n \text{ in } \mathbf{Z}^+ \text{ and } n > N_\epsilon \Rightarrow \left|\dfrac{(-1)^n}{n} - 0\right| < \epsilon.$$

4. Prove that $\lim \left\{\dfrac{n+2}{n}\right\} = 1$.

5. Prove that $\lim \left\{\dfrac{3n^2+5}{n^2}\right\} = 3$.

6. For each positive integer n, let $S_n = \sum_{k=1}^{n} 1/k^3$. Prove that the sequence S is convergent. No numeral for the limit of this sequence is known, but it is some nameless real number between 1 and 2.

Technical Points

Next we point out a few facts which are frequently used, but seem too slight in content to be called theorems or lemmas. Perhaps "technical observation" is a reasonable label for them.

1. If a is real and $\epsilon > 0$, and $|x - a| < \epsilon$ and $|y - a| < \epsilon$, then $|x - y| < 2\epsilon$.

2. If a and b are real numbers and, for every $\epsilon > 0$, $|a - b| < \epsilon$, then $a = b$.

3. $|x - L| < \epsilon \Rightarrow |x| < |L| + \epsilon$.

4. To prove that the sequence u converges to the number L, it is sufficient to prove, for example, that for each $\epsilon > 0$ there is a number N_ϵ such that

$$n > N_\epsilon \Rightarrow |u_n - L| < 2\epsilon$$

or

$$n > N_\epsilon \Rightarrow |u_n - L| < 5\epsilon.$$

The argument for this fourth "technical observation" runs as follows. Suppose that for each $\epsilon > 0$ there is a number N_ϵ such that

$$n > N_\epsilon \Rightarrow |u_n - L| < 3\epsilon.$$

Then, given any $\epsilon > 0$, set $\epsilon' = \epsilon/3$. There is also an $N_{\epsilon'}$ such that

$$n > N_{\epsilon'} \Rightarrow |u_n - L| < 3\epsilon' = \epsilon.$$

An example of observation 3 is

$$|x - (-8)| < 1 \Rightarrow -9 < x < -7 \Rightarrow |x| < 8 + 1.$$

Observation 3 is true because

$$|x| = |x - L + L| \le |x - L| + |L|.$$

Observation 2 is true because $|a - b|$ cannot be negative; if, also, $|a - b|$ is less than every positive number, then $|a - b| = 0$.

Observation 1 is obvious: if x and y are both in the open interval $(a - \epsilon, a + \epsilon)$ of length 2ϵ, then $|x - y| < 2\epsilon$. Or $|x - y| = |x - a + a - y| \le |x - a| + |y - a|$.

Lemma about $(1 + x)^n$. If $x > -1$, then, for every positive integer n,

$$(1 + x)^n \ge 1 + nx.$$

PROOF: For $x > 0$ this is clear from the binomial theorem, but for $x < 0$ it is not clear. In any case the lemma is much less profound than the binomial theorem. For $n = 1$ it says that $1 + x \ge 1 + x$. If $x > -1$ and, for some n, $(1 + x)^n \ge 1 + nx$, then $1 + x > 0$ and we can multiply both sides of the inequality by $1 + x$ to get

$$(1 + x)^{n+1} \ge (1 + nx)(1 + x)$$
$$= 1 + (n + 1)x + nx^2 \ge 1 + (n + 1)x. \quad \blacksquare$$

As an example,

$$\left(\frac{99}{100}\right)^{50} = \left(1 + \frac{-1}{100}\right)^{50} \ge 1 - \frac{50}{100} = \frac{1}{2}.$$

Corollary 1. If $|r| > 1$, the sequence $\{r^n\}$ is unbounded.

If $|r| > 1$, then $r^2 = 1 + x$, where $x > 0$. For every n in Z^+, $r^{2n} = (1 + x)^n > nx$. But for any positive B, $nx > B$ if $n > B/x$.

Corollary 2. If $|r| < 1$, the sequence $\{r^n\}$ converges to 0.

PROOF: If $r = 0$, then each term $0^n = 0$. If $r \ne 0$ but $|r| < 1$, then $|1/r| > 1$, and the sequence $\{|1/r|^n\}$ is unbounded. Thus for each $\epsilon > 0$ there is some integer k such that $|1/r|^k > 1/\epsilon$, which implies $|r^k| < \epsilon$. But $|r^{k+1}| = |r^k| \cdot |r| < |r^k|$. It follows that, for all $n > k$, $|r^n| < \epsilon$. Since $|r^n| = |r^n - 0|$, this establishes the corollary. $\quad \blacksquare$

Lemma. Every convergent real sequence is bounded.

PROOF: Let u be a sequence on Z^+ converging to the number L. Since $1 > 0$, there is some N_1 such that $n > N_1 \Rightarrow |u_n - L| < 1$. By "technical observation" 3, $n > N_1 \Rightarrow |u_n| < |L| + 1$. Let k be the largest integer $\leq N_1$. The finite set of numbers $|u_1|, |u_2|, \ldots, |u_k|$ has a largest member, say B. The larger of B and $|L| + 1$ is a bound for $\{|u_n| \,|n \text{ in } Z^+\}$. Let M be the larger of B and $|L| + 1$. Then, for all n in Z^+, $-M \leq u_n \leq M$. ∎

As a corollary to the above lemma and Corollary 1, if $|r| > 1$, the sequence $\{r^n\}$ does not converge.

The Limit Theorems

Suppose a sequence u converges to L and a sequence v converges to L'. For all large n, u_n is close to L and v_n is close to L'. If these "close" values are close enough, then $u_n + v_n$ should be close to $L + L'$ and $u_n v_n$ close to LL'. It seems that $u + v$ should converge to $L + L'$, and uv to LL'. The definition of limit is designed precisely to handle such matters.

One preliminary definition will be convenient. For real numbers a and b, let max $\{a, b\}$ denote the larger of a and b; if $a = b$, then max $\{a, b\} = a = b$. Clearly,

$$n > \max \{a, b\} \Rightarrow n > a \quad \text{and} \quad n > b.$$

Theorem 4.5. (*Uniqueness of Limits*). If the sequence u converges to L and to M, then $L = M$.

PROOF: For all n in Z^+,

$$|L - M| = |L - u_n + u_n - M| \leq |u_n - L| + |u_n - M|.$$

For $\epsilon > 0$ there are numbers N_ϵ and N'_ϵ such that

$$n > N_\epsilon \Rightarrow |u_n - L| < \epsilon,$$
$$n > N'_\epsilon \Rightarrow |u_n - M| < \epsilon.$$

Let n be an integer such that $n > \max \{N_\epsilon, N'_\epsilon\}$. Then $|u_n - L| < \epsilon$ and $|u_n - M| < \epsilon$. By technical observation 1, $|L - M| < 2\epsilon$. Thus for every $\epsilon > 0$, $|L - M| < 2\epsilon$, and, by observation 2, $L = M$. ∎

Theorem 4.6. If u and v are convergent sequences on Z^+ converging respectively to L and L', then

$$\lim (u + v) = L + L',$$
$$\lim (uv) \quad\; = LL',$$
$$\lim (u - v) = L - L'.$$

PROOF: Before starting the proof, notice that it is important that both sequences have domain Z^+, or at least that the intersection of their domains be an unbounded subset of Z^+. If the domain of u is the set of odd positive integers and that of v the even ones, then none of $u + v$, uv, or $u - v$ is a sequence.

We first consider $u + v$. We want to prove that for each $\epsilon > 0$ there is some N_ϵ such that

$$n > N_\epsilon \Rightarrow |(u_n + v_n) - (L + L')| < \epsilon.$$

In this statement (and for the rest of this section) we stipulate that the symbol n is understood to denote a positive integer.

To begin with, for all n,

$$|(u_n + v_n) - (L + L')| = |(u_n - L) + (v_n - L')|$$
$$\leq |u_n - L| + |v_n - L'|.$$

If $\epsilon > 0$, then $\epsilon/2 > 0$ and, since u converges to L, there is some $N_{\epsilon/2}$ such that

$$n > N_{\epsilon/2} \Rightarrow |u_n - L| < \frac{\epsilon}{2}.$$

Similarly, there is $N'_{\epsilon/2}$ such that

$$n > N'_{\epsilon/2} \Rightarrow |v_n - L'| < \frac{\epsilon}{2}.$$

Let $N_\epsilon = \max\{N_{\epsilon/2}, N'_{\epsilon/2}\}$. Then $n > N_\epsilon \Rightarrow |u_n - L| < \epsilon/2$, and $|v_n - L'| < \epsilon/2$. By the first step in the proof,

$$n > N_\epsilon \Rightarrow |(u_n + v_n) - (L + L')| < \epsilon.$$

The proof that $u - v$ converges to $L - L'$ is the same except that it begins, for all n,

$$|(u_n - v_n) - (L - L')| = |(u_n - L) - (v_n - L')|$$
$$\leq |u_n - L| + |v_n - L'|.$$

Now for the product. To begin with, for all n,

$$|u_n v_n - LL'| = |u_n v_n - Lv_n + Lv_n - LL'|$$
$$\leq |u_n v_n - Lv_n| + |Lv_n - LL'|$$
$$= |v_n|\,|u_n - L| + |L|\,|v_n - L'|.$$

Since v converges, v is bounded: there is some positive B such that for all n, $|v_n| < B$. Also, although $|L|$ might be 0, $|L| + 1$ is positive and larger than $|L|$.

For convenience, set $K = \max\{B, |L| + 1\}$. Then we can continue: for all n,

$$|u_n v_n - LL'| < K|u_n - L| + K|v_n - L'|,$$

which finishes the thoughtful part of the proof. A theorem-proving machine can now observe that, if $\epsilon > 0$, then $\epsilon/K > 0$. Therefore, since u converges to L and v converges to L', there are numbers N and N' such that

$$n > N \Rightarrow |u_n - L| < \frac{\epsilon}{K},$$

$$n > N' \Rightarrow |v_n - L'| < \frac{\epsilon}{K}.$$

Then it follows that

$$n > \max \{N, N'\} \Rightarrow |u_n v_n - LL'| < 2\epsilon. \qquad \blacksquare$$

Theorem 4.7. If the sequence v converges to L and $L \neq 0$ and, for all n, $v_n \neq 0$, then $1/v$ converges to $1/L$.

PROOF: To prove this it is necessary to establish first that the sequence $1/v$ is bounded. To this end observe that, since $L \neq 0$, $|L|/2 > 0$. Thus there exists some N such that

$$n > N \Rightarrow |v_n - L| < \frac{|L|}{2}.$$

This can be translated into

$$-\frac{|L|}{2} < v_n - L < \frac{|L|}{2},$$

$$L - \frac{|L|}{2} < v_n < L + \frac{|L|}{2},$$

and

$$n > N \Rightarrow |v_n| > \frac{|L|}{2} \quad \text{and} \quad \left|\frac{1}{v_n}\right| < \frac{2}{|L|}.$$

Let k be the largest integer $\leq N$; let p be the largest of $\left|\frac{1}{v_1}\right|, \left|\frac{1}{v_2}\right|, \cdots, \left|\frac{1}{v_k}\right|$.
Let $P = \max \left\{\frac{2}{|L|}, p\right\}$. For all n, $\left|\frac{1}{v_n}\right| \leq P$.

Now, for all n,

$$\left|\frac{1}{v_n} - \frac{1}{L}\right| = \left|\frac{L - v_n}{v_n L}\right|$$

$$= \frac{|v_n - L|}{|L| \, |v_n|}$$

$$\leq \frac{P}{|L|} |v_n - L|.$$

If $\epsilon > 0$, then $\epsilon|L|/P > 0$ and there is some N' such that

$$n > N' \Rightarrow |v_n - L| < \frac{\epsilon|L|}{P} \quad \text{and} \quad \frac{P}{|L|} |v_n - L| < \epsilon.$$

Thus

$$n > N' \Rightarrow \left|\frac{1}{v_n} - \frac{1}{L}\right| < \epsilon. \qquad \blacksquare$$

Remark: The hypothesis that $v_n \neq 0$ for all n was not really necessary. The assumption that v converges to L guarantees the existence of N such that $n > N \Rightarrow |v_n| > \frac{|L|}{2}$. Hence the sequence mapping n to $1/v_n$ for $n > N$ may not be a sequence on Z^+, but is a sequence converging to $1/L$.

By virtue of this remark and the product theorem we can assert

Theorem 4.8. If u and v are sequences on $\mathbf{Z}^+$ converging to L and L', and $L' \neq 0$, then u/v converges to L/L'.

Examples

1. $\{1/n\}$ converges to 0 and any constant sequence $\{k\}$ converges to k. Since

$$\left\{ \frac{n^2 + 3n}{2n^2 + 5} \right\} = \left\{ \frac{1 + \dfrac{3}{n}}{2 + \dfrac{5}{n^2}} \right\}$$

$$= \frac{\{1\} + \{3\}\left\{\dfrac{1}{n}\right\}}{\{2\} + \{5\}\left\{\dfrac{1}{n}\right\}\left\{\dfrac{1}{n}\right\}},$$

by the limit theorems, this sequence converges to

$$\frac{1 + 3\cdot 0}{2 + 5\cdot 0\cdot 0} = \frac{1}{2}.$$

2. Since, for all $n > 0$,

$$\frac{n^3 + 5n}{3n^2 + 2} > \frac{n^3}{3n^2 + 2} \geq \frac{n^3}{3n^2 + 2n^2} \geq \frac{n}{5},$$

the sequence $\left\{ \dfrac{n^3 + 5n}{3n^2 + 2} \right\}$ is unbounded. By the lemma on page 89, it does not converge.

Exercises

1. Each formula below defines a sequence on $\mathbf{Z}^+$. In each case determine whether the sequence converges and, if so, what the limit is.

a. $\dfrac{5n^3 - 1000}{n^3 + n^2 + 100}$.

b. $\dfrac{n^4 + 1}{10000n^3}$.

c. $\dfrac{1 + (-1)^n}{n}$.

d. $\dfrac{1 + n(-1)^n}{n}$.

e. $\dfrac{7n^4 + n^3}{n^4 - 10n^2 + 53}$.

f. $\dfrac{2^n}{n!}$.

g. $(1.001)^n$.

h. $(\sqrt{3} - 2)^n$.

i. $1 + \dfrac{1}{10} + \dfrac{1}{10^2} + \cdots + \dfrac{1}{10^n}$.

2. Prove that a bounded real sequence which is monotone increasing on the set of all integers $> 10^{10}$ converges.

3. Give an example of divergent sequences u and v such that $u + v$ converges. If u and v both diverge, can uv converge? [*Hint:* Try $u_n = (-1)^n$ for all n.]

4. Let $u_1 = \sqrt{3}$ and, for all n, $u_{n+1} = \sqrt{3 + u_n}$. Does this sequence converge?

5. [*The real number e.*]

a. For each positive integer n, let

$$E_n = \left(1 + \frac{1}{n}\right)^n.$$

Either from the binomial theorem or from the Lemma about $(1 + x)^n$ [page 89], it is clear that $E_n \geq 2$ for all n.

The exercise is to prove that the sequence E converges. Its limit is called e. You can establish the existence of the limit by proving that the sequence is monotone increasing and bounded. Some hints may be helpful.

First, since $E_n > 0$ for all n, $E_{n+1} > E_n$ if and only if $E_{n+1}/E_n > 1$. This can be established by filling in the outline below. For all n in $\mathbb{Z}^+$,

$$\frac{E_{n+1}}{E_n} = \frac{n+2}{n+1}\left(1 - \frac{1}{(n+1)^2}\right)^n \geq \frac{n+2}{n+1}\left(1 - \frac{n}{(n+1)^2}\right) > 1.$$

One way to establish an upper bound is to observe that if for $n \geq 2$ you set

$$F_n = \left(1 - \frac{1}{n}\right)^{-n} = \left(\frac{n}{n-1}\right)^n,$$

then you can apply the method of the last paragraph to prove that, for $n \geq 2$, $F_n/(F_n + 1) > 1$, and the sequence F is strictly decreasing. Finally then, for $n \geq 2$, $E_n < F_n \leq F_2 = 4$. This completes the proof that E converges and that the limit e satisfies $2 < e < 4$.

b. Prove that E/F converges to 1 and consequently F also converges to e.

c. For each $n \geq 2$, we have $E_n < e < F_n$. Using $n = 4$ or 6, find a decimal approximation to e.

d. Prove that $\left\{\left(1 + \frac{1}{n}\right)^n \left(1 - \frac{1}{n}\right)^n\right\}$ converges to 1 and consequently $\left\{\left(1 - \frac{1}{n}\right)^n\right\}$ converges to e^{-1}.

§ 7. *The Cauchy Completeness of* $\mathfrak{R}$

The French mathematician Augustin-Louis Cauchy (1789–1857) was one of the first to treat convergence and limits in a rigorous way. The theorem of this section is known as the *second principal convergence criterion* or the *Cauchy criterion.*

Let u be a sequence converging to a number L. For each $\epsilon > 0$ there is a corresponding N such that for all $n > N$, $|u_n - L| < \epsilon/2$. From this it follows that if n and m are both larger than N, then $|u_n - u_m| < \epsilon$.

Definition 4.6. Let u be a real sequence on $\mathbb{Z}^+$. If for each $\epsilon > 0$ there is a corresponding N such that, for all n and m larger than N, $|u_n - u_m| < \epsilon$, then u is a **Cauchy sequence.**

The paragraph above the definition gives the proof that every convergent real sequence on $\mathbb{Z}^+$ is a Cauchy sequence. The converse of this simple theorem is what we want.

Lemma. Every Cauchy sequence is bounded.

PROOF: Let u be a Cauchy sequence. Since $1 > 0$, there is some N such that, for all n and $m > N$, $|u_n - u_m| < 1$. Let p be an integer larger than N, say the smallest integer larger than N. For any $n > N$, $|u_n - u_p| < 1$ and hence $|u_p| - 1 < u_n < |u_p| + 1$. And, as in the proof that every convergent sequence is bounded, the finite set $\{u_1, \ldots, u_{p-1}\}$ is bounded.

Theorem 4.9. [*Cauchy Criterion*]. Every real Cauchy sequence converges to a real number.

PROOF: Let c be a Cauchy sequence. By the Lemma there are numbers L and U such that, for all n, $L \leq c_n \leq U$. Specifically we take L and U to be respectively the greatest lower bound and least upper bound [glb and lub] of the range of c. The sequence c may not be monotone and there is no reason to suppose it converges to either L or U.

We construct a monotone increasing sequence l and a monotone decreasing sequence u such that for every n in $\mathbb{Z}^+$, $l_n \leq c_n \leq u_n$. The idea is to have the sequences l and u converge to the same limit and thus ensure that c also converges to this limit.

For each positive integer n let l_n be the greatest lower bound of the set $\{c_k | k \geq n\}$, and let u_n be the least upper bound of the same set. The set $\{c_k | k \geq n + 1\}$ is a subset of $\{c_k | k \geq n\}$ from which, for all n, $l_{n+1} \geq l_n$ and $u_{n+1} \leq u_n$.

The monotone increasing sequence l has an upper bound: for all n, $l_n \leq c_n \leq U$. Similarly, for all n, $u_n \geq L$. Set $A = \text{lub } \{l_n\}$ and $B = \text{glb } \{u_n\}$. By the first principal convergence criterion, l converges to A and u converges to B.

It is also true that $A \leq B$. For suppose that $A > B$. Then B is not an upper bound of $\{l_n\}$ and there is some k such that $l_k > B$. But this is absurd, because $l_k \leq c_k \leq u_k \leq B$.

Given $\epsilon > 0$, since the sequence c is a Cauchy sequence, there is some N such that, for all n and m larger than N, $|c_n - c_m| < \epsilon$.

Also, since $\{l_n\}$ converges up to A, there is some M such that, for $n > M$, $A - \epsilon < l_n \leq A$. Similarly, there is some K such that, for $n > K$, $B \leq u_n < B + \epsilon$.

Let $P = \max \{N, M, K\}$ and let k be an integer larger than P. For any integer m larger than k we have

(1) $c_k - \epsilon < c_m < c_k + \epsilon$.

From (1), $c_k - \epsilon$ and $c_k + \epsilon$ are lower and upper bounds of $\{c_m | m \geq k\}$. Since l_m and u_m are the greatest lower and least upper bounds of this set, we have

(2) $c_k - \epsilon \leq l_m \leq A \leq B \leq u_m \leq c_k + \epsilon$.

For any $\epsilon > 0$ there is a number m such that inequality (2) gives $|B - A| < 2\epsilon$. Therefore $A = B$.

But also, since by construction $l_m \leq c_m \leq u_m$, we have, for all $m > k > P$,

$$l_m \leq A = B \leq u_m,$$

$$l_m \leq c_m \leq u_m,$$

and

$$u_m - l_m < 2\epsilon.$$

Thus for each $\epsilon > 0$ there is a number k_ϵ such that, for all $m > k_\epsilon$, $|c_m - A| < 2\epsilon$, which establishes the convergence of c to A.   ■

Given only the rational numbers we can consider rational sequences. Many of them [for example, all infinite nonrepeating decimals] seem to converge to something, but this something is not a rational number. In this sense the rational field might be called incomplete.

Theorem 4.9 says that any real sequence that seems as though it should converge to something [that is, any Cauchy sequence] does converge to a real number. The real field is complete in the sense that consideration of sequences does not lead to any need for a larger number system. This is the *Cauchy completeness* of $\mathfrak{R}$.

We shall have little need for Theorem 4.9 in this book, but shall indicate how to use it to deduce *Leibnitz's test for alternating series*.

Let p be a sequence of positive numbers, monotone decreasing and converging to 0. From p form a sequence S of partial sums:

$$S_1 = p_1,$$

$$S_2 = p_1 - p_2,$$

$$S_3 = p_1 - p_2 + p_3,$$

$$\cdots$$

$$S_n = \sum_{k=1}^{n} (-1)^{k+1} p_k, \text{ for all } n \text{ in } \mathbf{Z}^+.$$

If S converges to a number L, we write

$$L = \sum_{k=1}^{\infty} (-1)^{k+1} p_k.$$

The infinite series on the right [which is the sequence S] is *alternating* because the terms $(-1)^{k+1} p_k$ are alternately positive and negative.

Exercises

1. Prove that for all n and m, with $m > n$,

$$|S_m - S_n| \leq |S_{n+1} - S_n| = p_{n+1}.$$

2. Prove that the sequence S is a Cauchy sequence.

3. Find a reasonable estimate for

$$1 - \frac{1}{2} + \frac{1}{3} - \frac{1}{4} + \cdots + \frac{(-1)^{n+1}}{n} + \cdots.$$

4. Find a reasonable estimate for $\sum\limits_{k=1}^{\infty} [(-1)^{k+1}/k!]$.

5. [More ambitious.] Without using Theorem 4.8, prove that S converges by proving that each of the subsequences

$$S_1, S_3, S_5, \ldots,$$
$$S_2, S_4, S_6, \ldots$$

is monotone and bounded, and that they converge to the same limit.

The sequence of Exercise 4 has an interesting property. The first four terms are

$$S_1 = 1,$$
$$S_2 = 1 - \cdot\tfrac{1}{2} = \tfrac{1}{2},$$
$$S_3 = S_2 + \tfrac{1}{6} = \tfrac{2}{3},$$
$$S_4 = S_3 - \tfrac{1}{24} = \tfrac{5}{8}.$$

It is clear that the limit of the sequence, say L, is between S_n and S_{n+1} for every n. This is true for any sequence convergent by Leibnitz's test.

For this particular sequence, $n!S_n$ is an integer for every n. Now suppose a rational number p/q, reduced, to be between S_n and S_{n+1} for some n. If n is odd, we have

$$S_{n+1} < \frac{p}{q} < S_n,$$

$$(n+1)! \, S_{n+1} < (n+1)! \frac{p}{q} < (n+1)! \, S_n.$$

However,

$$S_{n+1} = S_n - \frac{1}{(n+1)!}.$$

Thus

$$(n+1)! \, S_n - 1 < (n+1)! \frac{p}{q} < (n+1)! \, S_n,$$

and

$$-1 < (n+1)! \frac{p}{q} - (n+1)! \, S_n < 0.$$

If n is even, the corresponding result is

$$0 < (n+1)! \frac{p}{q} - (n+1)! \, S_n < 1.$$

From these results we can see that if the rational number p/q is between S_n and S_{n+1}, then $(n+1)! \, (p/q) - (n+1)! \, S_n$ is not an integer. But $(n+1)! \, (p/q)$ is an integer if $n+1 \geq q$.

Conclusion: a rational number p/q can be between S_n and S_{n+1} only for a few small n, at most all n with $1 \leq n \leq q$, and the limit of the sequence must be irrational.

5

Elements of Analytic Geometry

The mathematical part of this chapter starts with Section 1. We preface it with a very brief historical sketch and some intuitive explanation of the approach taken in the chapter.

Synthetic Geometry

One of the greatest contributions of the Greeks to Western intellectual life is Euclid's *Elements*. Nothing is known of the man Euclid, who probably lived around 300 B.C., nor is much known about his predecessors who worked out the theorems that Euclid presumably collected together in an orderly way in the *Elements*.

If we take *Euclid* to mean the early Greek school of geometers—the book, rather than the man—we can say that Euclid created the first example of a deductive system. If one singles out some of the self-evident truths about the physical world as axioms, then one can logically deduce as theorems other truths which may or may not be self-evident. Later geometers have discovered some flaws in the *Elements*, but nevertheless the book is regarded as one of man's greatest achievements.

One of Euclid's axioms, the *fifth postulate* or *parallel postulate*, is equivalent to the statement that if L is a line and $\mathbf{p}$ a point not on L, then there is one and only one line through $\mathbf{p}$ parallel to L. From early Greek times until the 19th century this was regarded as less self-evident than the other axioms, and many people attempted to prove it as a theorem. In the early 19th century the existence of *non-Euclidean* geometries was discovered by Gauss, Bolyai, and Lobachevski. One may replace the parallel postulate by either (a) there is *no* line through $\mathbf{p}$ parallel to L, or (b) their is *more than one* line through $\mathbf{p}$ parallel to L. Either leads to a geometry just as consistent as Euclid's. Gauss suppressed his results, apparently on the grounds that the world wasn't yet ready to know that one must deal with "geometries" rather than "geometry." Later in the century Riemann discovered many more geometries.

These discoveries raised two questions, now seen to be quite distinct. Is the geometry of the physical universe Euclidean? This is a nonmathematical question, to be answered on the basis of experimental evidence. The current answer is that this part of the universe at this time seems to be Euclidean to within experimental error. Whether physical geometry on an astronomical scale is Euclidean is an interesting, unanswered question.

The mathematical question about the validity of a geometry is whether the axioms are consistent, or whether one can deduce some theorem and also its denial. No mathematical system as complicated as a plane geometry has ever been proved consistent, but it has been proved that Euclidean geometry is consistent if and only if the non-Euclidean geometries are consistent. Thus all are equally valid, or invalid.

It has also been proved that the Pythagorean theorem and its converse are true only in the Euclidean geometries: one way then to test physical space would be to measure the sides of astronomically large right triangles.

Axioms are no longer regarded as self-evident truths. Current synthetic plane geometry starts out with two explicitly undefined terms, *point* and *line*, and an undefined possible event: *point* **p** *is on line L*. Then comes a rather lengthy list of axioms, then theorems.

Intuitive Analytic Geometry

The intuitive plane is an infinite table top or blackboard. If on it two mutually perpendicular lines are drawn, with a direction indicated on each, and a unit of length is chosen, then these lines and the choice of unit form a *Cartesian coordinate system*. It is named after Descartes, whose *Essais philosophiques* of 1637 is regarded as the beginning of analytic geometry.

Intuitions about geometry and real numbers assert that to each point **p** in the plane we can assign an ordered pair of real numbers (p_1, p_2), where p_1 and p_2 are directed distances from the axes to **p**. Conversely, given any ordered pair (d_1, d_2) of real numbers, there should be a point at distance d_1 from the vertical axis and at distance d_2 from the horizontal axis.

The two axes split the plane into four quadrants: the first is the one containing the triangle **abc**; the others are numbered II, III, IV.

Assume that triangle **abc** has a right angle at **c** and that the Pythagorean theorem is true. Writing $\overline{\textbf{ac}}$ for the length of the segment joining **a** and **c**, we note the following: because **a** and **c** have the same first coordinate, line **ac** should be parallel to the vertical axis; by our construction, then, $\overline{\textbf{ac}} = |a_2 - b_2|$. Similarly, $\overline{\textbf{cb}} = |a_1 - b_1|$. By the Pythagorean theorem,

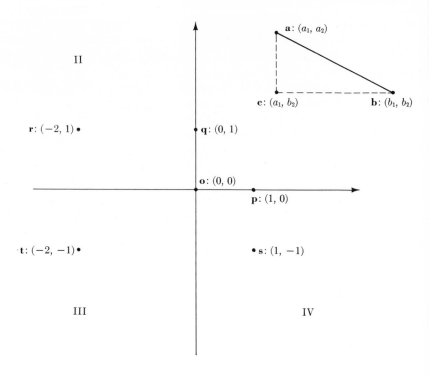

$$\overline{\mathbf{ab}}^2 = \overline{\mathbf{ac}}^2 + \overline{\mathbf{cb}}^2$$
$$= |a_2 - b_2|^2 + |a_1 - b_1|^2,$$
$$\overline{\mathbf{ab}} = \sqrt{(a_1 - b_1)^2 + (a_2 - b_2)^2}.$$

Although **a** and **b** are shown in the first quadrant, the formula above for the distance between **a** and **b** does not depend on their placement. For example,

$$\overline{\mathbf{ts}} = |-2 - 1| = 3,$$
$$\overline{\mathbf{tr}} = |1 - (-1)| = 2,$$
$$\overline{\mathbf{rs}} = \sqrt{3^2 + 2^2} = \sqrt{13}.$$

The conclusion is that if one can assign coordinates to points as in the intuitive construction, and if the Pythagorean theorem holds, then the distance between a point with coordinates (a_1, a_2) and one with coordinates (b_1, b_2) is the square root of sums of squares displayed above.

The analogous intuitive assignment of coordinates to points in space goes as follows. Choose a unit length and three mutually perpendicular planes: those determined by the front wall, left wall, and floor of an ordinary room will do. Assign to a point **p** the ordered triple (p_1, p_2, p_3), where p_1 is the directed distance to **p** from the front plane, p_2 the directed distance from the left plane, p_3 the directed distance from the floor plane. Choose signs so that distances measured into the room are positive.

Consider now a rectangular box with a bottom of length l, width w, and height h. Let c be the length of the diagonal of the bottom rectangle and d the length of the diagonal of the box. If the Pythagorean theorem holds, then

$$c^2 = l^2 + w^2,$$

and

$$d^2 = c^2 + h^2 = l^2 + w^2 + h^2.$$

If we assign coordinates (p_1, p_2, p_3) and (q_1, q_2, q_3) to the diagonally opposite points of the box at distance d from each other, we get

$$\overline{\mathbf{pq}} = d = \sqrt{(p_1 - q_1)^2 + (p_2 - q_2)^2 + (p_3 - q_3)^2}.$$

The real line or *number line* is a one-dimensional space. For real numbers a_1 and b_1, points on the line, we have $|a_1 - b_1| = \sqrt{(a_1 - b_1)^2}$ for the distance between two points.

The object of this chapter is to use the real number system to build formal models of Euclidean spaces. In our model a point in the plane *is* an ordered pair of real numbers, and a point in space *is* an ordered triple of real numbers. Distance between points will be defined by the formulas which we have seen above are intuitively correct [to. Euclidean intuitions]. A formal proof that we have a correct model of, for example, the Euclidean plane would call for listing a generally accepted set of axioms for the Euclidean plane and checking that each is verified in our model. We shall not be this formal, but many of the usual axioms appear as theorems or exercises.

The formulas for distance in one, two, and three dimensions are so similar that a feeling for economy dictates some attempt to exploit the similarity. Also, although there may be no intuitive geometric counterpart, there is nothing to prevent one from calling the set of all ordered sextuples of real numbers a six-dimensional space and defining distance in this space by the analogous formula.

We shall define an n-dimensional Euclidean space $\mathfrak{R}^n$ for each positive integer n. Although the spaces $\mathfrak{R}^n$ for $n > 3$ have no obvious intuitive counterparts, they are important to physics and chemistry as well as to mathematics. For example, a mathematical atom with 3 protons and 3 electrons lives in an 18-dimensional space.

Our primary motive for doing some geometry in $\mathfrak{R}^n$ for arbitrary n is not the usefulness of $\mathfrak{R}^{18}$, but the light it sheds on some ways in which $\mathfrak{R}^2$ and $\mathfrak{R}^3$ are very much alike and other ways in which they are very different. We shall give no detailed theorems about $\mathfrak{R}^n$ for $n > 3$, and shall try to prove a theorem in its most general form only if the proof for $\mathfrak{R}^n$ is not essentially more difficult than proofs for $\mathfrak{R}^2$ and $\mathfrak{R}^3$.

Intuitive Congruences and Similarities

The original Greek idea of *congruence* seems to have been that two plane figures are congruent if one could be superimposed on the other so that they match up exactly.

In our intuitive analytic model we can think of this as follows. Start with two indistinguishable sheets of infinite graph paper, initially super-imposed so that each point (a, b) of the top plane is exactly above the point (a, b) in the bottom plane. If we think of the top model of $\Re^2$ as domain and the bottom model as range, we have a picture of the identity function on $\Re^2$: this pairing of points assigns to each (a, b) in $\Re^2$ [thought of as top plane] the point (a, b) in $\Re^2$ [thought of as bottom plane].

Suppose now that the top plane is moved to rest in a new position on the bottom plane. The moving must be done very carefully, with no stretch-ing or tearing or other distortion: in short, the motion is to be accomplished without changing the distance between any two points in the top plane. Now, just under each point **p** in the top model is a corresponding point **p**′ in the bottom model; and just above each **q**′ in the bottom is a point **q** in the top. This gives a picture of a function K, which is a one-to-one cor-respondence of $\Re^2$ [as top plane] to $\Re^2$ [as bottom plane]. Furthermore, for any **p** and **q** in $\Re^2$, the distance between **p** and **q**, measured in the top plane, is the same as the distance between $K(\mathbf{p})$ and $K(\mathbf{q})$ measured in the bottom plane. This function K is a congruence.

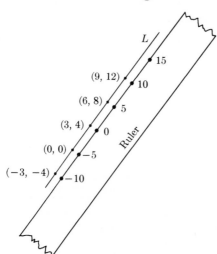

Above is a partial picture of a congruence of $\Re^1$ to a line in $\Re^2$. We pick up $\Re^1$ very carefully on the edge of a ruler and match it with the line L so that the distance between any two points of $\Re^1$ is the same as the distance between the corresponding points of L. The congruence is the function assign-ing to each point of $\Re^1$ a point of L.

If measurements in a plane are recorded in feet and we lay on the plane a ruler marked in centimeters, then all ruler readings will be wrong, but all by the same scale factor. Then the function matching points on the ruler with points on a line in the plane will be a *similarity* but not a congruence.

Two plane figures are *similar* if an enlargement of a photograph of one can be exactly superimposed on the other. In three dimensions a properly made scale model of a house is similar to the house.

Definitions and Usage

We shall give definitions of basic terms such as line, plane, parallel, perpendicular, circle, and line segment. It seems unnecessary to define derivative terms such as semicircle, right triangle, or regular hexagon.

In our model a line or a plane or a circle is a set of points and a point can be *in* a set. However, common usage calls for *on*, and we prefer this usual geometric language.

A *triangle* is a plane curve made out of three line segments. The *area* of the triangle is not the area of the curve, which is 0, but the area of the region enclosed by the triangle. The same abuse of language holds for circles, parallelograms, and other geometric figures.

It is possible that a formal definition of *angle* is called for. Measurement of angles is not at issue. The question is: what is an angle? Here is a formal definition, even though no use will be made of it.

An angle from a ray **ab** to a ray **ac** is an ordered quadruple: the first entry is the ray **ab** and the second is the ray **ac**; the third entry is a plus or a minus [+ or −], to be interpreted as counterclockwise or clockwise; the fourth entry is a nonnegative integer to be interpreted as the number of extra complete revolutions. An example is pictured below.

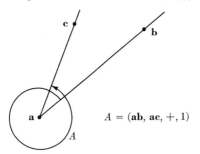

$$A = (\mathbf{ab}, \mathbf{ac}, +, 1)$$

The diagram seems superior to the quadruple.

Preview of the Sections

The basic preliminary definitions constitute § 1. Each of the next three sections introduces a new algebraic operation with geometric significance. You must learn to handle these operations algebraically and to interpret them geometrically before you can make much progress. The powerful theorems are in § 5 and § 6.

The reader who draws pictures for himself in the intuitive $\mathfrak{R}^2$ and $\mathfrak{R}^3$— and every reader should do this—will undoubtedly see all sorts of obvious theorems that are suggested by, but not asserted in, the text. You may be able to prove some, but others will require machinery that has not yet been presented. This can be very frustrating, but you should often drop the affair and try again later. Only one exercise is intentionally frustrating and unfair.

Analytic geometry is often described as a happy marriage of algebra and geometry: a geometric interpretation may make the solution to an algebraic puzzle obvious, or solving an equation may settle a problem where geometric intuition is in doubt. In terms of the marriage, this chapter is much more concerned with the courtship than with the honeymoon.

§ 1. *Basic Definitions*

Definition 5.1. For each positive integer n let $\mathfrak{R}^n$ be the set of all ordered n-tuples of real numbers. Each such n-tuple will be called a **point** of, or in, $\mathfrak{R}^n$.

For example, $(2, 5, 7)$ is a point in $\mathfrak{R}^3$, $(1, 1, 2, -5)$ a point in $\mathfrak{R}^4$. Unless a point $\mathbf{a}$ or $\mathbf{p}$ is actually specified, we adopt the convention that $\mathbf{a} = (a_1, \ldots, a_n)$, $\mathbf{p} = (p_1, \ldots, p_n)$, and so on. Therefore $\mathbf{a} = \mathbf{p}$ iff $a_k = p_k$ for $k = 1, \ldots, n$. The numbers in the n-tuple which is the point $\mathbf{q}$ will be called the *components* of $\mathbf{q}$.

The point in $\mathfrak{R}^n$ with all components 0 will be called $\mathbf{o}$ or $\mathbf{o}^n$. Thus $\mathbf{o}^2 = (0, 0)$ and $\mathbf{o}^5 = (0, 0, 0, 0, 0)$; $\mathbf{o}$ will also be called the *origin* in $\mathfrak{R}^n$. For $n = 1$ we shall drop the parentheses around a one-tuple and regard 3, for example, sometimes as a number and sometimes as a point of $\mathfrak{R}^1$.

Definition 5.2. For each positive integer n let d_n be the following function: the domain of d_n is the set of all pairs $(\mathbf{p}, \mathbf{q})$ such that $\mathbf{p}$ and $\mathbf{q}$ are points of $\mathfrak{R}^n$; to the pair $(\mathbf{p}, \mathbf{q})$, d_n assigns the number

$$d_n(\mathbf{p}, \mathbf{q}) = \sqrt{\sum_{k=1}^{n} (p_k - q_k)^2}.$$

Each function d_n is known as the *Euclidean metric* or *Euclidean distance function* for the set $\mathfrak{R}^n$. The *n-dimensional Euclidean space* $\mathfrak{R}^n$ is the set $\mathfrak{R}^n$ paired with the distance function d_n; in other words, the space is the set given a structure by specifying that the distance between two points $\mathbf{a}$ and $\mathbf{b}$ in the set is $d_n(\mathbf{a}, \mathbf{b})$. Replacement of d_n by a different function with the four properties listed below would give a *metric space*, but perhaps not a Euclidean space.

Properties of the Metric. Let **a**, **b**, **c** be points of $\mathcal{R}^n$. Then the following properties hold.

1. $d_n(\mathbf{a}, \mathbf{b}) \geq 0$.

2. $d_n(\mathbf{a}, \mathbf{b}) = 0$ iff $\mathbf{a} = \mathbf{b}$.

3. $d_n(\mathbf{a}, \mathbf{b}) = d_n(\mathbf{b}, \mathbf{a})$.

4. [*Triangle inequality*]. $d_n(\mathbf{a}, \mathbf{b}) \leq d_n(\mathbf{a}, \mathbf{c}) + d_n(\mathbf{c}, \mathbf{b})$.

The first and third of these are immediate from the definition. For the second, $d_n(\mathbf{a}, \mathbf{b}) = 0$ iff $(d_n(\mathbf{a}, \mathbf{b}))^2 = 0$—that is, iff $\sum_{k=1}^{n} (a_k - b_k)^2 = 0$. But a sum of squares of real numbers is 0 iff each term is 0—that is, iff $a_k - b_k = 0$ for $1 \leq k \leq n$, and $\mathbf{a} = \mathbf{b}$.

The Triangle Inequality is proved in § 5.

Definition 5.3 [*Congruence and Similarity*]. Let F be a mapping with domain a subset of $\mathcal{R}^n$ and range a subset of $\mathcal{R}^m$, where n and m are positive integers not necessarily different.

Then F is a **congruence** iff, for all **a** and **b** in the domain of F,

$$d_m(F(\mathbf{a}), F(\mathbf{b})) = d_n(\mathbf{a}, \mathbf{b}).$$

And F is a **similarity of scale factor** r iff there is some positive number r such that, for all **a** and **b** in the domain of F,

$$d_m(F(\mathbf{a}), F(\mathbf{b})) = r d_n(\mathbf{a}, \mathbf{b}).$$

Examples

1. For all real t let $F(t) = (2t, 3t)$ in $\mathcal{R}^2$. For any real t and s,

$$
\begin{aligned}
d_2(F(t), F(s)) &= d_2((2t, 3t), (2s, 3s)) \\
&= \sqrt{(2t - 2s)^2 + (3t - 3s)^2} \\
&= \sqrt{13(t - s)^2} = \sqrt{13}\,|t - s| = \sqrt{13}\,d_1(t, s).
\end{aligned}
$$

Thus F is a similarity of scale factor $\sqrt{13}$ mapping $\mathcal{R}^1$ onto a subset of $\mathcal{R}^2$.

2. For all (a, b, c) in $\mathcal{R}^3$ let $G(a, b, c) = (2, a, 3, b, c)$ in $\mathcal{R}^5$. For any (a, b, c) and (d, e, f) in $\mathcal{R}^3$,

$$
\begin{aligned}
d_5(G(a, b, c), G(d, e, f)) \\
&= \sqrt{(2 - 2)^2 + (a - d)^2 + (3 - 3)^2 + (b - e)^2 + (c - f)^2} \\
&= \sqrt{(a - d)^2 + (b - e)^2 + (c - f)^2} \\
&= d_3((a, b, c), (d, e, f)).
\end{aligned}
$$

Thus G is a congruence mapping $\mathcal{R}^3$ onto a subset of $\mathcal{R}^5$.

3. For all (a, b) in $\mathcal{R}^2$ let $\mathbf{X}(a, b) = (-b, a)$. For any (a, b) and (c, d) in $\mathcal{R}^2$,

$$
\begin{aligned}
d_2(\mathbf{X}(a, b), \mathbf{X}(c, d)) &= d_2((-b, a), (-d, c)) \\
&= \sqrt{(-b + d)^2 + (a - c)^2} \\
&= \sqrt{(a - c)^2 + (b - d)^2} \\
&= d_2((a, b), (c, d)).
\end{aligned}
$$

Thus $\mathbf{X}$ is a congruence mapping $\mathcal{R}^2$ onto $\mathcal{R}^2$. [Why onto?]

4. For all real t let $H(t) = t/(1 + |t|)$. Then $H(0) = 0$, $H(1) = \frac{1}{2}$, and $H(2) = \frac{2}{3}$. The three points 0, 1, 2 are equally spaced in $\Re^1$, but their images under H are not equally spaced; therefore H, which is a one-to-one correspondence of the real line to the open interval $(-1, 1)$, is not a similarity.

Theorem 5.1. A similarity of scale factor $r > 0$ is a one-to-one mapping of its domain onto its range; its inverse is a similarity of scale factor r^{-1}. In particular, a congruence is one-to-one and its inverse is a congruence.

PROOF: Let S be a similarity of scale factor $r > 0$ with domain in $\Re^n$. If $\mathbf{a}$ and $\mathbf{b}$ are in the domain of S and $S(\mathbf{a}) = S(\mathbf{b})$, then, by the second metric property,

$$0 = d_m(S(\mathbf{a}), S(\mathbf{b})) = rd_n(\mathbf{a}, \mathbf{b}).$$

Since $r \neq 0$, $d_n(\mathbf{a}, \mathbf{b}) = 0$ and $\mathbf{a} = \mathbf{b}$.

That S^{-1} is a similarity of scale factor r^{-1} is now clear. The corollary about congruences follows because a congruence is a similarity of scale factor 1.   ■

Theorem 5.2. If S is a similarity of scale factor r and S' a similarity of scale factor r' and the domain of S includes the range of S', then $S \circ S'$ is a similarity of scale factor rr'.

PROOF: If $\mathbf{a}$ and $\mathbf{b}$ are in the domain of S', then by hypothesis $S'(\mathbf{a})$ and $S'(\mathbf{b})$ are in the domain of S and, letting d represent the appropriate distance functions, we have

$$d(S(S'(\mathbf{a})), S(S'(\mathbf{b}))) = rd(S'(\mathbf{a}), S'(\mathbf{b}))$$
$$= rr'd(\mathbf{a}, \mathbf{b}).$$

Definition 5.4. Let U be a subset of $\Re^n$ and V a subset of $\Re^m$. Then U **is similar to** V iff there is a similarity mapping U onto V; U **is congruent to** V iff there is a congruence mapping U onto V.

Theorem 5.3 (*And Definition*). Each of *is similar to* and *is congruent to* is an **equivalence relation** in the collection of all subsets of all the Euclidean spaces; that is, each relation is reflexive, symmetric, and transitive.

PROOF FOR *"is similar to"*:

1. *Reflexivity.* Let U be a subset of $\Re^n$: the identity function on $\Re^n$ is a similarity mapping U onto U, so U is similar to U.

2. *Symmetry.* If U is similar to V, then there is a similarity S mapping U onto V. By Theorem 5.1, S^{-1} is a similarity mapping V onto U, and V is similar to U.

3. *Transitivity.* If U is similar to V and V is similar to W, then there are similarities S' mapping U onto V and S mapping V onto W. Therefore $S \circ S'$ maps U onto W and is a similarity, by Theorem 5.2. ∎

Definitions 5.5. Let U be a subset of $\mathfrak{R}^n$. Then the following statements obtain.
1. U is a **line** iff U is congruent to $\mathfrak{R}^1$.
2. U is a **closed segment** iff U is congruent to some closed interval $[a, b]$.
3. U is an **open segment** iff U is congruent to some open interval (a, b).
4. U is a **ray** iff U is congruent to $\{t | t \geq 0\}$.
5. U is a **plane** iff U is congruent to $\mathfrak{R}^2$.
6. U is a **plane figure** iff U is congruent to some subset of $\mathfrak{R}^2$.

Definition 5.6. 1. Let $\mathbf{a}$ be a point in $\mathfrak{R}^2$ and r be a positive number. The *circle* with radius r and center $\mathbf{a}$ is the set of all $\mathbf{p}$ in $\mathfrak{R}^2$ such that $d_2(\mathbf{p}, \mathbf{a}) = r$. The *open disc* with center $\mathbf{a}$ and radius r is the set of all $\mathbf{p}$ in $\mathfrak{R}^2$ such that $d_2(\mathbf{p}, \mathbf{a}) < r$. The *closed disc* with center $\mathbf{a}$ and radius r is the set of all $\mathbf{p}$ in $\mathfrak{R}^2$ such that $d_2(\mathbf{p}, \mathbf{a}) \leq r$. The open disc is the *interior* of the circle, and the circle is the *boundary* of the disc (open or closed). In particular, the circle of radius 1 with center at $(0, 0)$ is the *unit circle* in the plane and its interior is the *open unit disc*.

2. Let $\mathbf{a}$ be a point in $\mathfrak{R}^n$ with $n \geq 3$ and r be a positive number. The *sphere* with radius r and center $\mathbf{a}$ is the set of all $\mathbf{p}$ in $\mathfrak{R}^n$ such that $d_n(\mathbf{p}, \mathbf{a}) = r$. The *open ball* with center $\mathbf{a}$ and radius r is the set of all $\mathbf{p}$ in $\mathfrak{R}^n$ such that $d_n(\mathbf{p}, \mathbf{a}) < r$. The *closed ball* with center $\mathbf{a}$ and radius r is the set of all $\mathbf{p}$ in $\mathfrak{R}^n$ such that $d_n(\mathbf{p}, \mathbf{a}) \leq r$. The open ball is the *interior* of the sphere, and the sphere is the *boundary* of the ball (open or closed). In particular, the sphere of radius 1 with center at $\mathbf{o}^n$ is the *unit sphere* in $\mathfrak{R}^n$ and its interior is the *open unit ball*.

Examples

1. Let S be the set of all (u, v, w) in $\mathfrak{R}^3$ such that $u^2 + v^2 + w^2 - 2u + 4v \leq 0$. The given inequality is equivalent to each of the following:

$$u^2 - 2u + 1 + v^2 + 4v + 4 + w^2 \leq 5,$$
$$\sqrt{(u - 1)^2 + (v + 2)^2 + w^2} \leq \sqrt{5},$$
$$d_3((u, v, w), (1, -2, 0)) \leq \sqrt{5}.$$

Thus S is the closed ball of radius $\sqrt{5}$ with center at $(1, -2, 0)$.

2. The sphere with radius $\sqrt{2}$ and center at $(0, 0, 0, 0)$ is the set of all (w, x, y, z) such that $w^2 + x^2 + y^2 + z^2 = 2$. There are exactly 24 such points with integer coordinates; two of them are $(1, 0, -1, 0)$ and $(0, 0, -1, -1)$.

3. Let U be the set of all (x, y, z) such that $z = y = 2x$. We readily verify that U is the image of $\mathcal{R}^1$ under the mapping K: for all real t,

$$K(t) = \left(\frac{t}{3}, \frac{2t}{3}, \frac{2t}{3}\right).$$

By computing, for real t and s,

$$d_3(K(t), K(s)) = |t - s| = d_1(t, s),$$

we see that K is a congruence and therefore, by Definitions 5.5, U is a line.

[The mapping $S: t \longrightarrow (t, 2t, 2t)$, is the natural one-to-one correspondence of $\mathcal{R}^1$ to U. However, S is not a congruence but a similarity of scale factor 3. By a very convenient theorem in § 3 of this chapter, any set similar to $\mathcal{R}^1$ is also congruent to $\mathcal{R}^1$.]

Exercises

1. Some of the equations below, interpreted in terms of points (x, y) or (x, y, z), describe circles in $\mathcal{R}^2$ or spheres in $\mathcal{R}^3$. For those that do, find the center and radius.

a. $x^2 + y^2 + z^2 + 3 = 0.$

b. $x^2 + y^2 - 6y = 0.$

c. $x^2 + y^2 + z^2 = 1.$

d. $4x^2 + 8x + 4y^2 - 40y + 7 = 0.$

e. $x^2 + x + y^2 - 3y + z^2 + 2z = 1.$

f. $x^2 + 4y^2 = 1.$

2. Give equations or inequalities which the components of a point $\mathbf{p}$ satisfy iff

a. $\mathbf{p}$ is in the open ball of radius 2 with center at $(0, 0, 0, 1)$.

[Ans.: $p_1{}^2 + p_2{}^2 + p_3{}^2 + (p_4 - 1)^2 < 4.$]

b. $\mathbf{p}$ is on the sphere with radius 5 and center at $(2, -3, 4)$.

c. $\mathbf{p}$ is in the closed unit ball in $\mathcal{R}^3$.

d. $\mathbf{p}$ is in the intersection of the open unit disc in $\mathcal{R}^2$ with the circle of radius 1 with center at $(1, 1)$.

3. Prove that the set of all points (x, y, z) such that $x = 2y = 3z$ is a line.

4. Find the intersection of the line in Exercise 3 with the unit sphere in $\mathcal{R}^3$.

5. Let $\mathbf{a} = (a_1, a_2, a_3)$ be in $\mathcal{R}^3$ and define F by: for all real t, $F(t) = (ta_1, ta_2, ta_3)$. Prove that F is a congruence if and only if $\mathbf{a}$ is on the unit sphere.

6. Let U be the set of all (x, y, z) such that $x = y$. Prove that U can also be described as the set of all (u, u, v) for real u and v. Is the mapping $T: (u, v) \longrightarrow (u, u, v)$ a one-to-one correspondence of $\mathcal{R}^2$ to U? a congruence? a similarity?

Answer the same questions for the mapping $S: (u, v) \longrightarrow (u, u, v\sqrt{2})$. Is U a plane by Definitions 5.5?

7. Define a function d^* on the set of all pairs of points of $\mathcal{R}^2$ by, if $\mathbf{a} = \mathbf{b}$, $d^*(\mathbf{a}, \mathbf{b}) = 0$, but if $\mathbf{a} \neq \mathbf{b}$, $d^*(\mathbf{a}, \mathbf{b}) = 1$. Prove that d^* is a metric.

8. Define a function d_2', for all (a_1, a_2) and (b_1, b_2), by

$$d_2'((a_1, a_2), (b_1, b_2)) = 3\sqrt{(a_1 - b_1)^2 + (a_2 - b_2)^2}.$$

Is d_2' a metric?

9. Define a function d'', for all (a_1, a_2) and (b_1, b_2), by

$$d''((a_1, a_2), (b_1, b_2)) = \sqrt{(a_1 - b_1)^2 + 2(a_2 - b_2)^2}.$$

If distances are measured by d'', what are the lengths of the sides of a triangle with vertices at $(0, 0)$, $(1, 0)$, and $(0, 1)$?

§ 2. *Translations and Addition in* $\mathfrak{R}^n$

Let T be the mapping with domain $\mathfrak{R}^2$ defined by

$$T(a_1, a_2) = (a_1 + 3, a_2 - 5).$$

Then $T(a_1, a_2) = (b_1, b_2)$ iff $(a_1, a_2) = (b_1 - 3, b_2 + 5)$, so T is a one-to-one correspondence of $\mathfrak{R}^2$ to $\mathfrak{R}^2$. Furthermore it is easily verified that, for all $\mathbf{a}$ and $\mathbf{b}$ in $\mathfrak{R}^2$, $d_2(T(\mathbf{a}), T(\mathbf{b})) = d_2(\mathbf{a}, \mathbf{b})$; in other words, T is a congruence of $\mathfrak{R}^2$ to $\mathfrak{R}^2$. This particular sort of congruence of a Euclidean space to itself is called a *translation*. If we define $(a_1, a_2) + (3, -5)$ to mean $(a_1 + 3, a_2 - 5)$, then the formula for T becomes, for all $\mathbf{a}$ in $\mathfrak{R}^2$, $T(\mathbf{a}) = \mathbf{a} + (3, -5)$. This notation is convenient and readily generalized.

Definition 5.7 [*Addition in* $\mathfrak{R}^n$]. In each Euclidean space $\mathfrak{R}^n$, the operation $+_n$ is defined, for all $\mathbf{a}$ and $\mathbf{b}$ in $\mathfrak{R}^n$, by $\mathbf{a} +_n \mathbf{b} = \mathbf{c}$, where $c_k = a_k + b_k$, $1 \leq k \leq n$.

Notation: We shall usually understand that $+$ means the appropriate one of the operations $+_1, +_2, +_3, \ldots$.

Theorem 5.4. Each of the above operations $+$ is commutative and associative. Each $\mathfrak{R}^n$ is closed under $+_n$. The origin $\mathbf{o}^n$ is the additive identity in $\mathfrak{R}^n$. Each point of $\mathfrak{R}^n$ has an additive inverse in $\mathfrak{R}^n$. In short, the algebraic system $(\mathfrak{R}^n; +_n)$ is a commutative group.

This theorem, whose proof is immediate from the corresponding properties of $(\mathfrak{R}; +)$, asserts that addition in $\mathfrak{R}^n$ satisfies the axioms for addition in a field. It follows that any field theorem whose statement and proof involve only addition is valid for $(\mathfrak{R}^n; +)$.

For example, if $\mathbf{a}$ and $\mathbf{b}$ are in $\mathfrak{R}^n$, there is one and only one point $\mathbf{x}$ such that $\mathbf{a} + \mathbf{x} = \mathbf{b}$: namely, $\mathbf{x} = -\mathbf{a} + \mathbf{b}$. As in $\mathfrak{R}$ we define subtraction by

$$\mathbf{p} - \mathbf{q} = \mathbf{p} + -\mathbf{q},$$

for all $\mathbf{p}$ and $\mathbf{q}$ in the same space $\mathfrak{R}^n$. For example,

$$(2, -3, 4) - (1, 7, -5) = (2, -3, 4) + (-1, -7, 5) = (1, -10, 9).$$

In $\mathfrak{R}^1$ the absolute value of a number is geometrically its distance from the origin 0. This idea extends immediately to each $\mathfrak{R}^n$.

Definition 5.8. For **a** in $\mathfrak{R}^n$ the **absolute value** of **a** is denoted by $|\mathbf{a}|$ and is defined to be the distance between **a** and $\mathbf{o}^n$. Thus

$$|\mathbf{a}| = \sqrt{\sum_{k=1}^{n} a_k^2}.$$

As an example of this, $|(1, 2, 3)| = \sqrt{14}$.

Definitions 5.7 and 5.8 fit together rather neatly. Let **a** and **b** be two points in $\mathfrak{R}^n$. Then $\mathbf{a} - \mathbf{b} = (a_1 - b_1, \ldots, a_n - b_n)$, and

$$|\mathbf{a} - \mathbf{b}| = \sqrt{\sum_{k=1}^{n} (a_k - b_k)^2} = d_n(\mathbf{a}, \mathbf{b}).$$

From here on we shall generally write $|\mathbf{a} - \mathbf{b}|$ rather than $d_n(\mathbf{a}, \mathbf{b})$ for the distance between **a** and **b**.

Definition 5.9. Let **a** be a point of $\mathfrak{R}^n$. The **translation** $T_{\mathbf{a}}$ is the function defined by: for all **p** in $\mathfrak{R}^n$, $T_{\mathbf{a}}(\mathbf{p}) = \mathbf{p} + \mathbf{a}$.

Theorem 5.5. Each translation $T_{\mathbf{a}}$ is a congruence of $\mathfrak{R}^n$ to $\mathfrak{R}^n$.

PROOF: If **b** is in $\mathfrak{R}^n$, then $T_{\mathbf{a}}(\mathbf{b} - \mathbf{a}) = (\mathbf{b} - \mathbf{a}) + \mathbf{a} = \mathbf{b}$, which establishes that the range of $T_{\mathbf{a}}$ is $\mathfrak{R}^n$.

Now let **p** and **q** be any two points of $\mathfrak{R}^n$. Then

$$|T_{\mathbf{a}}(\mathbf{p}) - T_{\mathbf{a}}(\mathbf{q})| = |(\mathbf{p} + \mathbf{a}) - (\mathbf{q} + \mathbf{a})|$$
$$= |\mathbf{p} - \mathbf{q}|,$$

showing that $T_{\mathbf{a}}$ is a congruence.   ■

The identity function on $\mathfrak{R}^n$ is the translation $T_{\mathbf{o}}$, which adds $(0, \ldots, 0)$ to each point. Clearly the composition inverse of $T_{\mathbf{a}}$ is $T_{-\mathbf{a}}$. Also, if **a** and **b** are points in the same $\mathfrak{R}^n$, then, for all **p** in $\mathfrak{R}^n$, $(\mathbf{p} + \mathbf{a}) + \mathbf{b} = \mathbf{p} + (\mathbf{a} + \mathbf{b})$. In other words, for all **p** in $\mathfrak{R}^n$, $T_{\mathbf{b}}(T_{\mathbf{a}}(\mathbf{p})) = T_{(\mathbf{a}+\mathbf{b})}(\mathbf{p})$: $T_{\mathbf{b}} \circ T_{\mathbf{a}} = T_{\mathbf{a}+\mathbf{b}} = T_{\mathbf{b}+\mathbf{a}}$.

Definition 5.10. Let L and L' be lines in $\mathfrak{R}^n$. Then L **is parallel to** L' iff there is a translation mapping L onto L'. Let P and P' be planes in $\mathfrak{R}^n$. Then P **is parallel to** P' iff there is a translation mapping P onto P'.

Theorem 5.6. The relation *is parallel to* is an equivalence relation in the set of all lines in each $\mathfrak{R}^n$ and in the set of all planes in each $\mathfrak{R}^n$.

PROOF: The proof is left to the reader, but the essentials are in the paragraph just preceding Definition 5.10.

Theorem 5.7. Each line in $\mathfrak{R}^n$ is parallel to a line through the origin in $\mathfrak{R}^n$, and each plane in $\mathfrak{R}^n$ is parallel to a plane through the origin in $\mathfrak{R}^n$.

PROOF: Let L be a line in R^n and $\mathbf{a}$ be a point of L. By definition of line there is a congruence K mapping $\mathfrak{R}^1$ onto L. The composition $T_{-\mathbf{a}} \circ K$ maps $\mathfrak{R}^1$ onto a set L', a subset of $\mathfrak{R}^n$. But each translation is a congruence, and the composition of two congruences is a congruence. Thus L' is congruent to $\mathfrak{R}^1$ and is a line. Finally, L' was constructed to contain $\mathbf{o} = T_{-\mathbf{a}}(\mathbf{a})$.

The proof for planes differs little from that for lines. ∎

Problem

Let C be the circle of radius 1 with center at $(3, 5)$. Let C' be the image of C under the translation $T = T_{(1,2)}$. What is C'?

Solution 1. Obviously C' is the circle of radius 1 with center at $(4, 7)$.

Solution 2. A point (u, v) is on C iff $(u - 3)^2 + (v - 5)^2 = 1$. A point (x, y) is on C', the image of C under T, *iff* $T^{-1}(x, y)$ *is on* C. But $T^{-1}(x, y) = (x - 1, y - 2)$. So (x, y) is on C' iff $(x - 1, y - 2)$ is on C, which is the case iff

$$(x - 1 - 3)^2 + (y - 2 - 5)^2 = 1$$

or

$$(x - 4)^2 + (y - 7)^2 = 1.$$

This last equation describes a circle of radius 1 with center at $(4, 7)$.

The method of the second solution seems laborious when one can see the answer. But it is of such great usefulness that it deserves a symbolic picture. The sets pictured need not be in Euclidean spaces.

Set C Set $C' =$ image of C under F

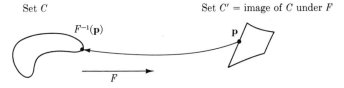

Given a one-to-one function F whose domain includes a set C, let C' be the image of C under F. A point $\mathbf{p}$ belongs to C' iff $F^{-1}(\mathbf{p})$ belongs to C.

Exercises

1. Let $\mathbf{a} = (1, 2)$, $\mathbf{b} = (5, 7)$, $\mathbf{c} = (2, -1, 3)$, $\mathbf{d} = (6, 2, 5)$. Exhibit or deny the existence of each of the following: $\mathbf{a} + \mathbf{b}$, $\mathbf{b} - \mathbf{a}$, $\mathbf{a} + \mathbf{c}$, $\mathbf{c} - \mathbf{d}$, $\mathbf{a} + \mathbf{a}$, $\mathbf{a} + \mathbf{a} + \mathbf{a}$, $\mathbf{a} + (\mathbf{b} - \mathbf{a}) + (\mathbf{a} - \mathbf{b}) - \mathbf{a}$, $-\mathbf{c}$.
2. Think of a good abbreviation for $\mathbf{x} + \mathbf{x} + \mathbf{x} + \mathbf{x} + \mathbf{x} + \mathbf{x}$.
3. With $\mathbf{a}$, $\mathbf{b}$, $\mathbf{c}$, $\mathbf{d}$ as in Exercise 1, compute or reject $T_{\mathbf{a}}(\mathbf{b})$, $T_{\mathbf{c}}(\mathbf{b})$, $T_{\mathbf{a}}(\mathbf{b} - \mathbf{a})$, $T_{\mathbf{b}} \circ T_{\mathbf{a}}(5, -5)$.
4. Let C be the set of all (x, y, z) such that $x^2 + 2y^2 + 3z^2 = 6$. What is the image of C under $T_{(1, 3, -2)}$?
5. Define S on $\mathfrak{R}^2$ by $S(x, y) = (x + y, x - y)$. Prove that S is a similarity of scale factor $\sqrt{2}$ and that

$$S^{-1}(x, y) = \left(\frac{x + y}{2}, \frac{x - y}{2} \right).$$

6. Let C be the set of all (x, y) such that $x^2 + 2xy + y^2 + y - x = 0$. Find the image of C under the similarity S of Exercise 5. Then sketch a diagram of C on graph paper.

7. Describe in words each of the following sets.

a. $\{\mathbf{p} \mid |\mathbf{p} - (2, 3)| = 5\}$.　　**c.** $\{\mathbf{p} \mid |\mathbf{p} + (1, -1)| > 1\}$.

b. $\{\mathbf{p} \mid |\mathbf{p} - (1, 1, 1)| \leq 2\}$.　　**d.** $\{\mathbf{p} \mid |\mathbf{p}| = 1\}$.

8. In the Triangle Inequality, set $\mathbf{p} = \mathbf{a} - \mathbf{c}$, $\mathbf{q} = \mathbf{c} - \mathbf{b}$, and deduce $|\mathbf{p} + \mathbf{q}| \leq |\mathbf{p}| + |\mathbf{q}|$.

§ 3.　*Dilations and Scalar Products*

In any set in which addition is defined it is natural to abbreviate $\mathbf{x} + \mathbf{x}$ to $2\mathbf{x}$, $\mathbf{x} + \mathbf{x} + \mathbf{x}$ to $3\mathbf{x}$, and so on. If, say, $5\mathbf{p} = \mathbf{q}$, it is difficult to resist writing $\mathbf{p} = \frac{1}{5}\mathbf{q} = \mathbf{q}/5$ or $3\mathbf{p} = \frac{3}{5}\mathbf{q}$.

In the case of the points of $\mathfrak{R}^n$ this leads to a natural definition of a *product* of a rational number t and a point $\mathbf{p}$. Because of the way addition is defined in $\mathfrak{R}^n$, we get, for example, $t(p_1, p_2, p_3) = (tp_1, tp_2, tp_3)$.

The reasoning that led to this formula depended on the rationality of t. But the right side is meaningful for all real t and thus can be used to define the left side for all real t.

Definition 5.11. For each real number t and each point $\mathbf{p}$ in each $\mathfrak{R}^n$, the **scalar product** $t\mathbf{p}$ is the point $(tp_1, \ldots, tp_n)$.

Although this product is not an operation in a set, we shall call it an operation. The properties listed in Theorem 5.8 are easily verified.

Theorem 5.8. Let $\mathbf{a}$ and $\mathbf{b}$ be points in the same space $\mathfrak{R}^n$ and let s and t be real numbers. Then

$$1\mathbf{a} = \mathbf{a} \quad \text{and} \quad 0\mathbf{a} = \mathbf{o},$$

$$t(\mathbf{a} + \mathbf{b}) = t\mathbf{a} + t\mathbf{b},$$

$$(s + t)\mathbf{a} = s\mathbf{a} + t\mathbf{a},$$

$$s(t\mathbf{a}) = (st)\mathbf{a},$$

$$|t\mathbf{a}| = |t| \, |\mathbf{a}|.$$

The scalar product has two primary geometric uses, one in connection with *dilations* and the other with lines through the origin.

Definition 5.12. Let r be a positive real number. On each space $\mathfrak{R}^n$ we define a **dilation** D_r by, for each $\mathbf{p}$ in $\mathfrak{R}^n$, $D_r(\mathbf{p}) = r\mathbf{p}$.

Remark: As with $+$, we are using the same symbol for many different dilations. There is a dilation D_2 mapping (x, y) to $(2x, 2y)$ and a different dilation D_2 mapping (u, v, w) to $(2u, 2v, 2w)$. If necessary, we can resort to $D_r{}^n$.

Theorem 5.9. For each $r > 0$ and each positive integer n, the dilation D_r with domain $\Re^n$ is a similarity of scale factor r mapping $\Re^n$ onto $\Re^n$.

PROOF: For **a** and **b** in $\Re^n$,

$$|D_r(\mathbf{a}) - D_r(\mathbf{b})| = |r\mathbf{a} - r\mathbf{b}|$$
$$= |r(\mathbf{a} - \mathbf{b})|$$
$$= |r| \, |\mathbf{a} - \mathbf{b}|$$
$$= r|\mathbf{a} - \mathbf{b}|.$$

The last step is from the positivity of r, the two previous from Theorem 5.8. This establishes that D_r is a similarity of scale factor r. To verify that the range is $\Re^n$, note that, if **a** is in $\Re^n$, then $D_r((1/r)\mathbf{a}) = \mathbf{a}$. ∎

For example, the unit circle in $\Re^2$ is the set of all **p** in $\Re^2$ with $|\mathbf{p}| = 1$. A dilation D_r maps **p** to $r\mathbf{p}$; if $|\mathbf{p}| = 1$, then $|r\mathbf{p}| = |r| \, |\mathbf{p}| = r$. The image of the unit circle is the circle of radius r with center at $(0, 0)$.

Theorem 5.10. If a subset of $\Re^n$ is similar to $\Re^1$ [or $\Re^2$], then it is congruent to $\Re^1$ [or $\Re^2$] and is a line [or plane].

PROOF: Let S be a similarity of scale factor s mapping $\Re^1$ onto L, a subset of $\Re^n$. Set $r = s^{-1}$. By Theorem 5.9 the dilation D_r on $\Re^1$ maps $\Re^1$ onto $\Re^1$ and is a similarity of scale factor r. The composition $S \circ D_r$ is a similarity of scale factor $sr = 1$ mapping $\Re^1$ onto L; L is congruent to $\Re^1$ and therefore a line.

The proof that any set similar to $\Re^2$ is congruent to $\Re^2$ is the same except that one applies the dilation to $\Re^2$ instead of $\Re^1$. ∎

Theorem 5.11. Let **a** be any point of $\Re^n$ except **o**. The set $\{t\mathbf{a}|t \text{ real}\}$ [the set of all scalar multiples of **a**] is a line through **o** and **a**.

PROOF: Given $\mathbf{a} \neq \mathbf{o}$ in $\Re^n$, define a mapping S, for all real t, by $S(t) = t\mathbf{a}$. For real s and t,

$$|S(t) - S(s)| = |t\mathbf{a} - s\mathbf{a}|$$
$$= |(t - s)\mathbf{a}|$$
$$= |t - s| \, |\mathbf{a}|,$$

which shows that S is a similarity of scale factor $|\mathbf{a}|$. Since the domain of S is $\Re^1$, the range of S is a line, by Theorem 5.10. Clearly $\mathbf{o} = 0\mathbf{a}$ and $\mathbf{a} = 1\mathbf{a}$ are in the range of S. ∎

Theorem 5.12. Let **a** and **b** be different points of the same space $\Re^n$.

The set

$$L_{\mathbf{ab}} = \{\mathbf{a} + t(\mathbf{b} - \mathbf{a})|t \text{ real}\} = \{t\mathbf{b} + (1 - t)\mathbf{a}|t \text{ real}\}$$

is a line through **a** and **b**.

PROOF: The translation $T_{-\mathbf{a}}$ maps the set $L_{\mathbf{ab}}$ onto the set $U = \{t(\mathbf{b} - \mathbf{a})|t \text{ real}\}$. Since $\mathbf{b} \neq \mathbf{a}$, $\mathbf{b} - \mathbf{a} \neq \mathbf{o}$, and by Theorem 5.11, U is a line through $\mathbf{o}$ and $\mathbf{b} - \mathbf{a}$. The translation $T_{\mathbf{a}}$ maps any line onto a line, but $T_{\mathbf{a}}$ maps U onto $L_{\mathbf{ab}}$, which then must be a line.   ∎

Diagrams for Theorems 5.11 and 5.12

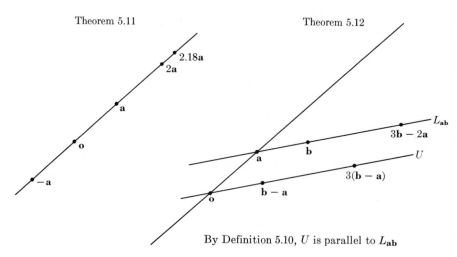

Theorem 5.11   Theorem 5.12

By Definition 5.10, U is parallel to $L_{\mathbf{ab}}$

Remark: Theorem 5.12 establishes that one of the basic axioms of synthetic geometry is a theorem in each of our models $\mathfrak{R}^1$, $\mathfrak{R}^2$, $\mathfrak{R}^3$, ... : two distinct points lie on at least one line. This axiom is usually adjoined to another which postulates that two distinct points lie on at most one line. From both axioms we have the theorem that two distinct points determine a unique line. A direct proof of this in our model is possible but difficult; it will follow easily from results in § 5.

A New Look at Addition

Let **a** and **b** be points of $\mathfrak{R}^n$. If $\mathbf{a} = \mathbf{o}$, then $\mathbf{a} + \mathbf{b} = \mathbf{b}$; if $\mathbf{b} = \mathbf{o}$, then $\mathbf{a} + \mathbf{b} = \mathbf{a}$; if $\mathbf{a} \neq \mathbf{o}$ and $\mathbf{b} \neq \mathbf{o}$, where is $\mathbf{a} + \mathbf{b}$? We consider two cases.

1. If **a** is a scalar multiple of **b**, say $\mathbf{a} = k\mathbf{b}$, k real and $k \neq 0$, then **a** is on a line through **o** and **b** and $\mathbf{a} + \mathbf{b} = (k + 1)\mathbf{b}$ is on the same line.

2. If **a** is not a scalar multiple of **b**, then we have not yet proved that **a** is *not* on some line through **o** and **b**, but we do know that the lines L_{oa} and L_{ob} [in the notation of Theorem 5.12] are different.

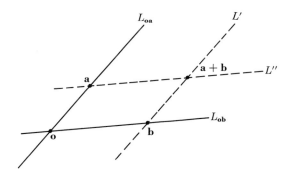

The translation T_b maps L_{oa} onto a line L' parallel to L_{oa}; in particular, $\mathbf{a} + \mathbf{b} = T_b(\mathbf{a})$ is on L'. The translation T_a maps L_{ob} onto a line L'' parallel to L_{ob}; in particular, $\mathbf{a} + \mathbf{b} = T_a(\mathbf{b})$ is on L''. Thus $\mathbf{a} + \mathbf{b}$ is in the intersection of L' and L''.

Later we shall prove that all the lines indicated in the diagram are indeed in a plane and that $\mathbf{a} + \mathbf{b}$ is the fourth vertex of a parallelogram with vertices at **o**, **a**, and **b**.

Vectors

Intuitively a *vector* is an arrow or directed line segment. The *parallelogram law* stated above is often put in terms of vectors: the sum of the arrow from **o** to **a** and the arrow from **o** to **b** is the arrow from **o** to $\mathbf{a} + \mathbf{b}$ at the fourth vertex of the parallelogram.

Corresponding to each $\mathbf{a} \neq \mathbf{o}$ is an arrow from **o** to **a**. Corresponding to each arrow with its tail at **o** is a point at its tip.

Formally a Euclidean *vector space* V^n is identical with the Euclidean point space $\mathcal{R}^n$: a set of ordered n-tuples of real numbers with the metric and algebraic structure described in this chapter.

Exercises

1. Let $\mathbf{a} = (1, 3)$. On graph paper locate $(0, 0)$, **a**, $2\mathbf{a}$, $-\mathbf{a}$, $-3\mathbf{a}$, $\frac{1}{2}\mathbf{a}$.
2. Let $\mathbf{a} = (1, 3)$ and $\mathbf{b} = (3, 1)$. Locate on graph paper the points $t\mathbf{b} + (1 - t)\mathbf{a}$ for $t = 0, 1, \frac{1}{2}, 2, 5, -1, -2$.
3. With L_{ab} as in Theorem 5.12, prove that the mapping $S: S(t) = \mathbf{a} + t(\mathbf{b} - \mathbf{a})$, for all real t, is a similarity of scale factor $|\mathbf{b} - \mathbf{a}|$.
4. Construct a congruence mapping $\mathcal{R}^1$ onto L_{ab}.
5. For each of the following conditions give an explicit description of a set of

points which is a line satisfying the conditions. Also list some points on each line. If practical, use a diagram as a check.

a. Through $(1, 1, 2)$ and $(3, 4, -1)$.
b. Through $(2, 1, 3)$ parallel to the line of (**a**).
c. Through $(0, 0, 0)$ and $(2, 4, 6)$.
d. Through $(0, 0, 0)$ and $(1, 2, 3)$.
e. Through $(0, 0)$ and $(1, 2)$.
f. Through $(-1, -2, 1)$ parallel to the line of (**d**).
g. Through $(5, 5)$ parallel to the line of (**e**).
h. Through $(0, 0, 0, 0)$ and $(1, 2, 3, 4)$.
i. Through $(1, 1, 1, 1)$ and $(2, 3, 4, 5)$, and parallel to the line of (**h**).

6. Let U be the set of all dilations in $\mathfrak{R}^3$. Discuss the algebraic system $(U; \circ)$. Give if possible a different system isomorphic to it.

7. Let D_r and $T_\mathbf{a}$ be a dilation and a translation in the same space $\mathfrak{R}^n$. Under what circumstances does $D_r \circ T_\mathbf{a} = T_\mathbf{a} \circ D_r$?

8. If **a** and **b** are distinct points in the same space $\mathfrak{R}^n$, prove that

$\{t\mathbf{b} + (1 - t)\mathbf{a}|t \geq 0\}$ is a ray,

$\{t\mathbf{b} + (1 - t)\mathbf{a}|0 \leq t \leq 1\}$ is a closed segment.

[See Definitions 5.5.] For the proof, either follow the lines of Theorem 5.10 or use Exercise 4 above.

9. Prove that, if $\mathbf{a} \neq \mathbf{o}$, the line $L_{\mathbf{oa}}$ is closed under addition.

10. Let **a** and **b** be distinct points of $\mathfrak{R}^n$, neither of them the origin. Prove that, if **o** is on $L_{\mathbf{ab}}$, then $L_{\mathbf{ab}}$ is closed under addition. [*Hint:* There is some real t such that $t\mathbf{b} + (1 - t)\mathbf{a} = \mathbf{o}$; prove that **b** is a scalar multiple of **a**.]

11. If **o** is not on $L_{\mathbf{ab}}$, can $L_{\mathbf{ab}}$ be closed under addition?

§ 4. *Inner Products*

The formula defining the distance between two points in R^n is basic to analytic geometry but is unpleasantly difficult to work with for large n. [Here "large" means >1.] The algebraic operations introduced in the last two sections enable us to discuss translations and dilations without explicit computations of square roots of sums of squares. In this section we define one more operation, an *inner product*, which assigns to each pair of points in the same space $\mathfrak{R}^n$ a real number. This inner product is introduced as merely a convenient abbreviation, but it is given some geometric meaning almost immediately and eventually acquires more.

Let **p** and **q** be points of $\mathfrak{R}^3$. The square of the distance between **p** and **q** is

$$|\mathbf{p} - \mathbf{q}|^2 = (p_1 - q_1)^2 + (p_2 - q_2)^2 + (p_3 - q_3)^2$$

$$= p_1{}^2 + p_2{}^2 + p_3{}^2 + q_1{}^2 + q_2{}^2 + q_3{}^2 - 2(p_1q_1 + p_2q_2 + p_3q_3).$$

For $p_1{}^2 + p_2{}^2 + p_3{}^2$ we have the convenient abbreviation $|\mathbf{p}|^2$, and the next three terms above add to $|\mathbf{q}|^2$. Furthermore, we have a standard abbreviation for $p_1q_1 + p_2q_2 + p_3q_3$: $\sum\limits_{k=1}^{3} p_kq_k$. Thus for $\mathbf{p}$ and $\mathbf{q}$ in $\mathfrak{R}^3$ we have

$$|\mathbf{p} - \mathbf{q}|^2 = |\mathbf{p}|^2 + |\mathbf{q}|^2 - 2 \sum_{k=1}^{3} p_kq_k.$$

In order to generalize to points in $\mathfrak{R}^n$ for any n, it is only necessary to replace 3 by n in the above formula. Nevertheless we want to replace $\sum\limits_{k=1}^{n} p_kq_k$ by a symbol which makes it clearer that this is a number determined by the pair of points $\mathbf{p}$ and $\mathbf{q}$. We shall use the first of the following four standard symbols: $\langle\mathbf{p}, \mathbf{q}\rangle$; $\mathbf{p}\cdot\mathbf{q}$; $[\mathbf{p}, \mathbf{q}]$; $(\mathbf{p}, \mathbf{q})$.

If either of the first two statements below is made a definition, the other becomes a theorem.

Definition 5.13 [*or Theorem*]. Let $\mathbf{p}$ and $\mathbf{q}$ be points in $\mathfrak{R}^n$; then their **inner product,** $\langle\mathbf{p}, \mathbf{q}\rangle$, is the number $\sum\limits_{k=1}^{n} p_kq_k$.

Theorem 5.13 [*or Definition*]. Let $\mathbf{p}$ and $\mathbf{q}$ be points in $\mathfrak{R}^n$; then their **inner product,** $\langle\mathbf{p}, \mathbf{q}\rangle$, is the number such that

$$|\mathbf{p} - \mathbf{q}|^2 = |\mathbf{p}|^2 + |\mathbf{q}|^2 - 2\langle\mathbf{p}, \mathbf{q}\rangle.$$

Theorem 5.14. For $\mathbf{a}$, $\mathbf{b}$, $\mathbf{c}$ in $\mathfrak{R}^n$ and any real t,

$$\langle\mathbf{a}, \mathbf{b}\rangle = \langle\mathbf{b}, \mathbf{a}\rangle,$$
$$\langle\mathbf{a}, \mathbf{b} + \mathbf{c}\rangle = \langle\mathbf{a}, \mathbf{b}\rangle + \langle\mathbf{a}, \mathbf{c}\rangle,$$
$$\langle\mathbf{a}, t\mathbf{b}\rangle = t\langle\mathbf{a}, \mathbf{b}\rangle,$$
$$\langle\mathbf{a}, \mathbf{a}\rangle = |\mathbf{a}|^2.$$

Exercises

For $\mathbf{a}$, $\mathbf{b}$, $\mathbf{c}$, $\mathbf{d}$ in $\mathfrak{R}^n$ and real a, b, c, d, prove that each of the following is a corollary to Theorem 5.14.

1. $\langle\mathbf{a} + \mathbf{b}, \mathbf{c}\rangle = \langle\mathbf{a}, \mathbf{c}\rangle + \langle\mathbf{b}, \mathbf{c}\rangle$.

2. $\langle a\mathbf{a}, b\mathbf{b}\rangle = ab\langle\mathbf{a}, \mathbf{b}\rangle$.

3. $\langle a\mathbf{a} + b\mathbf{b}, c\mathbf{c} + d\mathbf{d}\rangle = ac\langle\mathbf{a}, \mathbf{c}\rangle + ad\langle\mathbf{a}, \mathbf{d}\rangle + bc\langle\mathbf{b}, \mathbf{c}\rangle + bd\langle\mathbf{b}, \mathbf{d}\rangle$.

4. $|\mathbf{a} - \mathbf{b}|^2 = \langle\mathbf{a} - \mathbf{b}, \mathbf{a} - \mathbf{b}\rangle$.

Examples

1. If $\mathbf{p} = (3, 2)$ and $\mathbf{q} = (1, -4)$, then $\langle\mathbf{p}, \mathbf{q}\rangle = 3 - 8 = -5$ and $\langle 2\mathbf{p}, 5\mathbf{q}\rangle = \langle(6, 4), (5, -20)\rangle = 30 - 80 = -50 = 10\langle\mathbf{p}, \mathbf{q}\rangle$.

2. $\langle (0, 0, 0), (q_1, q_2, q_3) \rangle = 0 + 0 + 0 = 0.$

3. $\langle (1, 1, 1, 1), (2, 3, 4, 5) \rangle = 14.$

The first geometric meaning of the inner product comes from interpreting the formula in Theorem 5.13. Let $\mathbf{p}$ and $\mathbf{q}$ be points in $\mathfrak{R}^n$, both different from $\mathbf{o}$. Then the numbers $|\mathbf{p} - \mathbf{q}|$, $|\mathbf{p}|$, and $|\mathbf{q}|$ are the distances illustrated below.

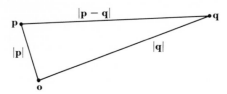

Our announced intention to make the Pythagorean theorem and its converse true by definition in our model requires that the triangle with vertices at $\mathbf{o}$, $\mathbf{p}$, $\mathbf{q}$ have a right angle at $\mathbf{o}$ iff

$$|\mathbf{p} - \mathbf{q}|^2 = |\mathbf{p}|^2 + |\mathbf{q}|^2.$$

This requirement, together with Theorem 5.13, leads to

Definition 5.14. Let $\mathbf{p}$ and $\mathbf{q}$ be points of $\mathfrak{R}^n$, both different from $\mathbf{o}$. The lines $L_{\mathbf{op}}$ and $L_{\mathbf{oq}}$ are **perpendicular,** or $L_{\mathbf{op}}$ is **perpendicular** to $L_{\mathbf{oq}}$, iff $\langle \mathbf{p}, \mathbf{q} \rangle = 0$.

Examples

1. If $\mathbf{a} = (1, -1)$ and $\mathbf{b} = (1, 1)$, then $\langle \mathbf{a}, \mathbf{b} \rangle = 0$. The lines $L_{\mathbf{oa}}$ and $L_{\mathbf{ob}}$ in $\mathfrak{R}^2$ are perpendicular.
2. If $\mathbf{c} = (1, 0, 0)$ and $\mathbf{d} = (0, 1, 0)$, then $\langle \mathbf{c}, \mathbf{d} \rangle = 0$. The lines $L_{\mathbf{oc}}$ and $L_{\mathbf{od}}$ in $\mathfrak{R}^3$ are perpendicular.
3. If $\mathbf{a} \neq \mathbf{o}$ is in $\mathfrak{R}^n$, then $\langle \mathbf{a}, \mathbf{a} \rangle > 0$. The line $L_{\mathbf{oa}}$ is not perpendicular to itself.
4. Let $\mathbf{a} = (a, b) \neq \mathbf{o}$ and $\mathbf{a}^* = (-b, a)$. The lines $L_{\mathbf{oa}}$ and $L_{\mathbf{oa}^*}$ are perpendicular.

Definition 5.15. Let $\mathbf{a}$, $\mathbf{b}$, $\mathbf{c}$ be three different points in $\mathfrak{R}^n$. The lines $L_{\mathbf{ab}}$ and $L_{\mathbf{ac}}$ are **perpendicular** iff $\langle \mathbf{b} - \mathbf{a}, \mathbf{c} - \mathbf{a} \rangle = 0$.

Remark: This amounts to saying that the lines are perpendicular iff their images under the translation $T_{-\mathbf{a}}$ are perpendicular.

Example

If $\mathbf{a} = (1, -2, 3)$, $\mathbf{b} = (2, 4, 5)$, and $\mathbf{c} = (3, -3, 5)$, then $\langle (\mathbf{b} - \mathbf{a}), (\mathbf{c} - \mathbf{a}) \rangle = \langle (1, 6, 2), (2, -1, 2) \rangle = 0$ and $L_{\mathbf{ab}}$ is perpendicular to $L_{\mathbf{ac}}$.

Let **a** and **b** be in $\mathfrak{R}^n$, both different from **o**, and let s and t be real numbers different from 0. Then

$$\langle s\mathbf{a}, t\mathbf{b}\rangle = st\langle\mathbf{a}, \mathbf{b}\rangle,$$

$$|s\mathbf{a}|\,|t\mathbf{b}| = |st|\,|\mathbf{a}|\,|\mathbf{b}|.$$

Consider the ratio

$$\frac{\langle s\mathbf{a}, t\mathbf{b}\rangle}{|s\mathbf{a}|\,|t\mathbf{b}|} = \pm\frac{\langle\mathbf{a}, \mathbf{b}\rangle}{|\mathbf{a}|\,|\mathbf{b}|}.$$

In particular, if $s > 0$ and $t > 0$, the $+$ sign holds. The sets $\{s\mathbf{a}|s \geq 0\}$ and $\{t\mathbf{b}|t \geq 0\}$ are [Exercise 8, page 116] rays from **o** through **a** and from **o** through **b**; call them **oa** and **ob**. If $\mathbf{c} \neq \mathbf{o}$ is on **oa** and $\mathbf{d} \neq \mathbf{o}$ on **ob**, then there are positive s and t such that $\mathbf{c} = s\mathbf{a}$ and $\mathbf{d} = t\mathbf{b}$. It follows that

$$\frac{\langle\mathbf{c}, \mathbf{d}\rangle}{|\mathbf{c}|\,|\mathbf{d}|} = \frac{\langle\mathbf{a}, \mathbf{b}\rangle}{|\mathbf{a}|\,|\mathbf{b}|}$$

for any **c** and **d** [except **o**] on the rays **oa** and **ob**.

The quotient is determined by the pair of rays from **o** rather than by the choice of points on the rays. [In the next section we shall also show that the quotient is invariant under any similarity of $\mathfrak{R}^n$ to $\mathfrak{R}^n$ which maps **o** to **o**.] The intuitive conclusion is irresistible: the quotient is determined by the size of an angle from **oa** to **ob** [or, since it is commutative, from **ob** to **oa**].

Definition 5.16. Let **a** and **b** be points of $\mathfrak{R}^n$ different from **o**. The number $\dfrac{\langle\mathbf{a}, \mathbf{b}\rangle}{|\mathbf{a}|\,|\mathbf{b}|}$ is the **cosine** of each and every angle from one to the other of rays **oa** and **ob**.

Examples

1. Let $\mathbf{a} \neq \mathbf{o}$ be in $\mathfrak{R}^n$. Then

$$\frac{\langle\mathbf{a}, \mathbf{a}\rangle}{|\mathbf{a}|\,|\mathbf{a}|} = 1.$$

The cosine of any angle from **oa** to **oa** is 1. Also,

$$\frac{\langle\mathbf{a}, -\mathbf{a}\rangle}{|\mathbf{a}|\,|-\mathbf{a}|} = -\frac{\langle\mathbf{a}, \mathbf{a}\rangle}{|\mathbf{a}|\,|\mathbf{a}|} = -1.$$

The cosine of any angle from **oa** to **o**$(-\mathbf{a})$ is -1.

2. Let $\mathbf{a} = (1, 0)$ and $\mathbf{b} = (x, y) \neq (0, 0)$. Set $r = |\mathbf{b}| = \sqrt{x^2 + y^2}$, and let A be any angle from **oa** to **ob**. Then the cosine of A is

$$\frac{\langle(1, 0), (x, y)\rangle}{|(1, 0)|\,|(x, y)|} = \frac{x}{r}.$$

Exercises

1. Let **a** and **b** be points in the same space $\mathfrak{R}^n$, both different from **o**, and let r and s be real numbers. Some of the symbols below represent points, others represent real numbers, and some are undefined. Classify them.

a. $|\mathbf{ab}|$.   **g.** $\mathbf{a}^2$.

b. $\langle \mathbf{a}, \mathbf{b} \rangle^2$.   **h.** $\dfrac{\mathbf{a}}{|\mathbf{a}|}$.

c. $(\mathbf{a} - \mathbf{b})^2$.   **i.** $r^{\mathbf{a}}$.

d. $|\mathbf{a} - \mathbf{b}|^2$.   **j.** $|\mathbf{a}| + \mathbf{b}$.

e. $|r\mathbf{a} + s\mathbf{b}|$.   **k.** $|\mathbf{a}| + \langle \mathbf{b}, \mathbf{b} \rangle$.

f. $\langle \mathbf{a}, \mathbf{b} \rangle \mathbf{a}$.   **l.** $|\mathbf{a}|\mathbf{b}$.

2. Let $\mathbf{a}$, $\mathbf{b}$, $\mathbf{c}$ be three points of $\mathcal{R}^2$, not all on one line. Let A be an angle from the ray $\mathbf{ab}$ to the ray $\mathbf{ac}$. Cosine A is defined to be the cosine of the image of this angle under the translation $T_{-\mathbf{a}}$. The figure below gives the standard notation: $a = |\mathbf{b} - \mathbf{c}|$, and so on. Prove the *law of cosines*:

$$a^2 = b^2 + c^2 - 2bc \cos A.$$

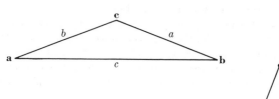
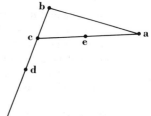

3. It is "obvious" that the line $L_{\mathbf{de}}$ intersects the segment $\mathbf{ba}$. In fact it is so obvious that apparently not until the 19th century did anyone wonder whether it could be proved from Euclid's axioms. Indeed, it cannot, and current formulations of synthetic axioms always include *Pasch's axiom*; M. Pasch discovered the need for some such axiom.

   Assume that by a similarity we can take the points to be as follows: $\mathbf{c} = (0, 0)$; $\mathbf{b} = (0, 1)$; $\mathbf{d} = (0, d_2)$, with either $d_2 < 0$ or $d_2 > 1$; $\mathbf{a} = (a_1, a_2)$, with $a_1 \neq 0$; $\mathbf{e} = t\mathbf{a}$, with $0 < t < 1$. Prove that the intersection of $L_{\mathbf{de}}$ and $L_{\mathbf{ab}}$ is the point $v\mathbf{a} + (1 - v)\mathbf{b}$, where

$$v = t\frac{1 - d_2}{t - d_2},$$

and that $0 < v < 1$.

4. Prove that, if $\mathbf{p}$ and $\mathbf{q}$ are in $\mathcal{R}^n$ and $|\mathbf{p}| = |\mathbf{q}|$ and $\langle \mathbf{p}, \mathbf{q} \rangle = \langle \mathbf{q}, \mathbf{q} \rangle$, then $\mathbf{p} = \mathbf{q}$. [*Hint:* Prove that $|\mathbf{p} - \mathbf{q}|^2 = 0$.]

§ 5. *Linear Similarities*

The only types of similarities for which we have given general formulas are translations and dilations, and the image of a line L under either of these is parallel to L [see Exercises]. It is intuitively clear, at least for $\mathcal{R}^2$ and $\mathcal{R}^3$, that there are also similarities which alter directions. Formulas for such similarities are in general more complicated than those for translations and dilations. In the next chapter we shall study them in detail for similarities in $\mathscr{R}^2$ and $\mathscr{R}^3$ [and, in brief outline, for similarities in $\mathscr{R}^n$, $n > 3$]. This section is concerned in a preliminary way with similarities having the special property that they map the origin in the domain onto the origin in the range; these similarities have important algebraic properties, some of them summarized in this section, which make it possible to work out formulas for them. Although such similarities are very special, the following theorem shows that we need consider only them and translations.

Theorem 5.15. Let S' be a similarity of scale factor k, with domain $\mathscr{R}^n$ and range a subset of $\mathscr{R}^m$. Then S' can be factored into $S' = T \circ S$, where T is a translation in $\mathscr{R}^m$ and S is a similarity of scale factor k such that $S(\mathbf{o}^n) = \mathbf{o}^m$.

PROOF: Set $S'(\mathbf{o}^n) = \mathbf{a}$ in $\mathscr{R}^m$ and define S by $S = T_{-\mathbf{a}} \circ S'$. Then S is a similarity of the same scale factor as S',

$$S(\mathbf{o}^n) = T_{-\mathbf{a}}(S'(\mathbf{o}^n)) = T_{-\mathbf{a}}(\mathbf{a}) = \mathbf{o}^m,$$

and $S' = T_{\mathbf{a}} \circ S$.   ∎

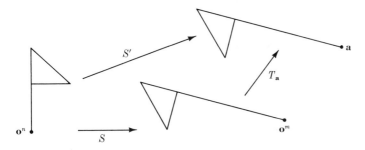

Lemma 1. Let S be a similarity of scale factor k with domain $\mathscr{R}^n$, and such that $S(\mathbf{o}^n) = \mathbf{o}^m$. Then, for all $\mathbf{a}$ and $\mathbf{b}$ in $\mathscr{R}^n$,

(1) $|S(\mathbf{a})| = k|\mathbf{a}|$,

(2) $\langle S(\mathbf{a}), S(\mathbf{b}) \rangle = k^2 \langle \mathbf{a}, \mathbf{b} \rangle$.

PROOF:

(1) $|S(\mathbf{a})| = |S(\mathbf{a}) - \mathbf{o}^m|$

$\qquad\quad\; = |S(\mathbf{a}) - S(\mathbf{o}^n)|$

$\qquad\quad\; = k|\mathbf{a} - \mathbf{o}^n|$

$\qquad\quad\; = k|\mathbf{a}|$.

(2) $|S(\mathbf{a}) - S(\mathbf{b})|^2 = |S(\mathbf{a})|^2 + |S(\mathbf{b})|^2 - 2\langle S(\mathbf{a}), S(\mathbf{b}) \rangle$

$\qquad\qquad\qquad\quad\; = k^2|\mathbf{a}|^2 + k^2|\mathbf{b}|^2 - 2\langle S(\mathbf{a}), S(\mathbf{b}) \rangle,$ by (1).

However,
$$|S(\mathbf{a}) - S(\mathbf{b})|^2 = k^2|\mathbf{a} - \mathbf{b}|^2$$
$$= k^2[|\mathbf{a}|^2 + |\mathbf{b}|^2 - 2\langle \mathbf{a}, \mathbf{b}\rangle].$$

Comparison of these two expansions of $|S(\mathbf{a}) - S(\mathbf{b})|^2$ establishes (2). ∎

Corollary. If S is as in Lemma 1 and $\mathbf{a}$ and $\mathbf{b}$ in $\mathfrak{R}^n$ are $\neq \mathbf{o}^n$, then
$$\frac{\langle S(\mathbf{a}), S(\mathbf{b})\rangle}{|S(\mathbf{a})|\ |S(\mathbf{b})|} = \frac{\langle \mathbf{a}, \mathbf{b}\rangle}{|\mathbf{a}|\ |\mathbf{b}|}.$$

Lemma 2. Let S be a similarity of scale factor k with domain $\mathfrak{R}^n$, and such that $S(\mathbf{o}^n) = \mathbf{o}^m$. Then, for all $\mathbf{a}$ and $\mathbf{b}$ in $\mathfrak{R}^n$ and all real t,

(1) $S(t\mathbf{a}) = tS(\mathbf{a})$,

(2) $S(\mathbf{a} + \mathbf{b}) = S(\mathbf{a}) + S(\mathbf{b})$.

PROOF: By Exercise 4 on page 120 we can prove that $\mathbf{p} = \mathbf{q}$ by establishing that $|\mathbf{p}| = |\mathbf{q}|$ and $\langle \mathbf{p}, \mathbf{q}\rangle = \langle \mathbf{q}, \mathbf{q}\rangle$. Also,

$$|tS(\mathbf{a})| = |t|\ |S(\mathbf{a})|$$
$$= |t|k|\mathbf{a}| \qquad \text{by Lemma 1}$$
$$= k|t\mathbf{a}|$$
$$= |S(t\mathbf{a})|,$$

and

$$\langle tS(\mathbf{a}), S(t\mathbf{a})\rangle = t\langle S(\mathbf{a}), S(t\mathbf{a})\rangle$$
$$= tk^2\langle \mathbf{a}, t\mathbf{a}\rangle$$
$$= t^2k^2\langle \mathbf{a}, \mathbf{a}\rangle$$
$$= k^2\langle t\mathbf{a}, t\mathbf{a}\rangle$$
$$= \langle S(t\mathbf{a}), S(t\mathbf{a})\rangle.$$

These two equations prove that $tS(\mathbf{a}) = S(t\mathbf{a})$. The approach to $S(\mathbf{a} + \mathbf{b})$ is much the same:

$$|S(\mathbf{a}) + S(\mathbf{b})|^2 = |S(\mathbf{a})|^2 + |S(\mathbf{b})|^2 + 2\langle S(\mathbf{a}), S(\mathbf{b})\rangle$$
$$= k^2|\mathbf{a}|^2 + k^2|\mathbf{b}|^2 + 2k^2\langle \mathbf{a}, \mathbf{b}\rangle$$
$$= k^2|\mathbf{a} + \mathbf{b}|^2$$
$$= |S(\mathbf{a} + \mathbf{b})|^2,$$

and

$$\langle S(\mathbf{a}) + S(\mathbf{b}), S(\mathbf{a} + \mathbf{b})\rangle = \langle S(\mathbf{a}), S(\mathbf{a} + \mathbf{b})\rangle + \langle S(\mathbf{b}), S(\mathbf{a} + \mathbf{b})\rangle$$
$$= k^2\langle \mathbf{a}, \mathbf{a} + \mathbf{b}\rangle + k^2\langle \mathbf{b}, \mathbf{a} + \mathbf{b}\rangle$$
$$= k^2\langle \mathbf{a} + \mathbf{b}, \mathbf{a} + \mathbf{b}\rangle$$
$$= \langle S(\mathbf{a} + \mathbf{b}), S(\mathbf{a} + \mathbf{b})\rangle. \qquad ∎$$

Before commenting on the geometric meaning of Lemma 2 we shall use it immediately to prove

Theorem 5.16. If $\mathbf{a} \neq \mathbf{o}$ is in $\mathfrak{R}^n$, then the set of all scalar multiples of $\mathbf{a}$ is the only line containing $\mathbf{o}$ and $\mathbf{a}$. If $\mathbf{a}$ and $\mathbf{b}$ are in $\mathfrak{R}^n$ and $\mathbf{a} \neq \mathbf{b}$, then the line $\mathbf{ab} = \{t\mathbf{b} + (1 - t)\mathbf{a} | t \text{ real}\}$ is the only line containing $\mathbf{a}$ and $\mathbf{b}$.

PROOF: Let L' be a line containing $\mathbf{o}$ and $\mathbf{a} \neq \mathbf{o}$. By the definition of line there is a congruence K' mapping $\mathfrak{R}^1$ onto L'. Let r be the number such that $K'(r) = \mathbf{o}$.

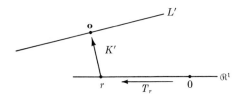

Consider $K = K' \circ T_r$, where T_r is the translation in $\mathfrak{R}^1$ mapping 0 to r. Since K is a congruence mapping $\mathfrak{R}^1$ to L' and, in particular, $K(0) = K'(r) = \mathbf{o}$, Lemma 2 applies to K.

Let a be the number such that $K(a) = \mathbf{a}$; since $\mathbf{a} \neq \mathbf{o}$, $a \neq 0$. For each real t, $t = (t/a)a$ and, by Lemma 2,

$$K(t) = \frac{t}{a} K(a) = \frac{t}{a} \mathbf{a}.$$

The range of K is the set of all scalar multiples of $\mathbf{a}$.

Now let $\mathbf{a}$ and $\mathbf{b}$ be distinct points in $\mathfrak{R}^n$. The translation $T_{-\mathbf{a}}$ maps $\mathbf{a}$ to $\mathbf{o}$ and any line through $\mathbf{a}$ and $\mathbf{b}$ to a line through $\mathbf{o}$ and $\mathbf{b} - \mathbf{a}$. But there is only one line through $\mathbf{o}$ and $\mathbf{b} - \mathbf{a}$, and $T_{\mathbf{a}}$ maps it onto the unique line through $\mathbf{a}$ and $\mathbf{b}$. ∎

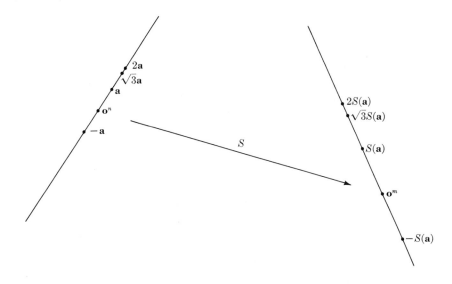

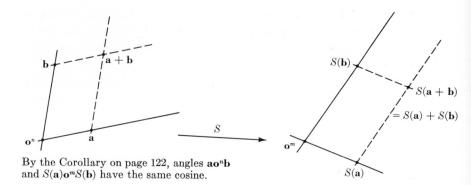

By the Corollary on page 122, angles $\mathbf{ao^n b}$
and $S(\mathbf{a})\mathbf{o^m} S(\mathbf{b})$ have the same cosine.

The diagram above shows S mapping a parallelogram with one vertex
at $\mathbf{o^n}$ to a parallelogram with one vertex at $\mathbf{o^m}$. This interpretation is correct,
but somewhat premature until we establish that each putative parallelogram
is in fact a plane figure. This will be a principal object of the rest of the section, but first we give an example of the algebraic usefulness of Lemma 2.

Intuition says that there should be a similarity [a composition of a
rotation and a dilation] mapping the points $(1, 0)$, $(0, 0)$, and $(0, 1)$, respectively, to $(1, 1)$, $(0, 0)$, and $(-1, 1)$.

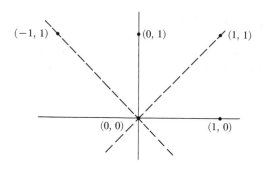

Suppose S is such a similarity: $S(0, 0) = (0, 0)$, $S(1, 0) = (1, 1)$, and
$S(0, 1) = (-1, 1)$. For all real u, $(u, 0) = u(1, 0)$. By Lemma 2, $S(u, 0) =$
$uS(1, 0) = u(1, 1) = (u, u)$.

Similarly, since $(0, v) = v(0, 1)$, Lemma 2 requires, for all real v, that

$$S(0, v) = vS(0, 1) = v(-1, 1) = (-v, v).$$

Finally, for all (u, v) in $\mathfrak{R}^2$, $(u, v) = (u, 0) + (0, v)$. By Lemma 2
there is only one possible formula for S: for all (u, v),

$$\begin{aligned}
S(u, v) &= S(u, 0) + S(0, v) \\
&= (u, u) + (-v, v) \\
&= (u - v, u + v).
\end{aligned}$$

If we now define S by this formula, it is easy to verify that S is a similarity of scale factor $\sqrt{2}$ and that S does map $(1, 0)$, $(0, 0)$, and $(0, 1)$, respectively, to $(1, 1)$, $(0, 0)$, and $(-1, 1)$.

This example suggests that we can now determine the algebraic structure of a plane in $\Re^n$. If P' is a plane in $\Re^n$, then by definition P' is the image of $\Re^2$ under a congruence K', and, by Theorem 5.15, $K' = T \circ K$, where T is a translation and K is a congruence mapping $\mathbf{o}^2$ to $\mathbf{o}^n$. Let P be the image of $\Re^2$ under K: P is a plane through $\mathbf{o}^n$ parallel to P'.

Set $K(1, 0) = \mathbf{a}$ and $K(0, 1) = \mathbf{b}$. By Lemma 1, $|\mathbf{a}| = |(1, 0)| = 1$ and $|\mathbf{b}| = |(0, 1)| = 1$, and $\langle \mathbf{a}, \mathbf{b} \rangle = \langle (1, 0), (0, 1) \rangle = 0$. For any (u, v) in $\Re^2$, we have

$$(u, v) = (u, 0) + (0, v)$$
$$= u(1, 0) + v(0, 1).$$

By Lemma 2,

$$K(u, v) = K(u, 0) + K(0, v)$$
$$= uK(1, 0) + vK(0, 1)$$
$$= u\mathbf{a} + v\mathbf{b}.$$

A sum of scalar multiples of points $\mathbf{a}$ and $\mathbf{b}$ is called a *linear combination* of $\mathbf{a}$ and $\mathbf{b}$. By what we have above, the plane P, the range of K, is just the set of all linear combinations of $K(1, 0)$ and $K(0, 1)$. The original plane P' is the image of P under a translation, say $T_{\mathbf{c}}$, so that $\mathbf{p}$ is in P' iff there are real numbers u and v such that $\mathbf{p} = u\mathbf{a} + v\mathbf{b} + \mathbf{c}$.

Theorem 5.17. If P' is a plane in $\Re^n$, then P' is parallel to a plane P containing $\mathbf{o}^n$. There are points $\mathbf{a}$ and $\mathbf{b}$ in P such that

$$|\mathbf{a}| = |\mathbf{b}| = 1, \quad \langle \mathbf{a}, \mathbf{b} \rangle = 0, \quad P = \{u\mathbf{a} + v\mathbf{b} | (u, v) \text{ in } \Re^2\},$$

the set of all linear combinations of $\mathbf{a}$ and $\mathbf{b}$.

This theorem says that each plane P through $\mathbf{o}^n$ is the set of all linear combinations of two points $\mathbf{a}$ and $\mathbf{b}$ in P with special properties, which came from special properties of $(1, 0)$ and $(0, 1)$ in $\Re^2$. We might have observed that each point of $\Re^2$ is a linear combination of $(1, 1)$ and $(0, 2)$:

$$(u, v) = u(1, 1) + \frac{v - u}{2}(0, 2).$$

If K is a congruence mapping $\Re^2$ to P such that $K(\mathbf{o}^2) = \mathbf{o}^n$ and we set $K(1, 1) = \mathbf{c}$ and $K(0, 2) = \mathbf{d}$, we would have a theorem asserting only that P is the set of all linear combinations of two points $\mathbf{c}$ and $\mathbf{d}$ such that $|\mathbf{c}| = \sqrt{2}$, $|\mathbf{d}| = 2$, and $\langle \mathbf{c}, \mathbf{d} \rangle = 2$. Clearly a more general theorem is wanted.

Let $\mathbf{a}$ and $\mathbf{b}$ be any points in $\Re^n$ and let C be the set of all linear combinations of $\mathbf{a}$ and $\mathbf{b}$. The set C has a striking algebraic property: it is closed under both addition and scalar multiplication. As a consequence of this closure, or directly from the definition of C, $\mathbf{o}^n$ is in C, and for each $\mathbf{p}$ in C $-\mathbf{p}$ is also in C. Thus C is a commutative group under addition and behaves like a Euclidean space under scalar multiplication.

If $\mathbf{a} = \mathbf{b} = \mathbf{o}^n$, then $C = \{\mathbf{o}^n\}$. This is trivially congruent to the set $\{0\}$, which we could harmlessly regard as a zero-dimensional Euclidean space $\mathfrak{R}^0$.

If $\mathbf{a} \neq \mathbf{o}^n$ but $\mathbf{b}$ is a scalar multiple of $\mathbf{a}$, say $\mathbf{b} = t\mathbf{a}$, then $u\mathbf{a} + v\mathbf{b} = (u + vt)\mathbf{a}$, and C is the line $\mathbf{oa}$.

We want to establish that, unless C is a point or a line, it is a plane.

Definition 5.17. Let F be a function with domain $\mathfrak{R}^n$ and range a subset of $\mathfrak{R}^m$. The function F is **linear** or is a **linear operator** if, for all $\mathbf{a}$ and $\mathbf{b}$ in $\mathfrak{R}^n$ and all real t,

(1) $F(t\mathbf{a}) = tF(\mathbf{a})$,

(2) $F(\mathbf{a} + \mathbf{b}) = F(\mathbf{a}) + F(\mathbf{b})$.

Equivalently, F is a linear operator if, for all $\mathbf{a}$ and $\mathbf{b}$ in $\mathfrak{R}^n$ and all real s and t,

(3) $F(s\mathbf{a} + t\mathbf{b}) = sF(\mathbf{a}) + tF(\mathbf{b})$.

We leave it to the reader to see that (1) and (2) are special cases of (3), but (1) and (2) jointly imply (3). To determine whether a function F is linear, we usually try (1) and (2); if F is a linear operator, we are free to use (3).

Theorem 5.18. A linear operator F with domain $\mathfrak{R}^n$ is a similarity of scale factor $k > 0$ iff, for all $\mathbf{a}$ and $\mathbf{b}$ in $\mathfrak{R}^n$,

$$\langle F(\mathbf{a}), F(\mathbf{b}) \rangle = k^2 \langle \mathbf{a}, \mathbf{b} \rangle.$$

PROOF: The *only if* is a restatement of Lemma 1, part (2). We must prove that *if* a linear operator F multiplies all inner products by k^2, then F also multiplies all distances by k.

For $\mathbf{a}$ and $\mathbf{b}$ in $\mathfrak{R}^n$, the linearity of F gives

$$F(\mathbf{a}) - F(\mathbf{b}) = F(\mathbf{a} - \mathbf{b}).$$

Thus
$$\begin{aligned}
|F(\mathbf{a}) - F(\mathbf{b})|^2 &= |F(\mathbf{a} - \mathbf{b})|^2 \\
&= \langle F(\mathbf{a} - \mathbf{b}), F(\mathbf{a} - \mathbf{b}) \rangle \\
&= k^2 \langle \mathbf{a} - \mathbf{b}, \mathbf{a} - \mathbf{b} \rangle \\
&= k^2 |\mathbf{a} - \mathbf{b}|^2. \quad \blacksquare
\end{aligned}$$

Theorem 5.19. Let F be a linear operator with domain $\mathfrak{R}^2$ and range a subset of $\mathfrak{R}^m$; set $F(1, 0) = \mathbf{a}$ and $F(0, 1) = \mathbf{b}$. Then F is a similarity of scale factor k iff

$$|\mathbf{a}| = |\mathbf{b}| = k, \quad \langle \mathbf{a}, \mathbf{b} \rangle = 0.$$

Let F be a linear operator with domain $\mathcal{R}^3$ and range a subset of $\mathcal{R}^m$; set $F(1, 0, 0) = \mathbf{a}$, $F(0, 1, 0) = \mathbf{b}$, and $F(0, 0, 1) = \mathbf{c}$. Then F is a similarity of scale factor k iff

$$|\mathbf{a}| = |\mathbf{b}| = |\mathbf{c}| = k \quad \text{and} \quad \langle \mathbf{a}, \mathbf{b} \rangle = \langle \mathbf{a}, \mathbf{c} \rangle = \langle \mathbf{b}, \mathbf{c} \rangle = 0.$$

PROOF: Again the *only if* proof comes from Lemma 1. Suppose then that F is linear with domain $\mathcal{R}^2$ and $\mathbf{a}$ and $\mathbf{b}$ are as stated in the theorem. For any (x, y) and (u, v) in $\mathcal{R}^2$,

$$
\begin{aligned}
\langle F(u, v), F(x, y) \rangle &= \langle u\mathbf{a} + v\mathbf{b}, x\mathbf{a} + y\mathbf{b} \rangle \\
&= ux\langle \mathbf{a}, \mathbf{a} \rangle + vy\langle \mathbf{b}, \mathbf{b} \rangle + (uy + vx)\langle \mathbf{a}, \mathbf{b} \rangle \\
&= uxk^2 + vyk^2 \\
&= k^2\langle (u, v), (x, y) \rangle.
\end{aligned}
$$

By Theorem 5.18, F is a similarity of scale factor k.

Now let F be linear with domain $\mathcal{R}^3$ and let $\mathbf{a}$, $\mathbf{b}$, $\mathbf{c}$ be as in the theorem. By two applications of Definition 5.17 we obtain, for all (x, y, z) in $\mathcal{R}^3$,

$$
\begin{aligned}
F(x, y, z) &= F((x, y, 0) + z(0, 0, 1)) \\
&= F(x, y, 0) + zF(0, 0, 1) \\
&= xF(1, 0, 0) + yF(0, 1, 0) + zF(0, 0, 1) \\
&= x\mathbf{a} + y\mathbf{b} + z\mathbf{c}.
\end{aligned}
$$

Thus, for any (x, y, z) and (u, v, w),

$$\langle F(u, v, w), F(x, y, z) \rangle = \langle u\mathbf{a} + v\mathbf{b} + w\mathbf{c}, x\mathbf{a} + y\mathbf{b} + z\mathbf{c} \rangle.$$

This inner product can be expanded into a sum of nine terms, six of which are 0. The other three add up to $k^2\langle (u, v, w), (x, y, z) \rangle$. ∎

Theorem 5.20. If $\mathbf{a} \neq \mathbf{o}^n$ is in $\mathcal{R}^n$ and $\mathbf{b}$ is in $\mathcal{R}^n$, then there are a unique number t and a point $\mathbf{c}$ such that

$$\mathbf{b} = t\mathbf{a} + \mathbf{c} \quad \text{and} \quad \langle \mathbf{a}, \mathbf{c} \rangle = 0.$$

Specifically,

$$t = \frac{\langle \mathbf{b}, \mathbf{a} \rangle}{\langle \mathbf{a}, \mathbf{a} \rangle} \quad \text{and} \quad \mathbf{c} = \mathbf{b} - \frac{\langle \mathbf{b}, \mathbf{a} \rangle}{\langle \mathbf{a}, \mathbf{a} \rangle} \mathbf{a}.$$

PROOF: Suppose that $\mathbf{b} = t\mathbf{a} + \mathbf{c}$ and $\langle \mathbf{a}, \mathbf{c} \rangle = 0$. Then

$$
\begin{aligned}
\langle \mathbf{b}, \mathbf{a} \rangle &= \langle t\mathbf{a} + \mathbf{c}, \mathbf{a} \rangle \\
&= t\langle \mathbf{a}, \mathbf{a} \rangle + 0.
\end{aligned}
$$

This determines t, as displayed, and $\mathbf{c} = \mathbf{b} - t\mathbf{a}$. It is easily verified that if t and $\mathbf{c}$ are as asserted, then $\mathbf{b} = t\mathbf{a} + \mathbf{c}$ and $\langle \mathbf{a}, \mathbf{c} \rangle = 0$. ∎

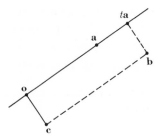

Theorem 5.21. If **a** and **b** are in $\mathfrak{R}^n$, $\mathbf{a} \neq \mathbf{o}$, and **b** is not a scalar multiple of **a**, then the set of all linear combinations of **a** and **b** is a plane.

PROOF: We shall construct a congruence mapping $\mathfrak{R}^2$ onto the set of all linear combinations of **a** and **b**.

By Theorem 5.20, $\mathbf{b} = t\mathbf{a} + \mathbf{c}$, where $t = \langle \mathbf{b}, \mathbf{a} \rangle / \langle \mathbf{a}, \mathbf{a} \rangle$ and $\langle \mathbf{a}, \mathbf{c} \rangle = 0$. Since **b** is not a scalar multiple of **a**, $\mathbf{c} \neq \mathbf{o}$.

Set $\mathbf{a}' = \mathbf{a}/|\mathbf{a}|$ and $\mathbf{c}' = \mathbf{c}/|\mathbf{c}|$. Then $|\mathbf{a}'| = 1$, $|\mathbf{c}'| = 1$, and

$$\langle \mathbf{a}', \mathbf{c}' \rangle = \frac{1}{|\mathbf{a}|\,|\mathbf{c}|} \langle \mathbf{a}, \mathbf{c} \rangle = 0.$$

Define K on $\mathfrak{R}^2$ by $K(x, y) = x\mathbf{a}' + y\mathbf{c}'$. For any t and (x, y),

$$K(t(x, y)) = K(tx, ty) = tx\mathbf{a}' + ty\mathbf{c}'$$
$$= t(x\mathbf{a}' + y\mathbf{c}') = tK(x, y).$$

For any (x, y) and (u, v),

$$K((x, y) + (u, v)) = K(x + u, y + v) = (x + u)\mathbf{a}' + (y + v)\mathbf{c}'$$
$$= x\mathbf{a}' + y\mathbf{c}' + u\mathbf{a}' + v\mathbf{c}' = K(x, y) + K(u, v).$$

We have established that K is linear. Now $K(1, 0) = \mathbf{a}'$ and $K(0, 1) = \mathbf{c}'$. By Theorem 5.19, K is a congruence. Since the domain of K is $\mathfrak{R}^2$, the range of K is a plane.

The range of K is the set of all linear combinations of $\mathbf{a}'$ and $\mathbf{c}'$. But

$$x\mathbf{a}' + y\mathbf{c}' = \frac{x}{|\mathbf{a}|} \mathbf{a} + \frac{y}{|\mathbf{c}|} \mathbf{c},$$

$$u\mathbf{a} + v\mathbf{c} = u|\mathbf{a}|\mathbf{a}' + v|\mathbf{c}|\mathbf{c}'.$$

The range of K is also the set of all linear combinations of **a** and **c**. However,

$$x\mathbf{a} + y\mathbf{c} = x\mathbf{a} + y(\mathbf{b} - t\mathbf{a}) = (x - yt)\mathbf{a} + y\mathbf{b}$$
$$u\mathbf{a} + v\mathbf{b} = u\mathbf{a} + v(t\mathbf{a} + \mathbf{c}) = (u + vt)\mathbf{a} + \mathbf{c}.$$

The range of K is also the set of all linear combinations of **a** and **b**.   ∎

Since we now know that the points $\mathbf{o}^n$, **a**, **b**, **c** and the lines determined by them all lie in a plane we can draw a diagram of K.

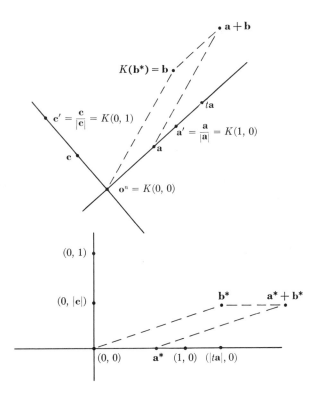

The area of a plane parallelogram is the product of the length of its base and its height. This is true either by definition or as a consequence of other definitions. The appendix to the next chapter discusses some "very elementary" formulas for area; here we shall simply accept this formula for the area of a parallelogram in $\mathcal{R}^2$. An essential part of the basic definition of area is that congruent plane figures have the same area. Thus the parallelogram in $\mathcal{R}^n$ with vertices at $\mathbf{o}^n$, $\mathbf{a}$, $\mathbf{a} + \mathbf{b}$, and $\mathbf{b}$ has the same area, say A, as has the parallelogram with vertices at $\mathbf{o}^2$, $\mathbf{a}^*$, $\mathbf{a}^* + \mathbf{b}^*$, and $\mathbf{b}^*$ in $\mathcal{R}^2$. Taking the base of this parallelogram to be the segment from $(0, 0)$ to $\mathbf{a}^*$, of length $|\mathbf{a}|$, its height is the distance of the point $\mathbf{b}$ from the line $\mathbf{o}\mathbf{a}^*$. In § 7 we give a method for calculating the distance of a point from a line in $\mathcal{R}^2$; this will of course give the height as $|\mathbf{c}|$ as in the diagram. Thus we have $A = |\mathbf{a}| \, |\mathbf{c}|$.

This formula turns out to be very interesting when applied to the original parallelogram in $\mathcal{R}^n$. We state the result as

Theorem 5.22. For $\mathbf{a}$ and $\mathbf{b}$ points in $\mathcal{R}^n$ let A be the area of the parallelogram with vertices at $\mathbf{o}$, $\mathbf{a}$, $\mathbf{a} + \mathbf{b}$, and $\mathbf{b}$:

$$A^2 = |\mathbf{a}|^2|\mathbf{b}|^2 - \langle \mathbf{a}, \mathbf{b} \rangle^2.$$

Note that if $\mathbf{a} = \mathbf{o}$ or $\mathbf{b}$ is a scalar multiple of $\mathbf{a}$, the parallelogram degenerates to a line segment or a point and the formula gives $A = 0$ [see Exercises].

PROOF: From the discussion above and the proof of Theorem 5.21, we have

$$A^2 = |\mathbf{a}|^2|\mathbf{c}|^2,$$

where

$$\mathbf{c} = \mathbf{b} - \frac{\langle \mathbf{b}, \mathbf{a} \rangle}{|\mathbf{a}|^2} \mathbf{a},$$

and

$$|\mathbf{a}|^2|\mathbf{c}|^2 = |\mathbf{a}|^2|\mathbf{b}|^2 - \langle \mathbf{a}, \mathbf{b} \rangle^2. \qquad \blacksquare$$

This equation is not only interesting in connection with areas of parallelograms, but it implies a famous inequality. With no reference to parallelograms, we note the following.

If $\mathbf{a} = \mathbf{o}^n$, then trivially, for any $\mathbf{b}$ and $\mathbf{c}$ in $\mathfrak{R}^n$,

$$|\mathbf{a}|^2|\mathbf{c}|^2 = |\mathbf{a}|^2|\mathbf{b}|^2 - \langle \mathbf{a}, \mathbf{b} \rangle^2.$$

If $\mathbf{a} \neq \mathbf{o}^n$, then, for any $\mathbf{b}$ in $\mathfrak{R}^n$, we can define $\mathbf{c}$ by

$$\mathbf{c} = \mathbf{b} - \frac{\langle \mathbf{b}, \mathbf{a} \rangle}{\langle \mathbf{a}, \mathbf{a} \rangle} \mathbf{a}$$

and conclude that

$$|\mathbf{a}|^2|\mathbf{c}|^2 = |\mathbf{a}|^2|\mathbf{b}|^2 - \langle \mathbf{a}, \mathbf{b} \rangle^2.$$

Since $|\mathbf{a}|^2|\mathbf{c}|^2 \geq 0$, we have proved that, for any $\mathbf{a}$ and $\mathbf{b}$ in R^n,

$$|\mathbf{a}|^2|\mathbf{b}|^2 \geq \langle \mathbf{a}, \mathbf{b} \rangle^2.$$

This inequality, stated in an equivalent form in the theorem below, is classically known as the *Cauchy-Schwarz inequality*; recently it has often been called the *Schwarz-Buniakowsky inequality*.

Theorem 5.23.   For all $\mathbf{a}$ and $\mathbf{b}$ in $\mathfrak{R}^n$,

$$|\langle \mathbf{a}, \mathbf{b} \rangle| \leq |\mathbf{a}|\,|\mathbf{b}|.$$

This theorem has an immediate corollary, which we give as

The Triangle Inequality.   For all $\mathbf{a}$ and $\mathbf{b}$ in $\mathfrak{R}^n$,

$$|\mathbf{a} + \mathbf{b}| \leq |\mathbf{a}| + |\mathbf{b}|.$$

PROOF: $|\mathbf{a} + \mathbf{b}|^2 = |\mathbf{a}|^2 + |\mathbf{b}|^2 + 2\langle \mathbf{a}, \mathbf{b} \rangle$

$$\leq |\mathbf{a}|^2 + |\mathbf{b}|^2 + 2|\langle \mathbf{a}, \mathbf{b} \rangle|$$

$$\leq |\mathbf{a}|^2 + |\mathbf{b}|^2 + 2|\mathbf{a}|\,|\mathbf{b}|$$

$$= (|\mathbf{a}| + |\mathbf{b}|)^2. \qquad \blacksquare$$

These two inequalities [Cauchy-Schwarz and triangle] are of crucial importance if one is studying convergence theory in $\mathfrak{R}^n$. For our purpose—to investigate basic elementary geometry and the associated linear algebra—they are of little interest, and we return to areas of parallelograms.

Theorem 5.22 applies in particular to $\mathfrak{R}^2$. Let $\mathbf{a} = (a_1, a_2)$ and $\mathbf{b} = (b_1, b_2)$ be in $\mathfrak{R}^2$. If $\mathbf{a} \neq \mathbf{o}$ and $\mathbf{b}$ is not a scalar multiple of $\mathbf{a}$, then the points $\mathbf{o}, \mathbf{a}, \mathbf{a} + \mathbf{b}$, and $\mathbf{b}$ are vertices of a nondegenerate parallelogram of area A, where

$$A^2 = |\mathbf{a}|^2 |\mathbf{b}|^2 - \langle \mathbf{a}, \mathbf{b} \rangle^2$$
$$= (a_1{}^2 + a_2{}^2)(b_1{}^2 + b_2{}^2) - (a_1 b_1 + a_2 b_2)^2$$
$$= (a_1 b_2 - a_2 b_1)^2.$$

The number $a_1 b_2 - a_2 b_1$ is often written as $\begin{vmatrix} a_1 a_2 \\ b_1 b_2 \end{vmatrix}$ and is called a *two-by-two determinant*. We shall regard *determinant* [abbreviated to det] as a function whose domain contains all ordered pairs of points in $\mathfrak{R}^2$. For $\mathbf{a} = (a_1, a_2)$, $\mathbf{b} = (b_1, b_2)$ we define it by

$$\det (\mathbf{a}, \mathbf{b}) = a_1 b_2 - a_2 b_1 = \begin{vmatrix} a_1 a_2 \\ b_1 b_2 \end{vmatrix}.$$

Note that $\det (\mathbf{b}, \mathbf{a}) = b_1 a_2 - b_2 a_1 = -\det (\mathbf{a}, \mathbf{b})$.

Definition 5.18. For $\mathbf{a}$ and $\mathbf{b}$ in $\mathfrak{R}^2$, $\det (\mathbf{a}, \mathbf{b})$ is the **oriented area** of the oriented parallelogram determined by $(\mathbf{a}, \mathbf{b})$. The vertices of this parallelogram are $\mathbf{o}, \mathbf{a}, \mathbf{a} + \mathbf{b}$, and $\mathbf{b}$, in that order. If $\mathbf{a}$ and $\mathbf{b}$ are $\neq \mathbf{o}$, the smallest angle from the ray $\mathbf{oa}$ to the ray $\mathbf{ob}$ is **counterclockwise** or **positive** iff $\det (\mathbf{a}, \mathbf{b}) > 0$.

Remark; Distance is an inherently nonnegative function: to a pair of points in $\mathfrak{R}^n$ it assigns a nonnegative number. *Directed distance* should be thought of as a single noun: to an ordered pair of points on a line it assigns a number which may be positive or negative, according to rather arbitrary conventions.

Area is an inherently nonnegative function: to a simple enough region in $\mathfrak{R}^2$ it assigns a nonnegative number. *Oriented area* should be thought of as a single noun: it assigns a number which may be positive or negative, according to a rather arbitrary definition. [See also Exercise 14 below.]

Now let $\mathbf{a} = (a_1, a_2, a_3)$, $\mathbf{b} = (b_1, b_2, b_3)$, and A be the area of the parallelogram [assuming $\mathbf{a} \neq \mathbf{o}$ and $b \neq t a$] with vertices at $\mathbf{o}, \mathbf{a}, \mathbf{a} + \mathbf{b}$, and $\mathbf{b}$. We have

$$A^2 = |\mathbf{a}|^2 |\mathbf{b}|^2 - \langle \mathbf{a}, \mathbf{b} \rangle^2$$
$$= (a_1{}^2 + a_2{}^2 + a_3{}^2)(b_1{}^2 + b_2{}^2 + b_3{}^2) - (a_1 b_1 + a_2 b_2 + a_3 b_3)^2$$
$$= (a_2 b_3 - a_3 b_2)^2 + (-a_1 b_3 + a_3 b_1)^2 + (a_1 b_2 - a_2 b_1)^2$$
$$= \begin{vmatrix} a_2 a_3 \\ b_2 b_3 \end{vmatrix}^2 + \begin{vmatrix} a_3 a_1 \\ b_3 b_1 \end{vmatrix}^2 + \begin{vmatrix} a_1 a_2 \\ b_1 b_2 \end{vmatrix}^2.$$

Example

Let A be the area of the parallelogram, two of whose sides are the segments from $(0, 0, 0)$ to $(1, 1, 1)$ and from $(0, 0, 0)$ to $(2, -1, 3)$:

$$A^2 = \begin{vmatrix} 1 & 1 \\ -1 & 3 \end{vmatrix}^2 + \begin{vmatrix} 1 & 1 \\ 3 & 2 \end{vmatrix}^2 + \begin{vmatrix} 1 & 1 \\ 2 & -1 \end{vmatrix}^2$$

$$= 4^2 + (-1)^2 + (-3)^2 = 26.$$

The point $(4, -1, -3)$ has the interesting property that

$$\langle (1, 1, 1), (4, -1, -3) \rangle = 0 \quad \text{and} \quad \langle (2, -1, 3), (4, -1, -3) \rangle = 0.$$

We conclude this section with one more, but not the last, definition of a term using the word *linear*.

Definition 5.19. A subset of $\mathfrak{R}^n$ is a **linear subspace** of $\mathfrak{R}^n$ iff it is closed under addition and under scalar multiplication.

For example, if $\mathbf{a} \neq \mathbf{o}^n$, the line $\mathbf{o}^n\mathbf{a} = \{t\mathbf{a} \,|\, t \text{ real}\}$ is closed under addition and scalar multiplication and is therefore a linear subspace of $\mathfrak{R}^n$.

Exercises

[In several of the following exercises you will need to use the fact that the line $\mathbf{ab}$ is the set $\{t\mathbf{b} + (1 - t)\mathbf{a} \,|\, t \text{ real}\}$.]

1. If $\mathbf{a}$ and $\mathbf{b}$ are in $\mathfrak{R}^n$ with $\mathbf{a} \neq \mathbf{b}$, prove that a dilation D_r maps the line $\mathbf{ab}$ onto the line $(r\mathbf{a})(r\mathbf{b})$.
2. With $\mathbf{a}$, $\mathbf{b}$ and r as in Exercise 1, prove that the translation mapping $\mathbf{a}$ to $r\mathbf{a}$ maps the line $\mathbf{ab}$ onto the line $(r\mathbf{a})(r\mathbf{b})$.
3. Let $L = \mathbf{ab}$ be a line in $\mathfrak{R}^n$ and T a translation. Prove that T maps L onto L if and only if $T(\mathbf{a})$ is on L.
4. Prove that, if two parallel lines L and L' have a point in common, then $L = L'$. [*Hint:* There is some translation T mapping L onto L'. Let $\mathbf{c}$ be a point on L and on L'. Since $\mathbf{c}$ is on L', there is some $\mathbf{a}$ on L such that $T(\mathbf{a}) = \mathbf{c}$. Now use the result from Exercise 3.]
5. Let L be a line in $\mathfrak{R}^n$ and $\mathbf{p}$ a point of $\mathfrak{R}^n$ not on L. Prove that there is one and only one line through $\mathbf{p}$ parallel to L.
6. Prove that, if $\mathbf{a} = \mathbf{o}$ or $\mathbf{b} = t\mathbf{a}$ for some t, then $|\mathbf{a}| \, |\mathbf{b}| = |\langle \mathbf{a}, \mathbf{b} \rangle|$.
7. Prove that $(-2, 3)$, $(-1, 4)$, $(0, 7)$, and $(-1, 6)$ are vertices of a parallelogram, and find its area. [*Hint:* Use a translation.]
8. Prove that a similarity mapping $\mathbf{a}$ to $\mathbf{a}'$ and $\mathbf{b}$ to $\mathbf{b}'$ maps the segment $\mathbf{ab}$ to the segment $\mathbf{a}'\mathbf{b}'$. [*Hint:* Use Theorem 5.15 and Lemma 2.]
9. Assuming $\mathbf{a} \neq \mathbf{o}$ and $\mathbf{b}$ not a scalar multiple of $\mathbf{a}$, prove that the triangles $\mathbf{oab}$ and $(\mathbf{a} + \mathbf{b})\mathbf{ba}$ are congruent. [*Hint:* By Exercise 8 you need only construct a congruence mapping $(\mathbf{o}, \mathbf{a}, \mathbf{b})$ to $(\mathbf{a} + \mathbf{b}, \mathbf{b}, \mathbf{a})$. The diagram suggests the mapping $\mathbf{p} \longrightarrow -\mathbf{p} + \mathbf{a} + \mathbf{b}$. Prove that this is a congruence.]

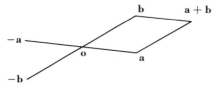

10. Prove that $(1, 2, 3, 0)$, $(2, 4, 3, 1)$, $(1, 5, 4, 2)$, and $(0, 3, 4, 1)$ are vertices of a parallelogram, and find its area.

11. For $\mathbf{a}$ and $\mathbf{b}$ in $\mathfrak{R}^4$, show that $|\mathbf{a}|^2 |\mathbf{b}|^2 - \langle \mathbf{a}, \mathbf{b} \rangle^2$ is the sum of the squares of six two-by-two determinants.

12. Let $\times$ be the mapping: for all $\mathbf{a} = (a_1, a_2)$ in $\mathfrak{R}^2$, $\times \mathbf{a} = (-a_2, a_1)$. [Read $\times \mathbf{a}$ as *cross* $\mathbf{a}$.] Prove that, if $\mathbf{a} \neq \mathbf{o}$, the smallest angle from the ray $\mathbf{oa}$ to the ray $\mathbf{o}(\times \mathbf{a})$ is counterclockwise, and that $\langle \mathbf{a}, \times \mathbf{a} \rangle = 0$ for all $\mathbf{a}$.

13. For $\mathbf{a} \neq \mathbf{o}$ in $\mathfrak{R}^2$, prove that, if $\langle \mathbf{a}, \mathbf{b} \rangle = 0$, then $\mathbf{b}$ is a scalar multiple of $\times \mathbf{a}$.

14. The idea of quadrants I through IV in the plane was partially defined by a picture in the introductory pages of this chapter, but the picture did not determine whether, for example, $(1, 0)$ is in I or IV or both or neither. Beginning with

$$I = \{(x, y) | x > 0 \text{ and } y \geq 0\},$$

give analogous definitions of the other three quadrants in such a way that each $\mathbf{a} \neq (0, 0)$ is in one and only one quadrant. Then prove that whatever quadrant $\mathbf{a}$ is in, $\times \mathbf{a}$ is in the next quadrant, where the ordering is I, II, III, IV, I, ...

15. For $\mathbf{a}$ and $\mathbf{b}$ in $\mathfrak{R}^2$, prove that det $(\mathbf{a}, \mathbf{b}) = \langle \times \mathbf{a}, \mathbf{b} \rangle$.

16. For each $\mathbf{a}$ in $\mathfrak{R}^3$, define a mapping $\mathbf{a} \times$ [read $\mathbf{a}$ *cross*] by: for all $\mathbf{b}$ in $\mathfrak{R}^3$,

$$\mathbf{a} \times \mathbf{b} = \left(\begin{vmatrix} a_2 & a_3 \\ b_2 & b_3 \end{vmatrix}, \begin{vmatrix} a_3 & a_1 \\ b_3 & b_1 \end{vmatrix}, \begin{vmatrix} a_1 & a_2 \\ b_1 & b_2 \end{vmatrix} \right).$$

Prove that $\langle \mathbf{a}, \mathbf{a} \times \mathbf{b} \rangle = 0$ and $\langle \mathbf{b}, \mathbf{a} \times \mathbf{b} \rangle = 0$.

17. Let $\mathbf{a} = (1, 1, 1)$ and $\mathbf{b} = (2, -1, 3)$. Prove that, if $\langle \mathbf{a}, \mathbf{p} \rangle = 0$ and $\langle \mathbf{b}, \mathbf{p} \rangle = 0$, then $\mathbf{p}$ is a scalar multiple of $\mathbf{a} \times \mathbf{b}$.

18. Let $\mathbf{a}, \mathbf{b}, \mathbf{c}$ be three points in $\mathfrak{R}^3$. We define the determinant of the three points, in this order, by det $(\mathbf{a}, \mathbf{b}, \mathbf{c}) = \langle \mathbf{a} \times \mathbf{b}, \mathbf{c} \rangle$. Prove, by a laborious computation, that

det $(\mathbf{a}, \mathbf{b}, \mathbf{c})$ = det $(\mathbf{b}, \mathbf{c}, \mathbf{a})$ = det $(\mathbf{c}, \mathbf{a}, \mathbf{b})$.

19. Let F be a linear operator with domain $\mathfrak{R}^n$ and range a subset of $\mathfrak{R}^m$. Prove that the range of F is a linear subspace of $\mathfrak{R}^m$.

20. For $\mathbf{a}$ in $\mathfrak{R}^n$, define a function $F_{\mathbf{a}}$, for all $\mathbf{p}$ in $\mathfrak{R}^n$, by $F_{\mathbf{a}}(\mathbf{p}) = \langle \mathbf{a}, \mathbf{p} \rangle$. Prove that $F_{\mathbf{a}}$ is a linear operator.

21. Let K be a linear operator mapping $\mathfrak{R}^2$ into $\mathfrak{R}^3$. If $K(1, 0) = (a_1, a_2, a_3)$ and $K(0, 1) = (b_1, b_2, b_3)$, show that the formula for K can be put in the form, for all $\mathbf{p}$ in $\mathfrak{R}^2$,

$$K(\mathbf{p}) = (\langle (a_1, b_1), \mathbf{p} \rangle, \langle (a_2, b_2), \mathbf{p} \rangle, \langle (a_3, b_3), \mathbf{p} \rangle).$$

22. Given $\mathbf{a}$ and $\mathbf{b}$ in $\mathfrak{R}^n$, define F, for all $\mathbf{p}$ in $\mathfrak{R}^n$, by

$$F(\mathbf{p}) = (\langle \mathbf{a}, \mathbf{p} \rangle, \langle \mathbf{b}, \mathbf{p} \rangle) \text{ in } \mathfrak{R}^2.$$

Prove that F is linear.

23. Let F be a linear operator with domain $\mathfrak{R}^n$ and range a subset of $\mathfrak{R}^m$. Let K_F be the set of all $\mathbf{a}$ in $\mathfrak{R}^n$ such that $F(\mathbf{a}) = \mathbf{o}^m$. Prove that K_F is a linear subspace of $\mathfrak{R}^n$.

24. Let $\mathbf{a} = (1, 1, 1)$ and $\mathbf{b} = (2, -1, 3)$. Define F, for all $\mathbf{p}$ in $\mathfrak{R}^3$, by

$$F(\mathbf{p}) = (\langle \mathbf{a}, \mathbf{p} \rangle, \langle \mathbf{b}, \mathbf{p} \rangle) \text{ in } \mathfrak{R}^2.$$

What is K_F?

§ 6. *Hyperplanes and Linear Equations*

For $\mathbf{a} \neq \mathbf{o}$ in $\Re^n$, let $H_\mathbf{a}$ be the set of all $\mathbf{p}$ in $\Re^n$ such that $\langle \mathbf{a}, \mathbf{p} \rangle = 0$. For any $\mathbf{p} \neq \mathbf{o}$ in $H_\mathbf{a}$, the line $\mathbf{op}$ is perpendicular, or *orthogonal*, to $\mathbf{oa}$. By Theorem 5.20 each $\mathbf{b}$ in $\Re^n$ has a unique representation, $\mathbf{b} = t\mathbf{a} + \mathbf{c}$, as the sum of a point of $\mathbf{oa}$ and a point $\mathbf{c}$ in $H_\mathbf{a}$. The subspaces $\mathbf{oa}$ and $H_\mathbf{a}$ are *complementary*, which means (1) their intersection is as small as possible, containing only $\mathbf{o}$, and (2) the set of all sums $\mathbf{p} + \mathbf{q}$, with $\mathbf{p}$ in $\mathbf{oa}$ and $\mathbf{q}$ in $H_\mathbf{a}$, is the whole space $\Re^n$.

> **Definition 5.20.**   For $\mathbf{a} \neq \mathbf{o}$ in $\Re^n$, the set $H_\mathbf{a} = \{\mathbf{p} | \langle \mathbf{a}, \mathbf{p} \rangle = 0\}$ is the **orthogonal complement of the line oa**. The image of $H_\mathbf{a}$ under a translation is a **hyperplane**.

Let $T_\mathbf{b}(H_\mathbf{a})$ be the image of $H_\mathbf{a}$ under the translation $T_\mathbf{b}$. A point $\mathbf{p}$ is in this hyperplane iff $\mathbf{p} - \mathbf{b}$ is in $H_\mathbf{a}$—that is, iff

$$\langle \mathbf{a}, \mathbf{p} - \mathbf{b} \rangle = \langle \mathbf{a}, \mathbf{p} \rangle - \langle \mathbf{a}, \mathbf{b} \rangle = 0.$$

Thus every hyperplane is the set of points $\mathbf{p}$ satisfying an equation of the form $\langle \mathbf{a}, \mathbf{p} \rangle - k = 0$, where $\mathbf{a} \neq \mathbf{o}$ and k is some real number.

In $\Re^1$ a hyperplane is the set of x satisfying an equation $ax - k = 0$, where $a \neq 0$; clearly this hyperplane contains only the point k/a.

In $\Re^2$ a hyperplane is the set of (x, y) satisfying $ax + by - k = 0$, where $(a, b) \neq \mathbf{o}^2$. Both intuition and Exercise 13 on page 133 say that a hyperplane in $\Re^2$ is a line.

In $\Re^3$ a hyperplane is the set of (x, y, z) such that $ax + by + cz - k = 0$, where $(a, b, c) \neq \mathbf{o}^3$. Intuition says that in $\Re^3$ the orthogonal complement of a line should be a plane. A principal object of this section is to develop enough of the theory of systems of linear equations to be able to prove this easily.

We have several times considered points $\mathbf{a}$ and $\mathbf{b}$ such that $\mathbf{a} \neq \mathbf{o}$ and $\mathbf{b}$ is not a scalar multiple of $\mathbf{a}$. This looks unsymmetric in $\mathbf{a}$ and $\mathbf{b}$, but actually it isn't: given those conditions, then $\mathbf{b} \neq 0\mathbf{a} = \mathbf{o}$, and $\mathbf{a} \neq t\mathbf{b}$ because this implies $\mathbf{b} = t^{-1}\mathbf{a}$. A symmetric phrasing of the condition is that neither $\mathbf{a}$ nor $\mathbf{b}$ is a scalar multiple of the other. Another symmetric phrasing is that $\mathbf{a}$ and $\mathbf{b}$ are not on a line through $\mathbf{o}$. The usual symmetric phrasing, which we shall now adopt, is that $\mathbf{a}$ and $\mathbf{b}$ are *linearly independent*.

> **Definition 5.21.**   Points $\mathbf{a}$ and $\mathbf{b}$ in $\Re^n$ are **linearly dependent** if there are numbers u and v, not both 0, such that $u\mathbf{a} + v\mathbf{b} = \mathbf{o}$. Points $\mathbf{a}$ and $\mathbf{b}$ in $\Re^n$ are **linearly independent** if the equation $u\mathbf{a} + v\mathbf{b} = \mathbf{o}$ implies $u = 0$ and $v = 0$.

Let $\mathbf{a}$ and $\mathbf{b}$ be linearly independent. Then $\mathbf{a} \neq \mathbf{o}$ because $1\mathbf{o} + 0\mathbf{b} = \mathbf{o}$ and 1 and 0 are not both 0. And $\mathbf{b} \neq t\mathbf{a}$ for any t because $-t\mathbf{a} + 1(t\mathbf{a}) = \mathbf{o}$

and $-t$ and 1 are not both 0. Rephrased: for any $\mathbf{b}$, $\mathbf{o}$ and $\mathbf{b}$ are linearly dependent; for any $\mathbf{a}$ and t, $\mathbf{a}$ and $t\mathbf{a}$ are linearly dependent.

This definition readily generalizes. Let $\mathbf{a}$, $\mathbf{b}$, $\mathbf{c}$ be three points in $\Re^n$. If there are numbers u, v, w not all 0 such that $u\mathbf{a} + v\mathbf{b} + w\mathbf{c} = \mathbf{o}^n$, then at least one of the points $\mathbf{a}$, $\mathbf{b}$, $\mathbf{c}$ is a linear combination of the other two. For example, if $v \neq 0$, $\mathbf{b} = -v^{-1}(u\mathbf{a} + w\mathbf{c})$, and $\mathbf{b}$ is in a plane containing $\mathbf{o}$, $\mathbf{a}$, and $\mathbf{c}$.

Definition 5.22. Let $a_1, \ldots, a_k$ be k points in $\Re^n$. They are **linearly dependent** if there are numbers $x_1, \ldots, x_k$, not all 0, such that

$$\sum_{i=1}^{k} x_i \mathbf{a}_i = \mathbf{o}^n.$$

They are **linearly independent** if this equation implies that each $x_i = 0$.

Consider the pair of equations

$$3c_1 + 2c_2 - c_3 = 0 \quad \text{and} \quad 37c_1 - 3c_2 + c_3 = 0.$$

They might arise from a puzzle about the ages of Carla, Charles, and Catherine. Once you establish that the only solution in reasonably small positive integers is $(c_1, c_2, c_3) = (1, 40, 83)$, you will admit that the puzzle is solvable.

One geometric problem leading to these equations is this: if $\mathbf{a} = (3, 2, -1)$ and $\mathbf{b} = (37, -3, 1)$, find the intersection of the orthogonal complements of $\mathbf{oa}$ and $\mathbf{ob}$.

Another geometric problem: are the points $(3, 37)$, $(2, -3)$, $(-1, 1)$ linearly dependent? That is, are there c_1, c_2, c_3 not all 0 such that $c_1(3, 37) + c_2(2, -3) + c_3(-1, 1) = (0, 0)$? From the solution displayed above, the answer is "yes," and $(3, 37) = -40(2, -3) - 83(-1, 1)$.

A *linear equation in n unknowns* is an equation of the form $\langle \mathbf{a}, \mathbf{x} \rangle = k$, where $\mathbf{a}$ is in $\Re^n$. Unless $\mathbf{a} = \mathbf{o}$, it is the equation of a hyperplane. If $\mathbf{a} = \mathbf{o}$, the equation reduces to $0 = k$, which is true for all $\mathbf{x}$ in $\Re^n$ if $k = 0$ but unsolvable if $k \neq 0$. The equation $\langle \mathbf{a}, \mathbf{x} \rangle = k$ is called *homogeneous* if $k = 0$. Thus a *homogeneous linear equation* is the equation of the orthogonal complement of a line, unless $\mathbf{a} = \mathbf{o}$.

We shall illustrate a very powerful method for finding all solutions of any system of linear equations. The general idea is to replace the system by a simpler equivalent system, where two systems are equivalent if they have exactly the same solutions.

First consider

$$(1) \quad \begin{aligned} 0x + y - z &= 2, \\ 0x \phantom{{}+y} + z &= 1. \end{aligned}$$

These equations put no condition on x, and the solution is the set of all (x, y, z) such that $y - z = 2$ and $z = 1$, which is the same as the set of all

(x, y, z) such that $z = 1$ and $y = 3$. These last two equations form the simplest equivalent system.

Now consider a more typical example:

$$\begin{aligned} -2w + 3x + y \qquad &= 1, \\ (2) \qquad 3w - 4x \qquad - z &= 0, \\ 2w - 2x + 4y - 2z &= 4, \end{aligned}$$

and

$$\begin{aligned} w - x + 2y - z &= 2, \\ (3) \qquad -2w + 3x + y \qquad &= 1, \\ 3w - 4x \qquad - z &= 0. \end{aligned}$$

Equations (3) were obtained from (2) by dividing both sides of one equation in (2) by 2 and writing down the equations in a different order. Obviously (3) and (2) are equivalent. Equations (3) are arranged so that the top equation has 1 as its first coefficient.

Now let $\mathbf{a}$, $\mathbf{b}$, $\mathbf{c}$ be points in $\Re^n$ and assume that the first component of $\mathbf{a}$ is 1. We claim the two systems

$$\begin{aligned} \langle \mathbf{a}, \mathbf{x} \rangle &= k_1 & \langle \mathbf{a}, \mathbf{x} \rangle &= k_1 \\ \langle \mathbf{b}, \mathbf{x} \rangle &= k_2, \qquad \text{and} \qquad & \langle \mathbf{b} - b_1\mathbf{a}, \mathbf{x} \rangle &= k_2 - b_1 k_1, \\ \langle \mathbf{c}, \mathbf{x} \rangle &= k_3, & \langle \mathbf{c} - c_1\mathbf{a}, \mathbf{x} \rangle &= k_3 - c_1 k_1 \end{aligned}$$

are equivalent. Because $\langle \mathbf{b} - b_1\mathbf{a}, \mathbf{x} \rangle = \langle \mathbf{b}, \mathbf{x} \rangle - b_1\langle \mathbf{a}, \mathbf{x} \rangle$ and $\langle \mathbf{c} - c_1\mathbf{a}, \mathbf{x} \rangle = \langle \mathbf{c}, \mathbf{x} \rangle - c_1\langle \mathbf{a}, \mathbf{x} \rangle$, this assertion is of the form

$$\begin{aligned} A &= k_1, & A &= k_1, \\ B &= k_2, \qquad \text{iff} \qquad & B - b_1 A &= k_2 - b_1 k_1, \\ C &= k_3, & C - c_1 A &= k_3 - c_1 k_1. \end{aligned}$$

This shows that system (3) is equivalent to

$$\begin{aligned} w - x + 2y - z &= 2, \\ (4) \qquad x + 5y - 2z &= 5, \\ - x - 6y + 2z &= -6. \end{aligned}$$

By the same principle we can retain the second equation above and add multiples of it to either or both the other two to obtain, for example,

$$\begin{aligned} w \qquad + 7y - 3z &= 7, \\ (5) \qquad x + 5y - 2z &= 5, \\ - y \qquad &= -1. \end{aligned}$$

One more application gives

$$\begin{aligned} w \qquad - 3z &= 0, \\ (6) \qquad x \qquad - 2z &= 0, \\ - y \qquad &= -1. \end{aligned}$$

The solutions of this last system, and therefore of system (2), are obviously all (w, x, y, z) such that $y = 1$, $x = 2z$, and $w = 3z$. Equivalently, the set of all $(3t, 2t, 1, t)$ or the set of all points $(0, 0, 1, 0) + t(3, 2, 0, 1)$. Geometrically the solutions are the points of the line through $(0, 0, 1, 0)$ parallel to the line through $\mathbf{o}^4$ and $(3, 2, 0, 1)$.

Exercises

Use the method outlined above to find all solutions of each of the systems below. If possible, give a geometric description of the set of solutions.

1. $x + 3y = 7$,
   $2x + 5y = 3$.

2. $x + y + z = 0$,
   $2x - y + 3z = 1$.

3. $x + 2y + 3z = 5$,
   $2x - y + z = 2$,
   $4x + 3y + 7z = 6$.

4. $x + 2y + 3z = 5$,
   $2x - y + z = 2$,
   $4x + 3y + 7z = 12$.

5. $0x + 2y + 3z = 1$,
   $0x + y - z = 2$.

6. $x + 2y + 3z = 0$,
   $4x + 5y + 6z = 0$,
   $7x + 8y + 9z = 0$.

7. $x + by = k_1$,
   $cx + dy = k_2$.

   [*Hint:* Make a special case of $d - bc = 0$.]

Theorem 5.24. 1. If $\mathbf{a}$ is in $\mathcal{R}^n$, with $n \geq 2$, there are $\mathbf{x}$ in $\mathcal{R}^n$ such that $\mathbf{x} \neq \mathbf{o}^n$, but $\langle \mathbf{a}, \mathbf{x} \rangle = 0$.

2. If $\mathbf{a}$ and $\mathbf{b}$ are in $\mathcal{R}^n$, with $n \geq 3$, there are $\mathbf{x}$ in $\mathcal{R}^n$ such that $\mathbf{x} \neq \mathbf{o}^n$, but $\langle \mathbf{a}, \mathbf{x} \rangle = 0$ and $\langle \mathbf{b}, \mathbf{x} \rangle = 0$.

3. If $\mathbf{a}$ and $\mathbf{b}$ and $\mathbf{c}$ are in $\mathcal{R}^n$, with $n \geq 4$, there are $\mathbf{x}$ in $\mathcal{R}^n$ such that $\mathbf{x} \neq \mathbf{o}^n$, but $\langle \mathbf{a}, \mathbf{x} \rangle = \langle \mathbf{b}, \mathbf{x} \rangle = \langle \mathbf{c}, \mathbf{x} \rangle = 0$.

4. If $n > m$, any system of m homogeneous linear equations in n unknowns has solutions other than $\mathbf{o}^n$.

PROOF OF 1: If $a_1 = 0$, let $x_1 = 1$ and $x_i = 0$ for $i > 1$. Then $\langle \mathbf{a}, \mathbf{x} \rangle = 0$ but $\mathbf{x} \neq \mathbf{o}^n$; also, for any real t, $\langle \mathbf{a}, t\mathbf{x} \rangle = 0$.

If $a_1 \neq 0$, let $x_1 = -a_2$, $x_2 = a_1$, and $x_i = 0$ for $2 < i < n$. Then $\mathbf{x} \neq \mathbf{o}^n$ because $x_2 \neq 0$, and $\langle \mathbf{a}, \mathbf{x} \rangle = a_1(-a_2) + a_2 a_1 + 0 = 0$; also, for any real t, $\langle \mathbf{a}, t\mathbf{x} \rangle = 0$.

PROOF OF 2: If $a_1 = 0$ and $b_1 = 0$, let $x_1 = 1$ and $x_i = 0$ for $i > 1$. Then $\langle \mathbf{a}, t\mathbf{x} \rangle = 0 = \langle \mathbf{b}, t\mathbf{x} \rangle$ for all real t.

If a_1 and b_1 are not both 0, then without loss of generality assume $a_1 \neq 0$ and set $\mathbf{a}' = \mathbf{a}/a_1 = (1, a_2', \ldots, a_n')$. The system $\langle \mathbf{a}, \mathbf{x} \rangle = 0$ and $\langle \mathbf{b}, \mathbf{x} \rangle = 0$ is equivalent to

$$x_1 + a_2'x_2 + \cdots + a_n'x_n = 0,$$
$$b_2'x_2 + \cdots + b_n'x_n = 0,$$

where $b_2' = b_2 - b_1 a_2', \ldots, b_n' = b_n - b_1 a_n'$; that is, we have replaced $\langle \mathbf{b}, \mathbf{x} \rangle = 0$ by $\langle \mathbf{b} - b_1\mathbf{a}', \mathbf{x} \rangle = 0$.

Now, since $n \geq 3$, the single equation $b_2'x_2 + \cdots + b_n'x_n = 0$ has, by Part 1, solutions $(x_2', \ldots, x_n') \neq \mathbf{o}^{n-1}$. Set $x_1' = -a_2'x_2' - \cdots - a_n'x_n'$, and $(x_1', x_2', \ldots, x_n')$ is a solution of the original system, and is not $\mathbf{o}^n$.

PROOF OF 3. If $a_1 = b_1 = c_1 = 0$, take $x_1 = 1$ and $x_i = 0$ for $i > 1$. Otherwise, construct an equivalent system of the form

$$x_1 + a_1'x_2 + \cdots + a_n'x_n = 0,$$
$$b_2'x_2 + \cdots + b_n'x_n = 0,$$
$$c_2'x_2 + \cdots + c_n'x_n = 0.$$

Since $n \geq 4$, the lower pair of equations is a system of two equations in at least three unknowns, and has nonzero solutions. Let $(x_2', \ldots, x_n') \neq \mathbf{o}^{n-1}$ be such a solution and, as in Part 2, set $x_1' = -a_1'x_2' - \cdots - a_n'x_n'$ to get a solution of the original system.

The inductive argument for statement 4 should now be clear.   ∎

Theorem 5.25.   Any three points in $\mathfrak{R}^2$ are linearly dependent.

PROOF: Points (a_1, a_2), (b_1, b_2), and (c_1, c_2) are linearly dependent if there are numbers x_1, x_2, x_3, not all 0, such that

$$x_1(a_1, a_2) + x_2(b_1, b_2) + x_3(c_1, c_2) = (0, 0).$$

But the system

$$a_1 x_1 + b_1 x_2 + c_1 x_3 = 0,$$
$$a_2 x_1 + b_2 x_2 + c_2 x_3 = 0$$

has solutions $(x_1, x_2, x_3) \neq (0, 0, 0)$, by Theorem 6.4.   ∎

Theorem 5.26.   If $\mathbf{a}$ and $\mathbf{b}$ are linearly independent points in $\mathfrak{R}^2$, then the set of all linear combinations of $\mathbf{a}$ and $\mathbf{b}$, the plane through $\mathbf{o}$, $\mathbf{a}$, and $\mathbf{b}$, is $\mathfrak{R}^2$.

PROOF: Let $\mathbf{c}$ be in $\mathfrak{R}^2$. By Theorem 5.25 there are numbers x_1, x_2, x_3, not all 0, such that $x_1\mathbf{a} + x_2\mathbf{b} + x_3\mathbf{c} = \mathbf{o}$. If $x_3 = 0$, we would have $x_1\mathbf{a} + x_2\mathbf{b} = \mathbf{o}$, with x_1 and x_2 not both 0. But this contradicts the linear independence of $\mathbf{a}$ and $\mathbf{b}$. Thus $x_3 \neq 0$ and $\mathbf{c} = -(x_1/x_3)\mathbf{a} - (x_2/x_3)\mathbf{b}$.   ∎

Theorem 5.27. If $\mathbf{a} \neq \mathbf{o}$ and $\mathbf{b} \neq \mathbf{o}$ but $\langle \mathbf{a}, \mathbf{b} \rangle = 0$, then $\mathbf{a}$ and $\mathbf{b}$ are linearly independent.

PROOF: Suppose that $u\mathbf{a} + v\mathbf{b} = \mathbf{o}$. Then

$$u\langle \mathbf{a}, \mathbf{a} \rangle + v\langle \mathbf{b}, \mathbf{a} \rangle = \langle \mathbf{o}, \mathbf{a} \rangle = 0,$$

$$u\langle \mathbf{a}, \mathbf{b} \rangle + v\langle \mathbf{b}, \mathbf{b} \rangle = \langle \mathbf{o}, \mathbf{b} \rangle = 0.$$

Since $\langle \mathbf{a}, \mathbf{b} \rangle = 0$ but $\langle \mathbf{a}, \mathbf{a} \rangle \neq 0$ and $\langle \mathbf{b}, \mathbf{b} \rangle \neq 0$, these equations imply $u = 0$ and $v = 0$. ∎

Theorem 5.28. Any four points in $\mathcal{R}^3$ are linearly dependent.

PROOF: Let $\mathbf{a}$, $\mathbf{b}$, $\mathbf{c}$, $\mathbf{d}$ be in $\mathcal{R}^3$. The equation $x_1\mathbf{a} + x_2\mathbf{b} + x_3\mathbf{c} + x_4\mathbf{d} = (0, 0, 0)$ is equivalent to the system

$$a_1x_1 + b_1x_2 + c_1x_3 + d_1x_4 = 0,$$

$$a_2x_1 + b_2x_2 + c_2x_3 + d_2x_4 = 0,$$

$$a_3x_1 + b_3x_2 + c_3x_3 + d_3x_4 = 0.$$

By Theorem 5.24 this system has solutions $(x_1, x_2, x_3, x_4) \neq (0, 0, 0, 0)$. ∎

Theorem 5.29. If $\mathbf{a}$, $\mathbf{b}$, $\mathbf{c}$ are three linearly independent points in $\mathcal{R}^3$, then the set of all linear combinations of $\mathbf{a}$, $\mathbf{b}$, $\mathbf{c}$ is $\mathcal{R}^3$.

PROOF: For any $\mathbf{d}$ in $\mathcal{R}^3$ there are x_1, x_2, x_3, x_4, not all 0, such that $x_1\mathbf{a} + x_2\mathbf{b} + x_3\mathbf{c} + x_4\mathbf{d} = \mathbf{o}^3$. In particular, $x_4 \neq 0$, as this would contradict the linear independence of $\mathbf{a}$, $\mathbf{b}$, $\mathbf{c}$. Thus $\mathbf{d}$ is a linear combination of $\mathbf{a}$, $\mathbf{b}$, and $\mathbf{c}$. ∎

Theorem 5.30. If $\mathbf{a}$, $\mathbf{b}$, and $\mathbf{c}$ in $\mathcal{R}^3$ are all $\neq \mathbf{o}^3$, but $\langle \mathbf{a}, \mathbf{b} \rangle = \langle \mathbf{a}, \mathbf{c} \rangle = \langle \mathbf{b}, \mathbf{c} \rangle = 0$, then $\mathbf{a}$, $\mathbf{b}$, $\mathbf{c}$ are linearly independent.

PROOF: If $x_1\mathbf{a} + x_2\mathbf{b} + x_3\mathbf{c} = 0$, then

$$x_1\langle \mathbf{a}, \mathbf{a} \rangle + x_2\langle \mathbf{b}, \mathbf{a} \rangle + x_3\langle \mathbf{c}, \mathbf{a} \rangle = 0,$$

which gives $x_1 = 0$. Similarly, $x_2 = x_3 = 0$. ∎

Theorem 5.31. Let $\mathbf{a} \neq \mathbf{o}$ be in $\mathcal{R}^3$. The orthogonal complement of $\mathbf{oa}$ is a plane.

PROOF: The equation $\langle \mathbf{a}, \mathbf{x} \rangle = 0$ has a solution other than $\mathbf{o}$; call it $\mathbf{b}$.

In $\mathcal{R}^3$ the system of two homogeneous equations, $\langle \mathbf{a}, \mathbf{x} \rangle = 0$ and $\langle \mathbf{b}, \mathbf{x} \rangle = 0$, has a solution $\mathbf{c} \neq \mathbf{o}$. By Theorem 5.30, $\mathbf{a}$, $\mathbf{b}$, $\mathbf{c}$ are linearly independent, and by Theorem 5.29 every point of $\mathcal{R}^3$ is a linear combination of them.

Let $\mathbf{d}$ be in the orthogonal complement of $\mathbf{oa}$. Since $\mathbf{d}$ is in $\mathcal{R}^3$, there are u, v, w such that $\mathbf{d} = u\mathbf{a} + v\mathbf{b} + w\mathbf{c}$. Now $0 = \langle \mathbf{a}, \mathbf{d} \rangle = u\langle \mathbf{a}, \mathbf{a} \rangle + v\langle \mathbf{a}, \mathbf{b} \rangle + w\langle \mathbf{a}, \mathbf{c} \rangle$. This gives $u = 0$ and $\mathbf{d} = v\mathbf{b} + w\mathbf{c}$. Thus the orthogonal complement of **oa** is the set of all linear combinations of **b** and **c**. But **b** and **c** are linearly independent, so this is a plane. ∎

Theorems 5.25 through 5.31 have obvious generalizations to $\mathfrak{R}^n$, $n > 3$. The proof, from Theorem 5.24, is straightforward. The generalization of Theorem 5.31 is clearly the statement that, for all n, the orthogonal complement of a line through $\mathbf{o}^n$ is congruent to $\mathfrak{R}^{n-1}$.

Exercises

1. Let **a** and **b** in $\mathfrak{R}^2$ be $\neq \mathbf{o}$ and such that $\langle \mathbf{a}, \mathbf{b} \rangle = 0$. Prove that, for every **c** in $\mathfrak{R}^2$,

$$\mathbf{c} = \frac{\langle \mathbf{c}, \mathbf{a} \rangle}{\langle \mathbf{a}, \mathbf{a} \rangle} \mathbf{a} + \frac{\langle \mathbf{c}, \mathbf{b} \rangle}{\langle \mathbf{b}, \mathbf{b} \rangle} \mathbf{b}.$$

2. Find u and v such that $(5, 7) = u(3, 4) + v(-4, 3)$.

3. Find all solutions of the system

$$3x - 4y = 5,$$
$$4x + 3y = 7.$$

4. Let $\mathbf{a} = (1, 2, 3)$. Find **b** and $\mathbf{c} \neq \mathbf{o}$ such that $\langle \mathbf{a}, \mathbf{b} \rangle = 0$, $\langle \mathbf{a}, \mathbf{c} \rangle = 0$, and $\langle \mathbf{b}, \mathbf{c} \rangle = 0$. Exhibit each of $(-2, 1, 0)$, $(0, -3, 2)$, $(-3, 0, 1)$, $(1, 1, -1)$ as a linear combination of **b** and **c**.

5. Let $\mathbf{a} = (1, 1, 1, 1)$. Find $\mathbf{b} \neq \mathbf{o}$ such that $\langle \mathbf{a}, \mathbf{b} \rangle = 0$. Then find $\mathbf{c} \neq \mathbf{o}$ such that $\langle \mathbf{a}, \mathbf{c} \rangle = 0$ and $\langle \mathbf{b}, \mathbf{c} \rangle = 0$. Then find $\mathbf{d} \neq \mathbf{o}$ such that $\langle \mathbf{a}, \mathbf{d} \rangle = 0$, $\langle \mathbf{b}, \mathbf{d} \rangle = 0$, and $\langle \mathbf{c}, \mathbf{d} \rangle = 0$. Are there planes through **o** perpendicular to **oa** other than the three generated by pairs of points **b**, **c**, and **d**?

6. Let L be the mapping $(x, y, z) \longrightarrow (x - y + z, x + 2y - z)$.

a. Find all **p** in $\mathfrak{R}^3$ such that $L(\mathbf{p}) = \mathbf{o}^2$.

b. If $\mathbf{a} = (2, 3, 4)$, then $L(\mathbf{a}) = (3, 4)$. If **q** in $\mathfrak{R}^3$ is such that $L(\mathbf{q}) = (3, 4)$, what is $L(\mathbf{q} - \mathbf{a})$?

c. With **a** as above, if $L(\mathbf{p}) = \mathbf{o}^2$, what is $L(\mathbf{a} + \mathbf{p})$?

d. Without solving any equations, write down the set of all **q** in $\mathfrak{R}^3$ such that $L(\mathbf{q}) = (3, 4)$.

e. Noting that $L(1, 1, 1) = (1, 2)$, what is the set of all **q** such that $L(\mathbf{q}) = (1, 2)$?

§ 7. *Coordinates*

Let $\mathbf{a} \neq \mathbf{o}$ be in $\mathfrak{R}^n$. For each **p** in $\mathfrak{R}^n$ we know that there is a unique **c** in $H_\mathbf{a}$, the orthogonal complement of **oa**, such that

$$\mathbf{p} = \frac{\langle \mathbf{p}, \mathbf{a} \rangle}{\langle \mathbf{a}, \mathbf{a} \rangle} \mathbf{a} + \mathbf{c}.$$

The illustration on page 128 [with **b** replaced by **p**] suggests that **c** is the point of $H_\mathbf{a}$ closest to **p** and that the distance of **p** from **c** is

$$|t\mathbf{a}| = \left| \frac{\langle \mathbf{p}, \mathbf{a} \rangle}{\langle \mathbf{a}, \mathbf{a} \rangle} \right| \mathbf{a} = \frac{|\langle \mathbf{p}, \mathbf{a} \rangle|}{|\mathbf{a}|}.$$

Set $t = \langle \mathbf{p}, \mathbf{a} \rangle / |\mathbf{a}|$ and let $\mathbf{q}$ be in $H_\mathbf{a}$, so that $\langle \mathbf{a}, \mathbf{q} \rangle = 0$. Then

$$|\mathbf{p} - \mathbf{q}|^2 = |t\mathbf{a} + \mathbf{c} - \mathbf{q}|^2$$
$$= |t\mathbf{a}|^2 + |\mathbf{c} - \mathbf{q}|^2 + 2t\langle \mathbf{a}, \mathbf{c} - \mathbf{q} \rangle.$$

But $\langle \mathbf{a}, \mathbf{c} \rangle = 0$ and $\langle \mathbf{a}, \mathbf{q} \rangle = 0$, and $|\mathbf{p} - \mathbf{q}|^2 = |t\mathbf{a}|^2 + |\mathbf{c} - \mathbf{q}|^2$. Unless $\mathbf{q} = \mathbf{c}$, $|\mathbf{p} - \mathbf{q}|^2 > |t\mathbf{a}|^2$. Thus $\mathbf{c}$ is the closest point to $\mathbf{p}$ in $H_\mathbf{a}$ and by definition the distance of $\mathbf{p}$ from $H_\mathbf{a}$ is

$$|\mathbf{p} - \mathbf{c}| = |t\mathbf{a}| = \frac{|\langle \mathbf{a}, \mathbf{b} \rangle|}{|\mathbf{a}|}.$$

Theorem 5.32. If $\mathbf{a} \neq \mathbf{o}$ is in $\mathfrak{R}^n$, then for each $\mathbf{p}$ in $\mathfrak{R}^n$ the distance of $\mathbf{p}$ from the orthogonal complement of $\mathbf{oa}$ is $|\langle \mathbf{a}, \mathbf{p} \rangle|/|\mathbf{a}|$. More generally, the distance of $\mathbf{p}$ from the hyperplane with equation $\langle \mathbf{a}, \mathbf{x} \rangle - k = 0$ is

$$\frac{|\langle \mathbf{a}, \mathbf{p} \rangle - k|}{|\mathbf{a}|}.$$

PROOF: We have proved the first statement. Any translation $T_\mathbf{b}$, such that $\langle \mathbf{a}, \mathbf{b} \rangle = k$, maps $H_\mathbf{a}$ onto the hyperplane H with equation $\langle \mathbf{a}, \mathbf{x} \rangle - k = 0$.

The distance of $\mathbf{p}$ from H is the same as the distance of $\mathbf{p} - \mathbf{b}$ from $H_\mathbf{a}$, which is

$$\frac{|\langle \mathbf{a}, \mathbf{p} - \mathbf{b} \rangle|}{|\mathbf{a}|} = \frac{|\langle \mathbf{a}, \mathbf{p} \rangle - k|}{|\mathbf{a}|}. \qquad \blacksquare$$

Examples

1. Let $\mathbf{a} = (3, 4)$. The orthogonal complement of $\mathbf{oa}$ is the line L through $(0, 0)$ and $(-4, 3)$. Regarded as a line, $L = \{(-4t, 3t) | t \text{ real}\}$. Regarded as a hyperplane, $L = \{(x, y) | 3x + 4y = 0\}$. The distance of a point $\mathbf{p}$ from L is $|3p_1 + 4p_2|/5$.

   The line through $(2, -1)$ parallel to L is the set $\{(2 - 4t, -1 + 3t) | t \text{ real}\}$. Regarded as a hyperplane, this line is the set of all (x, y) such that $3x + 4y - 2 = 0$. [Since $2 = \langle (3, 4), (2, -1) \rangle$.]

2. If $\mathbf{a} = (2, 1, -2)$, then $H_\mathbf{a}$, the orthogonal complement of $\mathbf{oa}$, is the set of all (x, y, z) such that $2x + y - 2z = 0$. For any (x, y, z) in $\mathfrak{R}^3$, the distance of (x, y, z) from $H_\mathbf{a}$ is $|2x + y - 2z|/3$.

   The parallel plane through $(1, 5, 10)$ is the set of all (x, y, z) such that

   $$2x + y - 2z - (2(1) + 5 - 2(10)) = 0,$$

   or

   $$2(x - 1) + (y - 5) - 2(z - 10) = 0.$$

   The points $\mathbf{b} = (-1, 2, 0)$ and $\mathbf{c} = (4, 2, 5)$ are in $H_\mathbf{a}$ and $\langle \mathbf{b}, \mathbf{c} \rangle = 0$. Thus $H_\mathbf{a}$ is the set of all linear combinations of $\mathbf{b}$ and $\mathbf{c}$.

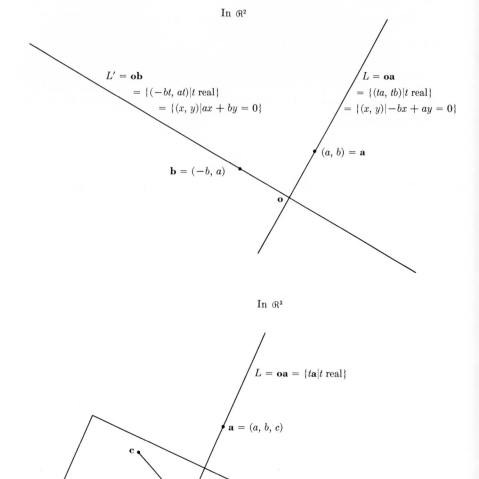

In $\mathfrak{R}^2$

$L' = \mathbf{ob}$
$\quad = \{(-bt,\, at)\,|\,t \text{ real}\}$
$\quad = \{(x,\, y)\,|\,ax + by = 0\}$

$L = \mathbf{oa}$
$\quad = \{(ta,\, tb)\,|\,t \text{ real}\}$
$\quad = \{(x,\, y)\,|\,-bx + ay = 0\}$

$(a,\, b) = \mathbf{a}$

$\mathbf{b} = (-b,\, a)$

$\mathbf{o}$

In $\mathfrak{R}^3$

$L = \mathbf{oa} = \{t\mathbf{a}\,|\,t \text{ real}\}$

$\mathbf{a} = (a,\, b,\, c)$

$\mathbf{c}$

$H_{\mathbf{a}}$

$\mathbf{o}$ $\mathbf{b}$

$H_{\mathbf{a}} = \{(x,\, y,\, z)\,|\,ax + by + cz = 0\}$
$\quad = \{u\mathbf{b} + v\mathbf{c}\,|\,(u,\, v) \text{ in } \mathfrak{R}^2\}$

Exercises

Describe each line in $\mathfrak{R}^2$ below as (a) a set of the form $\{t\mathbf{a} + (1 - t)\mathbf{b}\,|\,t \text{ real}\}$, and (b) the set of (x, y) satisfying a linear equation.

1. Through $(0, 0)$ and $(1, 0)$.
2. Through $(-3, 5)$ and $(2, 7)$.
3. Through $(5, 2)$ and $(5, 8)$.

4. Through $(3, 1)$ parallel to the line through $(0, 0)$ and $(2, -5)$.
5. Through $(3, 1)$ perpendicular to the lines in Exercise 4.
6. Through (a_1, a_2) and (b_1, b_2).

We have seen that a hyperplane in $\mathfrak{R}^1$ is a point, in $\mathfrak{R}^2$ a line, and in $\mathfrak{R}^3$ a plane. Intuitive question: how is a point in $\mathfrak{R}^1$ like a line in $\mathfrak{R}^2$ and like a plane in $\mathfrak{R}^3$? An answer: each separates its space into two pieces.

Now let H be a hyperplane in $\mathfrak{R}^n$ with an equation $\langle \mathbf{a}, \mathbf{x} \rangle - k = 0$. If $\mathbf{b}$ is not on H, then either $\langle \mathbf{a}, \mathbf{b} \rangle - k < 0$ or $\langle \mathbf{a}, \mathbf{b} \rangle - k > 0$. In some sense H has two sides in $\mathfrak{R}^n$.

Theorem 5.33. Let H be a hyperplane in $\mathfrak{R}^n$ with equation $\langle \mathbf{a}, \mathbf{x} \rangle - k = 0$. If $\langle \mathbf{a}, \mathbf{b} \rangle - k < 0$ and $\langle \mathbf{a}, \mathbf{c} \rangle - k > 0$, then a point of the open segment from $\mathbf{b}$ to $\mathbf{c}$ is on H.

PROOF: Set $\langle \mathbf{a}, \mathbf{b} \rangle - k = b < 0$ and $\langle \mathbf{a}, \mathbf{c} \rangle - k = c > 0$. The point $t\mathbf{b} + (1 - t)\mathbf{c}$ is on H iff

$$\langle \mathbf{a}, t\mathbf{b} + (1 - t)\mathbf{c} \rangle - k = 0$$

or

$$tb + (1 - t)c = 0,$$

or

$$t = \frac{c}{c - b}.$$

Since $c > 0$ and $b < 0$, $c < c - b$ and $0 < c/(c - b) < 1$. The corresponding point on H and on the line $\mathbf{bc}$ is between $\mathbf{b}$ and $\mathbf{c}$. ∎

Definition 5.23. Let $\mathbf{a} \neq \mathbf{o}$ be in $\mathfrak{R}^n$. The **directed distance** from the orthogonal complement of $\mathbf{oa}$ to $\mathbf{p}$ in $\mathfrak{R}^n$ is $\langle \mathbf{a}, \mathbf{p} \rangle/|\mathbf{a}|$.

Remark: If $\mathbf{b} = t\mathbf{a}$ and $t \neq 0$, the orthogonal complement of $\mathbf{oa}$ is the same as the orthogonal complement of $\mathbf{ob}$:

$$\frac{\langle t\mathbf{a}, \mathbf{b} \rangle}{|t\mathbf{a}|} = \frac{t\langle \mathbf{a}, \mathbf{b} \rangle}{|t|\,|\mathbf{a}|} = \pm\frac{\langle \mathbf{a}, \mathbf{b} \rangle}{|\mathbf{a}|}.$$

The $+$ holds if $t > 0$, otherwise the $-$ holds. This leaves us free to choose sides as we wish. Since $\langle \mathbf{a}, \mathbf{a} \rangle > 0$, the positive side of the orthogonal complement of $\mathbf{oa}$ is the side $\mathbf{a}$ is on.

Now let $\mathbf{a} = (a_1, a_2) \neq \mathbf{o}$. As in Exercise 12 on page 133, we set $\times\mathbf{a} = (-a_2, a_1)$. Then $|\times\mathbf{a}| = |\mathbf{a}|$, $\langle \mathbf{a}, \times\mathbf{a} \rangle = 0$, and, since $\det(\mathbf{a}, \times\mathbf{a}) = a_1^2 + a_2^2 > 0$, the right angle from the ray $\mathbf{oa}$ to the ray $\mathbf{o}(\times\mathbf{a})$ is counter-clockwise. The triangle $\mathbf{ao}(\times\mathbf{a})$ is congruent to the triangle $(a, 0)\,(0, 0)\,(0, a)$ if $a = |\mathbf{a}|$. We exploit this fact to set up a *coordinate system* with the pair of points $(\mathbf{a}, \times\mathbf{a})$ as a *basis*.

Definition 5.24. For $\mathbf{a} \neq \mathbf{o}$ in $\mathfrak{R}^2$, the **coordinate mappings** $x_\mathbf{a}$ and $y_\mathbf{a}$ relative to the **positively oriented orthogonal basis** $(\mathbf{a}, \times\mathbf{a})$

are defined by: for all $\mathbf{p}$ in $\mathfrak{R}^2$, $x_{\mathbf{a}}(\mathbf{p})$ is the directed distance to $\mathbf{p}$ from the orthogonal complement of $\mathbf{oa}$ and $y_{\mathbf{a}}(\mathbf{p})$ is the directed distance to $\mathbf{p}$ from the orthogonal complement of $\mathbf{o}(\times\mathbf{a})$. For $\mathbf{a} = (1, 0)$, we call $((1, 0), (0, 1))$ the **usual basis** and call the associated coordinate mappings simply x and y.

Evidently we have, for all $\mathbf{p}$,

$$x_{\mathbf{a}}(\mathbf{p}) = \frac{\langle \mathbf{a}, \mathbf{p} \rangle}{|\mathbf{a}|} = \frac{a_1 p_1 + a_2 p_2}{\sqrt{a_1{}^2 + a_2{}^2}},$$

$$y_{\mathbf{a}}(\mathbf{p}) = \frac{\langle \times\mathbf{a}, \mathbf{p} \rangle}{|\times\mathbf{a}|} = \frac{-a_2 p_1 + a_1 p_2}{\sqrt{a_1{}^2 + a_2{}^2}}.$$

In particular, for all $\mathbf{p}$,

$$x(\mathbf{p}) = \frac{1 p_1 + 0 p_2}{1} = p_1,$$

$$y(\mathbf{p}) = \frac{0 p_1 + 1 p_2}{1} = p_2.$$

Finally, we have recovered the original intuitive model of $\mathfrak{R}^2$. The components of a point $\mathbf{p}$ are its coordinates $x(\mathbf{p})$ and $y(\mathbf{p})$ relative to the usual basis, and are directed distances to $\mathbf{p}$ from the orthogonal complements of $\mathbf{o}(1, 0)$ and $\mathbf{o}(0, 1)$.

The notation $x_{\mathbf{a}}$ and $y_{\mathbf{a}}$ is appropriate but somewhat cumbersome. Appropriate notation for a coordinate system in $\mathfrak{R}^3$, or for a system in $\mathfrak{R}^2$ taking the origin at a point other than $(0, 0)$, is necessarily very cumbersome. The usual device is to use ad hoc names such as $\bar{x}$, $\bar{y}$ or x', y'. They are easily specified by a diagram.

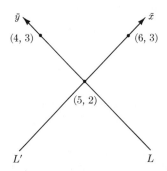

For every point $\mathbf{p}$, $\bar{x}(\mathbf{p})$ is the distance to $\mathbf{p}$ from L, and $\bar{y}(\mathbf{p})$ is the distance to $\mathbf{p}$ from L'. They are directed so that $\bar{x}(6, 3) > 0$ and $\bar{y}(4, 3) > 0$.

Exercises

1. Work out formulas for $\bar{x}$ and $\bar{y}$ in the example above. As a partial check note that $\bar{x}(5, 2) = \bar{y}(5, 2) = 0$ and $\bar{x}(6, 3) = \sqrt{2} = \bar{y}(4, 3)$.

2. Give the formulas for $x_{(3,4)}$, $y_{(3,4)}$ and for $x_{(3/5,4/5)}$, $y_{(3/5,4/5)}$.

3. If $x_{\mathbf{a}}(1, 0) = \sqrt{\tfrac{1}{2}}$, what can you say about $\mathbf{a}$?

4. If $x_{\mathbf{a}}(1, 0) = \sqrt{5}$, what can you say about $\mathbf{a}$?

Turning now to $\mathfrak{R}^3$, we want coordinates of a point to be its directed distances from three mutually perpendicular planes. Fortunately, planes in $\mathfrak{R}^3$ are hyperplanes, and we have formulas available for the coordinate mappings.

Suppose, for example, we select $\mathbf{a} = (2, 1, -2)$ and let the orthogonal complement of $\mathbf{oa}$ be the first coordinate plane. We define $\bar{x}$ to be the mapping: for all p in $\mathfrak{R}^3$, $\bar{x}(p)$ is the directed distance to $\mathbf{p}$ from the orthogonal complement of $\mathbf{oa}$. Then

$$\bar{x}(\mathbf{p}) = \frac{2p_1 + p_2 - 2p_3}{3}.$$

Now we want $\mathbf{b}$ such that $\mathbf{ob}$ is perpendicular to $\mathbf{oa}$. The situation is very different from that in $\mathfrak{R}^2$: there are many lines $\mathbf{ob}$ perpendicular to $\mathbf{oa}$, and none of them seems to have any special virtue. Quite arbitrarily we choose $\mathbf{b} = (0, 2, 1)$. One might ask whether the right angle from $\mathbf{oa}$ to $\mathbf{ob}$ is counterclockwise, but, as one can see by looking from both sides at an angle drawn on a window pane, this question has no intuitive meaning. This choice of $\mathbf{b}$ gives us a second coordinate mapping, $\bar{y}$: for all $\mathbf{p}$ in $\mathfrak{R}^3$,

$$\bar{y}(\mathbf{p}) = \frac{2p_2 + p_3}{\sqrt{5}}.$$

Now we want $\mathbf{c}$ such that $\mathbf{oc}$ is orthogonal to both $\mathbf{oa}$ and $\mathbf{ob}$ and such that the rays $\mathbf{oa}$, $\mathbf{ob}$, $\mathbf{oc}$ [in that order] form a *right-handed* or *positively oriented* system.

One intuitive definition is as follows: with the origin at the base of the index finger of your *right* hand, aim the index finger along $\mathbf{oa}$ and the middle finger comfortably along $\mathbf{ob}$; the system is right-handed if the extended thumb points in the direction $\mathbf{oc}$. A biologically equivalent formulation is that, looked at from $\mathbf{c}$, the right angle from $\mathbf{oa}$ to $\mathbf{ob}$ is seen as counterclockwise. Clearly this paragraph is about people, not space.

To return to our example, we want $\mathbf{c}$ such that $\langle \mathbf{a}, \mathbf{c} \rangle = 0$ and $\langle \mathbf{b}, \mathbf{c} \rangle = 0$. This is true iff $\mathbf{c}$ is a scalar multiple of $\mathbf{a} \times \mathbf{b} = (5, -2, 4)$. We assert that in the intuitive model the rays $\mathbf{oa}$, $\mathbf{ob}$, $\mathbf{o}(\mathbf{a} \times \mathbf{b})$ form a right-handed system according to the rule of thumb given. This particular coordinate system is completed by defining the third coordinate mapping $\bar{z}$: for all $\mathbf{p}$ in $\mathfrak{R}^3$,

$$\bar{z}(\mathbf{p}) = \frac{5p_1 - 2p_2 + 4p_3}{\sqrt{45}}.$$

Definition 5.25. For linearly independent $\mathbf{a}$ and $\mathbf{b}$ in $\mathfrak{R}^3$, with $\langle \mathbf{a}, \mathbf{b} \rangle = 0$, the triple $\langle \mathbf{a}, \mathbf{b}, \mathbf{a} \times \mathbf{b} \rangle$ is a **positively oriented orthogonal**

basis for $\Re^3$. The coordinates of a point relative to this basis are its directed distances from the orthogonal complements of $\mathbf{oa}$, $\mathbf{ob}$, $\mathbf{o(a \times b)}$. The **usual basis** for $\Re^3$ is $((1, 0, 0), (0, 1, 0), (0, 0, 1))$. The coordinate mappings relative to the usual basis are called x, y, and z.

Remark: The correspondence of this definition to the intuitive rule of thumb is not subject to mathematical proof. It will gain considerable plausibility later, when we can prove that there is a rotation mapping $\mathbf{a}$, $\mathbf{b}$, and $\mathbf{a} \times \mathbf{b}$ to $(|\mathbf{a}|, 0, 0)$, $(0, |\mathbf{b}|, 0)$, and $(0, 0, |\mathbf{a}|\,|\mathbf{b}|)$, respectively. The last three points taken as a basis determine the same rays, coordinate planes, and coordinate mappings as the usual basis. It seems intuitively clear that a rotation can't map a right hand onto a left hand.

Exercises

1. Let $\mathbf{a} = (3, 0, 0)$ and $\mathbf{b} = (0, 5, 0)$. Let $\bar{x}$, $\bar{y}$, $\bar{z}$ be the coordinate mappings relative to the basis $(\mathbf{a}, \mathbf{b}, \mathbf{a} \times \mathbf{b})$. Prove that $\bar{x} = x$, $\bar{y} = y$, and $\bar{z} = z$.
2. Give formulas for the coordinate mappings x', y', z' relative to the basis $(\mathbf{a}, \mathbf{b}, \mathbf{a} \times \mathbf{b})$, where $\mathbf{a} = (3, 1, 7)$ and $\mathbf{b} = (2, 1, -1)$.
3. Set up a coordinate system in which the origin is at $(1, 1, 1)$, the positive $\bar{x}$-axis is the ray from $(1, 1, 1)$ through $(4, 2, 8)$, and the positive $\bar{y}$-axis is the ray from $(1, 1, 1)$ through $(3, 2, 0)$.
4. Prove that if $\mathbf{a}$ and $\mathbf{b}$ are in $\Re^3$, with $|\mathbf{a}| = |\mathbf{b}| = 1$ and $\langle \mathbf{a}, \mathbf{b} \rangle = 0$, then $|\mathbf{a} \times \mathbf{b}| = 1$.
5. Let $\mathbf{a}$ and $\mathbf{b}$ be linearly independent in $\Re^3$ and such that $\langle \mathbf{a}, \mathbf{b} \rangle = 0$. Set $\mathbf{c} = \mathbf{a}/|\mathbf{a}|$ and $\mathbf{d} = \mathbf{b}/|\mathbf{b}|$, so that $|\mathbf{c}| = |\mathbf{d}| = 1$. The basis $(\mathbf{c}, \mathbf{d}, \mathbf{c} \times \mathbf{d})$ is called *orthonormal*, and the formulas for coordinates relative to it look particularly simple. Prove that they are, however, exactly the same as coordinates relative to $(\mathbf{a}, \mathbf{b}, \mathbf{a} \times \mathbf{b})$.

We conclude the chapter with the three-dimensional analogue of the material on two-by-two determinants and oriented areas.

Let $\mathbf{a}$, $\mathbf{b}$, $\mathbf{c}$ be linearly independent in $\Re^3$. Then $\mathbf{a}$ and $\mathbf{b}$ generate a parallelogram with vertices at $\mathbf{0}$, $\mathbf{a}$, $\mathbf{a} + \mathbf{b}$, and $\mathbf{b}$. The translation $T_{\mathbf{c}}$ maps these four points to the vertices of a parallel parallelogram, and these eight points are the vertices of a *parallelepiped*; it has three pairs of parallel faces, each a parallelogram.

The volume of the parallelepiped is the volume of the space enclosed by the surface and is defined to be the product of the height by the area of the base. Taking the base to be the parallelogram generated by $\mathbf{a}$ and $\mathbf{b}$, which has area $|\mathbf{a} \times \mathbf{b}|$, the height h is the distance of $\mathbf{c}$ from the plane through $\mathbf{o}$, $\mathbf{a}$, and $\mathbf{b}$. This plane is the orthogonal complement of the line through $\mathbf{o}$ and $\mathbf{a} \times \mathbf{b}$. Thus

$$h = \frac{|\langle \mathbf{a} \times \mathbf{b}, \mathbf{c} \rangle|}{|\mathbf{a} \times \mathbf{b}|}.$$

The denominator is just the area of the base and thus the volume is $|\langle \mathbf{a} \times \mathbf{b}, \mathbf{c} \rangle| = |\det (\mathbf{a}, \mathbf{b}, \mathbf{c})|$.

By Exercise 18 on page 133, $\det (\mathbf{a}, \mathbf{b}, \mathbf{c}) = \det (\mathbf{b}, \mathbf{c}, \mathbf{a}) = \det (\mathbf{c}, \mathbf{a}, \mathbf{b})$, so the volume is the same no matter which two of $\mathbf{a}, \mathbf{b}, \mathbf{c}$ are chosen to generate the base.

Definition 5.26. For $\mathbf{a}, \mathbf{b}, \mathbf{c}$ in $\mathfrak{R}^3$, the **oriented volume** of the parallelepiped generated by $(\mathbf{a}, \mathbf{b}, \mathbf{c})$ is $\det (\mathbf{a}, \mathbf{b}, \mathbf{c})$.

For example, the parallelepiped generated by $\mathbf{a} = (1, 1, 1)$, $b = (2, -1, 3)$, and $\mathbf{c} = (1, 5, -2)$ has its other vertices at $(0, 0, 0)$, $(3, 0, 4)$, $(2, 6, -1)$, $(3, 4, 1)$, and $(4, 5, 2)$. We have $\mathbf{a} \times \mathbf{b} = (4, -1, -3)$, and $\langle \mathbf{a} \times \mathbf{b}, \mathbf{c} \rangle = 5$ is the oriented volume.

Remark: The oriented volume of the parallelepiped generated by a positively oriented basis is always positive, since $\det (\mathbf{a}, \mathbf{b}, \mathbf{a} \times \mathbf{b}) = \langle \mathbf{a} \times \mathbf{b}, \mathbf{a} \times \mathbf{b} \rangle > 0$ for linearly independent $\mathbf{a}$ and $\mathbf{b}$.

Generalizations

Given one linearly independent point $\mathbf{a}$ in $\mathfrak{R}^2$, the point $\times \mathbf{a}$ was defined so that $|\times\mathbf{a}| = |\mathbf{a}|$, and $\langle \mathbf{a}, \times\mathbf{a} \rangle = 0$. The right angle from $\mathbf{o}\mathbf{a}$ to $\mathbf{o}(\times\mathbf{a})$ is counterclockwise.

Given two linearly independent points $\mathbf{a}$ and $\mathbf{b}$ in $\mathfrak{R}^3$, the point $\mathbf{a} \times \mathbf{b}$ was defined so that $|\mathbf{a} \times \mathbf{b}|$ is the area of the parallelogram generated by $\mathbf{a}$ and $\mathbf{b}$; $\langle \mathbf{a}, \mathbf{a} \times \mathbf{b} \rangle = \langle \mathbf{b}, \mathbf{a} \times \mathbf{b} \rangle = 0$. The three points $\mathbf{a}, \mathbf{b}, \mathbf{a} \times \mathbf{b}$ generate a positively oriented parallelepiped; if, also, $\langle \mathbf{a}, \mathbf{b} \rangle = 0$, they form an orthogonal basis.

In $\mathfrak{R}^n$, with $n > 1$, $n - 1$ linearly independent points are all in the orthogonal complement of a unique line. On this line we want to single out the point $\mathbf{p}$ such that $|\mathbf{p}|$ is the $(n - 1)$-dimensional volume of the base and the orientation is positive.

The idea is relatively recent and there is no standard notation except in $\mathfrak{R}^3$. Even our $\times\mathbf{a}$ in $\mathfrak{R}^2$ is not standard. During the 19th century physicists working with their rules of thumb for electricity and magnetism developed, in $\mathfrak{R}^3$, the formula we have given for $\mathbf{a} \times \mathbf{b}$. This was regarded not as the image of $\mathbf{b}$ under $\mathbf{a} \times$, but as the image of $(\mathbf{a}, \mathbf{b})$ under an operation called the cross product. This operation $\times$ is neither associative nor commutative, and there is no identity element.

It was a contemporary theoretical physicist, N. Wheeler, who pointed out to me the advantages of discarding this sick operation and considering instead the mappings $\mathbf{a} \times$. These are linear, and map $\mathfrak{R}^3$ onto the orthogonal complement of $\mathbf{o}\mathbf{a}$, for $\mathbf{a} \neq \mathbf{o}$.

The theory of determinants and oriented volumes in $\mathfrak{R}^n$, when $n > 3$, proceeds by analogy from $\mathfrak{R}^n$, when $n \leq 3$. It is, however, substantially more difficult, and to develop it would be contrary to the stated objectives of this chapter.

Miscellaneous Exercises on Chapter 5

1. Let $\mathbf{a}$ and $\mathbf{b}$ be in $\mathfrak{R}^n$, with $|\mathbf{a}| = |\mathbf{b}| \neq 0$. Let U be the set of $\mathbf{p}$ in $\mathfrak{R}^n$ such that $|\langle \mathbf{a}, \mathbf{p} \rangle| = |\langle \mathbf{b}, \mathbf{p} \rangle|$. Investigate the geometric nature of U for $n = 2, 3$, and 1, making a special case of linearly dependent $\mathbf{a}$ and $\mathbf{b}$.

2. Let $\mathbf{a} = (8, 1)$ and $\mathbf{b} = (7, 5)$. Give an equation of the line which bisects the acute angle from $\mathbf{oa}$ to $\mathbf{ob}$. Also give an equation of the other bisector.

3. Let $\mathbf{a}, \mathbf{b}, \mathbf{c}, \mathbf{d}$ be four distinct points in $\mathfrak{R}^n$, not all on a line. Prove that the midpoints of the segments $\mathbf{ab}, \mathbf{bc}, \mathbf{cd}, \mathbf{da}$ are vertices of a parallelogram. For $n = 3$ give an equation of the plane in which the parallelogram lies. [*Hint:* Translate one of the midpoints, say $(\mathbf{a} + \mathbf{b})/2$, to the origin, and show that the other three are, in some order, of the form $\mathbf{p}, \mathbf{q}, \mathbf{p} + \mathbf{q}$.]

4. Let $\mathbf{a} = (1, 1)$ and $\mathbf{b} = (1, 4)$. For a point to be in the interior of the parallelogram generated by $\mathbf{a}$ and $\mathbf{b}$, it must be on the correct side of each of four lines. Show that if $0 < u < 1$ and $0 < v < 1$, then $u\mathbf{a} + v\mathbf{b}$ is in the interior.

5. With $\mathbf{a}$ and $\mathbf{b}$ as in Exercise 4, the four lines $\mathbf{oa}, \mathbf{ob}, \mathbf{a}(\mathbf{a} + \mathbf{b}), \mathbf{b}(\mathbf{a} + \mathbf{b})$ split $\mathfrak{R}^2$ into nine regions. Each point of $\mathfrak{R}^2$ is of the form $u\mathbf{a} + v\mathbf{b}$ for some u and v. Can the nine regions be characterized by inequalities for u and v? If so, what are the corresponding nine regions where (u, v) might be?

6. With the same $\mathbf{a}$ and $\mathbf{b}$, under what conditions will $u\mathbf{a}$ and $v\mathbf{b}$ be in the interior of the triangle with vertices at $\mathbf{o}, \mathbf{a}, \mathbf{b}$?

7. Describe the generalization of the last three exercises to three linearly independent points in $\mathfrak{R}^3$.

Exercises 8–13 are concerned with $\mathfrak{R}^2$ only.

8. Prove that $\times$ is a linear operator.

9. For $\mathbf{a}, \mathbf{b}, \mathbf{c}, \mathbf{d}$ in $\mathfrak{R}^2$ and real s and t, prove that

$$\det (\mathbf{a} + \mathbf{b}, \mathbf{c} + \mathbf{d}) = \det (\mathbf{a}, \mathbf{c}) + \det (\mathbf{a}, \mathbf{d}) + \det (\mathbf{b}, \mathbf{c}) + \det (\mathbf{b}, \mathbf{d}),$$

$$\det (s\mathbf{a}, t\mathbf{b}) = st \det (\mathbf{a}, \mathbf{b}).$$

[*Hint:* Since $\det (\mathbf{p}, \mathbf{q}) = \langle \times \mathbf{p}, \mathbf{q} \rangle$, use the linearity of $\times$ and properties of the inner product.]

10. Let $\mathbf{a}, \mathbf{b}, \mathbf{c}$ be vertices of a triangle in $\mathfrak{R}^2$ such that the interior angle from $\mathbf{ab}$ to $\mathbf{ac}$ is counterclockwise. Use the translation $T_{-\mathbf{a}}$ and the results of Exercise 9 to prove that the area of the triangle is

$$\tfrac{1}{2} \det (\mathbf{b} - \mathbf{a}, \mathbf{c} - \mathbf{a}) = \tfrac{1}{2} (\det (\mathbf{a}, \mathbf{b}) + \det (\mathbf{b}, \mathbf{c}) + \det (\mathbf{c}, \mathbf{a})).$$

Check the formula for the triangles with vertices at $(1, 1)$, $(3, 1)$, $(5, 7)$ and $(2, 1)$, $(3, -2)$, $(10, 5)$.

11. Let the vertices of a quadrilateral be $\mathbf{a}, \mathbf{b}, \mathbf{c}, \mathbf{d}$ in a counterclockwise order. Draw the diagonal $\mathbf{ac}$ and deduce that the area of the quadrilateral is $\tfrac{1}{2} (\det (\mathbf{a}, \mathbf{b}) + \det (\mathbf{b}, \mathbf{c}) + \det (\mathbf{c}, \mathbf{d}) + \det (\mathbf{d}, \mathbf{a}))$.

12. Derive a formula for the area of a pentagon and check it on the pentagon with

vertices at $(0, 0)$, $(2, 0)$, $(2, 2)$, $(1, 1)$, $(0, 2)$. Investigate what happens if the vertices are assigned various random orders.

13. Deduce from Exercise 9 that det $(\mathbf{a}, \mathbf{b}) = $ det $(\mathbf{a}, \mathbf{b} - t\mathbf{a})$. Illustrate for $\mathbf{a} = (1, 1)$, $\mathbf{b} = (2, 1)$, and $t = 2$. Sketch a figure showing the parallelograms generated by $(\mathbf{a}, \mathbf{b})$ and by $(\mathbf{a}, \mathbf{b} - t\mathbf{a})$, having the same base, height, and orientation.

6
Linear Algebra in $\mathfrak{R}^2$ and $\mathfrak{R}^3$

§ 1. *Linear Transformations in* $\mathfrak{R}^2$

A transformation in $\mathfrak{R}^2$ is a mapping with domain $\mathfrak{R}^2$ and range a subset of $\mathfrak{R}^2$. It is clear that the composition of two transformations in $\mathfrak{R}^2$ is a transformation in $\mathfrak{R}^2$. If F and G are transformations in $\mathfrak{R}^2$, then $F + G$ is the mapping: for all $\mathbf{p}$ in $\mathfrak{R}^2$,

$$(F + G)(\mathbf{p}) = F(\mathbf{p}) + G(\mathbf{p}),$$

and $F + G$ is also a transformation in $\mathfrak{R}^2$.

Also, the sum and composition of linear transformations are linear. We give part of the proof and leave the rest to the reader. Let $\mathbf{A}$ and $\mathbf{B}$ be linear transformations in $\mathfrak{R}^2$. For any real t and any $\mathbf{a}$ in $\mathfrak{R}^2$,

$$(\mathbf{A} + \mathbf{B})(t\mathbf{a}) = \mathbf{A}(t\mathbf{a}) + \mathbf{B}(t\mathbf{a}) = t\mathbf{A}(\mathbf{a}) + t\mathbf{B}(\mathbf{a}) = t(\mathbf{A} + \mathbf{B})(\mathbf{a}).$$

For any $\mathbf{p}$ and $\mathbf{q}$ in $\mathfrak{R}^2$,

$$(\mathbf{A} \circ \mathbf{B})(\mathbf{p} + \mathbf{q}) = \mathbf{A}(\mathbf{B}(\mathbf{p} + \mathbf{q})) = \mathbf{A}(\mathbf{B}(\mathbf{p}) + \mathbf{B}(\mathbf{q}))$$
$$= \mathbf{A}(\mathbf{B}(\mathbf{p})) + \mathbf{A}(\mathbf{B}(\mathbf{q})) = (\mathbf{A} \circ \mathbf{B})(\mathbf{p}) + (\mathbf{A} \circ \mathbf{B})(\mathbf{q}).$$

We have partly proved

> **Theorem 6.1.** The set of all linear transformations in $\mathfrak{R}^2$ is closed under addition and composition. The set is a commutative group under addition. For any $\mathbf{A}$, $\mathbf{B}$, $\mathbf{C}$ in the set,
>
> $\mathbf{A} \circ (\mathbf{B} + \mathbf{C}) = \mathbf{A} \circ \mathbf{B} + \mathbf{A} \circ \mathbf{C},$
>
> $(\mathbf{B} + \mathbf{C}) \circ \mathbf{A} = \mathbf{B} \circ \mathbf{A} + \mathbf{C} \circ \mathbf{A}.$
>
> PROOF: The additive identity is the linear transformation $\mathbf{O}$: $\mathbf{O}(\mathbf{p}) = \mathbf{o}$, for all $\mathbf{p}$ in $\mathfrak{R}^2$. If $\mathbf{A}$ is a linear transformation in $\mathfrak{R}^2$, then the trans-

formation $\mathbf{p} \longrightarrow -\mathbf{A}(\mathbf{p})$ is easily seen to be linear and to be the additive inverse of $\mathbf{A}$.

The proof of one distributive law goes as follows. For any $\mathbf{p}$ in $\Re^2$,

$$[\mathbf{A} \circ (\mathbf{B} + \mathbf{C})](\mathbf{p}) = \mathbf{A}([\mathbf{B} + \mathbf{C}](\mathbf{p}))$$
$$= \mathbf{A}(\mathbf{B}(\mathbf{p}) + \mathbf{C}(\mathbf{p}))$$
$$= \mathbf{A}(\mathbf{B}(\mathbf{p})) + \mathbf{A}(\mathbf{C}(\mathbf{p})),$$

by the linearity of $\mathbf{A}$. The proof of the other distributive law is immediate from the definitions of the operations and does not use linearity.   ∎

It is rather natural to define a scalar product $t\mathbf{A}$ of a real number t and a linear transformation $\mathbf{A}$ by $(t\mathbf{A})(\mathbf{p}) = t(\mathbf{A}(\mathbf{p}))$, for all $\mathbf{p}$ in the domain of $\mathbf{A}$. We can easily prove

Theorem 6.2. The set of all linear transformations in $\Re^2$ is closed under scalar multiplication; that is, if $\mathbf{A}$ is a linear transformation in $\Re^2$, so is $t\mathbf{A}$ for all real t.

The two theorems above show that the set of all linear transformations in $\Re^2$ has a rich algebraic structure. We shall eventually see that there are subsystems isomorphic to some more familiar algebraic systems.

Let $\mathbf{A}$ be a linear transformation in $\Re^2$ and set $\mathbf{A}(1, 0) = (a, c)$ and $\mathbf{A}(0, 1) = (b, d)$. As we have seen in the last chapter, the linearity of $\mathbf{A}$ produces the formula, for all (x, y) in $\Re^2$,

$$\mathbf{A}(x, y) = x\mathbf{A}(1, 0) + y\mathbf{A}(0, 1) = x(a, c) + y(b, d)$$
$$= (ax + by, cx + dy).$$

A linear transformation in $\Re^2$ is completely determined by the images of $(1, 0)$ and $(0, 1)$.

Conversely, let (a', c') and (b', d') be any two points in $\Re^2$ and define a mapping $\mathbf{A}'$ by: for all (x, y) in $\Re^2$,

$$\mathbf{A}'(x, y) = (a'x + b'y, c'x + d'y).$$

It is easily proved that $\mathbf{A}'$ is linear and that $\mathbf{A}'(1, 0) = (a', c')$ and $\mathbf{A}'(0, 1) = (b', d')$. Furthermore, it is clear that $\mathbf{A} = \mathbf{A}'$ iff $(a, c) = (a', c')$ and $(b, d) = (b', d')$.

There is, then, a one-to-one correspondence of the set of all linear transformations in $\Re^2$ to the set of all ordered pairs of points in $\Re^2$. An ordered pair of points in $\Re^2$ is essentially an ordered set of four real numbers.

Given four real numbers, a, b, c, d, we can form the *matrix* $A = \begin{pmatrix} a & b \\ c & d \end{pmatrix}$.

We shall use this matrix as a name for the linear transformation $\mathbf{A}$ mapping $(1, 0)$ to (a, c) and $(0, 1)$ to (b, d). In the early grades of school we learned to get results in adding and multiplying numbers by manipulating the numerals which are the standard names of the numbers. Similarly, we can get results about the algebra of linear transformations by manipulating the matrices which are the standard [relative to the usual coordinate system] names of the transformations.

Definition 6.1. Let $A = \begin{pmatrix} a & b \\ c & d \end{pmatrix}$ be the **matrix, relative to the usual basis,** of the linear transformation **A** such that $\mathbf{A}(1, 0) = (a, c)$ and $\mathbf{A}(0, 1) = (b, d)$. Then $\begin{pmatrix} a & b \\ c & d \end{pmatrix} = \begin{pmatrix} a' & b' \\ c' & d' \end{pmatrix}$ iff $a = a'$, $b = b'$, $c = c'$, and $d = d'$.

Examples

1. The matrix $B = \begin{pmatrix} 2 & 1 \\ 3 & 5 \end{pmatrix}$ is the matrix of the linear transformation **B** such that $\mathbf{B}(1, 0) = (2, 3)$ and $\mathbf{B}(0, 1) = (1, 5)$. For all (x, y), $\mathbf{B}(x, y) = (2x + y, 3x + 5y)$.

2. The matrix of the linear transformation **I** mapping $(1, 0)$ to $(1, 0)$ and $(0,1)$ to $(0, 1)$ is $I = \begin{pmatrix} 1 & 0 \\ 0 & 1 \end{pmatrix}$. Clearly **I** is the identity function on $\Re^2$.

3. The matrix of the linear transformation **O** mapping $\Re^2$ onto $(0, 0)$ is $O = \begin{pmatrix} 0 & 0 \\ 0 & 0 \end{pmatrix}$.

Definition 6.2. Let $A = \begin{pmatrix} a & b \\ c & d \end{pmatrix}$ and $A' = \begin{pmatrix} a' & b' \\ c' & d' \end{pmatrix}$ be matrices and **A** and **A'** the corresponding linear transformations. We define $A + A'$ to be the matrix corresponding to the transformation $\mathbf{A} + \mathbf{A}'$, and AA' to be the matrix corresponding to $\mathbf{A} \circ \mathbf{A}'$. Also, for real t we define tA to be the matrix corresponding to $t\mathbf{A}$.

Remark: Properly, each "corresponding" above should be followed by: "relative to the usual basis." A later section furnishes examples of correspondences of linear transformations to matrices relative to other bases. Unless the basis is mentioned explicitly, we always mean it to be the usual basis, $((1, 0), (0, 1))$.

Theorem 6.3. If $A = \begin{pmatrix} a & b \\ c & d \end{pmatrix}$ and $A' = \begin{pmatrix} a' & b' \\ c' & d' \end{pmatrix}$, then

$$A + A' = \begin{pmatrix} a + a' & b + b' \\ c + c' & d + d' \end{pmatrix},$$

$$AA' = \begin{pmatrix} aa' + bc' & ab' + bd' \\ ca' + dc' & cb' + dd' \end{pmatrix},$$

and, for real t,

$$tA = \begin{pmatrix} ta & tb \\ tc & td \end{pmatrix}.$$

PARTIAL PROOF: If **A** maps $(1, 0)$ to (a, c) and $(0, 1)$ to (b, d), then $t\mathbf{A}$ maps $(1, 0)$ to (ta, tc) and $(0, 1)$ to (tb, td). The matrix corresponding to $t\mathbf{A}$ is tA and is displayed in the theorem.

To compute the first column of AA' we must find the image of $(1, 0)$ under $\mathbf{A} \circ \mathbf{A}'$:

$$\mathbf{A}'(1, 0) = (a', c'),$$
$$\mathbf{A}(a', c') = (aa' + bc', ca' + dc').$$

We leave it to the reader to work out the second column of AA' and to establish the formula for $A + A'$. The formula for the product is easily remembered if one notices that each entry in AA' is the inner product of a row of A and a column of A'. ∎

Following are a few examples of this result.

$$\begin{pmatrix} 2 & 3 \\ -2 & 1 \end{pmatrix} \begin{pmatrix} 1 & -7 \\ 2 & 5 \end{pmatrix} = \begin{pmatrix} 8 & 1 \\ 0 & 19 \end{pmatrix}.$$

$$\begin{pmatrix} 1 & -7 \\ 2 & 5 \end{pmatrix} \begin{pmatrix} 2 & 3 \\ -2 & 1 \end{pmatrix} = \begin{pmatrix} 16 & -4 \\ -6 & 11 \end{pmatrix}.$$

$$\begin{pmatrix} 1 & 1 \\ 2 & 2 \end{pmatrix} \begin{pmatrix} -2 & -4 \\ 2 & 4 \end{pmatrix} = \begin{pmatrix} 0 & 0 \\ 0 & 0 \end{pmatrix}.$$

Let us summarize what has been accomplished so far in this chapter. The algebraic system—the set of all linear transformations in $\mathcal{R}^2$, along with the operations of addition of transformations, composition of transformations, and the scalar product of a number and a transformation—is a complicated system. We have given each linear transformation in $\mathcal{R}^2$ a name, a two-by-two matrix, and have shown that there is a one-to-one correspondence of the set of linear transformations in $\mathcal{R}^2$ to the set of all two-by-two matrices. Then Definition 6.2 defined matrix addition, matrix multiplication, and the scalar product of a number and a matrix, in such a way that the set of all two-by-two matrices, along with the matrix operations, is isomorphic to the original system.

A linear transformation is a somewhat abstract object, and the algebra of the set of all linear transformations in $\mathcal{R}^2$ is hard to work with. But a matrix such as $\begin{pmatrix} 1 & 2 \\ 3 & 4 \end{pmatrix}$ is as concrete as are the four numbers, and with a little practice matrices are easy to work with.

Example

Let $\mathbf{A}(x, y) = (2x - 2y, 3x + 3y)$ for all (x, y). The corresponding matrix is $A = \begin{pmatrix} 2 & -2 \\ 3 & 3 \end{pmatrix}$. It is easily verified that

$$A = \begin{pmatrix} 2 & 0 \\ 0 & 3 \end{pmatrix} \begin{pmatrix} 1 & -1 \\ 1 & 1 \end{pmatrix} = BC,$$

where C is the matrix of the linear transformation **C** mapping $(1, 0)$ to $(1, 1)$ and $(0, 1)$ to $(-1, 1)$. From the last chapter [or by inspection] **C** is a similarity of scale factor $\sqrt{2}$ and is the composition of a dilation with a congruence, which is a $45°$ rotation around the origin. The corresponding matrix factorization is

$$\begin{pmatrix} 1 & -1 \\ 1 & 1 \end{pmatrix} = \begin{pmatrix} \sqrt{2} & 0 \\ 0 & \sqrt{2} \end{pmatrix} \begin{pmatrix} \dfrac{1}{\sqrt{2}} & \dfrac{1}{-\sqrt{2}} \\ \dfrac{1}{\sqrt{2}} & \dfrac{1}{\sqrt{2}} \end{pmatrix}.$$

The transformation **B** corresponding to B is not a similarity, but is easily visualized: $\mathbf{B}(x, y) = (2x, 3y)$, so that **B** stretches horizontal distances by 2 and vertical distances by 3. The linear transformation **A** is now seen as the composition of three simpler linear transformations, each rather easily visualized geometrically.

Exercises

1. If $A = \begin{pmatrix} 3 & -4 \\ 2 & -3 \end{pmatrix}$, $B = \begin{pmatrix} 1 & 0 \\ 5 & -1 \end{pmatrix}$, and $C = \begin{pmatrix} -1 & k \\ 0 & 1 \end{pmatrix}$, compute each of the following: $A + B$, AB, BA, AC, CA, BC, CB, A^2, B^2, C^2.

2. Give a careful proof that if a and b are numbers and $a^2 = b^2$, then $a = b$ or $-b$. Which steps in the proof remain valid if you replace a and b by the matrices A and B in Exercise 1?

3. Prove that multiplication of two-by-two matrices is associative. [*Hint:* The easy way is to use Definition 6.2 rather than Theorem 6.3.]

4. If $I = \begin{pmatrix} 1 & 0 \\ 0 & 1 \end{pmatrix}$, prove, without using Theorem 6.3, that $IA = AI = A$ for every two-by-two matrix A.

5. Prove that if A, B, C are two-by-two matrices, then $A(B + C) = AB + AC$ and $(B + C)A = BA + CA$.

6. Under what circumstances does $(A + B)^2 = A^2 + 2AB + B^2$?

7. A matrix of the form $\begin{pmatrix} a & 0 \\ 0 & a \end{pmatrix}$ is called a *scalar matrix*. Prove that a scalar matrix commutes with every two-by-two matrix. Discuss the linear transformation corresponding to $\begin{pmatrix} a & 0 \\ 0 & a \end{pmatrix}$, considering separately $a > 0$, $a = 0$, and $a < 0$.

8. Let $A = \begin{pmatrix} a & 0 \\ 0 & a \end{pmatrix}$. Prove that, for every two-by-two matrix B, $AB = aB$.

9. Let S be the set of all two-by-two scalar matrices. Prove that the algebraic system $(S; \text{matrix addition, matrix multiplication})$ is isomorphic to $(\mathbb{R}; +, \cdot)$.

10. Prove that if $AB = BA$ for every two-by-two matrix B, then A is scalar. [*Hint:* If A commutes with every B, then in particular A commutes with some very simple matrices such as $\begin{pmatrix} 0 & 1 \\ 0 & 0 \end{pmatrix}$.]

11. Let $A = \begin{pmatrix} 1 & 2 \\ 2 & 4 \end{pmatrix}$. Find B and C such that $B \ne C$ but $AB = AC$.

The theorems and exercises above say a good deal about the algebra of two-by-two matrices. Clearly the set is a commutative group under addition. Multiplication is distributive over addition and is associative, and $I = \begin{pmatrix} 1 & 0 \\ 0 & 1 \end{pmatrix}$ is the multiplicative identity. Multiplication is not commutative, and this makes the algebra somewhat different from that of the real numbers.

If the matrix A in Exercise 11 above had a multiplicative inverse A^{-1}, then from $AB = AC$ would follow $A^{-1}AB = A^{-1}AC$ and $B = C$. However, this is not the case, and therefore A has no multiplicative inverse. This will be immediately clear if you look at the corresponding transformation $\mathbf{A}$ with $\mathbf{A}(1, 0) = (1, 2)$ and $\mathbf{A}(0, 1) = (2, 4) = 2\mathbf{A}(1, 0)$; $\mathbf{A}$ maps $\mathbb{R}^2$ onto the line through $(0, 0)$ and $(1, 2)$, is not one-to-one, and has no composition inverse. Hence A has no multiplicative inverse.

The problem of determining whether a function is one-to-one and has an inverse can be difficult. But for linear transformations it is much easier than for functions in general. We first give a general definition and theorem and then a specific theorem for linear transformations in $\mathbb{R}^2$.

Definition 6.3. Let **L** be a linear transformation. The **kernel** of **L** is the set of all **p** in the domain of **L** such that $\mathbf{L}(\mathbf{p}) = \mathbf{o}$, the zero of the range of **L**.

Theorem 6.4. A linear transformation **L** is one-to-one and has an inverse iff the kernel of **L** contains only **o**, the zero of the domain of **L**.

PROOF: A linear transformation necessarily maps **o** in the domain to **o** in the range. If the kernel of **L** contains $\mathbf{p} \neq \mathbf{o}$, then $\mathbf{L}(\mathbf{p}) = \mathbf{o} = \mathbf{L}(\mathbf{o})$ and **L** is not one-to-one.

Conversely, if **L** is not one-to-one, there are **p** and **q** in the domain with $\mathbf{p} \neq \mathbf{q}$ but $\mathbf{L}(\mathbf{p}) = \mathbf{L}(\mathbf{q})$. Then $\mathbf{p} - \mathbf{q} \neq \mathbf{o}$, but $\mathbf{L}(\mathbf{p} - \mathbf{q}) = \mathbf{L}(\mathbf{p}) - \mathbf{L}(\mathbf{q}) = \mathbf{o}$, and $\mathbf{p} - \mathbf{q}$ is in the kernel but $\neq \mathbf{o}$.   ∎

Theorem 6.5. Let **A** be a linear transformation in $\mathbb{R}^2$. Then **A** is one-to-one and has an inverse iff $\mathbf{A}(1, 0)$ and $\mathbf{A}(0, 1)$ are linearly independent.

PROOF: Suppose $\mathbf{A}(1, 0)$ and $\mathbf{A}(0, 1)$ are linearly dependent. If either is $(0, 0)$, then the kernel of **A** contains $(1, 0)$ or $(0, 1)$ and **A** is not one-to-one. If neither is $(0, 0)$, then $\mathbf{A}(0, 1)$ is a scalar multiple of $\mathbf{A}(1, 0)$; say $\mathbf{A}(0, 1) = k\mathbf{A}(1, 0)$. But also $\mathbf{A}(k, 0) = k\mathbf{A}(1, 0)$, and **A** is not one-to-one. We have established that if $\mathbf{A}(1, 0)$ and $\mathbf{A}(0, 1)$ are linearly dependent, then **A** is not one-to-one.

Now suppose $\mathbf{A}(1, 0)$ and $\mathbf{A}(0, 1)$ are linearly independent. If $\mathbf{A}(x, y) = (0, 0)$, then $x\mathbf{A}(1, 0) + y\mathbf{A}(0, 1) = (0, 0)$, and $(x, y) = (0, 0)$ by definition of linear independence. The kernel of A contains $(0, 0)$ only, and **A** is one-to-one.   ∎

Remark: Recall that, if $\mathbf{A}(1, 0)$ and $\mathbf{A}(0, 1)$ are linearly independent, then the set of all linear combinations of them, which is the range of $\mathbf{A}$, is all of $\Re^2$. Thus $\mathbf{A}$ is a one-to-one mapping of $\Re^2$ onto $\Re^2$.

Theorem 6.6.   Let $A = \begin{pmatrix} a & b \\ c & d \end{pmatrix}$. If (a, c) and (b, d) are linearly independent, then

$$A^{-1} = \frac{1}{ad - bc} \begin{pmatrix} d & -b \\ -c & a \end{pmatrix}.$$

PROOF: By Theorem 6.5, A has a multiplicative inverse: there is some $B = \begin{pmatrix} w & x \\ y & z \end{pmatrix}$ such that $AB = BA = \begin{pmatrix} 1 & 0 \\ 0 & 1 \end{pmatrix}$. This gives us systems of linear equations, guaranteed to have unique solutions for the entries in $B = A^{-1}$. You can readily verify that, with A^{-1} as displayed, $AA^{-1} = A^{-1}A = I$.

Definition 6.4.   Let $A = \begin{pmatrix} a & b \\ c & d \end{pmatrix}$ and let $\mathbf{A}$ be the corresponding linear transformation. Then $\det A = \det \mathbf{A} = ad - bc$.

This defines two new functions that are called *determinant*. One function assigns to each two-by-two matrix a number; the other assigns the same number to the corresponding linear transformation. With A as above, $\det A$ is also the previously defined $\det ((a, c), (b, d))$, which leads to a geometric interpretation.

The square with vertices at $(0, 0)$, $(1, 0)$, $(1,1)$, $(0,1)$ has oriented area $+1$. The linear transformation $\mathbf{A}$ respectively maps these points to $(0, 0)$, (a, c), $(a + b, c + d)$, (b, d). If (a, c) and (b, d) are linearly dependent, then $\mathbf{A}$ maps the square onto a line segment, or else onto $(0, 0)$. If (a, c) and (b, d) are linearly independent, $\mathbf{A}$ maps the square onto a parallelogram of oriented area $\det \mathbf{A}$. If we agree that a line segment or a point is a degenerate parallelogram of area 0, then we can say that in every case the image of the unit square under $\mathbf{A}$ has oriented area $\det \mathbf{A}$.

This last remark can be generalized considerably as a result of Theorem 6.7 below. There is no brief elegant proof of the theorem, and we leave it to the reader to do the necessary computations.

Theorem 6.7.   If A and B are two-by-two matrices, then $\det (AB) = \det A \det B$.

Now let $\mathbf{A}$ be the linear transformation with matrix $A = \begin{pmatrix} a & b \\ c & d \end{pmatrix}$. Let (a', c') and (b', d') be any two points in $\Re^2$, and set $B = \begin{pmatrix} a' & b' \\ c' & d' \end{pmatrix}$. The parallelogram with vertices at $(0, 0)$, (a', c'), $(a' + b', c' + d')$, and (b', d') has oriented area det $((a', c'), (b', d')) = \det B$.

The image of this parallelogram under $\mathbf{A}$ is the same as the image of the unit square under the linear transformation corresponding to AB, and has oriented area det (AB).

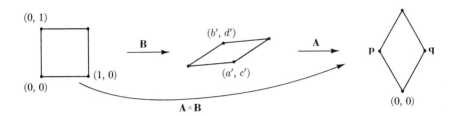

Since det $(AB) = \det A \det B$, we see that if P is any parallelogram with a vertex at the origin and P' is the image of P under a linear transformation $\mathbf{A}$, then the oriented area of P' is det $\mathbf{A}$ times the oriented area of P.

By using a translation we can deduce [see Exercises] that the oriented area of the image of any parallelogram under $\mathbf{A}$ is the product of det $\mathbf{A}$ and the oriented area of the original. This result is easily extended [or shrunk?] to triangles. Any plane region which has an area can be approximated by a union of triangles. The general result, which we shall not prove, is that a linear transformation $\mathbf{A}$ in $\mathcal{R}^2$ multiplies all oriented areas by det $\mathbf{A}$ and all areas by $|\det \mathbf{A}|$.

To complete the basic matrix machinery for linear transformations in $\mathcal{R}^2$, we shall call the symbol $\begin{pmatrix} x \\ y \end{pmatrix}$ a *column matrix*. Clearly there is a one-to-one correspondence of points to column matrices. If $A = \begin{pmatrix} a & b \\ c & d \end{pmatrix}$, we define the product of A and a column matrix by

$$\begin{pmatrix} a & b \\ c & d \end{pmatrix} \begin{pmatrix} x \\ y \end{pmatrix} = \begin{pmatrix} ax + by \\ cx + dy \end{pmatrix}.$$

For example, $\begin{pmatrix} 1 & 2 \\ 3 & 4 \end{pmatrix} \begin{pmatrix} 5 \\ 6 \end{pmatrix} = \begin{pmatrix} 17 \\ 39 \end{pmatrix}$.

Corresponding to the formula $\mathbf{A}(x, y) = (ax + by, cx + dy)$, we have the matric equation $A \begin{pmatrix} x \\ y \end{pmatrix} = \begin{pmatrix} ax + by \\ cx + dy \end{pmatrix}$. If $\mathbf{A}$ and $\mathbf{B}$ are linear transformations in $\mathcal{R}^2$, then, for all (x, y), $(\mathbf{A} \circ \mathbf{B})(x, y) = \mathbf{A}(\mathbf{B}(x, y))$. The corresponding matrix equation is $(AB) \begin{pmatrix} x \\ y \end{pmatrix} = A \left(B \begin{pmatrix} x \\ y \end{pmatrix} \right)$, which can be regarded as an associative law in which A and B are two-by-two matrices and the right-hand factor is a column matrix.

This newly defined product, $\begin{pmatrix} a & b \\ c & d \end{pmatrix}\begin{pmatrix} x \\ y \end{pmatrix}$, follows the old rule that the entries in the product are inner products of rows of the left factor with columns of the right factor. This rule does not allow symbols such as $\begin{pmatrix} x \\ y \end{pmatrix}\begin{pmatrix} a & b \\ c & d \end{pmatrix}$, which are not defined.

Exercises

1. Write down the multiplicative inverse of each of the following: $\begin{pmatrix} 2 & 3 \\ 1 & 1 \end{pmatrix}$, $\begin{pmatrix} 5 & 7 \\ -2 & 3 \end{pmatrix}$, $\begin{pmatrix} 5 & 7 \\ 2 & 3 \end{pmatrix}$, $\begin{pmatrix} 0 & 1 \\ 1 & 0 \end{pmatrix}$.

2. Replace the system of equations
$$3x + 4y = 7,$$
$$x + \ y = 5$$
by a single matrix equation.

3. Solve the equation $\begin{pmatrix} 5 & 4 \\ 1 & 1 \end{pmatrix}\begin{pmatrix} x \\ y \end{pmatrix} = \begin{pmatrix} 2 \\ 3 \end{pmatrix}$ by multiplying both sides by $\begin{pmatrix} 5 & 4 \\ 1 & 1 \end{pmatrix}^{-1}$.

4. Assume that $ad - bc \neq 0$, and solve the equation
$$\begin{pmatrix} a & b \\ c & d \end{pmatrix}\begin{pmatrix} x \\ y \end{pmatrix} = \begin{pmatrix} k_1 \\ k_2 \end{pmatrix}.$$

5. Let $\mathbf{A}$ be the linear transformation with matrix $A = \begin{pmatrix} 1 & 2 \\ 2 & 4 \end{pmatrix}$. Find the kernel of $\mathbf{A}$ and describe it geometrically.

6. Find all solutions of $\begin{pmatrix} 1 & 2 \\ 2 & 4 \end{pmatrix}\begin{pmatrix} x \\ y \end{pmatrix} = \begin{pmatrix} 3 \\ 6 \end{pmatrix}$ and describe the set of solutions geometrically.

7. Let P be a parallelogram with vertices at $\mathbf{a}, \mathbf{b}, \mathbf{c}, \mathbf{d}$ in $\Re^2$. A translation maps P onto a parallelogram P^* with vertices at $\mathbf{o}, \mathbf{b} - \mathbf{a}, \mathbf{c} - \mathbf{a}, \mathbf{d} - \mathbf{a}$. Then P^* has the same oriented area as has P. Let $\mathbf{A}$ be a linear transformation in $\Re^2$ mapping P to Q and P^* to Q^*. Show that Q^* is the image of P^* under a translation, so Q^* and P^* have the same oriented area. Now deduce that the oriented area of $Q = \det \mathbf{A}$ times the oriented area of P.

8. Describe in geometric terms as clearly as you can the effect of the linear transformation corresponding to each of the following: $\begin{pmatrix} 1 & 0 \\ 0 & -1 \end{pmatrix}$, $\begin{pmatrix} 0 & 1 \\ 1 & 0 \end{pmatrix}$, $\begin{pmatrix} 1 & -1 \\ 3 & -3 \end{pmatrix}$, $\begin{pmatrix} 0 & -1 \\ 1 & 0 \end{pmatrix}$.

9. Find many matrices A such that $A^2 = A + I$.

§ 2. Linear Similarities in $\Re^2$

Let $A = \begin{pmatrix} a & b \\ c & d \end{pmatrix}$. By Theorem 5.19 (page 126), the corresponding linear transformation is a similarity of scale factor r iff $|(a, c)| = |(b, d)| = r$ and $ab +$

$cd = 0$. Geometrically speaking, $\mathbf{A}$ is a linear similarity iff it maps the triangle with vertices at $(0, 0)$, $(1, 0)$, $(0, 1)$ to an isosceles right triangle. The condition $ab + cd = 0$ puts (b, d) on the orthogonal complement of the line through $(0, 0)$ and (a, c). Thus (b, d) is a scalar multiple of $(-c, a)$. From $|(b, d)| = |(a, c)| = |(-c, a)|$, it follows that (b, d) can only be either $(-c, a)$ or $(c, -a)$.

Thus the matrix of a linear similarity of scale factor r can only be of the form $\begin{pmatrix} a & -c \\ c & a \end{pmatrix}$ or $\begin{pmatrix} a & c \\ c & -a \end{pmatrix}$, with $a^2 + c^2 = r^2$; and, for any $(a, c) \neq (0, 0)$, each of these matrices is the matrix of a linear similarity. This fits intuition very well: a linear similarity must map $(0, 0)$ to $(0, 0)$; once the image of $(1, 0)$ is chosen, there are only two intuitively acceptable locations for the image of $(0, 1)$.

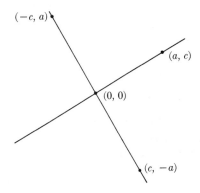

Since $\det \begin{pmatrix} a & -c \\ c & a \end{pmatrix} = a^2 + c^2 = r^2$, the corresponding similarity multiplies lengths by r and areas by r^2. Again, $\det \begin{pmatrix} a & c \\ c & -a \end{pmatrix} = -a^2 - c^2 = -r^2$.

The corresponding transformation multiplies lengths by r and areas by r^2, but multiplies oriented areas by $-r^2$. This fits with the fact that the corresponding similarity maps the counterclockwise angle from the positive horizontal axis to the positive vertical axis onto a clockwise angle.

A simple example of an orientation-reversing similarity is the congruence $\mathbf{H}$ with matrix $H = \begin{pmatrix} 1 & 0 \\ 0 & -1 \end{pmatrix}$ and formula

$$\mathbf{H}(x, y) = (x, -y).$$

The congruence $\mathbf{H}$ is called a *reflection* in the horizontal axis. The illustration shows a triangle and its image under $\mathbf{H}$.

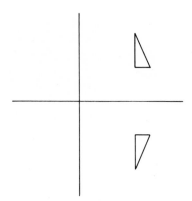

It is not physically possible to superimpose the triangle on its image by moving it in the plane; one must pick it up and turn it over. This raises a real doubt about whether the two triangles should be regarded as congruent. The mathematical answer is that H is an *improper* congruence.

Summary and Definition 6.5.   For $(a, b) \neq (0, 0)$, set $P(a, b) = \begin{pmatrix} a & -b \\ b & a \end{pmatrix}$ and $Q(a, b) = \begin{pmatrix} a & b \\ b & -a \end{pmatrix}$. The transformation $\mathbf{P}(a, b)$ is a **proper linear similarity**; the transformation $\mathbf{Q}(a, b)$ is an **improper linear similarity**. Each similarity has scale factor $\sqrt{a^2 + b^2}$. Every linear similarity in $\mathfrak{R}^2$ has a matrix of the form $P(a, b)$ or $Q(a, b)$.

The matrices $P(a, b)$ and $Q(a, b)$ satisfy the equations $P(a, b)H = Q(a, b)$ and $Q(a, b)H = P(a, b)$, where $H = \begin{pmatrix} 1 & 0 \\ 0 & -1 \end{pmatrix}$, as above. Thus each proper linear similarity is the composition of an improper linear similarity with $\mathbf{H}$, and each improper one is the composition of a proper one with $\mathbf{H}$. Since $\mathbf{H}$ is easily comprehended, this suggests that a thorough study of either proper or improper linear similarities would lead to an understanding of both types. The theorem below gives some grounds for a choice.

Theorem 6.8.   If $\mathbf{P}$ and $\mathbf{P}'$ are proper linear similarities, then $\mathbf{P} \circ \mathbf{P}' = \mathbf{P}' \circ \mathbf{P}$ and is a proper linear similarity. If $\mathbf{Q}$ and $\mathbf{Q}'$ are improper linear similarities, then probably $\mathbf{Q} \circ \mathbf{Q}' \neq \mathbf{Q}' \circ \mathbf{Q}$, but each is a proper linear similarity.

PROOF:

$$\begin{pmatrix} a & -b \\ b & a \end{pmatrix} \begin{pmatrix} a' & -b' \\ b' & a' \end{pmatrix} = \begin{pmatrix} aa' - bb' & -ab' - ba' \\ ba' + ab' & -bb' + aa' \end{pmatrix}$$

$$= \begin{pmatrix} a'' & -b'' \\ b'' & a'' \end{pmatrix} = P'',$$

and P'' is the matrix of a proper similarity unless $a'' = b'' = 0$. This would make $\det P'' = 0$, but $\det P'' = \det P \det P' \neq 0$. The commutativity is seen by observing that interchanging (a, b) and (a', b') does not change a'' or b''.

Now consider the product of two matrices of improper similarities:

$$\begin{pmatrix} a & b \\ b & -a \end{pmatrix} \begin{pmatrix} a' & b' \\ b' & -a' \end{pmatrix} = \begin{pmatrix} aa' + bb' & ab' - ba' \\ ba' - ab' & bb' + aa' \end{pmatrix} = \begin{pmatrix} c & -d \\ d & c \end{pmatrix}.$$

Again, $(c, d) \neq (0, 0)$ by a determinant argument, and the product is the matrix of a proper similarity. Interchanging the order of the factors gives $\begin{pmatrix} c & d \\ -d & c \end{pmatrix} \neq \begin{pmatrix} c & -d \\ d & c \end{pmatrix}$ unless $d = 0$, which is the case iff (a', b') is a scalar multiple of (a, b). [The "probably" in the theorem means that (a', b') is unlikely to be a scalar multiple of (a, b).] ∎

The only reason for displaying the products in the proof is the commutativity question. The composition of linear similarities is a linear similarity. It is proper if it has a positive determinant, improper if it has a negative determinant. Thus the theorem that the determinant of a product is the product of the determinants settles the propriety question.

Theorem 6.8 shows that the set of proper linear similarities is closed under composition and that composition is commutative in the set. These are very pleasant algebraic properties. Let C' be the set of all matrices of proper linear similarities in $\Re^2$: $I = \begin{pmatrix} 1 & 0 \\ 0 & 1 \end{pmatrix}$ is in C'. Furthermore, each matrix in C' has a multiplicative inverse in C'. For $(a, b) \neq (0, 0)$,

$$\begin{pmatrix} a & -b \\ b & a \end{pmatrix}^{-1} = \frac{1}{a^2 + b^2} \begin{pmatrix} a & b \\ -b & a \end{pmatrix},$$

which is in C'.

Interpreted geometrically, the composition inverse of the proper linear similarity mapping $(1, 0)$ to (a, b) is the proper linear similarity mapping $(1, 0)$ to $\left(\dfrac{a}{a^2 + b^2}, \dfrac{-b}{a^2 + b^2} \right)$. The original similarity has scale factor $\sqrt{a^2 + b^2}$; the inverse has scale factor

$$\sqrt{\left(\frac{a}{a^2 + b^2} \right)^2 + \left(\frac{-b}{a^2 + b^2} \right)^2} = \frac{1}{\sqrt{a^2 + b^2}}.$$

Of course the product of these two scale factors is 1, the scale factor of the identity mapping.

Theorem 6.9. Let C' be the set of all matrices of the form $\begin{pmatrix} a & -b \\ b & a \end{pmatrix}$, (a, b) in $\Re^2$, and $(a, b) \neq (0, 0)$. Let $\mathbf{C}'$ be the set of all proper linear similarities in $\Re^2$. The isomorphic algebraic systems $(\mathbf{C}'; \circ)$ and $(C'; \text{matrix multiplication})$ are commutative groups.

The commutativity of proper linear similarities leads to a very pleasant, purely geometric way of locating the image of a point under a proper linear similarity. Theorem 6.10 also confirms the intuitive feeling that a proper linear similarity is the composition of a dilation with a rotation around the origin.

Theorem 6.10.   Let $\mathbf{p}'$ be the image of $\mathbf{p}$ under the similarity $\mathbf{P}(a, b)$. If $b = 0$, then $\mathbf{p}' = a\mathbf{p}$. Otherwise the triangle $\mathbf{opp}'$ is the image of the triangle $\mathbf{o}(1, 0)(a, b)$ under a proper similarity with scale factor $r = \sqrt{a^2 + b^2}$.

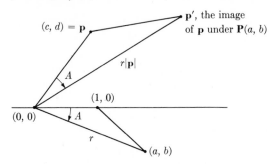

PROOF: To obtain the image of (c, d) under $\mathbf{P}(a, b)$, we look at the column matrix $\begin{pmatrix} a & -b \\ b & a \end{pmatrix}\begin{pmatrix} c \\ d \end{pmatrix}$. That is, we look at the first column of $\begin{pmatrix} a & -b \\ b & a \end{pmatrix}\begin{pmatrix} c & -d \\ d & c \end{pmatrix}$. By the commutativity of this product,

$$\begin{pmatrix} a & -b \\ b & a \end{pmatrix}\begin{pmatrix} c \\ d \end{pmatrix} = \begin{pmatrix} c & -d \\ d & c \end{pmatrix}\begin{pmatrix} a \\ b \end{pmatrix}.$$

The image of (c, d) under $\mathbf{P}(a, b)$ is the same as the image of (a, b) under $\mathbf{P}(c, d)$. Thus the proper similarity $\mathbf{P}(c, d)$ maps $(0, 0)$ to $(0, 0)$, $(1, 0)$ to (c, d), and (a, b) to $\mathbf{p}'$, the image of (a, b) under $\mathbf{P}(c, d)$ and also the image of (c, d) under $\mathbf{P}(a, b)$.   ∎

Exercises

1. Using straightedge and compasses, ruler and protractor, polar coordinate paper and a ruler, or any other appropriate tools, construct the following on the basis of Theorem 6.10.

   a. The images under $\mathbf{P}(3, 4)$ of $(1, 0)$, $(0, 1)$, $(1, 1)$, $(-1, 2)$, $(1, -1)$.

   b. The image under $\mathbf{P}(-2, 0)$ of $(1, 0)$, $(2, 3)$, $(-1, 1)$. What rotation is involved?

   c. The images under $\mathbf{P}(\frac{5}{13}, \frac{12}{13})$ of $(1, 0)$, $(\frac{3}{5}, \frac{4}{5})$, $(\frac{5}{13}, \frac{12}{13})$, $(-1, 0)$.

2. Show that $\begin{pmatrix} 0 & -1 \\ 1 & 0 \end{pmatrix}^2 = \begin{pmatrix} -1 & 0 \\ 0 & -1 \end{pmatrix} = -I$ and $\begin{pmatrix} 0 & -1 \\ 1 & 0 \end{pmatrix}^4 = I$. Interpret geometrically. What is $\begin{pmatrix} 0 & -1 \\ 1 & 0 \end{pmatrix}^{103}$? $\begin{pmatrix} 0 & -1 \\ 1 & 0 \end{pmatrix}^{-5}$?

3. Show that the cube of $P\left(-\dfrac{1}{2}, \dfrac{\sqrt{3}}{2}\right)$ is I. Interpret geometrically.

4. The question of whether there is any positive integer n such that $(P(\tfrac{3}{4}, \tfrac{4}{5}))^n = I$ is interesting and nontrivial. Explain the essence of the question.

5. Use the fact that $Q(0, 1)$ is the product of $P(0, 1)$ and H, in that order, to study the geometric effect of $Q(0, 1)$. Also study the similarity corresponding to $HP(0, 1)$.

6. Prove that the function $F: \begin{pmatrix} a & -b \\ b & a \end{pmatrix} \longrightarrow \begin{pmatrix} a & b \\ -b & a \end{pmatrix}$ is an isomorphism of $(C'; \cdot)$ to $(C'; \cdot)$. That is, prove that F is a one-to-one correspondence of C' to C' and that, for any A and B in C', $F(AB) = F(A)F(B)$.

7. Prove that, if (a, b) is on the unit circle, then $\begin{pmatrix} a & -b \\ b & a \end{pmatrix}^{-1} = \begin{pmatrix} a & b \\ -b & a \end{pmatrix}$.

Explain geometrically why this is as it should be.

8. For each of several points (a, b) not on the unit circle, and not $(0, 0)$, locate geometrically

$$\mathbf{q} = \left(\frac{a}{a^2 + b^2}, \frac{-b}{a^2 + b^2}\right).$$

Theorem 6.10 can be applied because the image of $\mathbf{q}$ under $\mathbf{P}(a, b)$ is $(1, 0)$, so that the triangle $\mathbf{oq}(1, 0)$ is similar to $\mathbf{o}(1, 0)(a, b)$.

9. Prove that, for all $\mathbf{a}$ and $\mathbf{b}$ in $\Re^2$,

$$\mathbf{H}(\mathbf{a} + \mathbf{b}) = \mathbf{H}(\mathbf{a}) + \mathbf{H}(\mathbf{b}).$$

Finish the sentence "$\mathbf{H}$ is an isomorphism of . . . ."

The set C' is almost in one-to-one correspondence with $\Re^2$. To each point (a, b) [except $(0, 0)$] corresponds the matrix $\begin{pmatrix} a & -b \\ b & a \end{pmatrix}$ in C'. Furthermore, C' is almost closed under addition:

$$\begin{pmatrix} a & -b \\ b & a \end{pmatrix} + \begin{pmatrix} a' & -b' \\ b' & a' \end{pmatrix} = \begin{pmatrix} a + a' & -b - b' \\ b + b' & a + a' \end{pmatrix},$$

which is in C' unless $a + a' = b + b' = 0$. That is, $P(a, b) + P(a', b')$ is in C' unless $P(a', b') = -P(a, b)$.

Suppose we extend the domain of the function P to include $(0, 0)$ and define $P(0, 0) = \begin{pmatrix} 0 & 0 \\ 0 & 0 \end{pmatrix}$. Then define C to be the set of all matrices $\begin{pmatrix} a & -b \\ b & a \end{pmatrix}$; in other words, enlarge C' to C by throwing in the O matrix. Geometrically this seems at first unreasonable, since $O = P(0, 0)$ is not the matrix of a similarity. Algebraically it is strikingly appropriate, for it is immediately clear that C is a commutative group under matrix addition, and that P is an isomorphism of $(\Re^2; +)$ to $(C; +)$.

The groups $(C; +)$ and $(C'; \cdot)$ are commutative, and matrix multiplication is distributive over matrix addition. In short, $(C; +, \cdot)$ is a field.

Let S be the set of all scalar matrices $\begin{pmatrix} a & 0 \\ 0 & a \end{pmatrix}$; S is closed under both addition and multiplication and thus $(S; +, \cdot)$ is a subfield. Furthermore, the mapping $\begin{pmatrix} a & 0 \\ 0 & a \end{pmatrix} \longrightarrow a$ is an isomorphism of this subfield to the real field. Thus we have a field of two-by-two matrices with a subfield isomorphic to the real field.

The simple fact that $(a, b) = a(1, 0) + b(0, 1)$ has been crucial for discussing linear transformations. Its analogue in the set C is

$$\begin{pmatrix} a & -b \\ b & a \end{pmatrix} = \begin{pmatrix} a & 0 \\ 0 & a \end{pmatrix} + \begin{pmatrix} 0 & -b \\ b & 0 \end{pmatrix}$$
$$= a \begin{pmatrix} 1 & 0 \\ 0 & 1 \end{pmatrix} + b \begin{pmatrix} 0 & -1 \\ 1 & 0 \end{pmatrix}$$
$$= aI + bJ.$$

In this field I is the multiplicative identity, playing the role that 1 plays in the real field; J is the matrix of the rotation mapping $(1, 0)$ to $(0, 1)$, and J^2 is the matrix of the rotation mapping $(1, 0)$ to $(-1, 0)$. Thus $J^2 = -I$. Either this field of matrices or its natural isomorph—a field of proper similarities in $\Re^2$ along with the 0 function—is a realization of the complex field.

Since the matrices in C are determined by their first columns, it is rather natural to define multiplication in $\Re^2$ in such a way that P is an isomorphism of $(\Re^2; +, \cdot)$ to $(C; +, \cdot)$. With their *complex product* defined by

$$(a, b)(c, d) = (ac - bd, ad + bc),$$

the points of $\Re^2$ are called *complex numbers*.

The set of complex numbers then can be taken to be the set of points of $\Re^2$, with the usual addition and with an extra operation called multiplication. To locate $(a, b)(c, d)$ geometrically, use Theorem 6.10. That is, apply to (c, d) the rotation and dilation which send $(1, 0)$ to (a, b).

Historically, complex numbers were used long before they were understood. If there were an imaginary number called i such that $i^2 = -1$, then, for any real a and b, $a + bi$ ought to be some sort of number. And if algebra is to look familiar it should be that

$$(a + bi)(c + di) = (ac + bdi^2) + (ad + bc)i$$
$$= (ac - bd) + (ad + bc)i.$$

Suppose for each real number a we set $a^* = (a, 0)$; in particular, then, $1^* = (1, 0)$ and $a^* = a(1, 0) = a1^*$, for all real a. Furthermore, set $i = (0, 1)$. Then, using the complex product defined above, we have

$$(0, b) = (0, 1)(b, 0) = ib^*,$$
$$(a, b) = (a, 0) + (0, b) = a^* + ib^*.$$

Multiplication of a point or complex number by i means applying the proper similarity mapping $(1, 0)$ to $(0, 1)$; but this similarity is just the rotation we have called $\times$:

$$\times(a, b) = (-b, a) = (0, 1)(a, b) = i(a, b).$$

Expressed just in terms of complex numbers,

$$i(a^* + ib^*) = -b^* + ia^*,$$
$$(a^* + ib^*)(c^* + id^*) = (a^*c^* - b^*d^*) + i(a^*d^* + b^*c^*).$$

The usual notation simply drops the stars and writes, for example, $3 + 4i$ for $3^* + 4^*i = (3, 4)$. Fortunately, scalar products work out properly: for real a, x, y, we have $a(x, y) = (ax, ay)$. We also have

$$a^*(x + iy) = (a, 0)(x, y) = (ax, ay) = ax + iay.$$

That is, for example, $3(4 + 2i) = 12 + 6i$ can be regarded as a scalar product of the real number 3 and the complex number $4 + 2i$, or as the complex product $(3 + 0i)(4 + 2i)$.

Regarding the point (a, b) as the complex number $z = a + bi$, we say that a is the *real* part of z and b is the *imaginary* part of z. The imaginary part of $3 + 7i$ is 7, not $7i$. *Imaginary* here is purely a technical term with no trace left of its original meaning.

In the language of complex numbers the reflection in the horizontal axis, **H**, is called the *conjugate mapping* and is denoted by an overbar. Thus the statement $\mathbf{H}(x, y) = (x, -y)$ becomes: if $z = x + iy$, then $\bar{z}$ (the conjugate of z) $= \overline{x + iy} = x - iy$. The absolute value mapping is unchanged: if $z = x + iy$, the absolute value of z is $|z| = \sqrt{x^2 + y^2}$.

Exercises

1. Prove that, for any two complex numbers z and w,
$$\overline{w + z} = \bar{w} + \bar{z},$$
$$\overline{wz} = \bar{w}\bar{z}.$$

2. For any complex number z, prove that both $z + \bar{z}$ and $z\bar{z}$ are real—that is, of the form $a + 0i$.

3. Prove that $z\bar{z} = |z|^2$.

4. For any complex number z [except 0], prove that $z^{-1} = \bar{z}/|z|^2$.

5. If $w = 2 + i$ and $z = 1 + 3i$, locate each of the following: $w + z$, wz, $\bar{w}$, $1/w = w^{-1}$, w^2, w^3, w^{-2}.

6. If $z = \frac{3}{5} + \frac{4}{5}i$, locate z^2, z^3, z^4, z^5, z^{-1}, and z^{-2}.

7. Consider the quadratic equation $\epsilon^2 - 4\epsilon + 5 = 0$.

a. Show that if 4, 5, and 0 are regarded as real numbers, there is no real number ϵ satisfying the equation.

b. Show that if 5 and 0 are regarded as the matrices $\begin{pmatrix} 5 & 0 \\ 0 & 5 \end{pmatrix}$ and $\begin{pmatrix} 0 & 0 \\ 0 & 0 \end{pmatrix}$, and 4 as either a real number or as $\begin{pmatrix} 4 & 0 \\ 0 & 4 \end{pmatrix}$, there are infinitely many matrices ϵ satisfying the equation.

c. Show that if 5 and 0 are regarded as the complex numbers $5 + 0i$ and $0 + 0i$, and 4 as either a real number or the complex number $4 + 0i$, there are just two complex numbers ϵ satisfying the equation.

8. Prove that if a two-by-two matrix M commutes with $\begin{pmatrix} 0 & -1 \\ 1 & 0 \end{pmatrix}$, the matrix corresponding to i, then M is in C. This shows that the field $(C; +, \cdot)$ is not a proper subfield of any larger field of two-by-two matrices.

§ 3. *The Circular Functions*

Given a point **a** on the unit circle in $\Re^2$, we can determine **a** by specifying an angle; the universal choice is to specify an angle from the positive horizontal axis to the ray **oa**. There is no universal agreement on which of the infinitely many possible angles to choose, nor on how to measure the angle chosen.

The Babylonians, having a number system partly based on 60 and knowing that the year has about 360 days, chose to divide a circle into 360 congruent arcs, each subtending a central angle of 1°. This system is still widely used, perhaps partly because of the tendency of printed tables to survive and partly because 360 has a conveniently large number of divisors. The U.S. Army prefers to divide a circle into 6400 *mils:* it is roughly true that on a circle of radius 1000 yards an arc of length 1 yard subtends a central angle of 1 mil.

Whatever system one adopts, the ultimate crucial question is how to determine the length of an arc of a circle. Euclid established the content of the statement that any similarity of scale factor r maps a circular arc of length l onto a circular arc of length rl. A consequence is that the ratio of the circumference to the length of the diameter is the same for all circles. This number has been called π since the 18th century.

Archimedes proved that $223/71 < \pi < 22/7$. The approximation $355/113$ was known by 1700 in both Europe and Japan. In 1761 Lambert proved that π is irrational. In 1882 Lindemann proved the much stronger statement that π is transcendental: π is not a root of any polymonial equation with rational coefficients. For example, if a, b, c, d are rational and not all 0, then $a\pi^3 + b\pi^2 + c\pi + d \neq 0$.

Later in this section we give the definition of arc length and prove the following theorem and some related inequalities. But first we shall apply the theorem, whose content is intuitively clear and familiar, to the geometry and algebra of the plane.

Theorem 6.11. 1. Each circular arc has a length, and a similarity of scale factor r maps an arc of length l onto an arc of length rl.

2. If **a**, **b**, **c** are on a circle, then the length of an arc from **a** to **c** is the sum of lengths of arcs from **a** to **b** and from **b** to **c**.

3. Define π to be the length of the upper arc of the unit circle from $(1, 0)$ to $(-1, 0)$. For each number t in the half-open interval $[0, 2\pi)$,

there is one and only one point on the unit circle, called $W(t)$, such that the counterclockwise arc from $(1, 0) = W(0)$ to $W(t)$ has length t.

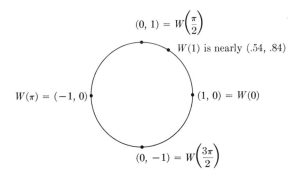

$(0, 1) = W\left(\dfrac{\pi}{2}\right)$

$W(1)$ is nearly $(.54, .84)$

$W(\pi) = (-1, 0)$

$(1, 0) = W(0)$

$(0, -1) = W\left(\dfrac{3\pi}{2}\right)$

This theorem has many immediate consequences. For example, the congruence with matrix $\begin{pmatrix} 0 & -1 \\ 1 & 0 \end{pmatrix}$ maps the quarter circle from $(1, 0)$ to $(0,1)$ onto the quarter circle from $(0, 1)$ to $(-1, 0)$. By statement 1, these arcs have the same length and, by 2 and 3, each has length $\pi/2$. The congruence with matrix $\begin{pmatrix} -1 & 0 \\ 0 & -1 \end{pmatrix}$ maps the upper half of the unit circle onto the lower half, establishing that the circumference of the unit circle is 2π. By 1, any circle of radius r has circumference $2\pi r$.

The theorem allows us to construct a *wrapping function* W, which assigns to each real number t a point $W(t)$ on the unit circle such that some directed arc from $(1, 0)$ to $W(t)$ has directed length t. Part 3 of the theorem defines W on the interval $[0, 2\pi)$. If n is a positive integer, then $2\pi n$ is n times the circumference of the unit circle and can be regarded as the directed length of the counterclockwise arc running n times around the circle from $(1, 0)$ back to $(1, 0)$. Thus we want $W(2\pi n) = (1, 0)$ for each integer $n \geq 0$.

Next, for any positive number t, set $t = 2\pi n + t_1$, where n is an integer and $0 \leq t_1 < 2\pi$. We want t to be the directed length of a counterclockwise arc from $(1, 0)$ to $W(t)$. An arc from $(1, 0)$ to $(1, 0)$ has length $2\pi n$, and the shortest counterclockwise arc from $(1, 0)$ to $W(t_1)$ has length t_1. Thus we want $W(t) = W(t_1)$.

We want to assign to each negative real t a point $W(t)$ on the unit circle in such a way that a *clockwise* arc from $(1, 0)$ to $W(t)$ has directed length t.

First consider t in the interval $(-2\pi, 0)$, so that $|t|$ is in $(0, 2\pi)$. The reflection $\mathbf{H}$ maps the shortest counterclockwise arc from $(1, 0)$ to $W(|t|)$ onto the shortest clockwise arc from $(1, 0)$ to $\mathbf{H}(W(|t|))$. Since $\mathbf{H}$ is a congruence, these arcs have the same length, but we want them to have directed lengths of opposite sign. Thus we want $W(t) = \mathbf{H}(W(|t|))$, at least if $-2\pi < t < 0$.

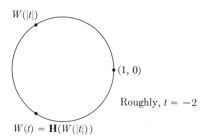

$W(|t|)$

$(1, 0)$

Roughly, $t = -2$

$W(t) = \mathbf{H}(W(|t|))$

For $t < -2\pi$ we can set $|t| = 2n\pi + t_1$, where n is a positive integer and $0 \leq t_1 < 2\pi$. Then $t = -2n\pi - t_1$ and, considering $-2n\pi$ as the directed length of an arc running clockwise n times from $(1, 0)$ to $(1, 0)$, we want

$$W(-2n\pi - t_1) = W(-t_1) = \mathbf{H}(W(t_1)).$$

Thus for any negative t we want

$$W(t) = \mathbf{H}(W(|t|)) = \mathbf{H}(W(-t)).$$

But since $\mathbf{H} = \mathbf{H}^{-1}$ this is equivalent to $\mathbf{H}(W(t)) = W(-t)$, and for all real t, $W(-t) = \mathbf{H}(W(t))$.

Finally, we note that this definition of $W(t)$ for $t < 0$ can be put in a form just like that for $t > 0$. If $t = -2n\pi - t_1$, where $0 < t_1 < 2\pi$, then also $t = -(2n + 2)\pi + 2\pi - t_1$ and $0 < 2\pi - t_1 < 2\pi$. The counterclockwise arc from $W(-t_1)$ to $(1, 0)$ has length t_1, and the counterclockwise arc from $(1, 0)$ to $W(2\pi - t_1)$ has length $2\pi - t_1$. Since $t_1 + 2\pi - t_1 = 2\pi$, we have

$$W(-t_1) = \mathbf{H}(W(t_1)) = W(2\pi - t_1).$$

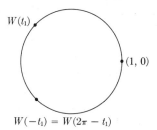

$W(t_1)$

$(1, 0)$

$W(-t_1) = W(2\pi - t_1)$

We summarize the foregoing discussion in the definition and theorem below.

Definition 6.6. The **wrapping function** W is defined on the real line as follows. Set $t = 2n\pi + t_1$, where n is an integer and $0 \leq t_1 \leq 2\pi$. Then $W(t) = W(t_1)$, the point on the unit circle at the end of a counterclockwise arc of length t_1 from $(1, 0)$.

Theorem 6.12. For all real t, $W(-t) = \mathbf{H}(W(t))$, and $W(t + 2n\pi) = W(t)$ for every integer n.

We have now in effect wrapped the real line around the unit circle, and can use it as a tape measure for measuring arcs. If $0 \le s_1 \le t_1 < 2\pi$, then by Theorem 6.11 the shortest counterclockwise arc from $W(s_1)$ to $W(t_1)$ has length $t_1 - s_1$. If $s = s_1 + 2n\pi$ and $t = t_1 + 2m\pi$, for integers n and m, then $t - s = t_1 - s_1 + 2(m - n)\pi$ and is the length of a directed arc from $W(s)$ to $W(t)$.

Definition 6.7. For real s and t, $t - s$ is the **radian measure** of an angle from the ray $oW(s)$ to the ray $oW(t)$, and is also the **radian measure** of any angle congruent to this by a proper congruence.

For example, 1 is the radian measure of an angle from $o(1, 0)$ to $oW(1)$. Approximately, $W(1) = (.54030, .84147)$. Some other angles from $o(1, 0)$ to $oW(1)$ have radian measures $1 + 2\pi, 1 - 2\pi, 1 + 4\pi, \ldots$

Definition 6.8. For each real t, let $\mathbf{R}_t$ be the proper linear congruence mapping $(1, 0)$ to $W(t)$, and let R_t be the corresponding matrix. [Equivalently, $R_t = P(W(t))$.] We shall call $\mathbf{R}_t$ a **rotation around o** through an angle of radian measure t.

Examples

1. $W\left(\dfrac{\pi}{2}\right) = W\left(\dfrac{5\pi}{2}\right) = (0, 1); R_{\pi/2} = R_{5\pi/2} = \begin{pmatrix} 0 & -1 \\ 1 & 0 \end{pmatrix}; \mathbf{R}_{\pi/2} = \mathbf{R}_{5\pi/2}$ and maps

   (x, y) to $\times(x, y) = (-y, x)$.

2. Approximately, $R_1 = \begin{pmatrix} .54 & -.84 \\ .84 & .54 \end{pmatrix}$.

3. $W(4\pi) = (1, 0); R_{4\pi} = \begin{pmatrix} 1 & 0 \\ 0 & 1 \end{pmatrix} = R_0$.

Remark: For some purposes a rotation through 4π is not the same as the identity function on $\mathcal{R}^2$. But our theory of congruences cannot distinguish them except to the extent that the different names $\mathbf{R}_{4\pi}$ and $\mathbf{R}_0$ are suggestive. To specify a congruence means to specify the image of each point; no description of a route is necessary.

Theorem 6.13. For all real t and s, $\mathbf{R}_t(W(s)) = W(s + t)$. Equivalently, regarding $W(t)$ and $W(s)$ as complex numbers and using the complex product,

$$W(t)W(s) = W(t + s).$$

The geometric statement of the theorem is a restatement of a special case of Theorem 6.10: $\mathbf{R}_t$ is a proper congruence mapping $(1, 0)$ to $W(t)$; the image of a point $\mathbf{p}$ under $\mathbf{R}_t$ is found geometrically from the fact that the triangle $\mathbf{opR}_t(\mathbf{p})$ is properly similar to the triangle $o(1, 0)W(t)$.

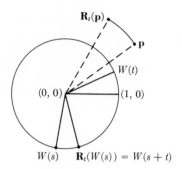

$W(s) \qquad \mathbf{R}_t(W(s)) = W(s+t)$

The form of the statement $W(t)W(s) = W(t+s)$ is very suggestive. For example the points $(\frac{3}{5}, \frac{4}{5}) = \frac{3}{5} + \frac{4}{5}i$ and $(\frac{5}{13}, \frac{12}{13}) = \frac{5}{13} + \frac{12}{13}i$ are on the unit circle, and there are real t and s such that $W(t) = (\frac{3}{5}, \frac{4}{5})$ and $W(s) = (\frac{5}{13}, \frac{12}{13})$. In principle we can read off appropriate t and s from our tape measure and very easily compute $(\frac{3}{5} + \frac{4}{5}i)(\frac{5}{13} + \frac{12}{13}i) = W(t+s)$, which is then located from the tape measure.

A glance at a fairly accurate tape gives, approximately, $\frac{3}{5} + \frac{4}{5}i = W(.93)$ and $\frac{5}{13} + \frac{12}{13}i = W(1.18)$. The product is $W(2.11)$ which, from the same tape, is approximately $(-.51 + .85i)$.

In order to use Theorem 6.13 for multiplying complex numbers it is convenient to have some tabulation of the function W. The one given here is extracted from a standard table called *Trigonometric Functions of Angles in Radians*.

In the diagram below, the number t is the radian measure of an angle from the ray $\mathbf{o}(1, 0)$ to the ray $\mathbf{o}W(t)$. If we set $W(t) = (c, s)$ then the cosine of this angle is

$$\frac{\langle (c, s), (1, 0)\rangle}{|(c, s)|\,|(1, 0)|} = c.$$

The *sine* of the same angle is s, which is also the cosine of an angle from $\mathbf{o}(0, 1)$ to $\mathbf{o}(c, s)$.

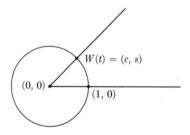

Definition 6.9. The functions **cosine** (cos) and **sine** (sin) are defined on R by: for all real t, $W(t) = (\cos t, \sin t)$. Also, $\cos t$ and $\sin t$ are the cosine and sine of any angle of radian measure t.

Table of Some Approximations [*correct to two decimal places*]

t	$W(t) = (\cos t, \sin t)$	t	$W(t) = (\cos t, \sin t)$
0	(1, 0)	1.0	(.54, .84)
0.1	(1.00, .10)	1.1	(.45, .89)
0.2	(.98, .20)	1.2	(.36, .93)
0.3	(.96, .30)	1.3	(.27, .96)
0.4	(.92, .39)	1.4	(.17, .99)
0.5	(.88, .48)	1.5	(.07, 1.00)
0.6	(.83, .56)	$\pi/2$	(0, 1)
0.7	(.76, .64)	1.6	($-.03$, 1.00)
0.8	(.70, .72)	1.7	($-.13$, .99)
0.9	(.62, .78)	1.8	($-.23$, .97)
		1.9	($-.32$, .95)

Exercises

1. Extend the table of the wrapping function by using the fact that

$$W\left(t + \frac{\pi}{2}\right) = \mathbf{R}_{\pi/2}(W(t)).$$

For example, using 1.57 as an approximation to $\pi/2$, 1.9 is nearly $(\pi/2) + .33$. From the table, $W(.33)$ is about $(.95, .33)$ and $\mathbf{R}_{\pi/2}(.95, .33) = (-.33, .95)$. Calculate approximations to $W(2)$, $W(2.5)$, $W(3)$.
2. Use the formula $W(2\pi - t) = W(-t) = \mathbf{H}(W(t))$ to calculate $W(4)$, $W(4.2)$, $W(6)$.
3. Below is a sketch of the graph of the sine function over the interval $[0, 2\pi]$. The first quarter of the curve looks congruent to the second quarter, and the first half to the second half. Give formulas for the congruences and prove they are correct. What congruence maps the graph of sine over $[0, 2\pi]$ onto the graph of sine over $[2\pi, 4\pi]$? over $[-2\pi, 0]$?

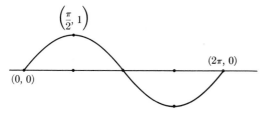

4. Sketch a good graph of the cosine function over the interval $[-\pi, 3\pi]$.
5. From Theorem 6.13, in the form $W(t)W(s) = W(t + s)$, follow, for example, $W(t)W(t) = W(2t)$, or $(W(t))^2 = W(2t)$, for all real t; also, $W(t)W(-t) = W(0) = 1 + 0i$, so that $(W(t))^{-1} = W(-t)$. Prove

De Moivre's Theorem: For all real t and every integer n, $(W(t))^n = W(nt)$. Alternatively,

$$(\cos t + i \sin t)^n = \cos nt + i \sin nt.$$

6. If $(a, b) \neq (0, 0)$, then, setting $r = |(a, b)|$,

$$(a, b) = r\left(\frac{a}{r}, \frac{b}{r}\right).$$

The point $(a/r, b/r)$ is on the unit circle and thus $(a, b) = rW(t)$ for some [many] real t. *Polar coordinates* of (a, b) are $r = |(a, b)|$ and any number t such that $W(t) = (a/r, b/r)$.

Find polar coordinates of $(3, 0)$, $(1, 1)$, $(0, 2)$, $(3, 4)$, $(-2, 5)$, $(5, -2)$.

7. If r and t are polar coordinates of (a, b), then

$$a + ib = rW(t) = r(\cos t + i \sin t).$$

The last expression is the *polar form* of the complex number $a + ib$. Use the polar form to compute the complex products $(1, 1)(0, 2) = (1 + i)(0 + 2i)$,

$$(3 + 4i)(-2 + 5i), \left(\frac{1}{\sqrt{2}} + \frac{i}{\sqrt{2}}\right)^2, \left(\frac{1}{\sqrt{2}} + \frac{i}{\sqrt{2}}\right)^{17}.$$

8. If $(rW(t))^3 = 8 + 0i = 8W(0)$, then $r^3 = 8$ and $W(3t) = W(0)$. Find all cube roots of $8 + 0i$.

9. Find all square roots of $2 - 2i$, all fourth roots of $81 + 0i$, and all fourth roots of $-81 + 0i$.

10. Find all cube roots of i.

11. Let $\epsilon = W(2\pi/5)$. Show that the set $\{1^*, \epsilon, \epsilon^2, \epsilon^3, \epsilon^4\}$ is closed under complex multiplication, and give the complete multiplication table.

12. If $\epsilon = W(2\pi/6)$, show that the set $\{1^*, \epsilon, \epsilon^2, \epsilon^3, \epsilon^4, \epsilon^5\}$ forms a group with respect to complex multiplication. List all subgroups.

13. Prove that the unit circle is a group with respect to complex multiplication, and that it has infinitely many finite subgroups.

14. For each integer n set $x_n = 2\pi n/5$, and let S be the set of all x_n. Show that S is a group with respect to addition. How is this group related to the group in Exercise 11?

15. For real a and b say that $a \equiv b \pmod{2\pi}$ if $a - b$ is an integer multiple of 2π. Prove that this relation, *congruence modulo* 2π, is an equivalence relation in $\Re$.

For each x_n in S [Exercise 14] let $[x_n]$ be the set of all x_m in S such that $x_m \equiv x_n \pmod{2\pi}$. Prove that S is the union of the sets $[x_0]$, $[x_1]$, $[x_2]$, $[x_3]$, $[x_4]$. Then define addition of these sets in such a way as to get a group isomorphic to the group of fifth roots of $1 + 0i$ [Exercise 11].

16. Use the definition $W(t) = (\cos t, \sin t)$, previous theorems of this section, and complex products as needed, to prove, for all real s and t, the following.

a. $\cos^2 t + \sin^2 t = 1$.

b. $\cos(-t) = \cos t$ and $\sin(-t) = -\sin t$.

c. For any integer n, $\cos(t + 2n\pi) = \cos t$ and $\sin(t + 2n\pi) = \sin t$.

d. *The addition theorems for sine and cosine:*

$$\cos(t + s) = \cos t \cos s - \sin t \sin s,$$
$$\sin(t + s) = \sin t \cos s + \cos t \sin s.$$

17. Prove that each of the statements below, for all real t and s, follows from the results of Exercise 16.

a. $\cos(t - s) = \cos t \cos s + \sin t \sin s$,

$$\sin(t - s) = \sin t \cos s - \cos t \sin s.$$

b. $\cos 2t = \cos^2 t - \sin^2 t$
$$= 1 - 2 \sin^2 t$$
$$= 2 \cos^2 t - 1,$$
$$\sin 2t = 2 \sin t \cos t.$$

c. $\sin t - \sin s = 2 \sin \dfrac{t - s}{2} \cos \dfrac{t + s}{2}.$

[*Hint:* From previous results, for real a and b,
$$\sin (a + b) - \sin (a - b) = 2 \sin b \cos a.]$$

d. $\cos t + \cos s = 2 \cos \dfrac{t + s}{2} \cos \dfrac{t - s}{2}.$

18. a. Without using any complex products or matrices, prove that the two segments shown have the same length.

b. From this derive
$$\cos (t - s) = \cos t \cos s + \sin t \sin s.$$

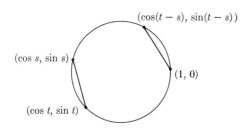

$(\cos(t - s),\ \sin(t - s))$

$(\cos s,\ \sin s)$

$(1, 0)$

$(\cos t,\ \sin t)$

c. From
$$\cos (t - s) = \cos t \cos s + \sin t \sin s,$$
together with $W(-s) = \mathbf{H}(W(s))$, follows
$$\cos (t + s) = \cos t \cos s - \sin t \sin s.$$

d. Use this and the relation between $W(t)$ and $W(t + (\pi/2))$ to derive
$$\sin (t + s) = \sin t \cos s + \cos t \sin s.$$

19. The function *tangent* (tan) is defined by $\tan = \sin/\cos$. Thus the domain of tan is the set of all real t such that $\cos t \neq 0$. Sketch the graph of tan over the open interval $(-\pi/2, \pi/2)$. Prove that for all t in the domain of tan, $\tan (t + \pi) = \tan t$.

20. Prove that if s, t, and $s + t$ are in the domain of tan, then
$$\tan (s + t) = \frac{\tan s + \tan t}{1 - \tan s \tan t}.$$

Why is it that, if $\tan s \tan t = 1$, then $\cos (s + t) = 0$?

21. From Exercise 17 (b), for all real t,
$$\sin^2 t = \frac{1 - \cos 2t}{2} \qquad \text{and} \qquad \cos^2 t = \frac{1 + \cos 2t}{2}.$$

For which t does $\sin t = \sqrt{\dfrac{1 - \cos 2t}{2}}$? $\cos t = \sqrt{\dfrac{1 + \cos 2t}{2}}$?

22. Find all real t in the interval $[0, 2\pi]$ such that

$$\tan\frac{t}{2} = \frac{1 - \cos t}{\sin t} = \frac{\sin t}{1 + \cos t}.$$

23. Functions F and G are defined on the interval $[-1, 1]$ by the graphs below, and are not defined anywhere else.

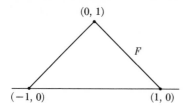

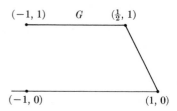

The domain of each function below is the set of all x for which the formula is defined. Sketch a graph of each on its domain.

a. $f(x) = F(3x)$.

b. $g(x) = F\left(\dfrac{x}{3}\right)$.

c. $h(x) = G(2x)$.

d. $j(x) = G(10x - 20)$.

e. $k(x) = 2F\left(\dfrac{x}{2}\right)$.

f. $l(x) = F(x + 1) + G(x - 1)$.

24. Sketch graphs of the following.

a. $y = \sin 2x$.

b. $y = 2\sin\dfrac{x}{2}$.

c. $y = \cos(x - \pi)$.

d. $y = \cos\left(x - \dfrac{\pi}{2}\right)$.

e. $y = 3\sin(2x + \pi)$.

f. $y = \sin(20\pi x)$.

We conclude this section by proving Theorem 6.11 and some basic inequalities which ultimately make it possible to calculate tables of sines and cosines. First, however, we introduce a usual notation.

Suppose we give a name to $W(1)$, say ϵ as a temporary one, and define ϵ^t for all real t by $\epsilon^t = W(t)$. Then $\epsilon^1 = W(1) = \epsilon$ and $\epsilon^0 = W(0) = 1 + 0i$. Both look reasonable. And, for all real t and s,

$$\epsilon^t\epsilon^s = W(t)W(s) = W(t + s) = \epsilon^{t+s}.$$

This also looks reasonable, and familiar, and shows the homomorphism of the additive group of the real numbers to the multiplicative group of the complex numbers on the unit circle in the most natural way.

The usual name for $W(1)$ is e^i, where $i = (0, 1)$ and e is the base for natural logarithms, defined in Chapters 8 and 9. [In Chapter 11 there is an explanation of why e^i is an appropriate name for $W(1)$; here we can give none.] For real t, e^{it} is defined to be

$$W(t) = \cos t + i \sin t,$$

so that $e^{it}e^{is} = e^{i(t+s)}$.

In particular, $e^{i\pi} = (-1, 0)$ and $e^{i\pi} + (1, 0) = (0, 0)$. In the usual language, writing x for $(x, 0)$, this becomes $e^{i\pi} + 1 = 0$, and is sometimes regarded as mysterious. In Chapter 9 we prove that, for all real x, e^x is positive, and that if $r > 0$ there is one and only one real x such that $e^x = r$. With the definition

$$e^{x+iy} = e^x e^{iy} \doteq e^x W(y),$$

the polar form of a complex number $\neq (0, 0)$ becomes strictly exponential: $(a, b) = e^{x+iy}$, where $e^x = |(a, b)|$ and y is any real number such that $W(y) = \dfrac{(a, b)}{|(a, b)|}$.

Any discussion of arc length uses the triangle inequality to get lower bounds, and some geometric inequality to get upper bounds. One possible choice is the lemma below.

Lemma. Consider an isosceles triangle with legs **ab** and **ac** of equal length. Let **d** be on ray **ab** but not in the segment **ab**, let **e** be on ray **ac** and either **e** = **c** or else **e** is not on the segment **ac**. Then $|\mathbf{d} - \mathbf{e}| > |\mathbf{b} - \mathbf{c}|$.

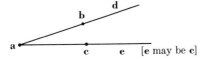

PROOF: Consider the similar triangle below.

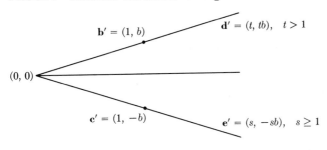

$$|\mathbf{b}' - \mathbf{c}'|^2 = 4b^2.$$
$$|\mathbf{d}' - \mathbf{e}'|^2 = (t - s)^2 + (tb + sb)^2$$
$$\geq (t + s)^2 b^2 > 4b^2,$$

since $t + s > 2$. ∎

Now let C be a circle, **a** and **b** points on C, and $C_{\mathbf{ab}}$ one of the arcs from **a** to **b**, considered as undirected and not containing any point twice unless $\mathbf{a} = \mathbf{b}$ and $C_{\mathbf{ab}}$ is the entire circle.

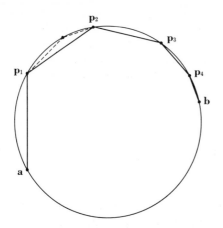

For any nonnegative integer n, select any n points in order on the arc, and draw chords as shown. The union of the chords is what we shall call a *broken-line approximation* to the arc. The length of the approximation is the sum of the lengths of the chords.

Let U be the set of all numbers l such that l is the length of a broken line approximation to $C_{\mathbf{ab}}$.

By the triangle inequality, from any broken-line approximation one can always derive a longer approximation by replacing a chord by two chords. Thus the set U has no largest member: for each l in U there are l' in U with $l' > l$.

However, U has an upper bound: for each l in U, $l < 4d$, where d is the diameter of the circle. To prove this we use the isosceles triangle lemma, first circumscribing about the circle a square of side d.

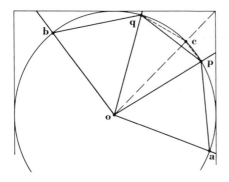

The length of each chord is less than that of the corresponding segment on the square. As in the diagram, it may be necessary to replace a chord **pq** by two chords **pc** and **cq**. The segments on the square do not overlap and their total length is at most $4d$.

By the least upper bound axiom U has a least upper bound. U has no largest member, but there is a smallest number which is larger than every member of U.

Definition 6.10. The **length of an arc of a circle** is the least upper bound of the set of all lengths of broken-line approximations to the arc.

PROOF OF THEOREM 6.11: [The proof will use some results of exercises on page 63.]

Let A be a circular arc and let A' be the image of A under a similarity S of scale factor r. If B is a broken-line approximation to A, of length l, then S maps B onto B', a broken-line approximation to A', of length rl. Furthermore, S^{-1} maps any approximation to A' onto an approximation to A.

Thus, if U is the set of all lengths of broken-line approximations to A and V is the set of all lengths of broken-line approximations to A', then $V = \{rl | l \text{ in } U\}$, from which lub $V = r(\text{lub } U)$: the length of A' is r times the length of A.

Next consider three points **a**, **b**, **c** on a circle.

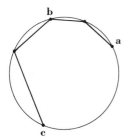

Let U be the set of all lengths of broken-line approximations to arc **ab**, V the set of all lengths of broken-line approximations to arc **bc**, and W the set of all lengths of broken-line approximations to arc **abc**.

If B is an approximation to **ab** of length l and B' an approximation to **bc** of length l', then the union of B and B' is an approximation to **abc**, of length $l + l'$. For each l in U and l' in V, $l + l'$ is in W; consequently, lub U + lub $V \le$ lub W.

Let C be an approximation to **abc**, of length L.

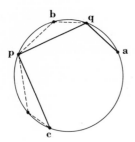

If **b** is not an end point of a chord of C, replace **pq** by **pb** and **bq** to get an approximation of length $> L$, which is the union of approximations to **ab** and to **bc**. If **b** is an end point of a chord of C, then C is the union of approximations to **ab** and to **bc**; replace any chord of C by two chords to get a longer approximation. This shows that for each L in W there are l in U and l' in V such that $l + l' > L$. Consequently, lub U + lub $V \geq$ lub W, and we now have lub U + lub V = lub W. Or,

length of arc **ab** + length of arc **bc** = length of arc **abc**.

Define π to be the length of the upper arc of the unit circle from $(1, 0)$ to $(0, 1)$, which finishes the proof of the first three parts of Theorem 6.11. We must still prove that for each t in the interval $[0, 2\pi)$ there is a point $W(t)$ such that the arc from $(1, 0)$ to $W(t)$ has length t. It is sufficient to prove this for t in the open interval $(0, \pi/2)$. [Why?]

Given t in $(0, \pi/2)$, let S be the set of all x between 0 and 1 such that the length of the arc from $(1, 0)$ to $(x, \sqrt{1 - x^2})$ is $< t$. Then S has 0 as a lower bound; let g be the greatest lower bound of S. We shall prove that the length of the arc from $(1, 0)$ to $(g, \sqrt{1 - g^2})$ is neither $< t$ nor $> t$, and consequently is t.

The proof involves one technical detail whose proof we postpone: given x with $0 < x < 1$ and given $\epsilon > 0$, then, for all u close enough to x, the arc from $(x, \sqrt{1 - x^2})$ to $(u, \sqrt{1 - u^2})$ has length $< \epsilon$.

Assuming the validity of this, let x be in S and let l be the length of the arc from $(1, 0)$ to $(x, \sqrt{1 - x^2})$. By definition of S, $l < t$; set $t - l = \epsilon > 0$. For $u < x$, but close enough to x, the arc from $(x, \sqrt{1 - x^2})$ to $(u, \sqrt{1 - u^2})$ has length $< \epsilon$, and hence the arc from $(1, 0)$ to $(u, \sqrt{1 - u^2})$ has length $< t$. For each x in S there is some u in S with $u < x$, and S has no smallest member. If g, the greatest lower bound of S were in S, it would be the smallest member of S. Consequently g is not in S and the length of the arc from $(1, 0)$ to $(g, \sqrt{1 - g^2})$ is not $< t$.

Suppose the arc length from $(1, 0)$ to $(g, \sqrt{1 - g^2})$ were $> t$, say equal to $t + \epsilon$ for $\epsilon > 0$. Then, by the technical detail [below], there would be some $u > g$ with the length of the arc from $(1, 0)$ to $(u, \sqrt{1 - u^2}) > t$. Also, then, for any x such that $g < x < u$, the length of the arc from $(1, 0)$ to $(x, \sqrt{1 - x^2}) >$ the length of the arc from $(1, 0)$ to $(u\sqrt{1 - u^2}) > t$. This would make u a lower bound of S with $u > g$, a contradiction.

Now for the technical detail.

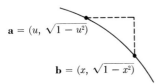

$\mathbf{a} = (u, \sqrt{1 - u^2})$

$\mathbf{b} = (x, \sqrt{1 - x^2})$

By the isosceles triangle inequality, the length of arc $\mathbf{ab}$ is less than the sum of the lengths of the dotted segments, which is $|x - u| + |\sqrt{1 - u^2} - \sqrt{1 - x^2}|$.

For $0 < a < b$, the inequality

$$\sqrt{b} - \sqrt{a} < \sqrt{b - a}$$

is equivalent to

$$b + a - 2\sqrt{ba} < b - a,$$
$$a < \sqrt{ba},$$

and

$$a^2 < ba,$$

which is true. Thus,

$$|\sqrt{1 - u^2} - \sqrt{1 - x^2}| < \sqrt{|x^2 - u^2|}$$
$$= \sqrt{|x + u|\,|x - u|}.$$

For x and u between 0 and 1, $\sqrt{x + u} < \sqrt{2}$. If $|x - u| < \epsilon^2/8$, then $\sqrt{|x - u|} < \epsilon/2\sqrt{2}$, and $\sqrt{|x^2 - u^2|} < \epsilon/2$.

Given $\epsilon > 0$, if x and u are between 0 and 1 and $|x - u| <$ the smaller of $\epsilon/2$ and $\epsilon^2/8$, then

$$|x - u| + |\sqrt{1 - u^2} - \sqrt{1 - x^2}| < \frac{\epsilon}{2} + \frac{\epsilon}{2},$$

which completes the technical detail and the proof of Theorem 6.11. ∎

For $0 < t < \pi/2$, consider the diagram below.

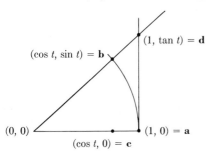

$(\cos t, \sin t) = \mathbf{b}$

$(1, \tan t) = \mathbf{d}$

$(0, 0)$

$(\cos t, 0) = \mathbf{c}$

$(1, 0) = \mathbf{a}$

The point called $(1, \tan t)$ is a scalar multiple of $(\cos t, \sin t)$. Since its first coordinate is 1, the scalar factor is $1/\cos t$ and the second coordinate is $\sin t/\cos t = \tan t$. We have

$$|\mathbf{b} - \mathbf{c}| < |\mathbf{b} - \mathbf{a}| < t < |\mathbf{d} - \mathbf{a}|,$$

or

$$\sin t < \sqrt{(\cos t - 1)^2 + \sin^2 t} < t < \tan t.$$

The second inequality is equivalent to

$$(\cos t - 1)^2 + \sin^2 t < t^2,$$

and to

$$2 - 2\cos t < t^2.$$

Thus, for $0 < t < \pi/2$, $\cos t > 1 - (t^2/2)$, and $t \cos t > t - (t^3/2)$. From the last inequality and $\sin t/\cos t > t$, we get

$$\sin t > t \cos t > t - \frac{t^3}{2}.$$

Theorem 6.14. If $t \neq 0$ and $|t| < \pi/2$, then

$$1 - \frac{t^2}{2} < \cos t < 1,$$

$\sin t$ is strictly between t and $t - (t^3/2)$, and

$$1 - \frac{t^2}{2} < \frac{\sin t}{t} < 1.$$

PROOF: The theorem was proved above for $0 < t < \pi/2$. Since $\cos(-t) = \cos t$, no change is needed for t negative in the cosine inequality. From $t - (t^3/2) < \sin t < t$, for $0 < t < \pi/2$, it follows that

$$-t - \frac{(-t)^3}{2} > -\sin t > -t,$$

$$-t - \frac{(-t)^3}{2} > \sin(-t) > (-t),$$

and

$$1 - \frac{(-t)^2}{2} < \frac{\sin(-t)}{-t} < 1. \qquad \blacksquare$$

Theorem 6.14 is strong enough to establish some of the entries in the table on page 171. For example, $1 - ((0.1)^2/2) < \cos(0.1) < 1$, or $.995 < \cos(0.1) < 1$; and, $0.1 - ((0.1)^3/2) < \sin(0.1) < 0.1$, or $.0995 < \sin(0.1) < 0.1$. Correct to two decimal places, $W(0.1) = (1.00, .10)$.

For $t = \frac{1}{2}$ we get $\frac{7}{8} < \cos\frac{1}{2} < 1$ and $\frac{7}{16} < \sin\frac{1}{2} < \frac{1}{2}$. This is compatible with, but does not establish that, $W(\frac{1}{2}) = (.88, .48)$ correct to two decimal places.

Corollary to Theorem 6.14. Let $\{t_n\}$ be any sequence converging to 0 but with $t_n \neq 0$ for all n. Then the sequence $\left\{\dfrac{\sin t_n}{t_n}\right\}$ converges to 1. From $\{t_n\}$ delete any terms t_n with $|t_n| \geq \pi$. [At most, a finite number of terms are deleted.] Then also $\left\{\dfrac{t_n}{\sin t_n}\right\}$ converges to 1.

Exercises

1. From $\sin \pi/4 < \pi/4 < \tan \pi/4$, deduce $2\sqrt{2} < \pi < 4$.
2. Prove that $W\,(\pi/6) = (\sqrt{3}/2,\ 1/2)$, and that $3 < \pi < 2\sqrt{3}$.
3. From Exercise 22, page 174,

$$\tan \frac{\pi}{12} = \frac{\sin \dfrac{\pi}{6}}{1 + \cos \dfrac{\pi}{6}}.$$

From this, derive $\tan \pi/12 = 2 - \sqrt{3}$, $\sin \pi/12 = \sqrt{2 - \sqrt{3}}/2$, $\cos \pi/12 = 1/2\sqrt{2 - \sqrt{3}}$, and $6\sqrt{2 - \sqrt{3}} < \pi < 12(2 - \sqrt{3})$.
4. Give a formal proof of the first part of the Corollary to Theorem 6.14. How does the rest of the corollary follow?
5. Prove from Exercise 3 that

$$\cos \frac{\pi}{12} = \frac{\sqrt{2 + \sqrt{3}}}{2}.$$

Then, use the fact that for all real t,

$$\cos^2 t = \frac{1 + \cos (2t)}{2}$$

to deduce

$$\cos \frac{\pi}{24} = \frac{\sqrt{2 + \sqrt{2 + \sqrt{3}}}}{2}.$$

6. Is there a simple formula for $\cos \pi/3 \cdot 2^n$ for every positive integer n? Is there a similar formula for $\cos t/2^n$ for any t such that $0 \leq t < \pi/2$?

§ 4. *Miscellaneous Examples*

In the last section we dropped improper similarities in favor of the proper ones, whose algebra is more pleasing. Consider now an improper linear similarity $\mathbf{Q}(a, b)$ with matrix

$$\begin{pmatrix} a & b \\ b & -a \end{pmatrix} = \begin{pmatrix} a & -b \\ b & a \end{pmatrix}\begin{pmatrix} 1 & 0 \\ 0 & -1 \end{pmatrix} = P(a, b)H.$$

With $r = |(a, b)|$ and any t such that $\cos t = a/r$ and $\sin t = b/r$,

$$\begin{pmatrix} a & b \\ b & -a \end{pmatrix} = \begin{pmatrix} r & 0 \\ 0 & r \end{pmatrix}\begin{pmatrix} \cos t & \sin t \\ \sin t & -\cos t \end{pmatrix}\begin{pmatrix} 1 & 0 \\ 0 & -1 \end{pmatrix} = D_r R_t H.$$

Forget the dilation for the moment and consider the improper congruence $\mathbf{K} = \mathbf{R}_t \circ \mathbf{H}$. As a linear congruence this maps the unit circle onto the unit circle: $\mathbf{H}$ maps $W(s)$ to $W(-s)$, and $\mathbf{R}_t$ maps this to $W(-s + t)$. In particular, $\mathbf{H}(W(\tfrac{1}{2}t)) = W(-\tfrac{1}{2}t)$ and $\mathbf{R}_t(W(-\tfrac{1}{2}t)) = W(-\tfrac{1}{2}t + t) = W(\tfrac{1}{2}t)$. Thus $\mathbf{K}$ maps $W(\tfrac{1}{2}t)$ to itself, and of course any scalar multiple $kW(\tfrac{1}{2}t)$ to $kW(\tfrac{1}{2}t)$; $\mathbf{K}$ maps each point of the line through $\mathbf{o}$ and $\mathbf{a} = W(\tfrac{1}{2}t)$ to itself.

What is $\mathbf{K}(\mathbf{b})$ for $\mathbf{b} = \times\mathbf{a} = W(\tfrac{1}{2}t + \tfrac{1}{2}\pi)$? Well, $\mathbf{H}(\mathbf{b}) = W(-\tfrac{1}{2}t - \tfrac{1}{2}\pi)$, and $\mathbf{R}_t$ maps this to

$$W(\tfrac{1}{2}t - \tfrac{1}{2}\pi) = W(\tfrac{1}{2}t + \tfrac{1}{2}\pi - \pi) = -W(\tfrac{1}{2}t + \tfrac{1}{2}\pi) = -W(\mathbf{b}).$$

Now $\mathbf{a}$ and $\mathbf{b}$ form a proper orthogonal basis for $\mathR^2$: $\mathbf{K}(\mathbf{a}) = \mathbf{a}$ and $\mathbf{K}(\mathbf{b}) = -\mathbf{b}$. Each point of $\mathR^2$ is a linear combination of $\mathbf{a}$ and $\mathbf{b}$ and, since $\mathbf{K}$ is linear, $\mathbf{K}(u\mathbf{a} + v\mathbf{b}) = u\mathbf{a} - v\mathbf{b}$.

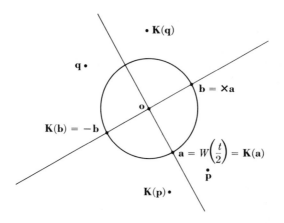

The congruence $\mathbf{K}$, with matrix $\begin{pmatrix} \cos t & -\sin t \\ \sin t & \cos t \end{pmatrix}$, relative to the usual basis, is a reflection in the line $\mathbf{oa}$. Geometrically $\mathbf{K}$ looks just like $\mathbf{H}$, provided one looks at $\mathbf{K}$ from the right viewpoint.

To do this algebraically use coordinates $\bar{x} = x_\mathbf{a}$ and $\bar{y} = y_\mathbf{a}$. Then $\bar{x}(u\mathbf{a} + v\mathbf{b}) = u$ and $\bar{y}(u\mathbf{a} + v\mathbf{b}) = v$.

[To see this, recall that $\bar{x}(\mathbf{p})$ is the directed distance of $\mathbf{p}$ from the orthogonal complement of $\mathbf{oa}$, which is defined to be $\dfrac{\langle \mathbf{a}, \mathbf{b} \rangle}{|\mathbf{a}|} = \langle \mathbf{a}, \mathbf{p} \rangle$, since $|\mathbf{a}| = 1$. Now

$$\langle \mathbf{a}, u\mathbf{a} + v\mathbf{b} \rangle = u\langle \mathbf{a}, \mathbf{a} \rangle + v\langle \mathbf{a}, \mathbf{b} \rangle = u1 + v0 = u.$$

Similarly, $\bar{y}(u\mathbf{a} + v\mathbf{b}) = v$.]

Suppose we understand that $[u, v] = u\mathbf{a} + v\mathbf{b}$. In particular, $[1, 0] = \mathbf{a}$ and $[0, 1] = \mathbf{b}$. In this language, $\mathbf{K}[1, 0] = [1, 0]$ and $\mathbf{K}[0, 1] = [0, -1]$.

The matrix of **K** relative to *this* coordinate system, is $\begin{pmatrix} 1 & 0 \\ 0 & -1 \end{pmatrix} = H$. For all u and v,

$$\mathbf{K}[u, v] = [u, -v].$$

Relative to the usual basis the matrix of **K** is $K = \begin{pmatrix} \cos t & \sin t \\ \sin t & -\cos t \end{pmatrix}$, but relative to the most natural basis to use in connection with **K** the matrix of **K** is H.

If we set $\mathbf{S} = \mathbf{D}_r \circ \mathbf{K}$, then the matrix of **S** relative to the usual basis is

$$D_r K = \begin{pmatrix} r \cos t & r \sin t \\ r \sin t & -r \cos t \end{pmatrix},$$

and **S** maps **a** to $r\mathbf{a}$ and **b** to $-r\mathbf{b}$. Relative to the basis $(\mathbf{a}, \mathbf{b})$ the matrix of **S** is $\begin{pmatrix} r & 0 \\ 0 & -r \end{pmatrix} = D_r H$. [Because $\mathbf{D}_r$ maps **a** to $r\mathbf{a}$ and **b** to $r\mathbf{b}$ for all **a** and **b**, relative to *any* basis the matrix of $\mathbf{D}_r$ is $\begin{pmatrix} r & 0 \\ 0 & r \end{pmatrix}$.]

Nothing more need be said about the geometric effect of improper linear congruences in $\mathcal{R}^2$, but there is a far-reaching generalization. The reason that **K** above has such a simple matrix relative to the basis $(\mathbf{a}, \mathbf{b})$ is that $\mathbf{K}(\mathbf{a}) = \mathbf{a}$ and $\mathbf{K}(\mathbf{b}) = -\mathbf{b}$.

If **c** and **d** are any two linearly independent points in $\mathcal{R}^2$, then each **p** in $\mathcal{R}^2$ has a unique representation: $\mathbf{p} = u\mathbf{c} + v\mathbf{d}$. Let **A** be any linear transformation in $\mathcal{R}^2$. Then $\mathbf{A}(\mathbf{c}) = a\mathbf{c} + c\mathbf{d}$ for some numbers a and c, and $\mathbf{A}(\mathbf{d}) = b\mathbf{c} + d\mathbf{d}$ for some b and d. Relative to the basis $(\mathbf{c}, \mathbf{d})$ the matrix of **A** is $\begin{pmatrix} a & b \\ c & d \end{pmatrix}$. In general, $\langle \mathbf{c}, \mathbf{d} \rangle \neq 0$ and the basis is not orthogonal. But the essential equation, $\mathbf{A}(u\mathbf{c} + v\mathbf{d}) = u\mathbf{A}(\mathbf{c}) + v\mathbf{A}(\mathbf{d})$, is unchanged. We have

$$\mathbf{A}(u\mathbf{c} + v\mathbf{d}) = u(a\mathbf{c} + c\mathbf{d}) + v(b\mathbf{c} + d\mathbf{d})$$
$$= (ua + vb)\mathbf{c} + (uc + vd)\mathbf{d},$$

or, in matrix formulation,

$$\begin{pmatrix} a & b \\ c & d \end{pmatrix} \begin{bmatrix} u \\ v \end{bmatrix} = \begin{bmatrix} au + bv \\ cu + dv \end{bmatrix}.$$

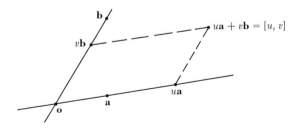

In this *oblique* system the coordinates u and v are *not* directed distances from the axes; they must be measured parallel to the axes.

For example, let $\mathbf{A}$ be the linear transformation whose matrix, relative to the usual coordinate system, is $A = \begin{pmatrix} 4 & -2 \\ 1 & 1 \end{pmatrix}$. Then, for all (x, y),

$$\mathbf{A}(x, y) = (4x - 2y, x + y).$$

Clearly $\mathbf{A}$ is not a similarity:

$$\mathbf{A}(1, 1) = (2, 2) = 2(1, 1),$$
$$\mathbf{A}(2, 1) = (6, 3) = 3(2, 1).$$

Setting $\mathbf{c} = (1, 1)$ and $\mathbf{d} = (2, 1)$, $\mathbf{c}$ and $\mathbf{d}$ are linearly independent: $\mathbf{A}(\mathbf{c}) = 2\mathbf{c}$ and $\mathbf{A}(\mathbf{d}) = 3\mathbf{d}$. For all real u and v,

$$\mathbf{A}(u\mathbf{c} + v\mathbf{d}) = u\mathbf{A}(\mathbf{c}) + v\mathbf{A}(\mathbf{d}) = 2u\mathbf{c} + 3v\mathbf{d}.$$

Relative to the basis $(\mathbf{c}, \mathbf{d})$ the matrix of $\mathbf{A}$ is $\begin{pmatrix} 2 & 0 \\ 0 & 3 \end{pmatrix}$.

The numbers 2 and 3 are called *eigenvalues* or *characteristic values* of $\mathbf{A}$. The points $(1, 1)$ and $(2, 1)$ [or more generally, (t, t) and $(2s, s)$ for any t and $s \neq 0$] are called *eigenvectors* or *characteristic vectors* of $\mathbf{A}$.

> **Definition 6.11.** Let $\mathbf{A}$ be any linear transformation, not necessarily in $\Re^2$. If $\mathbf{p} \neq \mathbf{o}$ and, for some real λ, $\mathbf{A}(\mathbf{p}) = \lambda\mathbf{p}$, then λ is an **eigenvalue** of $\mathbf{A}$ and $\mathbf{p}$ an **eigenvector** of $\mathbf{A}$ corresponding to λ.

If $\mathbf{A}(\mathbf{p}) = \lambda\mathbf{p}$, then for any scalar k, $\mathbf{A}(k\mathbf{p}) = k\mathbf{A}(\mathbf{p}) = k(\lambda\mathbf{p}) = \lambda(k\mathbf{p})$. Thus any scalar multiple of an eigenvector, except $\mathbf{o}$, is an eigenvector.

Example

Let $\mathbf{B}$ have the matrix $B = \begin{pmatrix} 1 & 3 \\ 2 & -4 \end{pmatrix}$, relative to the usual basis. Are there any number λ and point $\mathbf{p}$ such that $\mathbf{B}(\mathbf{p}) = \lambda\mathbf{p}$?

Now $\mathbf{B}(p_1, p_2) = (p_1 + 3p_2, 2p_1 - 4p_2)$. Can $(p_1 + 3p_2, 2p_1 - 4p_2) = (\lambda p_1, \lambda p_2)$ for some p_1, p_2 and λ? The equations to be solved are

$$(1) \quad \begin{aligned} (1 - \lambda)p_1 + 3p_2 &= 0, \\ 2p_1 - (4 + \lambda)p_2 &= 0. \end{aligned}$$

For each λ, an equivalent system is

$$(2) \quad \begin{aligned} p_1 - \left(2 + \frac{\lambda}{2}\right) p_2 &= 0, \\ \left(3 - (\lambda - 1)\left(2 + \frac{\lambda}{2}\right)\right) p_2 &= 0. \end{aligned}$$

Unless the coefficient of p_2 in the last equation is 0, the unique solution is $(p_1, p_2) = (0, 0)$, which is not an eigenvector.

Thus the only possible eigenvalues are λ such that $3 - (\lambda - 1)(2 + (\lambda/2)) = 0$, or $\lambda^2 + 3\lambda - 10 = 0$. Possible eigenvalues then are $\lambda_1 = 2$, $\lambda_2 = -5$.

Using $\lambda_1 = 2$, Equations (2) become

$$p_1 - 3p_2 = 0,$$
$$0p_2 = 0.$$

Any scalar multiple of $(3, 1)$ is an eigenvector corresponding to the eigenvalue 2.

With $\lambda_2 = -5$, we have

$$p_1 + \tfrac{1}{2}p_2 = 0,$$
$$0p_2 = 0.$$

Any scalar multiple of $(-1, 2)$ is an eigenvector corresponding to the eigenvalue -5.

Check: $\mathbf{B}(3, 1) = (6, 2) = 2(3, 1)$,

$\mathbf{B}(-1, 2) = (5, -10) = -5(-1, 2)$.

For any u and v, $\mathbf{B}(u(3, 1) + v(-1, 2)) = 2u(3, 1) - 5v(-1, 2)$. Relative to the basis $((3, 1), (-1, 2))$, the matrix of $\mathbf{B}$ is $\begin{pmatrix} 2 & 0 \\ 0 & -5 \end{pmatrix}$.

The eigenvalues 2 and -5 can be found much more elegantly. Suppose, for some $(x, y) \neq (0, 0)$,

$$B\begin{pmatrix} x \\ y \end{pmatrix} = \lambda \begin{pmatrix} x \\ y \end{pmatrix} = \lambda I \begin{pmatrix} x \\ y \end{pmatrix}.$$

Then $(B - \lambda I) \begin{pmatrix} x \\ y \end{pmatrix} = \begin{pmatrix} 0 \\ 0 \end{pmatrix}$. Since $(x, y) \neq (0, 0)$, the transformation corresponding to $B - \lambda I$ is not one-to-one and has no inverse. Thus the matrix $B - \lambda I$ has no multiplicative inverse, and consequently $\det (B - \lambda I) = 0$.

But $B - \lambda I = \begin{pmatrix} 1 - \lambda & 3 \\ 2 & -4 - \lambda \end{pmatrix}$ and

$$\det \begin{pmatrix} 1 - \lambda & 3 \\ 2 & -4 - \lambda \end{pmatrix} = \lambda^2 + 3\lambda - 10 = (\lambda - 2)(\lambda + 5).$$

Exercises

1. With $\mathbf{B}$ as in the preceding example, locate several linear combinations of $(3, 1)$ and $(-1, 2)$ and their images under $\mathbf{B}$.
2. If $\mathbf{A}(x, y) = (x, x + 2y)$ for all (x, y), show that $\mathbf{A}$ has two eigenvalues and find corresponding eigenvectors. What is the matrix of $\mathbf{A}$ relative to a basis of two linearly independent eigenvectors? How many answers are there to this question?
3. Let $R_t = \begin{pmatrix} \cos t & -\sin t \\ \sin t & \cos t \end{pmatrix}$. Prove that $\det (R_t - \lambda I) > 0$ for all λ unless $R_t = \begin{pmatrix} 1 & 0 \\ 0 & 1 \end{pmatrix}$ or $\begin{pmatrix} -1 & 0 \\ 0 & -1 \end{pmatrix}$.
4. Prove that if $\mathbf{A}$ corresponds to $\begin{pmatrix} 1 & 1 \\ 0 & 1 \end{pmatrix}$ relative to the usual basis, then $\mathbf{A}$ has only one eigenvalue and only one linearly independent eigenvector.

   5. Let **A** have matrix $\begin{pmatrix} 1 & 3 \\ -2 & 1 \end{pmatrix}$ relative to the usual basis. Prove that **A** is not
   a similarity and has no eigenvectors. Study the geometric effect of **A** as best
   you can.

   6. Describe in lucid detail the geometric effect of the linear transformation
   mapping $(1, 0)$ to $(3, -4)$ and $(0, 1)$ to $(-4, -3)$.

   7. The original reason for our studying linear transformations was the theorem
   that every similarity is a composition $T \circ \mathbf{S}$, where T is a translation in the
   range space and $\mathbf{S}$ is a linear similarity. Prove that every similarity F with
   domain $\Re^2$ and range a subset of $\Re^2$ has a formula of one of two sorts. Either,
   for all (x, y) in $\Re^2$,

   $$F(x, y) = (ax - by + h, bx + ay + k),$$

   for some (h, k) and some $(a, b) \neq (0, 0)$; or else, for all (x, y) in $\Re^2$,

   $$F(x, y) = (ax + by + h, bx - ay + k),$$

   for some (h, k) and some $(a, b) \neq (0, 0)$.

   8. Prove, using the explicit formulas above, that every similarity with domain $\Re^2$
   and range a subset of $\Re^2$ actually maps $\Re^2$ onto $\Re^2$.

   9. Let

   $$F = \mathbf{R}_{\pi/4} \circ T_{(1,2)} \circ \mathbf{R}_{\pi/2}.$$

   Find a translation T and linear similarity $\mathbf{S}$ such that $F = T \circ \mathbf{S}$.

   10. Write $\mathbf{R}_t \circ T_\mathbf{a}$ in the form $T \circ \mathbf{S}$.

   11. Give a formula for the congruence which rotates the plane through an angle
   of radian measure $\pi/6$ around the point $(5, 7)$.

   12. Give a formula for a reflection in the line $3x - 2y = 0$.

   13. Give a formula for a reflection in the line $3x - 2y + 10 = 0$.

   14. Let $F(x, y) = (5x - 12y + 10, 12x + 5y - 17)$ for all (x, y). Prove there is
   one and only one point (x, y) such that $F(x, y) = (x, y)$. Then describe F
   geometrically.

   15. Let F be any proper similarity in $\Re^2$. For some $(a, b) \neq (0, 0)$ and some (h, k),

   $$F(x, y) = (ax - by + h, bx + ay + k)$$

   for all (x, y). Prove that, unless $(a, b) = (1, 0)$, F has just one fixed point:
   there is one and only one point (x, y) with $F(x, y) = (x, y)$. What are the fixed
   points of F if $(a, b) = (1, 0)$?

   16. Investigate the existence of fixed points for the improper similarity mapping
   (x, y) to $(ax + by + h, bx - ay + k)$.

§ 5. *Conic Sections*

In $\Re^3$ a *right circular conical surface* [*cone* for brevity] is the union of an
infinite ice cream cone [sans ice cream] with its reflection in a plane through
the vertex [tip] perpendicular to the axis of symmetry. More formally, let
a $\neq$ **o** be in $\Re^3$ and let α be a number strictly between 0 and $\pi/2$. The line

oa is the *axis* and the point **o** the *vertex* of the cone which is the set of all points **p** such that

$$\frac{|\langle \mathbf{a}, \mathbf{p} \rangle|}{|\mathbf{a}|\,|\mathbf{p}|} = \cos \alpha.$$

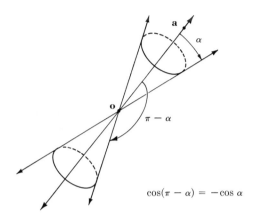

$$\cos(\pi - \alpha) = -\cos \alpha$$

The intersection of a cone with a plane is a *conic section*. Such sections were studied for their intrinsic interest by Greek mathematicians of Euclid's time. A century or two later Apollonius of Perga made notable contributions to the theory. Much later they became *important* with the discovery that the orbit of a particle traveling in the gravitational field of a massive object must, according to Newtonian gravitational theory, be a conic section, or part of one.

The exercises below outline some of the basic parts of a subject with a vast literature. In order to study the intersection of a cone with a plane it is convenient to note that a rotation [details in next section] will map the plane onto a plane perpendicular to the z-axis. Any conic section is congruent to one obtained by intersecting a cone with vertex at **o** with a plane having the equation $z = z_o \geq 0$. The congruence $(x, y, z_o) \longrightarrow (x, y)$ maps the conic section into $\mathfrak{R}^2$.

Exercises

Given $\mathbf{a} = (a_1, a_2, a_3) \neq (0, 0, 0)$ and given α such that $0 < \alpha < \pi/2$, the intersection of the cone with the plane $z = z_0$ is the set of all (x, y, z_0) such that

(1) $|a_1 x + a_2 y + a_3 z_0| = u \sqrt{x^2 + y^2 + z_0^2}$,

where $u = |\mathbf{a}| \cos \alpha$.

Let C be the set of (x, y) in $\mathfrak{R}^2$ such that (x, y, z_0) satisfies equation (1).
1. Why are $\alpha = 0$ and $\alpha = \pi/2$ excluded?
2. For $\mathbf{a} = (1, 1, 1)$, sketch a graph of the set of all **p** such that

$$\frac{|\langle \mathbf{a}, \mathbf{p} \rangle|}{|\mathbf{a}|\,|\mathbf{p}|} = \cos \frac{3\pi}{4}.$$

3. Show that each point of C satisfies an equation of the form

(2) $ax^2 + bxy + cy^2 + dx + ey + f = 0,$

with the three coefficients a, b, c not all 0.

4. Each equation below is a special case of Equation (2). Investigate intuitively whether the locus of each can be the intersection of a plane with a cone.

(a) $x^2 + y^2 = 0.$ (d) $y^2 = 0.$

(b) $x^2 - 9y^2 = 0.$ (e) $x^2 + y^2 - 1 = 0.$

(c) $x^2 - 1 = 0.$

5. In Equation (1) set $z_0 = 0$: the cutting plane contains the vertex of the cone. Prove that C is either a point or a line or a pair of lines. [C is called a *degenerate conic.*]

If $z_0 \neq 0$ a dilation will map the plane $z = z_0$ onto the plane P with equation $z = 1$. Every nondegenerate conic is similar to the intersection of a cone with vertex at $\mathbf{o}$ with the plane P. Now consider the mapping

$(x, y, z) \longrightarrow (x \cos t - y \sin t, x \sin t + y \cos t, z).$

This maps P, or any plane parallel to P, onto itself by a rotation. Choosing t so that $a_1 \sin t + a_2 \cos t = 0$ gives a cone congruent to the original one, with vertex at the origin and axis through some point $(a'_1, 0, a'_3)$.

Every nondegenerate conic is similar to the locus of

(3) $|kx + l| = u\sqrt{x^2 + y^2 + 1}$

for some $u > 0$ and some $(k, l) \neq (0, 0)$. Here

$u = \cos \alpha \sqrt{k^2 + l^2} < \sqrt{k^2 + l^2},$

and the axis of the cone is the line through $(0, 0, 0)$ and $(k, 0, l)$.

6. In Equation (3) set $k = 0$ so that the axis of the cone is the z-axis. Prove that the conic is a circle in the plane P.

7. For $k \neq 0$ show that (3) is equivalent to

(4) $|x + p| = \cos \alpha \sqrt{1 + p^2} \, \sqrt{x^2 + y^2 + 1}$

$= v\sqrt{x^2 + y^2 + 1},$

where $p = 1/k$ and $v = \cos \alpha \sqrt{1 + p^2}$, and to

(5) $(v^2 - 1)x^2 + v^2y^2 - 2px + v^2 - p^2 = 0.$

Geometric summary: If the cutting plane goes through the vertex of the cone, the conic is degenerate. Otherwise a dilation gives a similar conic in the plane $z = 1$, and a rotation puts the axis of the cone in the plane $y = 0$. If the axis of the cone is the z-axis, the conic is a circle. Otherwise the axis of the cone is the line through $(0, 0, 0)$ and $(1, 0, p)$ for some real p. In the plane $y = 0$, unless $p = 0$, we can visualize its appearance as follows.

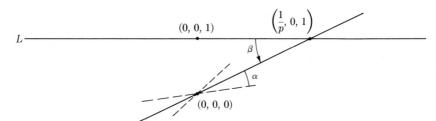

The dotted lines are the intersection of the cone with the plane $y = 0$. Evidently the relative size of α and β determines the intersection of the dotted lines with L.

8. In (5) set $y = 0$ and solve for x. Prove that, if $v = 1$, then $p \neq 0$ and there is just one solution: $(1 - p^2)/2p$. Also prove that in these circumstances (5) reduces to

$$(5a) \quad y^2 = 2p\left(x - \frac{1 - p^2}{2p}\right).$$

9. Prove that the locus of Equation (5a) is congruent to the locus of $y^2 = 2px$ and similar [by a reflection and dilation] to the locus of $y = x^2$. The locus of (5a) is a *parabola*.

10. Prove that, if $y^2 = 2px$, then (x, y) is equally distant from the point $(p/2, 0)$ and the line $x = -p/2$. This point and line are respectively the *focus* and *directrix* of the parabola.

11. Verify that the similarity mapping the parabola with equation $y^2 = 2px$ onto the parabola with equation $y = x^2$ maps focus to focus and directrix to directrix.

12. For $v \neq 1$ set $y = 0$ in (5a) and verify that the points $(x_1, 0, 1)$ and $(x_2, 0, 1)$ are on the cone, where

$$x_1 = \frac{p}{v^2 - 1} - \frac{v \sin \alpha}{2(v^2 - 1)},$$

$$x_2 = \frac{p}{v^2 - 1} + \frac{v \sin \alpha}{2(v^2 - 1)},$$

$$\frac{x_1 + x_2}{2} = \frac{p}{v^2 - 1}.$$

13. Prove that the locus of (5), for $v \neq 1$, is congruent by a translation to the locus of

$$(5b) \quad (v^2 - 1)x^2 + v^2 y^2 = \frac{v^2(1 + p^2 - v^2)}{v^2 - 1}$$

$$= \frac{v^2(1 + p^2)\sin^2 \alpha}{v^2 - 1}.$$

The locus of Equation (5b) is an *ellipse* if $v > 1$ and an *hyperbola* if $v < 1$. Set $1/v = e$; e is called the *eccentricity* of the conic. The parabola has eccentricity 1; each ellipse, eccentricity between 0 and 1; and each hyperbola, eccentricity greater than 1.

The locus of (5b) cannot be a circle because $v^2 - 1 \neq v^2$ for any real v. However,

$$\frac{v^2}{v^2 - 1} = \frac{1}{1 - e^2}.$$

Our definition of the eccentricity e makes $e > 0$. But a circle is regarded as a conic with eccentricity 0.

14. Show that Equation (5b) can be rewritten as

$$(5c) \quad \frac{x^2}{a^2} + \frac{y^2}{a^2(1 - e^2)} = 1,$$

where

$$a = \left| \frac{e}{1 - e^2} \sin \alpha \sqrt{1 + p^2} \right|$$

$$= \left| \frac{e}{1 - e^2} \tan \alpha \right|.$$

For $e = 0$, Equation (5c) is the equation of a circle of radius $a = \tan \alpha$. [This must be regarded as a special definition of a for $e = 0$.]

15. Equation (5c) can be rewritten as

$$x^2 + y^2 = e^2 x^2 + a^2(1 - e^2).$$

For any real h this is equivalent to

$$x^2 - 2hx + h^2 + y^2 = e^2 x^2 - 2hx + h^2 + a^2(1 - e^2).$$

The left side of this equation is the square of the distance of (x, y) from $(h, 0)$. The right side might, for appropriate h, have the form $e^2(x - q)^2$: this is e^2 times the square of the distance of (x, y) from the line $x = q$.

Prove that the right side can be so interpreted iff $h = ae$ or $-ae$, and that Equation (5c) is equivalent to each of the equations

$$|(x, y) - (ae, 0)| = e\left| x - \frac{a}{e} \right|$$

and

$$|(x, y) - (-ae, 0)| = e\left| x - \frac{-a}{e} \right|.$$

The points $(ae, 0)$ and $(-ae, 0)$ are the *foci* of the conic; the lines $x = a/e$ and $x = -a/e$ are the corresponding *directrices*. The conic is the locus of all points $\mathbf{p}$ such that the distance of $\mathbf{p}$ from a focus is e times the distance of $\mathbf{p}$ from the corresponding directrix.

16. Let C be the conic defined by Equation (5c), and prove the following.

a. A reflection in either axis maps C onto itself; so does the mapping $(x, y) \longrightarrow (-x, -y)$.

b. If (x_0, y_0) is on C, then the line with equation

$$\frac{x_0 x}{a^2} + \frac{y_0 y}{a^2(1 - e^2)} = 1$$

intersects C at (x_0, y_0) only. [It is in fact tangent to C at (x_0, y_0).]

c. C is similar to the curve with equation

$$x^2 + \frac{y^2}{1 - e^2} = 1.$$

d. C cannot intersect either of its directrices.

17. For $0 < e < 1$, let $E(e)$ be the ellipse with equation

$$(1 - e^2)x^2 + y^2 = 1 - e^2.$$

Prove that $E(e)$ must be contained in the rectangular region in the following diagram and that the sketch is in accord with the results of Exercise 16.

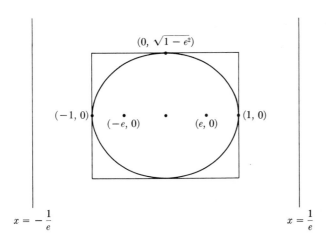

18. Sketch respectable graphs of $E(\frac{3}{5})$, $E(\frac{4}{5})$, $E(\frac{5}{13})$, and then of their images under a dilation D_a.

19. Prove that a point (x, y) is on $E(e)$ if and only if $|(x, y) - (e, 0)| + |(x, y) - (-e, 0)| = 2$.

20. For $e > 1$ let $H(e)$ be the hyperbola with equation
$$(1 - e^2)x^2 + y^2 = 1 - e^2.$$
The part in the first quadrant is the graph of
$$y = \sqrt{(e^2 - 1)x^2 - (e^2 - 1)},$$
where $x \geq 1$, or, setting $w = \sqrt{e^2 - 1}$,
$$y = w\sqrt{x^2 - 1}.$$
Prove that, for $x > 1$,
$$\sqrt{x^2 - 1} = x - \frac{1}{x + \sqrt{x^2 - 1}}.$$
Prove that, for any positive w and ϵ, there is some N such that, for all $x > N$,
$$|w\sqrt{x^2 - 1} - wx| < \epsilon.$$

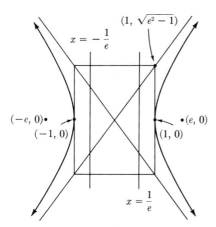

Use this result and the symmetries of Exercise 16 to see that the preceding graph of a hyperbola is essentially correct. The hyperbola is *asymptotic* to the lines $y = \pm\sqrt{e^2 - 1}\,x$.

21. Sketch the hyperbolas $H(\frac{13}{12})$, $H(2)$, $H(10)$.

22. For $\mathbf{p}$ on $H(e)$, what can be said about the distances of $\mathbf{p}$ from the foci?

23. For the ellipse it is customary to set $b^2 = a^2(1 - e^2)$ and write the standard equation as

$$\frac{x^2}{a^2} + \frac{y^2}{b^2} = 1.$$

Sketch this and label the vertices, foci, and directrices in terms of a and b.

24. For the hyperbola it is customary to set $b^2 = a^2(e^2 - 1)$ and write the standard equation as

$$\frac{x^2}{a^2} - \frac{y^2}{b^2} = 1.$$

Sketch this and label the important points and lines in terms of a and b.

25. Let C be the set of (x, y) such that

$$(6) \quad ax^2 + bxy + cy^2 + dx + ey + f = 0,$$

where a, b, c are not all 0. Prove that, unless $b^2 - 4ac = 0$, C is congruent by a translation to the locus of

$$(6a) \quad ax^2 + bxy + cy^2 + g = 0.$$

26. $D = b^2 - 4ac$ is known as *the discriminant* of Equations (6) and (6a). [So, unfortunately, are $-D$, $D/4$, $-D/4$. The literature is extensive, and inconsistent in notation.] Prove that, if $D = 0$, the locus of Equation (6) is either degenerate or a parabola. *Hint:*

$$4a^2x^2 + 4abxy + 4acy^2 = (2ax + by)^2 - Dy^2.$$

27. Prove that the locus of Equation (6a) is congruent by a rotation to the locus of

$$a'x^2 + b'xy + c'y^2 + g' = 0,$$

where

$$a' = a\cos^2 t - b\cos t \sin t + c\sin^2 t,$$

$$b' = (a - c)\sin 2t + b\cos 2t,$$

$$c' = a\sin^2 t + b\sin t \cos t + c\cos^2 t,$$

$$g' = g.$$

Note: Most elementary texts discuss *rotation of axes* rather than rotations in our sense. In the following graph E is the image of E' under the rotation $\mathbf{R}_{-\pi/4}$.

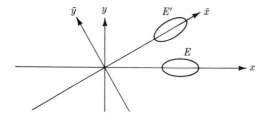

In the context of this book use $\mathbf{R}_{-\pi/4}$ to map E' onto E, which has a simple equation. In the rotation-of-axes theory a rotation $\mathbf{R}_{\pi/4}$ gives E' the same equation in $\bar{x}$ and $\bar{y}$ as has E in x and y. A rotation in our sense through an angle of radian measure t corresponds to a rotation of axes through an angle of radian measure $-t$. Translations and translations of axes are similarly related.

28. With a', b', c' and a, b, c, related as above, prove that

$$b'^2 - 4a'c' = b^2 - 4ac.$$

The discriminant of a conic is invariant under rotations. [Also, from Exercise 25, D is invariant under translations.] This can be done by a straightforward computation or by verifying the following matrix equation and using determinants:

$$\begin{pmatrix} \cos t & -\sin t \\ \sin t & \cos t \end{pmatrix} \begin{pmatrix} a & \dfrac{b}{2} \\ \dfrac{b}{2} & c \end{pmatrix} \begin{pmatrix} \cos t & \sin t \\ -\sin t & \cos t \end{pmatrix} = \begin{pmatrix} a' & \dfrac{b'}{2} \\ \dfrac{b'}{2} & c' \end{pmatrix}.$$

29. It is clearly always possible to choose t so as to make $b' = 0$ in (27). The locus of Equation (6a) is congruent to the locus of

(7) $a'x^2 + c'y^2 + g = 0.$

The same rotation maps the locus of Equation (6) onto the locus of

(7a) $a'x^2 + c'y^2 + d'x + e'y + f' = 0.$

a. Give examples showing that the locus of either (7) or (7a) can be empty, or be a point, or be a line or two lines.

b. By Exercise 28, the dicriminant of Equations (6) and (6a) is

$$D = b^2 - 4ac = -4a'c'.$$

Prove that in nondegenerate cases the locus is

a parabola	if $D = 0$,
a ellipse	if $D < 0$,
a hyperbola	if $D > 0$.

30. For each equation below find a congruence mapping the locus onto a conic with one of the standard equations. Then sketch the original locus.

a. $xy = 1.$

b. $4x^2 + 9y^2 - 24x + 36y + 36 = 0.$

c. $9x^2 + 24xy + 16y^2 - 170x - 60y + 125 = 0.$

d. $73x^2 - 72xy + 52y^2 - 90x - 120y + 125 = 0.$

e. $x^2 + xy + y^2 = 1.$

31. Define F, for $0 \le t \le 2\pi$, by $F(t) = (2 \cos t, 5 \sin t)$ in $\mathfrak{R}^2$. The range of F is the set of all (x, y) such that, for some t in $[0, 2\pi]$,

$$x = 2 \cos t,$$

$$y = 5 \sin t.$$

These equations are called *parametric equations* of the range of F.

Prove that F maps $[0, 2\pi]$ onto an ellipse, one-to-one except that $F(0) = F(2\pi)$.

Parametric comes from a Greek verb meaning "to measure by or with [something else]." A mapping from $\mathcal{R}^n$ to $\mathcal{R}^m$ is frequently described by parametric equations, especially if $n \leq m$. We append two examples of parametric equations.

  1. $x = 2t + 3$,

     $y = 5t - 7$, t real,

are parametric equations of the line through $(3, -7)$ and $(5, -2)$.

  2. Let a and b be positive numbers and let U be the unit square in $\mathcal{R}^2$, the set of (u, v) such that $0 \leq u \leq 1$ and $0 \leq v \leq 1$. For (u, v) in U, let

   $G(u, v) = (au \cos 2\pi v, bu \sin 2\pi v, u)$

in $\mathcal{R}^3$. The range of G has the parametric equations

   $x = au \cos 2\pi v$,

   $y = bu \sin 2\pi v$,

   $z = u$,   for (u, v) in U.

Since $G(0, v) = (0, 0, 0)$ for all relevant v, G maps the segment from $(0, 0)$ to $(0, 1)$ onto $(0, 0, 0)$.

G maps the segment from $(1, 0)$ to $(1, 1)$ onto a set with the parametric equations

   $x = a \cos 2\pi v$,

   $y = b \sin 2\pi v$,

   $z = 1$.

For such $(x, y, 1)$, $(x^2/a^2) + (y^2/b^2) = 1$, and G maps the segment from $(1, 0)$ to $(1, 1)$ onto an ellipse in the plane $z = 1$.

For $0 < u \leq 1$, $G(u, v) = uG(1, v)$. Each segment from $(u, 0)$ to $(u, 1)$ is mapped onto an ellipse similar to the one above, in the plane $z = u$.

The range of G is a part of a conical surface with an elliptical cross-section.

32. Give a geometric description of the set defined by each following set of parametric equations.

  a. $x = \cos t,$
         $y = \sin t,$ for all real t.
         $z = t,$

  b. $x = 2t,$
         $y = 2t + 1,$ for $0 \leq t \leq 5$.

  c. $x = u + v,$
         $y = u - v,$ for all (u, v) in $\mathcal{R}^2$.
         $z = 2u + v,$

  d. $x = 3 \sin t,$
         $y = 5 \cos t,$ for all $t \geq 0$.
         $z = t^2,$

  e. $x = 3 \sin u \cos v,$
         $y = 3 \sin u \sin v,$ for $0 \leq u \leq \pi$, and $0 \leq v \leq 2\pi$.
         $z = 3 \cos u,$

§ 6. *Similarities in $\mathfrak{R}^3$*

Linear transformations in $\mathfrak{R}^3$ can be assigned matrices relative to the usual basis, just as in $\mathfrak{R}^2$. If **A** is linear and maps $\mathfrak{R}^3$ into $\mathfrak{R}^3$, let

$$A(1, 0, 0) = \mathbf{a}, \quad A(0, 1, 0) = \mathbf{b}, \quad A(0, 0, 1) = \mathbf{c}.$$

The matrix of **A** relative to the usual basis is

$$A = \begin{pmatrix} a_1 & b_1 & c_1 \\ a_2 & b_2 & c_2 \\ a_3 & b_3 & c_3 \end{pmatrix}.$$

This notation is a little awkward, and we usually adopt a double subscript notation:

$$A = \begin{pmatrix} a_{11} & a_{12} & a_{13} \\ a_{21} & a_{22} & a_{23} \\ a_{31} & a_{32} & a_{33} \end{pmatrix}$$

is the matrix relative to the usual basis of the linear transformation **A**, with

$$A(1, 0, 0) = (a_{11}, a_{21}, a_{31}) = \mathbf{a}_1,$$
$$A(0, 1, 0) = (a_{12}, a_{22}, a_{32}) = \mathbf{a}_2,$$
$$A(0, 0, 1) = (a_{13}, a_{23}, a_{33}) = \mathbf{a}_3.$$

Just as in $\mathfrak{R}^2$, if A corresponds in this way to **A** and B to **B**, then AB is defined to be the matrix corresponding to $\mathbf{A} \circ \mathbf{B}$. Multiplication works as before. If $AB = C$, then c_{ij}, the entry in the ith row and jth column of C, is the inner product of the ith row of A with the jth column of B:

$$c_{ij} = a_{i1}b_{1j} + a_{i2}b_{2j} + a_{i3}b_{3j}.$$

The *transpose*, A^T, of any matrix A is defined to be the matrix whose kth column, for each k, is the kth row of A. For example,

$$\begin{pmatrix} a & b \\ c & d \end{pmatrix}^T = \begin{pmatrix} a & c \\ b & d \end{pmatrix},$$

$$\begin{pmatrix} 2 \\ 3 \end{pmatrix}^T = (2, 3),$$

$$\begin{pmatrix} 1 & 2 & 3 \\ 4 & 5 & 6 \\ 7 & 8 & 9 \end{pmatrix}^T = \begin{pmatrix} 1 & 4 & 7 \\ 2 & 5 & 8 \\ 3 & 6 & 9 \end{pmatrix}.$$

It is clear from the above that for a two-by-two matrix A, $\det A^T = \det A$.

For A, a three-by-three matrix with columns $\mathbf{a}_1, \mathbf{a}_2, \mathbf{a}_3$ as above, we define $\det A$ by $\det A = \det(\mathbf{a}_1, \mathbf{a}_2, \mathbf{a}_3)$. Written out in full,

$$\det\begin{pmatrix} a_{11} & a_{12} & a_{13} \\ a_{21} & a_{22} & a_{23} \\ a_{31} & a_{32} & a_{33} \end{pmatrix} = \begin{vmatrix} a_{21} & a_{22} \\ a_{31} & a_{32} \end{vmatrix} a_{13} + \begin{vmatrix} a_{31} & a_{32} \\ a_{11} & a_{12} \end{vmatrix} a_{23} + \begin{vmatrix} a_{11} & a_{12} \\ a_{21} & a_{22} \end{vmatrix} a_{33}.$$

We leave it to the reader to prove the following two theorems.

Theorem 6.15. For every three-by-three matrix A,

$\det A^T = \det A.$

Theorem 6.16. If A and B are both two-by-two or both three-by-three matrices, then

$(AB)^T = B^T A^T.$

We assert without proof that if A and B are n-by-n matrices, n any positive integer, then $\det AB = \det A \det B$. For $n = 1$, $\det(a) = a$, and the assertion is obvious. You were asked to prove this for $n = 2$ earlier in the chapter; of course you could prove it for $n = 3$ by a lengthy direct computation. For $n = 3$ the geometric content is that a linear transformation $\mathbf{A}$, of determinant $\det \mathbf{A} = \det A$, multiplies oriented volumes by $\det A$.

Definition 6.12. If the matrix A is

$$A = \begin{pmatrix} a_{11} & a_{12} & a_{13} \\ a_{21} & a_{22} & a_{23} \\ a_{31} & a_{32} & a_{33} \end{pmatrix},$$

then

$$A^* = \begin{pmatrix} \begin{vmatrix} a_{22} & a_{23} \\ a_{32} & a_{33} \end{vmatrix} & -\begin{vmatrix} a_{12} & a_{13} \\ a_{32} & a_{33} \end{vmatrix} & \begin{vmatrix} a_{12} & a_{13} \\ a_{22} & a_{23} \end{vmatrix} \\[2mm] -\begin{vmatrix} a_{21} & a_{23} \\ a_{31} & a_{33} \end{vmatrix} & \begin{vmatrix} a_{11} & a_{13} \\ a_{31} & a_{33} \end{vmatrix} & -\begin{vmatrix} a_{11} & a_{13} \\ a_{21} & a_{23} \end{vmatrix} \\[2mm] \begin{vmatrix} a_{21} & a_{22} \\ a_{31} & a_{32} \end{vmatrix} & -\begin{vmatrix} a_{11} & a_{12} \\ a_{31} & a_{32} \end{vmatrix} & \begin{vmatrix} a_{11} & a_{12} \\ a_{21} & a_{22} \end{vmatrix} \end{pmatrix}.$$

Note that if the columns of A are $\mathbf{a}$, $\mathbf{b}$, $\mathbf{c}$, the rows of A^* are $\mathbf{b} \times \mathbf{c}$, $\mathbf{c} \times \mathbf{a}$, $\mathbf{a} \times \mathbf{b}$. From previous exercises and definitions we have, for example, $\langle \mathbf{b} \times \mathbf{c}, \mathbf{a} \rangle = \det A$, $\langle \mathbf{b} \times \mathbf{c}, \mathbf{b} \rangle = 0$. Such observations establish

Theorem 6.17. With A and A^* as in Definition 6.12,

$$A^*A = \begin{pmatrix} \det A & 0 & 0 \\ 0 & \det A & 0 \\ 0 & 0 & \det A \end{pmatrix} = (\det A)I,$$

where

$$I = \begin{pmatrix} 1 & 0 & 0 \\ 0 & 1 & 0 \\ 0 & 0 & 1 \end{pmatrix}.$$

Theorem 6.18. Let A be a three-by-three matrix and $\mathbf{A}$ the corresponding linear transformation. Then $\mathbf{A}$ is a one-to-one mapping of $\mathcal{R}^3$ onto $\mathcal{R}^3$ iff $\det A \neq 0$. If $\det A \neq 0$, then

$$A^{-1} = \frac{1}{\det A} A^*,$$

where A^* is as in Definition 6.12.

PROOF: Let $\mathbf{A}$ map $(1, 0, 0)$, $(0, 1, 0)$, $(0, 0, 1)$ respectively to $\mathbf{a}$, $\mathbf{b}$, $\mathbf{c}$. For all (x, y, z) in $\mathcal{R}^3$, then

$$\mathbf{A}(x, y, z) = x\mathbf{a} + y\mathbf{b} + z\mathbf{c}.$$

If $\mathbf{a}$, $\mathbf{b}$, $\mathbf{c}$ are linearly independent then, from Chapter 5, each point of $\mathcal{R}^3$ is a unique linear combination of $\mathbf{a}$, $\mathbf{b}$, $\mathbf{c}$: for $\mathbf{p}$ in $\mathcal{R}^3$ there is one and only one (x, y, z) in $\mathcal{R}^3$ such that $\mathbf{A}(x, y, z) = \mathbf{p}$. But if $\mathbf{a}$, $\mathbf{b}$, $\mathbf{c}$ are linearly dependent, then $\mathbf{A}(x, y, z) = (0, 0, 0)$ for some $(x, y, z) \neq (0, 0, 0)$. Thus $\mathbf{A}$ is a one-to-one mapping of $\mathcal{R}^3$ onto $\mathcal{R}^3$ iff the columns of A are linearly independent.

If the columns of A are linearly dependent, one is a linear combination of the other two. Suppose, for example, that $\mathbf{c} = u\mathbf{a} + v\mathbf{b}$. Then

$$\det A = \langle \mathbf{a} \times \mathbf{b}, u\mathbf{a} + v\mathbf{b} \rangle$$
$$= u\langle \mathbf{a} \times \mathbf{b}, \mathbf{a} \rangle + v\langle \mathbf{a} \times \mathbf{b}, \mathbf{b} \rangle = 0.$$

Conversely, suppose $\det A = 0$. If $\mathbf{a}$ and $\mathbf{b}$ are linearly dependent, then $x\mathbf{a} + y\mathbf{b} + 0\mathbf{c} = \mathbf{o}$ for some x and y not both 0, and $\mathbf{a}$, $\mathbf{b}$, $\mathbf{c}$ are linearly dependent. If $\mathbf{a}$ and $\mathbf{b}$ are linearly independent, then, from Chapter 5, $\mathcal{R}^3$ is the set of all linear combinations of $\mathbf{a}$, $\mathbf{b}$, $\mathbf{a} \times \mathbf{b}$. For some u, v, w,

$$\mathbf{c} = u\mathbf{a} + v\mathbf{b} + w(\mathbf{a} \times \mathbf{b}),$$

and

$$0 = \det A = \langle \mathbf{a} \times \mathbf{b}, \mathbf{c} \rangle = u\langle \mathbf{a} \times \mathbf{b}, \mathbf{a} \rangle + v\langle \mathbf{a} \times \mathbf{b}, \mathbf{b} \rangle + w\langle \mathbf{a} \times \mathbf{b}, \mathbf{a} \times \mathbf{b} \rangle$$
$$= w\langle \mathbf{a} \times \mathbf{b}, \mathbf{a} \times \mathbf{b} \rangle.$$

From this equation, $w = 0$ and $\mathbf{c}$ is a linear combination of $\mathbf{a}$ and $\mathbf{b}$.

We have proved that $\mathbf{A}$ is one-to-one onto $\mathcal{R}^3$ iff the columns of A are linearly independent, which is the case iff $\det A \neq 0$.

Now assume $\det A \neq 0$. From Theorem 6.17,

$$\frac{1}{\det A} A^* A = I = \begin{pmatrix} 1 & 0 & 0 \\ 0 & 1 & 0 \\ 0 & 0 & 1 \end{pmatrix}.$$

From the argument above, $\mathbf{A}$ has a composition inverse $\mathbf{A}^{-1}$ and hence A has a multiplicative inverse A^{-1}. Thus

$$\left(\frac{1}{\det A} A^* A \right) A^{-1} = I A^{-1} = A^{-1},$$

and, by associativity,

$$\frac{1}{\det A} A^* = A^{-1}. \quad \blacksquare$$

Corollary to theorem 6.18. If $\det A \neq 0$, then also $AA^* = (\det A)I$.

PROOF: $A^{-1}A = AA^{-1} = I$. $\quad \blacksquare$

We turn now to similarities in $\Re^3$. Each similarity in $\Re^3$ is a composition of a translation with a linear similarity, and each linear similarity is the composition of a dilation with a linear congruence.

Let **A** map $(1, 0, 0)$, $(0, 1, 0)$, $(0, 0, 1)$ respectively to **a**, **b**, **c** in $\Re^3$. From Chapter 5, **A** is a congruence iff

$$|\mathbf{a}| = |\mathbf{b}| = |\mathbf{c}| = 1,$$
$$\langle \mathbf{a}, \mathbf{b} \rangle = \langle \mathbf{b}, \mathbf{c} \rangle = \langle \mathbf{c}, \mathbf{a} \rangle = 0.$$

These six equations are equivalent to one matrix equation.

Theorem 6.19. A three-by-three matrix A is the matrix of a congruence iff $A^T = A^{-1}$.

PROOF:

$$A^T A = \begin{pmatrix} 1 & 0 & 0 \\ 0 & 1 & 0 \\ 0 & 0 & 1 \end{pmatrix}$$

iff the columns of A satisfy the six equations above.

From Chapter 5 these six conditions assure that **a**, **b**, **c** are linearly independent and that the associated transformation **A** is one-to-one onto $\Re^3$. From Theorem 6.18 and its proof, $\det A \neq 0$ and A has an inverse. From $A^T A = I$ follows $A^T = A^{-1}$. $\quad \blacksquare$

The matrix of a linear congruence is usually called an *orthogonal* matrix. Theorem 6.19 can then be rephrased: A [three-by-three] is orthogonal iff $A^T = A^{-1}$.

Theorem 6.20. If A is orthogonal, then the inner product of any row of A with itself is 1, and the inner product of any two different rows is 0.

PROOF: The equation $AA^T = I$ holds. $\quad \blacksquare$

Theorems 6.19 and 6.20 impose many conditions, partly redundant, on the entries of a three-by-three orthogonal matrix A. Furthermore, we have

$$A^T = A^{-1} = \frac{1}{\det A} A^*,$$

where A^*, whose entries are generically two-by-two determinants, is simply a scalar multiple of A^T.

This can be seen in a different way as follows. The segments **oa** and **ob** are perpendicular and each of length 1. Thus $|\mathbf{a} \times \mathbf{b}|$, the area of the parallelogram generated by **a** and **b**, is 1. Line **oc** is perpendicular to both **oa** and **ob**. Hence **c** is a scalar multiple of $\mathbf{a} \times \mathbf{b}$. But $|\mathbf{c}| = 1$, so either $\mathbf{c} = \mathbf{a} \times \mathbf{b}$ or $\mathbf{c} = -\mathbf{a} \times \mathbf{b}$. Then $\det A = \langle \mathbf{a} \times \mathbf{b}, \mathbf{c} \rangle$ is either 1 or -1.

Precisely the same argument applies to $\mathbf{b} \times \mathbf{c}$ and to $\mathbf{c} \times \mathbf{a}$, and we have

Theorem 6.21. Let A be a three-by-three orthogonal matrix with columns **a**, **b**, **c**.
Either $\det A = 1$,

$$\mathbf{a} \times \mathbf{b} = \mathbf{c}, \qquad \mathbf{b} \times \mathbf{c} = \mathbf{a}, \qquad \text{and} \qquad \mathbf{c} \times \mathbf{a} = \mathbf{b},$$

or else $\det A = -1$,

$$\mathbf{a} \times \mathbf{b} = -\mathbf{c}, \qquad \mathbf{b} \times \mathbf{c} = -\mathbf{a}, \qquad \text{and} \qquad \mathbf{c} \times \mathbf{a} = -\mathbf{b}.$$

This theorem says that $A^T = (1/\det A)A^*$ and furthermore that $\det A$ is either 1 or -1.

Note that since $\det A^T = \det A$ the equation $A^T A = I$ implies, via the unproved assertion that the determinant of a product is the product of the determinants, that $(\det A)^2 = \det I = 1$.

Definition 6.13. A linear congruence **A** in $\Re^3$ with matrix A is **proper** if $\det A = 1$, **improper** if $\det A = -1$.

Theorem 6.22. Set

$$H = \begin{pmatrix} 1 & 0 & 0 \\ 0 & 1 & 0 \\ 0 & 0 & -1 \end{pmatrix}.$$

Then **A** is proper or improper according as **AH** is improper or proper.

PROOF: If the columns of A are **a**, **b**, **c**, then those of AH are **a**, **b**, $-\mathbf{c}$. Moreover, $\langle \mathbf{a} \times \mathbf{b}, -\mathbf{c} \rangle = -\langle \mathbf{a} \times \mathbf{b}, \mathbf{c} \rangle$. ∎

Theorem 6.23. If **A** is a proper linear congruence in $\Re^3$, there is some $\mathbf{p} \neq \mathbf{o}$ such that $\mathbf{A}(\mathbf{p}) = \mathbf{p}$.
If **A** is an improper linear congruence in $\Re^3$, there is some $\mathbf{p} \neq \mathbf{o}$ such that $\mathbf{A}(\mathbf{p}) = -\mathbf{p}$.

Remarks: The improper congruence **H** in $\Re^3$ cannot be performed physically. This amounts to the assertion that a person cannot put himself into the space occupied by his image in a mirror. Assuming that every proper congruence can be accomplished in a physical model, it follows that no improper congruence in $\Re^3$ can be accomplished physically.

Consider now a bowling ball sitting in a saucerlike depression which fixes its center. Move the ball any way you like, but finally return it to the saucer so that the center is back where it was. You have performed a proper linear congruence. The theorem says that some point $\mathbf{p} \neq \mathbf{o}$ [the center of the ball] is just where it used to be. Since $\mathbf{A}(\mathbf{p}) = \mathbf{p}$ implies $\mathbf{A}(t\mathbf{p}) = t\mathbf{p}$ for all t, some point on the surface of the ball is just where it used to be. Whatever contortions you went through, all you accomplished was to rotate the ball around the axis $\mathbf{op}$.

PROOF OF THEOREM 6.23: Suppose, for some $\mathbf{p} \neq \mathbf{o}$ and some real λ, $\mathbf{A}(\mathbf{p}) = \lambda\mathbf{p}$. Let $\mathbf{I}$ with matrix I be the identity function on $\mathfrak{R}^3$ and set $\mathbf{B} = \mathbf{A} - \lambda\mathbf{I}$. Then

$$\mathbf{B}(\mathbf{p}) = \mathbf{A}(\mathbf{p}) - \lambda\mathbf{I}(\mathbf{p}) = \lambda\mathbf{p} - \lambda\mathbf{p} = \mathbf{o}.$$

Thus $\mathbf{B}$ is not one-to-one and $\det B = 0$.

If the columns of A are $\mathbf{a}$, $\mathbf{b}$, $\mathbf{c}$, then

$$\det (A - \lambda I) = \det \begin{pmatrix} a_1 - \lambda & b_1 & c_1 \\ a_2 & b_2 - \lambda & c_2 \\ a_3 & b_3 & c_3 - \lambda \end{pmatrix}.$$

A straightforward calculation gives

$$\det (A - \lambda I) = -\lambda^3 + \lambda^2(a_1 + b_2 + c_2) - \lambda \left(\begin{vmatrix} b_2 & c_2 \\ b_3 & c_3 \end{vmatrix} + \begin{vmatrix} a_1 & c_1 \\ a_3 & c_3 \end{vmatrix} + \begin{vmatrix} a_1 & b_1 \\ a_2 & b_2 \end{vmatrix} \right) + \det A.$$

Set $a_1 + b_2 + c_3 = k$. By Theorem 6.21 the coefficient of $-\lambda$ above is k if $\det \lambda = 1$ and $-k$ if $\det A = -1$. Setting $F(\lambda) = \det (A - \lambda I)$, we have, if $\det A = 1$,

$$F(\lambda) = -\lambda^3 + k^2 - k + 1$$
$$= (\lambda - 1)(-\lambda^2 + (k - 1)\lambda - 1).$$

If $\det A = -1$,

$$F(\lambda) = -\lambda^3 + k\lambda^2 + k\lambda - 1$$
$$= (\lambda + 1)(-\lambda^2 + (k + 1)\lambda - 1).$$

Evidently, if $\det A = 1$, then $F(1) = 0$, and if $\det A = -1$, then $F(-1) = 0$.

To finish the argument for $\det A = 1$, then $\det (A - I) = 0$. Therefore $\mathbf{A} - \mathbf{I}$ is not one-to-one and there is some $\mathbf{p} \neq \mathbf{o}$ in the kernel of $\mathbf{A} - \mathbf{I}$, some $\mathbf{p} \neq \mathbf{o}$ with $(\mathbf{A} - \mathbf{I})(\mathbf{p}) = \mathbf{o}$, and hence $\mathbf{A}(\mathbf{p}) = \mathbf{p}$. In just the same way one proves that, if $\det A = -1$, there is some $\mathbf{p}$ with $\mathbf{A}(\mathbf{p}) = -\mathbf{p}$. ∎

Example

Let

$$A = \frac{1}{3} \begin{pmatrix} 1 & 2 & 2 \\ 2 & 1 & -2 \\ -2 & 2 & -1 \end{pmatrix}, \qquad A^T = \frac{1}{3} \begin{pmatrix} 1 & 2 & -2 \\ 2 & 1 & 2 \\ 2 & -2 & -1 \end{pmatrix},$$

$$A^T A = \frac{1}{9}\begin{pmatrix} 9 & 0 & 0 \\ 0 & 9 & 0 \\ 0 & 0 & 9 \end{pmatrix} = I.$$

Det $A = 1$, and

$$A - I = \frac{1}{3}\begin{pmatrix} -2 & 2 & 2 \\ 2 & -2 & -2 \\ -2 & 2 & -4 \end{pmatrix}.$$

Also, $A(\mathbf{p}) = \mathbf{p}$ iff $3A(\mathbf{p}) = 3\mathbf{p}$, iff

$$p_1 + 2p_2 + 3p_3 = 3p_1,$$
$$2p_1 + p_2 - 2p_3 = 3p_2,$$
$$-2p_1 + 2p_2 - p_3 = 3p_3,$$

or

$$-2p_1 + 2p_2 + 2p_3 = 0,$$
$$2p_1 - 2p_2 - 2p_3 = 0,$$
$$-2p_1 + 2p_2 - 4p_3 = 0,$$

or

$$-2p_1 + 2p_2 + 2p_3 = 0,$$
$$0 = 0,$$
$$-6p_3 = 0,$$

or $\mathbf{p}$ is a scalar multiple of $(1, 1, 0)$.

Take $\mathbf{p} = (1, 1, 0)$. Let $\mathbf{d} = (-1, 1, 0)$ and $\mathbf{e} = (0, 0, 1)$ so that $\mathbf{d}$ and $\mathbf{e}$ are in the orthogonal complement of $\mathbf{op}$ and $\langle \mathbf{d}, \mathbf{e} \rangle = 0$. Then

$$\mathbf{A(d)} = \tfrac{1}{3}(1, -1, 4) = -\tfrac{1}{3}\mathbf{d} + \tfrac{4}{3}\mathbf{e},$$
$$\mathbf{A(e)} = \tfrac{1}{3}(2, -2, -1) = -\tfrac{2}{3}\mathbf{d} - \tfrac{1}{3}\mathbf{e},$$

and $(\mathbf{p}, \mathbf{d}, \mathbf{e})$ is a right-handed basis for $\Re^3$. Relative to this basis the matrix of our transformation is

$$\begin{pmatrix} 1 & 0 & 0 \\ 0 & -\tfrac{1}{3} & -\tfrac{2}{3} \\ 0 & \tfrac{4}{3} & -\tfrac{1}{3} \end{pmatrix}.$$

This matrix is not orthogonal because the basis is not orthonormal. Relative to the orthonormal basis $\left(\dfrac{\mathbf{p}}{\sqrt{2}}, \dfrac{\mathbf{d}}{\sqrt{2}}, \mathbf{e} \right)$, the matrix is

$$\begin{pmatrix} 1 & 0 & 0 \\ 0 & -\dfrac{1}{3} & -\dfrac{2\sqrt{2}}{3} \\ 0 & \dfrac{2\sqrt{2}}{3} & -\dfrac{1}{3} \end{pmatrix},$$

which is orthogonal. [From $\mathbf{A(d)} = 0\mathbf{p} - \tfrac{1}{3}\mathbf{d} + \tfrac{4}{3}\mathbf{e}$ follows

$$A\frac{\mathbf{d}}{\sqrt{2}} = 0\frac{\mathbf{p}}{\sqrt{2}} - \frac{1}{3}\frac{\mathbf{d}}{\sqrt{2}} + \frac{4}{3\sqrt{2}}\mathbf{e},$$

which gives the second column above.]

The matrix

$$R = \frac{1}{3}\begin{pmatrix} -1 & -2\sqrt{2} \\ 2\sqrt{2} & -1 \end{pmatrix}$$

is the matrix of a rotation in $\mathfrak{R}^2$. Our transformation **A** leaves the line **op** fixed pointwise and rotates the orthogonal complement of **op** through an angle of radian measure t such that $W(t) = \left(-\dfrac{1}{3}, \dfrac{2\sqrt{2}}{3}\right)$.

If **q** is in $\mathfrak{R}^3$, then $\mathbf{q} = u\mathbf{p} + \mathbf{r}$, where **r** is in the orthogonal complement of **op**. Also,

$$\mathbf{A}(\mathbf{q}) = \mathbf{A}(u\mathbf{p}) + \mathbf{A}(\mathbf{r}) = u\mathbf{p} + A(\mathbf{r}),$$

showing that both **q** and **A(q)** are in the plane through $u\mathbf{p}$ perpendicular to **op**. Thus **A** rotates this plane around the axis **op**.

Exercises

1. Set

$$B = \tfrac{1}{9}\begin{pmatrix} 1 & 8 & -4 \\ 8 & 1 & 4 \\ -4 & 4 & 7 \end{pmatrix}.$$

Verify that $B^T B = I$, that $\det B = -1$, and that $\det(B + I) = 0$. Find a point **p** such that $\mathbf{B}(\mathbf{p}) = -\mathbf{p}$.

2. With **B** as above, find two linearly independent points **q** and **r** such that $\mathbf{B}(\mathbf{q}) = \mathbf{q}$ and $\mathbf{B}(\mathbf{r}) = \mathbf{r}$.

3. Prove that the three points **p**, **q**, **r** found in Exercises 1 and 2 are linearly independent. Thus each point of $\mathfrak{R}^3$ has a unique representation as a linear combination of **p**, **q**, **r**. What is the geometric effect of **B**? What is the matrix of **B** relative to the basis (**p**, **q**, **r**)? relative to ($u\mathbf{p}$, $v\mathbf{q}$, $w\mathbf{r}$) for nonzero scalars u, v, w?

4. Let **L** be the linear transformation mapping $(1, 0, 0)$, $(0, 1, 0)$, $(0, 0, 1)$ respectively to $(3, 0, 4)$, $(4, 0, -3)$, $(0, 5, 0)$. Show that **L** is a composition of a dilation with an orthogonal transformation, say $\mathbf{L} = \mathbf{D} \circ \mathbf{A}$. Find all **p** such that $\mathbf{A}(\mathbf{p}) = \mathbf{p}$, and all **q** such that $\mathbf{A}(\mathbf{q}) = -\mathbf{q}$. Then work out a simple geometric description of **L**.

5. If

$$A = \begin{pmatrix} k & o & o \\ o & a & b \\ o & c & d \end{pmatrix},$$

prove that $\det A = k(ad - bc)$. If A is orthogonal, then k is either 1 or -1 and $\det A$ is either 1 or -1. For each of the four possibilities say all you can about $\begin{pmatrix} a & b \\ c & d \end{pmatrix}$.

6. If **A** is orthogonal and $\mathbf{A}(\mathbf{p}) = \lambda\mathbf{p}$, where $\mathbf{p} \neq 0$ and $\lambda = 1$ or -1, prove that **A** maps the orthogonal complement of **op** onto itself, and also each plane parallel to the orthogonal complement onto itself.

7. Give an example of two proper orthogonal matrices A and B such that $AB \neq BA$.

8. Prove that, if $A^T A = I$ and $B^T B = I$, then $(AB)^T AB = I$. The product of orthogonal matrices is orthogonal.

Remarks: From Exercise 8 above, the set of orthogonal transformations in $\mathcal{R}^3$ is closed under composition. By the theorem about the determinant of a product, if $\det A = 1$ and $\det B = 1$, then $\det AB = 1$. Because dilations commute with all linear transformations, we have $D_r A D_s B = D_{r+s} AB$. The set of all proper linear similarities in $\mathcal{R}^3$ is a group under composition.

It is natural to ask if we have some extension of the complex field. Exercise 7 is discouraging: the group is not commutative. If we consider addition, the algebra becomes worse. Both

$$\begin{pmatrix} 1 & 0 & 0 \\ 0 & 1 & 0 \\ 0 & 0 & 1 \end{pmatrix} \text{ and } \begin{pmatrix} 1 & 0 & 0 \\ 0 & -1 & 0 \\ 0 & 0 & -1 \end{pmatrix}$$

are matrices of proper congruences. Their sum,

$$\begin{pmatrix} 2 & 0 & 0 \\ 0 & 0 & 0 \\ 0 & 0 & 0 \end{pmatrix},$$

is the matrix of a linear transformation mapping $\mathcal{R}^3$ onto the line through $(0, 0, 0)$ and $(2, 0, 0)$. The set is not closed under addition, and this cannot be remedied, as in $\mathcal{R}^2$, by throwing in the O matrix.

In $\mathcal{R}^2$, a proper linear similarity is determined by the image of $(1, 0)$, which produces a natural one-to-one correspondence of similarities to points. In $\mathcal{R}^3$, if the image of $(1, 0, 0)$ is chosen, the image of $(0, 1, 0)$ can be anywhere on a circle. There are, in one sense, many more proper linear similarities than points.

In summary, then, the set of proper linear similarities in $\mathcal{R}^3$ provides a moderately complicated example of an infinite noncommutative group. But it is less interesting than the complex field.

Some extensions to $\mathcal{R}^n$, $n > 3$, are easy. A linear transformation in $\mathcal{R}^n$ has a matrix relative to the usual basis constructed just as in $\mathcal{R}^2$ and $\mathcal{R}^3$. It is easily established that an n-by-n matrix A is the matrix of a congruence iff $A^T A$ is the identity matrix. But an effective theory needs an adequate theory of determinants, or an adequate substitute for this.

In this chapter we have looked only at transformations in $\mathcal{R}^2$ or in $\mathcal{R}^3$, and thus only at square matrices. This restriction is not necessary. For example,

$$\begin{pmatrix} 1 & 0 \\ 2 & 2 \\ 3 & 5 \end{pmatrix}$$

is the matrix, relative to the usual basis in $\mathcal{R}^2$ and the usual basis in $\mathcal{R}^3$, of the linear transformation mapping $(1, 0)$ to $(1, 2, 3)$ and $(0, 1)$ to $(0, 2, 5)$.

We can compute products of rectangular matrices provided the corresponding linear transformations can be composed. That is, if domain **A** includes range **B** then AB is defined to be the matrix of $\mathbf{A} \circ \mathbf{B}$.

Examples

1. $\begin{pmatrix} 1 & 0 \\ 2 & 2 \\ 3 & 5 \end{pmatrix} \begin{pmatrix} 1 & 2 & 5 \\ 1 & 3 & 7 \end{pmatrix} = \begin{pmatrix} 1 & 2 & 5 \\ 4 & 10 & 24 \\ 8 & 21 & 50 \end{pmatrix}.$

2. $\begin{pmatrix} 1 & 2 & 5 \\ 1 & 3 & 7 \end{pmatrix} \begin{pmatrix} 1 & 0 \\ 2 & 2 \\ 3 & 5 \end{pmatrix} = \begin{pmatrix} 20 & 29 \\ 28 & 41 \end{pmatrix}.$

3. $(1, 2, 3) \begin{pmatrix} 4 \\ 5 \\ 6 \end{pmatrix} = (32).$

Exercise

What linear transformations are involved in the above examples?

§ 7. *Appendix*

Elementary Areas

A square of side 1 has area 1; a similarity of scale factor r maps a region of area A onto a region of area r^2A; a rectangle with sides of lengths a and b has area ab; a triangle with base b and height h has area $\frac{1}{2}bh$; a circle of radius r has area πr^2.

Which of these statements are definitions and which are theorems? There is no unique answer to this question. If we went to the extreme of regarding them all as definitions, we might reasonably be required to prove that they are mutually consistent and conform to the following *intuitive requirements*.

1. If a plane region having area is cut into a finite number of non-overlapping subregions, each having an area, then the sum of the areas of the subregions is the area of the whole region.

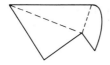

2. If U and V are regions having area and U is a subset of V, then the area of U is not larger than the area of V.

3. Congruent regions have the same area.

Conditions 1 and 3 imply that a definition of the area of a rectangle settles the areas of triangles and parallelograms. Alternatively, a definition of the area of triangles settles rectangles and parallelograms.

　　If we accept 1, 2, 3, and the definition that the area of the unit square is 1, we can prove the following statements.

　　(a) Any square of rational side r has area r^2.

　　(b) Any square of side a has area a^2.

　　(c) Any rectangle of sides a and b has area ab.

　　(d) Any triangle of base b and height h has area $\frac{1}{2}bh$.

　　(e) The area of a circle of radius r is πr^2.

　　To get (a), observe that a square of side n, with n a positive integer, can be cut into n^2 squares of side 1. The unit square can be cut into n^2 squares each of side $1/n$. Finally, if a square has side m/n, then n^2 copies of it can be pieced together to make a square of side m, and area m^2. If A is the area of the original square, then $n^2A = m^2$ and $A = (m/n)^2$.

　　Let a square S have side a, irrational, and assume the square has area A. For n a positive integer, the sequence D, $1/n$, $2/n$, $3/n$, ... is unbounded. Let m be the integer such that

$$\frac{m}{n} < a < \frac{m+1}{n}.$$

Since S is the square of side a, containing a square of side m/n and contained in a square of side $(m+1)/n$, then, by condition 2 and statement (a),

$$\left(\frac{m}{n}\right)^2 \le A \le \left(\frac{m+1}{n}\right)^2 = \left(\frac{m}{n}\right)^2 + \frac{2m+1}{n^2}.$$

Also,

$$\left(\frac{m}{n}\right)^2 < a^2 < \left(\frac{m+1}{n}\right)^2.$$

Since $m/n < a$,

$$\frac{2m+1}{n^2} < \frac{2a}{n} + \frac{1}{n^2}.$$

Conclusion: for every positive integer n,

$$|A - a^2| < \frac{2a}{n} + \frac{1}{n^2},$$

from which $A = a^2$.

　　Consider now a rectangle with sides a and b. It is natural to try to cut it into squares of side $a/n = b/m$.

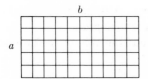

But, as the Greeks were dismayed to discover, this can be done only if $a/b = n/m$ is rational! A rectangle cannot be so subdivided into squares unless its length is a rational multiple of its width.

One remedy is to subdivide the side of length a into n congruent intervals and let m be the integer such that

$$m \frac{a}{n} < b < (m+1) \frac{a}{n}.$$

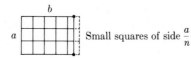

Small squares of side $\dfrac{a}{n}$

Assume the rectangle has area A and, using condition 2 and statement (b), we have

$$mn \left(\frac{a}{n}\right)^2 \leq A \leq (m+1)n \left(\frac{a}{n}\right)^2$$

and also

$$m \frac{a^2}{n} < ab < (m+1) \frac{a^2}{n}.$$

For each positive integer n, $|A - ab| < a^2/n$, and $A = ab$.

Triangles and parallelograms now follow by the usual construction, using conditions 1 and 3 and statement (c).

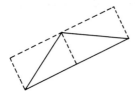 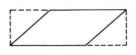

Now consider a circle of radius r.

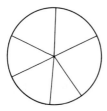

The basic intuition is that we can approximate the disc by a union of triangles. Below is one with central angle of radian measure t and hence intercepted arc of length rt.

The triangle has area $\frac{1}{2}|\mathbf{p} - \mathbf{q}|h$. For small enough t, the chord $\mathbf{pq}$ has length nearly rt, and the height is nearly r. The area of the triangle is somewhat less than $\frac{1}{2}r^2t$. If we have used n triangles with central angles of measure $t_1, t_2, \ldots, t_n$, the sum of their areas is somewhat less than

$$\tfrac{1}{2}r^2(t_1 + t_2 + \cdots + t_n) = \tfrac{1}{2}r^2 2\pi = \pi r^2.$$

Choosing each t_i small enough will make each individual error in approximating a sector by a triangle small; but the smaller each t_i, the more errors there are to be considered. Thus a more precise analysis is needed.

Let n be any positive integer > 8, so that $2\pi/n < \pi/4$, and approximate the disc from within by n congruent triangles, each of central angle $2\pi/n$.

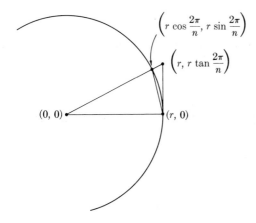

Assume the circle has area A. By condition 1, the one sector shown has area A/n. It contains a triangle of area $\frac{1}{2}rr \sin (2\pi/n)$ and is contained in a triangle of area $\frac{1}{2}rr \tan (2\pi/n)$. By condition 2,

$$\frac{1}{2}r^2 \sin \frac{2\pi}{n} \leq \frac{A}{n} \leq \frac{1}{2}r^2 \tan \frac{2\pi}{n},$$

and

$$\frac{n}{2\pi} \sin \frac{2n}{n} \leq \frac{A}{\pi r^2} \leq \frac{n}{2\pi} \tan \frac{2\pi}{n}.$$

Setting $t = 2\pi/n < \pi/4 < 1$, we have

$$\frac{\sin t}{t} \le \frac{A}{\pi r^2} \le \frac{\sin t}{t} \cdot \frac{1}{\cos t}.$$

From the inequalities at the end of the section on the circular functions,

$$1 - \frac{t^2}{2} < \frac{\sin t}{t} < 1 \quad \text{and} \quad \frac{1}{\cos t} < \frac{1}{1 - \dfrac{t^2}{2}}.$$

Thus

$$1 - \frac{1}{2}\left(\frac{2\pi}{n}\right)^2 < \frac{A}{\pi r^2} < \frac{1}{1 - \dfrac{1}{2}\left(\dfrac{2\pi}{n}\right)^2},$$

for every integer $n > 8$. The sequence $\{(2\pi/n)^2\}$ converges to 0. Thus $A/\pi r^2$ is trapped between corresponding terms of two sequences, both converging to 1, and therefore $A/\pi r^2 = 1$.

It is now easy to prove that any sector of a circle has area $\frac{1}{2}$ base times height or $\frac{1}{2}rs$, where s is the length of the arc.

If t is a rational multiple of 2π, this follows immediately from the above: if $t = m2\pi/n$, the area is m times $\pi r^2/n$, or

$$\frac{m\pi r^2}{n} = \frac{1}{2} r^2 t = \frac{1}{2} rs.$$

If t is not a rational multiple of 2π, then for each positive integer n there is an integer m such that

$$\frac{m2\pi}{n} < t < \frac{(m+1)2\pi}{n}.$$

We proceed as with rectangles.

7
Curves and Continuity

The word *curve* has some connotations in ordinary usage which it does not have in this chapter. Here it is not used in contrast to *straight*: a line is just a particularly simple curve; a polygon, made up of line segments, is a curve in spite of the sharp corners. We repudiate any esthetic connotations.

An intuitive model underlying the definitions below goes something as follows. Start with the idealization of a piece of thin string or wire. Don't cut it and don't melt it into a non-wire or beat it out flat. However you bend and knot it, the result is a curve.

For almost all of the chapter we consider only plane curves, subsets of $\mathcal{R}^2$, and furthermore only those which are graphs of real functions. This very considerable restriction does not eliminate any real difficulties, but does avoid some complications by temporarily eliminating curves such as that below.

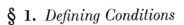

§ 1. *Defining Conditions*

The object of this section is to formulate analytic conditions which must be imposed on a real function if its graph is to be regarded as a curve. The first of these is very simple: the domain of the function must be a connected stretch of the line. The graph of $y = \sqrt{x^2 - 1}$ is two disconnected curves rather than a curve.

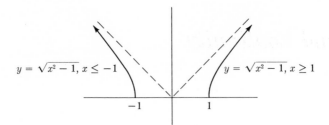

$y = \sqrt{x^2 - 1},\ x \le -1$ $y = \sqrt{x^2 - 1},\ x \ge 1$

Or if, from the semicircle $y = \sqrt{1 - x^2}$, we delete the point $(0, 1)$, two curves are left.

A *connected stretch* of the line is one of nine types of intervals given below in the most usual notation.

Bounded Intervals

Given two real numbers a and b, with $a < b$, we have previously defined the closed interval $[a, b]$ and open interval (a, b). There are also two half-open intervals:

$$[a, b) = \{x | a \le x < b\},$$
$$(a, b] = \{x | a < x \le b\}.$$

Unbounded Intervals

Any real number a is an end point of four different unbounded intervals:

$$(a, \infty) = \{x | x > a\},$$
$$[a, \infty) = \{x | x \ge a\},$$
$$(-\infty, a) = \{x | x < a\},$$
$$(-\infty, a] = \{x | x \le a\}.$$

Finally, $(-\infty, \infty) = \mathfrak{R}^1$ is an unbounded interval.

Our first condition for the graph of a function to be a curve is that the domain of the function be an interval. This of course is not nearly enough. If $f(x) = 1$ for x rational, 2 for x irrational, the graph of f consists of a dense but disconnected set of points on the line $y = 1$ and another such set on the line $y = 2$.

We might also insist that the range of the function be an interval, but the diagram below shows that this is not enough. The function f in the picture has domain $[0, 1]$ and range $[0, 1]$ but is not a curve.

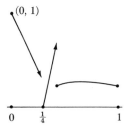

This function fails to have what is known as the *intermediate value property*: $f(0) = 1$ and $f(\frac{1}{4}) = 0$, but, on the interval $[0, \frac{1}{4}]$, f does not take on every value between 1 and 0.

Definition 7.1 [*The Intermediate Value Property*]. Let f be a real function on an interval: f has the **intermediate value property** if, for any two numbers x_1 and x_2 in the domain of f and each number k between $f(x_1)$ and $f(x_2)$, there is at least one number c between x_1 and x_2 with $f(c) = k$.

An intuitive interpretation of the intermediate value property is that the graph of a function with this property cannot get from below [above] a horizontal line $y = k$ to above [below] it without intersecting the line.

$(x_1, f(x_1)) \bullet$

$\underline{\hspace{5cm}\bullet\hspace{3cm}}\;\;y = k$
$\qquad\qquad (c, f(c))$

$\qquad\qquad\qquad\bullet\,(x_2, f(x_2))$

Preliminary Summary

In order that the graph of a real function f be regarded as a curve we insist that (1) the domain of f be an interval, and (2) f have the intermediate value property.

Next we give an example of a function which has both properties (1) and (2) but whose graph is not intuitively acceptable as a curve. We shall call the function a *squeezed sawtooth* function and name it sst. It is defined as follows: for each positive integer n sst $(1/n) = (-1)^n$, sst $(0) = 0$, and over the interval $(1/(n + 1), 1/n)$ the graph of sst is the segment from $(1/(n + 1), (-1)^{n+1})$ to $(1/n, (-1)^n)$.

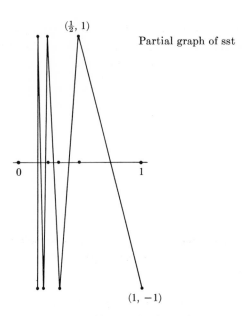

$(\tfrac{1}{2}, 1)$

Partial graph of sst

0   1

$(1, -1)$

The domain of sst is the interval [0, 1] and the function has the intermediate value property. In particular, on any interval [0, b], for $0 < b \leq 1$, sst takes on every value between 0 and sst (b) infinitely often. But the point $(0, 0) = (0, \text{sst } (0))$ is somehow not hooked on.

We note that for any number a with $0 < a < 1$, the graph of sst over the interval [a, 1] consists of a finite number of line segments, properly joined at their end points, and will be a curve by our final definition. Also, the graph of sst over the half-open interval (0, 1] will be a curve; but there is no way of redefining sst (0) so as to get a curve over the closed interval [0, 1].

The motivation for our third and final condition for the graph of a function to be a curve comes from the most famous of all curves, the circle. In the present context of graphs of functions we can consider at most a semi-circle, but this is enough. To define the length of a circular arc we considered the lengths of broken-line approximations to the arc, approximations to the arc by chords. Surely the reason that this has been considered a satisfactory approach for some 2500 years is that although no arc of a circle is a line segment the eye finds it difficult to distinguish the arc from a set of many short chords.

This brings us to a crucial distinction which we shall, at least for this chapter, pose as the distinction between qualitative and quantitative viewpoints. From what we shall here consider a qualitative viewpoint, an arc of a circle is completely different from an approximation to it by chords. The one is made up of straight pieces and has sharp corners; the other is the classical model of the absence of these two features.

From the quantitative point of view we consider the upper half of the unit circle, for example, as the graph of a function f: for $-1 \leq x \leq 1$, $f(x) = \sqrt{1 - x^2}$. If we are willing to tolerate any errors no larger than ϵ, for some preassigned positive number ϵ, then we can approximate f by a broken-line function, a finite collection of chords, with an error everywhere less than ϵ.

Our final condition for the graph of a function to be a curve will be that over any bounded subinterval of the domain the function can be approximated arbitrarily well by a finite collection of line segments. This needs to be spelled out in more detail, but the condition does not imply that a curve in any qualitative sense looks like a broken-line function.

Definition 7.2. Let $[a, b]$ be a closed interval. A **partition** of $[a, b]$ is an ordered set $\{x_0, x_1, \ldots, x_n\}$ of $n + 1$ points, for some positive integer n, such that $a = x_0 < x_1 < \cdots < x_n = b$. The intervals $[x_0, x_1], \ldots, [x_{n-1}, x_n]$ are the **intervals of the partition.**

For example, $\{1, 1.1, 2, 2.5, 3\}$ is a partition of the interval $[1, 3]$.

Definition 7.3. Let f be a real function whose domain includes the interval $[a, b]$ and let $p = \{x_0, \ldots, x_n\}$ be a partition of $[a, b]$. The function f and partition p determine a unique function $B_{f,p}$ [abbreviated to B whenever possible], defined by: for each x_k in p with $1 \leq k \leq n$, over the interval $[x_{k-1}, x_k]$, the graph of B is the line segment with end points $(x_{k-1}, f(x_{k-1}))$ and $(x_k, f(x_k))$.

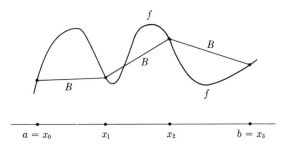

Definition 7.4. Let f be a real function whose domain includes the closed interval $[a, b]$. The statement that f is **uniformly well approximable by broken-line functions over** $[a, b]$ means that for each $\epsilon > 0$ there is a partition $p(\epsilon)$ of $[a, b]$ such that, if B is the broken-line function $B_{f,p(\epsilon)}$, then for all x in $[a, b]$, $|f(x) - B(x)| < \epsilon$.

Definition 7.5 [*First Formulation*]. A real function f is a **curve** [or the graph of f is a **curve**] if
(1)   the domain of f is an interval,
(2) f has the intermediate value property, and

(3) f is uniformly well approximable by broken-line functions over any closed bounded subinterval of its domain.

Remarks: 1. The second formulation will be in terms of *continuity*. That is, (3) will be shown equivalent to (3′):

f is uniformly continuous on each closed bounded subinterval of its domain.

We shall establish that (3′) or (3) implies (2); we shall drop (2) as a defining condition, but retain it as an important theorem.

2. We impose no more conditions because those of Definition 7.5 are equivalent to the classical and well-established definition. This definition is retained in spite of the fact that Karl Weierstrass (1815–1897), to the considerable shock of his contemporaries, constructed curves failing to have a tangent at any point. From the work of Weierstrass and Lebesgue it is now known that the graph of a function can be a curve as defined in Definition 7.5, even though the function is not monotone on any interval. The graph of such a function does not seem to conform to any intuitive idealization of streaks drawn with sharp pencils. The existence of such curves is a principal reason why we don't offer a diagram purporting to be a picture of a typical curve.

3. In this section we have used the word *connected* in an informal intuitive way. The word is also a technical term with a formal definition.

Definition 7.6. If S is a set of real numbers, S is *connected* in case each number between two members of S is also a member of S. Somewhat more precisely, S is a *connected* set of real numbers iff, for any x_1 and x_2 in S with $x_1 < x_2$, each number in the interval $[x_1, x_2]$ is also in S.

The null set is trivially connected, as is any set with only one member. A set containing just one real number, a one-point set, is sometimes called a *degenerate interval*. For the purpose of this chapter a one-point set is *not* an interval.

Exercises

1. Establish that a subset of $\Re$ containing more than one member is connected iff it is one of the nine sorts of intervals listed on page 210. The next paragraph makes a start.

    Suppose S is a connected set of reals having a greatest lower bound, a, but no upper bound. We want to show that S is either $[a, \infty)$ or (a, ∞). To begin with, if $x < a$, then x is not in S because a is a lower bound of S. Next consider $x > a$. Since a is the greatest lower bound, x is not a lower bound and there is some x_1 in S with $x_1 < x$. Also, since S has no upper bound, x is not an upper bound and there is some x_2 in S with $x < x_2$. Thus any number $x > a$ is between two members of S and, since S is connected, is itself a member of S. We have established that S contains no number less than a, but contains every number larger than a. Thus S is either $[a, \infty)$ if a is member of S, or (a, ∞) if a is not a member of S.

2. Let c and d be two different numbers in the domain of a real function f. Show that the line through the points $(c, f(c))$ and $(d, f(d))$ has the equation

$$y = f(c) + \frac{f(d) - f(c)}{d - c} (x - c).$$

Also draw a diagram to show how, for (x, y) a point on this line, the equation

$$\frac{y - f(c)}{x - c} = \frac{f(d) - f(c)}{d - c}$$

can be interpreted in terms of similar triangles.

Definition 7.7. The number

$$\frac{f(d) - f(c)}{d - c}$$

is the **slope** of the line through $(c, f(c))$ and $(d, f(d))$. Any nonvertical line has a slope, the ratio of its **direction numbers.** If (x_1, y_1) and (x_2, y_2) are any two points on the line, its slope is

$$\frac{y_2 - y_1}{x_2 - x_1}.$$

Examples

1. *The graph of* sst *is not a curve.* If it were a curve we could approximate it uniformly well by broken-line functions over any closed interval $[0, b]$ with $0 < b \leq 1$. For example, taking $\epsilon = \frac{1}{2}$ in the definition, we could find a partition of $[0, 1]$ such that the corresponding broken-line approximation nowhere differs from sst by as much as $\frac{1}{2}$. For any partition of $[0, 1]$, consider the first interval $[0, x_1]$. In this interval there are infinitely many x with sst $(x) = 1$, and also infinitely many x with sst $(x) = -1$. The segment from $(0, 0)$ to $(0, \text{sst} (x_1))$ either does not go below the x-axis, in which case it is no good as an approximation to sst $(x) = -1$; or else it does go below the axis and is no good as an approximation to sst (x) for sst $(x) = 1$.

2. *A tapered sawtooth curve.* Define a function tst on $[0, 1]$ as follows: tst $(0) = 0$ and, for every positive integer n, tst $(1/n) = 0$. Over each interval $[1/(n + 1), 1/n]$ the graph of tst consists of the legs of an isosceles triangle of height $1/n$.

$0 \qquad \frac{1}{5}\frac{1}{4}\ \frac{1}{3} \qquad \frac{1}{2} \qquad\qquad\qquad 1$

This function is something like the squeezed sawtooth in that its graph is composed of one point, $(0, 0)$, and infinitely many line segments. Obviously, as is the case with the squeezed sawtooth, the domain is an interval and the function has the intermediate value property. The crucial difference is that this tapered sawtooth can be uniformly well approximated by broken-line functions.

Given $\epsilon > 0$, let n be the smallest positive integer such that $1/n < \epsilon$ and approximate tst by the function B_ϵ, defined by

$$\text{for } 0 \leq x \leq \frac{1}{n}, \quad B_\epsilon(x) = 0,$$

$$\text{for } \frac{1}{n} \leq x \leq 1, \quad B_\epsilon(x) = \text{tst } (x).$$

Then B_ϵ is a broken-line function composed of $2n - 1$ segments, which approximates tst perfectly on the interval $[1/n, 1]$ and with error less than ϵ on $[0, 1/n]$. Thus for each $\epsilon > 0$ we can find a partition of $[0, 1]$ such that the corresponding broken-line function approximates tst with an error everywhere less than ϵ, and the graph of tst is a curve.

The remarks made before about how a set of chords can approximate a circular arc in a way that is quantitatively good although qualitatively wrong can be applied here too. The teeth of our tapered saw are almost all very sharp. The tooth over the interval $[1/(n + 1), 1/n]$ has height $1/n$ and base length $1/(n + 1)n$, so that the height is $(n + 1)$ times the base. Thus we are approximating [quantitatively very well] an infinite set of sharp teeth by a totally blunt horizontal segment.

The moral of this is that although the graph of a curve over a closed interval can be uniformly well approximated by broken-line functions, it does not follow that the shape of a broken-line approximation is anything like the shape, if any, of the curve.

3. *The graph of $y = x^2$ is a curve.* The domain is an interval, the whole line. That the function has the intermediate value property is equivalent to the assertion that each positive real number has a positive square root, which we have proved.

Now consider two numbers c and d, with $c < d$. The line through (c, c^2) and (d, d^2) has the equation

$$y = c^2 + \frac{d^2 - c^2}{d - c} (x - c).$$

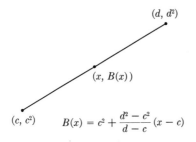

(d, d^2)

$(x, B(x))$

$(c, c^2) \qquad B(x) = c^2 + \dfrac{d^2 - c^2}{d - c} (x - c)$

For $c < x < d$ we want to investigate the difference between x^2 and the approximation $B(x)$:

$$x^2 - B(x) = x^2 - c^2 - \frac{d^2 - c^2}{d - c}(x - c).$$

In the graph above, $d^2 - c^2 > 0$. But this is not the case if, for example, $d = -2$ and $c = -3$. We claim that for any c, d, x, such that $c < x < d$, $x^2 - B(x) < 0$ or, equivalently, $x^2 < B(x)$. In fact,

$$\begin{aligned}
x^2 - B(x) &= x^2 - c^2 - (d + c)(x - c) \\
&= (x - c)[x + c - d - c] \\
&= (x - c)(x - d).
\end{aligned}$$

This shows that $x^2 < B(x)$ and that

$$|x^2 - B(x)| = B(x) - x^2 = (x - c)(d - x).$$

Now $0 < x - c < d - c$ and $0 < d - x < d - c$. Thus

$$|x^2 - B(x)| < (d - c)^2.$$

Given a closed interval $[a, b]$ and a positive number ϵ, let $p = \{x_0, x_1, \ldots, x_n\}$ be a partition of $[a, b]$ such that each subinterval has length $< \sqrt{\epsilon}$. If B is the corresponding broken-line function, the argument above shows that on each subinterval $[x_{k-1}, x_k]$

$$|x^2 - B(x)| < (x_k - x_{k-1})^2 < \epsilon.$$

This example has one atypical feature: how close together the partition points must be to get an ϵ-good approximation depends only on ϵ and not on the particular interval $[a, b]$.

4. *The graph of $y = 1/x$, with $x > 0$, is a curve.* The entire graph of $y = 1/x$, $x \neq 0$, is one hyperbola with two branches. Each branch is a curve, but the hyperbola is not. The domain has a hole in it at 0 and is not an interval.

The branch we are considering has as domain the interval $(0, \infty)$. The intermediate value property is easy: if $x_1 < x_2$ and $1/x_1 > k > 1/x_2$, then $k = 1/(1/k)$ and $x_1 < 1/k < x_2$.

Now let $[a, b]$ be a closed interval, with $a > 0$, and let $[c, d]$ be any subinterval. Let B be the line segment from $(c, 1/c)$ to $(d, 1/d)$. We shall exploit the fact that $y = 1/x$ is the graph of a strictly monotone decreasing function to get a crude but useful estimate for $|B(x) - (1/x)|$.

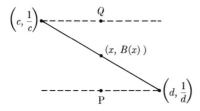

By the monotonicity the point $(x, 1/x)$ is somewhere between P and Q, and so is $(x, B(x))$; thus

$$\left|B(x) - \frac{1}{x}\right| < |P - Q| = \frac{1}{c} - \frac{1}{d} = \frac{d - c}{cd}.$$

Since $[c, d]$ is a subinterval of $[a, b]$, $c \geq a$ and $d > a$. It follows that $1/cd < 1/a^2$ and

$$\left| B(x) - \frac{1}{x} \right| < \frac{|d - c|}{a^2}.$$

Given $\epsilon > 0$, let p be a partition of $[a, b]$ such that each subinterval has length no greater than $a^2\epsilon$. Then the corresponding broken-line function approximates $1/x$ on the interval $[a, b]$ with error everywhere less than ϵ.

Exercises

1. In considering $y = x^2$ we found that $|B(x) - x^2| = (x - c)(d - x) < (d - c)^2$. Show that in fact, for $c < x < d$, $(x - c)(d - x) \leq (d - c)^2/4$, and actually $<$ except for $x = (c + d)/2$.
2. Partition the interval $[0, 1]$ into five subintervals of length 0.2 and draw the corresponding broken-line approximation to $y = x^2$.
3. Over the interval $[10, 20]$ find a broken-line approximation to $1/x$, with error everywhere less than 0.01.
4. Prove that over any interval (c, d), with $c > 0$, the graph of $y = 1/x$ is below the segment from $(c, 1/c)$ to $(d, 1/d)$.

§ 2. *Uniform Continuity*

Definition 7.8. Let f be a real function and S a subset of the domain of f. The function f is **uniformly continuous on the set S** in case: for each $\epsilon > 0$ there is a number $\delta > 0$ such that: if x and t are in S and $|x - t| < \delta$, then $|f(x) - f(t)| < \epsilon$.

Examples

1. The identity function is uniformly continuous on the real line. For given $\epsilon > 0$, let the δ of the definition be ϵ: if x and t are real numbers and $|x - t| < \epsilon$, then $|x - t| < \epsilon$.
2. Any nonvertical line or line segment L is the graph of a function uniformly continuous on its domain. To see this, let m be the slope of the line or segment L. Then, for any two points $(x, L(x))$ and $(t, L(t))$ on L,

$$\frac{L(x) - L(t)}{x - t} = m \quad \text{and} \quad |L(x) - L(t)| = |m| \, |x - t|.$$

Given $\epsilon > 0$, if $m \neq 0$ set $\delta = \epsilon/|m|$; then, for x and t in the domain of L,

$$|x - t| < \delta \Longrightarrow |L(x) - L(t)| < \epsilon.$$

3. The square root function is uniformly continuous on the interval $[0, \infty)$. It is easily verified, by squaring both sides, that if $0 \leq t < x$, then $0 < \sqrt{x} - \sqrt{t} \leq \sqrt{x - t}$. Given $\epsilon > 0$, let $\delta = \epsilon^2$; then, if x and t are nonnegative and $|x - t| < \delta$,

$$|\sqrt{x} - \sqrt{t}| \leq \sqrt{|x - t|} < \sqrt{\delta} = \epsilon.$$

Lemma 1. If B is any broken-line function on a bounded closed interval $[a, b]$, then B is uniformly continuous on $[a, b]$.

PROOF: Let $p = \{x_0, \ldots, x_n\}$ be the partition associated with B and let δ_1 be the length of a shortest interval $[x_{k-1}, x_k]$. Then, if x and t are in $[a, b]$ and $|x - t| < \delta_1$, x and t are either in the same subinterval or in adjacent subintervals. Let $m_1, \ldots, m_n$ be the slopes of the segments composing B and let m be the largest of $|m_1|, \ldots, |m_n|$.

If x and t are in the same partition interval $[x_{k-1}, x_k]$, then $B(x) - B(t) = m_k(x - t)$ and

$$|B(x) - B(t)| = |m_k| \, |x - t| \leq m|x - t|.$$

If x and t are in adjacent intervals, say $x_{k-1} \leq x < x_k < t \leq x_{k+1}$, then

$$\begin{aligned}
|B(x) - B(t)| &= |B(x) - B(x_k) + B(x_k) - B(t)| \\
&\leq |m_k| \, |x - x_k| + |m_{k+1}| \, |x_k - t| \\
&\leq m|x - x_k| + m|x_k - t| \\
&= m|x - t|.
\end{aligned}$$

Now, given $\epsilon > 0$, let δ be the smaller of δ_1 and ϵ/m. If x and t are in $[a, b]$ and $|x - t| < \delta$, then $|x - t| < \delta_1$ and, as established above, $|B(x) - B(t)| < m|x - t|$. But also $|x - t| < \epsilon/m$, so that $|B(x) - B(t)| < \epsilon$. ∎

Theorem 7.1. If the function f is uniformly well approximable by broken-line functions on an interval $[a, b]$, then f is uniformly continuous on $[a, b]$.

PROOF: Given $\epsilon > 0$, there is by hypothesis a broken-line function B such that, for every number z in $[a, b]$, $|B(z) - f(z)| < \epsilon/3$.

By Lemma 1, B is uniformly continuous on $[a, b]$, and there is a number $\delta > 0$ such that, if x and t are in $[a, b]$ and $|x - t| < \delta$, then $|B(x) - B(t)| < \epsilon/3$.

Now let x and t be any two numbers in $[a, b]$ such that $|x - t| < \delta$. Then

$$f(x) - f(t) = f(x) - B(x) + B(x) - B(t) + B(t) - f(t)$$

and

$$|f(x) - f(t)| < \frac{\epsilon}{3} + \frac{\epsilon}{3} + \frac{\epsilon}{3}. \qquad ∎$$

Theorem 7.2. If the function f is uniformly continuous on an interval $[a, b]$, then f is uniformly well approximable by broken-line functions on $[a, b]$.

PROOF: Let $[c, d]$ be a subinterval of $[a, b]$ and let B be the line segment from $(c, f(c))$ to $(d, f(d))$. Then, for $c \leq x \leq d$,

$$|f(x) - B(x)| = \left| f(x) - f(c) - \frac{f(d) - f(c)}{d - c} (x - c) \right|$$

$$\leq |f(x) - f(c)| + \left| (f(d) - f(c)) \frac{x - c}{d - c} \right|$$

$$\leq |f(x) - f(c)| + |f(d) - f(c)|.$$

Now, given $\epsilon > 0$, there is, since f is uniformly continuous on $[a, b]$, a positive number δ_ϵ such that if x and t are in $[a, b]$ and $|x - t| < \delta_\epsilon$, then $|f(x) - f(t)| < \epsilon$. Let p_ϵ be a partition of $[a, b]$ such that each interval of the partition has length less than δ_ϵ, and let B_ϵ be the corresponding broken-line approximation to f.

By the first paragraph of the proof we have, over each interval $[x_{k-1}, x_k]$ of p_ϵ,

$$|f(x) - B_\epsilon(x)| \leq |f(x) - f(x_{k-1})| + |f(x_k) - f(x_{k-1})|.$$

But $|x - x_{k-1}| < \delta_\epsilon$ and $|x_k - x_{k-1}| < \delta_\epsilon$, so $|f(x) - B_\epsilon(x)| < 2\epsilon$. ∎

This concludes the demonstration that on a closed bounded interval $[a, b]$ a function is uniformly continuous iff it can be uniformly well approximated by broken-line functions. Uniform continuity is, however, the broader of the two concepts because it applies to sets other than bounded intervals. For example, the square root function is uniformly continuous on $[0, \infty)$, but a broken-line function as we have defined it must have a bounded interval as domain.

With appropriate restrictions on domains, ranges, zero denominators, and so on, it is true that if each of two functions is uniformly continuous then so are their sum, difference, product, quotient, and compositions. This means that as soon as a few basic functions are proved uniformly continuous on certain intervals it follows that a large class of functions built out of these are uniformly continuous on these intervals. In this section we prove some of the most straightforward results along these lines; the next section considers more delicate aspects of continuity.

Theorem 7.3. If each of the functions f and g is uniformly continuous on an interval I, then so are $f + g$ and $f - g$ uniformly continuous on I.

PROOF: We will give the proof for $f + g$. Given $\epsilon > 0$, there is a corresponding $\delta_1 > 0$ such that if x and t are in I and $|x - t| < \delta_1$, then $|f(x) - f(t)| < \epsilon/2$. Also, there is $\delta_2 > 0$ such that if x and t are in I and $|x - t| < \delta_2$, then $|g(x) - g(t)| < \epsilon/2$. Let δ be the smaller of δ_1 and δ_2.

For x and t in I with $|x - t| < \delta$,

$$|[f + g](x) - [f + g](t)| = |f(x) - f(t) + g(x) - g(t)|$$

$$\leq |f(x) - f(t)| + |g(x) - g(t)|$$

$$< \frac{\epsilon}{2} + \frac{\epsilon}{2}.$$ ∎

Theorem 7.4. If each of the functions f and g is uniformly continuous on an interval I, and furthermore each is bounded on I, then the product fg is uniformly continuous on I.

PROOF: By hypothesis, each of the sets $\{|f(x)| \mid x$ in $I\}$ and $\{|g(x)| \mid x$ in $I\}$ has an upper bound. Let $M > 0$ be an upper bound for both sets.

For any x and t in I,

$$|f(x)g(x) - f(t)g(t)| = |f(x)g(x) - f(x)g(t) + f(x)g(t) - f(t)g(t)|$$
$$\leq |f(x)| \, |g(x) - g(t)| + |f(x) - f(t)| \, |g(t)|$$
$$\leq M|g(x) - g(t)| + M|f(x) - f(t)|.$$

Given $\epsilon > 0$, the uniform continuity of f on I guarantees the existence of $\delta_1 > 0$ such that, for x and t in I,

$$|x - t| < \delta_1 \Rightarrow |f(x) - f(t)| < \frac{\epsilon}{2M}.$$

Similarly, there exists $\delta_2 > 0$ such that, for x and t in I,

$$|x - t| < \delta_2 \Rightarrow |g(x) - g(t)| < \frac{\epsilon}{2M}.$$

Now let δ be the smaller of δ_1 and δ_2. If x and t are in I and $|x - t| < \delta$, then

$$|f(x)g(x) - f(t)g(t)| \leq M \frac{\epsilon}{2M} + M \frac{\epsilon}{2M} = \epsilon. \qquad \blacksquare$$

This theorem becomes particularly useful in conjunction with

Theorem 7.5. If the real function f is uniformly continuous on a *bounded* interval I, then f is bounded on I.

PROOF: Let the left end point of I be a, the right endpoint b; I may be closed, open, or neither. Since $1 > 0$ and f is uniformly continuous on I, there is some $\delta > 0$ such that, if x and t are in I and $|x - t| < \delta$, then $|f(x) - f(t)| < 1$. Let $\{x_0, \ldots, x_n\}$ be a partition of the closed interval $[a, b]$ such that each interval $[x_{k-1}, x_k]$ has length less than δ. For any x in the half-open interval $(x_0, x_2]$, $|x - x_1| < \delta$ and hence $|f(x) - f(x_1)| < 1$. If a is in I, then also $|f(a) - f(x_1)| < 1$. Thus $|f(x_1)| + 1$ is a bound for $\{|f(x)| \mid x$ in I and $x \leq x_2\}$.

For any x in the interval $[x_2, x_3]$, $|x - x_2| < \delta$ and $|f(x) - f(x_2)| < 1$. But $|f(x_2) - f(x_1)| < 1$, so for x in $[x_2, x_3]$, $|f(x) - f(x_1)| < 2$.

By an obvious induction we get to the last interval in the partition and can assert that, for all x in I,

$$f(x_1) - (n - 1) < f(x) < f(x_1) + (n - 1). \qquad \blacksquare$$

Corollary to Theorems 7.4 and 7.5. If functions f and g are each uniformly continuous on a bounded interval I, then their product fg is uniformly continuous on I.

Theorem 7.6.   If g is uniformly continuous on an interval I and f is uniformly continuous on a set S such that the range of g is a subset of S, then the composition $f \circ g$ is uniformly continuous on I.

PROOF: As an aid to the memory we have been consistent in associating the δ with domains and the ϵ with ranges. For this theorem the range of g is also the domain of f, or a subset of the domain of f, and we need some neutral symbol, say θ.

Given $\epsilon > 0$, since f is uniformly continuous on S, there is some $\theta > 0$ such that if u and v are in S and $|u - v| < \theta$, then $|f(u) - f(v)| < \epsilon$.

Since $\theta > 0$ and g is uniformly continuous on I, there is some $\delta > 0$ such that if x and t are in I and $|x - t| < \delta$, then $|g(x) - g(t)| < \theta$.

But the range of g is a subset of S, so that from $|g(x) - g(t)| < \theta$ follows $|f(g(x)) - f(g(t))| < \epsilon$.   ∎

Example

The sine function is uniformly continuous on the real line. For any real x and t we have [Exercise 17 on page 172]

$$\sin x - \sin t = 2 \cos \frac{x + t}{2} \sin \frac{x - t}{2}.$$

Since $|\cos u| \leq 1$ for all real u,

$$|\sin x - \sin t| \leq 2 \left| \sin \frac{x - t}{2} \right|.$$

If $|x - t| < \pi$, then

$$\left| \frac{x - t}{2} \right| < \frac{\pi}{2} \quad \text{and} \quad \left| \sin \frac{x - t}{2} \right| = \sin \left| \frac{x - t}{2} \right|.$$

But by Theorem 6.14 [page 180],

$$\sin \left| \frac{x - t}{2} \right| \leq \left| \frac{x - t}{2} \right|.$$

Given $\epsilon > 0$, let δ be the smaller of π and ϵ. Then for any real x and t, with $|x - t| < \delta$,

$$|\sin x - \sin t| \leq 2 \left| \frac{x - t}{2} \right| = |x - t| < \epsilon.$$

Exercises

1. Show that each statement below follows rather directly from theorems or examples given so far in this chapter.
   a. A constant function is uniformly continuous on any interval.
   b. The identity function is uniformly continuous on any interval.
   c. The squaring function is uniformly continuous on any bounded interval.
   d. A polynomial of degree two is uniformly continuous on any bounded interval.
   e. For each positive integer n the function x^n is uniformly continuous on any bounded interval.

f. The function $1/x$ is *not* uniformly continuous on the interval $(0, 1]$. [*Hint:* Use Theorem 7.5.]

g. For any number a in $(0, 1)$, the function $1/x$ is uniformly continuous on the interval $[a, 1]$.

h. If $h(x) = \sqrt{1 - x^2}$, h is uniformly continuous on $[-1, 1]$.

i. For each positive integer n, any polynomial of degree n is uniformly continuous on any bounded interval.

j. The cosine function is uniformly continuous on the real line. [*Hint:* If, for all x, $g(x) = (\pi/2) - x$, then $\cos = \sin \circ g$.]

k. If $F(x) = \sqrt{5 + x^2} - \cos(x - 5)$, F is uniformly continuous on the real line.

2. Prove directly from Definition 7.8 that the absolute value function is uniformly continuous on the interval $[-2, 2]$.

3. Prove that the squaring function is not uniformly continuous on $[0, \infty)$. [*Hint:* Given a positive number δ, however small, show that there are positive numbers x and t such that $|x - t| < \delta$ but $|x^2 - t^2| > 1$. For instance, $x = 1/\delta$ and $t = (1/\delta) + (\delta/2)$.]

4. Suppose that a function f is uniformly continuous on an interval I and that the set $\{f(x)|x \text{ in } I\}$ has a positive lower bound, a. Prove that $1/f$ is uniformly continuous on I. [*Hint:* Think of $1/f$ as a composition rather than as a quotient.]

§ 3. *Continuity at Points*

If we start with a function whose graph is a curve and change the value of the function at just one point, the result is two curves and an isolated point— a point that is in the wrong place to join the two curves.

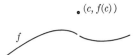

$\bullet\,(c, f(c))$

The diagram above illustrates one of the many ways in which a function f can fail to be continuous at the point c. The definition of continuity at a point is given by

Definition 7.9. A real function f is **continuous at the number c** iff corresponding to each $\epsilon > 0$ there exists $\delta > 0$ such that

$$\left.\begin{array}{l} x \text{ in the domain of } f \\ |x - c| < \delta \end{array}\right\} \Rightarrow |f(x) - f(c)| < \epsilon.$$

Remarks: 1. The definition clearly implies that in order for f to be continuous at c, c must be in the domain of f.

2. If f is uniformly continuous on a set S, then f is continuous at c for each c in S.

3. A function f may be continuous at each point of an interval, but not uniformly continuous on the interval. [See Example 1, below.]

Examples

1. A usual example of Remark 3 is $f(x) = 1/x$ for $0 < x \leq 1$. From Exercise 1(f) on page 223, we know that f is not uniformly continuous on $(0, 1]$ because f is not bounded on $(0, 1]$. We now prove that f is continuous at each number c in $(0, 1]$.

Given a number c in $(0, 1]$, set $\delta_1 = c/2$. Then, for x in

$$(c - \delta_1, c + \delta_1) = (c/2, 3c/2),$$

$x \neq 0$ and we can speak of $1/x$. For such x,

$$\left| \frac{1}{x} - \frac{1}{c} \right| = \left| \frac{c - x}{xc} \right| \leq \frac{|x - c|}{\dfrac{cc}{2}} = \frac{2}{c^2} |x - c|.$$

Now for each $\epsilon > 0$ let δ_ϵ be the smaller of $c/2$ and $\epsilon c^2/2$. Then

$$|x - c| < \delta_\epsilon \Rightarrow \left| \frac{1}{x} - \frac{1}{c} \right| \leq \frac{2}{c^2} |x - c| < \frac{2}{c^2} \frac{\epsilon c^2}{2} = \epsilon.$$

The δ we have found depends crucially on c. Given a function f and an interval I in its domain, f is uniformly continuous on I if corresponding to each $\epsilon > 0$ there is some $\delta_\epsilon > 0$ such that, for every c in I,

$$x \text{ in } I \text{ and } |x - c| < \delta_\epsilon \Rightarrow |f(x) - f(c)| < \epsilon.$$

But f is continuous at each point of I if corresponding to each $\epsilon > 0$ there is, for each c in I, some $\delta = \delta_\epsilon(c) > 0$ such that x is in I and

$$|x - c| < \delta_\epsilon(c) \Rightarrow |f(x) - f(c)| < \epsilon.$$

Oversimplified and abbreviated, the distinction is as follows: f is uniformly continuous on I if for each $\epsilon > 0$ there is a single $\delta > 0$ which works for all c in I; f is continuous on I, but not uniformly, if for each c there is a δ_c which works, but no single δ which works for all c.

2. The squeezed sawtooth function sst is a broken-line function on any interval $[a, 1]$, where $0 < a < 1$. Thus sst is uniformly continuous on any such interval. As a consequence sst is continuous at each number c in the half-open interval $(0, 1]$: given c in $(0, 1)$, choose a such that $0 < a < c$; sst is uniformly continuous on $[a, 1]$ and therefore continuous at c.

But sst is not uniformly continuous on $(0, 1]$. This can be seen as follows. For each positive integer n, the graph of sst over the interval $[1/(n + 1), 1/n]$ is a line segment with a slope whose absolute value is $2n(n + 1)$. For x and t in this interval,

$$|\text{sst } x - \text{sst } t| = 2n(n + 1)|x - t|.$$

To make $|\text{sst } x - \text{sst } t| < 1$, for example, it is necessary to have $|x - t| < 1/2n(n + 1)$. There is no positive number δ which is less than $1/2n(n + 1)$ for every positive integer n; thus corresponding to $\epsilon = 1$ there is no δ which works for sst on the interval $(0, 1]$, which includes every interval $[1/(n + 1),$ $1/n]$.

3. If, for $x \neq 0$, $f(x) = \sin \pi/x$, then f is, on the interval $(0, 1]$, something like a smoothed-out sst. For each integer n, $f(1/n) = \sin n\pi = 0$. In each interval $[1/(n + 2), 1/n]$, for n a positive integer, there is a number x_n with $f(x_n) = 1$ and a number t_n with $f(t_n) = -1$. On any closed interval not containing 0, f is uniformly continuous because it is the composition of sine, uniformly continuous on the real line, with the function mapping x to π/x, which is uniformly continuous on any closed interval not containing 0.

We turn now to examine what positive inferences we can draw from the continuity of a function f at a point c, and also what we can deduce about a function continuous at each point of an interval.

The diagram below is a picture of Definition 7.8. If f is continuous at c, then corresponding to each $\epsilon > 0$ is $\delta > 0$ such that, if x is in the interval $(c - \delta, c + \delta)$, either x is not in the domain of f or else x is in the domain of f and $|f(x) - f(c)| < \epsilon$. Then the point $(x, f(x))$ is in the white rectangle between the two shaded strips. The diagram becomes most useful when the domain of f includes every point of the interval $(c - \delta, c + \delta)$, or at least every point of either $(c - \delta, c]$ or $[c, c + \delta)$. The graph of f over this interval is inside the white rectangle.

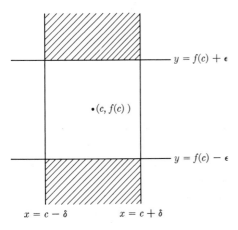

$y = f(c) + \epsilon$

$\bullet (c, f(c))$

$y = f(c) - \epsilon$

$x = c - \delta$ $x = c + \delta$

Basic picture about a function f continuous at c: for each $\epsilon > 0$ there is $\delta > 0$ such that no point on the graph of f is in either shaded infinite strip.

Basic Lemmas

Let the domain of a function f include a closed interval $[a, b]$, and let c be an interior point of $[a, b]$ at which f is continuous.

Lemma 2. If $f(c)$ is positive [negative], there is an interval $(c - \delta, c + \delta)$ such that, for each x in this interval, $f(x)$ is positive [negative].

Lemma 3. If k is any number larger than [smaller than] $f(c)$, then there is an interval $(c - \delta, c + \delta)$ over which the graph of f remains below [above] the line $y = k$.

Let the domain of a function f include a closed interval $[a, b]$.

Lemma 4. If f is continuous at a, and k is any number larger than [smaller than] $f(a)$, then there is an interval $[a, a + \delta)$ over which the graph of f remains below [above] the line $y = k$.

Lemma 5. If f is continuous at b, and k is any number larger than [smaller than] $f(b)$, then there is an interval $(b - \delta, b]$ over which the graph of f remains below [above] the line $y = k$.

Before proving these lemmas we note that they all have essentially the same content. Lemma 2 is a special case of 3; Lemmas 4 and 5 are merely the appropriate one-sided modifications of 3 for an end point of the domain. We give an illustration of the proof of Lemma 2 for $f(c) < 0$ and then prove Lemma 3 for $f(c) > k$.

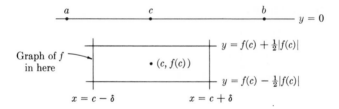

There are no points of the graph of f in the strip of width 2δ that are above the line $y = f(c) + \frac{1}{2}|f(c)|$, so certainly none above or on $y = 0$.

PROOF OF LEMMA 3: Let f be defined on $[a, b]$ and continuous at some number c, with $a < c < b$. Let δ_c be the smaller of $c - a$ and $b - c$. Then the domain of f contains the interval $(c - \delta_c, c + \delta_c)$.

Now let k be any number such that $f(c) > k$. Set

$$\epsilon = \frac{f(c) - k}{2} > 0.$$

Since f is continuous at c and $\epsilon > 0$, there is a positive number δ_ϵ such that if x is in the domain of f and $|x - c| < \delta_\epsilon$, then

$$|f(x) - f(c)| < \frac{f(c) - k}{2},$$

or,

$$f(c) - \frac{f(c) - k}{2} < f(x) < f(c) + \frac{f(c) - k}{2}.$$

Now let δ be the smaller of δ_c and δ_ϵ. Then the last inequality above holds for any x in $(c - \delta, c + \delta)$. Its left side says that

$$f(x) > \frac{f(c) + k}{2}.$$

But $f(c) > k$, so for x in $(c - \delta, c + \delta)$,

$$f(x) > \frac{k + k}{2} = k.$$

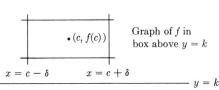

$\bullet\,(c, f(c))$

Graph of f in
box above $y = k$

$x = c - \delta$ $x = c + \delta$

$y = k$

Theorem 7.7 [*The Intermediate Value Theorem*]. Let f be a non-constant real function continuous on an interval I. If x_1 and x_2 are any two numbers of I such that $f(x_1) \neq f(x_2)$, then for each number k between $f(x_1)$ and $f(x_2)$ there is some number c between x_1 and x_2 such that $f(c) = k$.

PROOF: Without loss of generality we can assume $x_1 < x_2$. As one of two possible cases we assume $f(x_1) < f(x_2)$. Let k be any number such that $f(x_1) < k < f(x_2)$. By Lemma 4 there is a positive number δ_1 such that over the interval $[x_1, x_1 + \delta_1)$ the graph of f is below the line $y = k$.

By Lemma 5 there is a positive number δ_2 such that over the interval $(x_2 - \delta_2, x_2]$ the graph of f is above the line $y = k$.

Let S be the set of those numbers x between x_1 and x_2 such that $f(x) < k$. Set S is not empty because each x in $(x_1, x_1 + \delta_1)$ is in S. Set S has upper bounds: any number in $(x_2 - \delta_2, x_2]$. Let c be the least upper bound of S, and consider $f(c)$.

If $f(c)$ were less than k, then by Lemma 3 the graph of f would stay below the line $y = k$ over some interval $[c, c + \delta)$, and c would not be an upper bound of S. Thus $f(c) \not< k$.

If $f(c)$ were larger than k, then by Lemma 3 the graph of f would stay above the line $y = k$ over some interval $(c - \delta, c]$, and c would not be the *least* upper bound of S. Thus $f(c) \not> k$.

By trichotomy, $f(c) = k$. ∎

Below is one possible illustration. The set S is indicated by heavy segments.

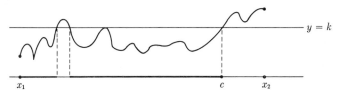

$y = k$

x_1 c x_2

Typical Applications of the Intermediate Value Theorem

1. For each positive integer n, let f_n be the function mapping each real x to x^n. By Exercise 1(e) on page 222, f_n is uniformly continuous on any bounded interval. Let k be a positive number. Then, for any positive integer n, $0^n < k < (k + 1)^n$. By the Intermediate Value Theorem there is a positive number c such that $c^n = k$. This positive c is labeled $\sqrt[n]{k}$ or $k^{1/n}$. For odd n the range of f_n has no lower bound and by the Intermediate Value Theorem each negative number has an nth root, unique because, for odd n, f_n is strictly monotone increasing on $\mathfrak{R}$.

2. Consider the equation $x^2 = \cos x + 3$. If we define f by: for all real x,

$$f(x) = x^2 - \cos x - 3,$$

the function f is uniformly continuous on any bounded interval. Also

$$f(1) = 1 - \cos 1 - 3 < 0, \quad f(2) = 4 - \cos 2 - 3 > 0.$$

By the Intermediate Value Theorem there is some x between 1 and 2 with $f(x) = 0$, or $x^2 = \cos x + 3$.

3. Let f be monotone increasing and continuous on an interval $[a, b]$. The monotonicity gives an upper bound to the set of lengths of all broken-line approximations to the graph of f over any interval $[a, c]$, with $a < c \leq b$. For let p be any partition of $[a, c]$: the length of the segment from $(x_{k-1}, f(x_{k-1}))$ to $(x_k, f(x_k))$ is less than $x_k - x_{k-1} + f(x_k) - f(x_{k-1})$ for each x_k in p. Moreover,

$$\sum_{k=1}^{n} [x_k - x_{k-1} + f(x_k) - f(x_{k-1})] = c - a + f(c) - f(a).$$

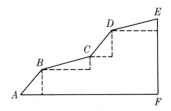

$$AB + BC + CD + DE < AF + FE$$

This lets us define an *arc length function*, say L. We let $L(a) = 0$ and, for each x in $(a, b]$, let $L(x)$ be the length of the graph of f over the interval $[a, x]$; that is, $L(x)$ is the least upper bound of the set of all lengths of broken-line approximations to f over the interval $[a, x]$.

We claim that L is continuous at each point of $[a, b]$, and therefore for each number t between 0 and $L(b)$ there is a point $(x, f(x))$ such that the graph of f over the interval $[a, x]$ has length t.

The argument for the continuity of L is much like that for the existence of L. For c any point of $[a, b)$, and for $\epsilon > 0$ let δ_c be less than $\epsilon/2$ and also small enough [by the continuity of f at c] so that, for x in $(c, c + \delta_c)$,

$$|f(x) - f(c)| < \frac{\epsilon}{2}.$$

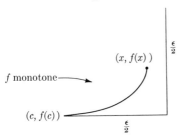

Then [see diagram] $(\epsilon/2) + (\epsilon/2)$ is an upper bound for the length of the arc from $(c, f(c))$ to $(x, f(x))$ and

$$|L(x) - L(c)| \leq \epsilon.$$

A similar argument is used for x to the left of c, unless $c = a$, and establishes that L is continuous on $[a, b]$.

Remark: This discussion for monotone increasing continuous functions can be applied with little change to monotone decreasing continuous functions. For a function made up from a few monotone pieces, such as cosine over $[0, 10]$, we could patch up a treatment of arc length. Anything beyond this is quite difficult.

Exercises

1. Prove that the equation $x^3 - 5x^2 + 6x - 1 = 0$ has a root in each of the intervals $(0, 1)$, $(1, 2)$, and $(3, 4)$.
2. Prove that there are at least three real numbers x such that $x^3 = \sin x$.
3. Say what you can about solutions of $x^3 = \cos x$.
4. Prove that there is one and only one real number k such that $k^3 = k + 1$.
5. Locate the number k of Exercise 4 in an interval of length less than 0.05.
6. If $g(x) = x^3 - x - 1$, find a positive number δ such that

   $$|x - 1| < \delta \Rightarrow |g(x) - g(1)| < \tfrac{1}{4}.$$

   [*Hint:* $g(x) - g(1)$ has $x - 1$ as a factor.]
7. Let P be a polynomial and a a number. Let $Q(x) = P(x) - P(a)$, for all x. Prove that $Q(x)$ has $x - a$ as a factor.

Quotients

We have proved that if each of two functions is uniformly continuous on an interval I, then their sum is uniformly continuous on I. We have also proved that if each of two functions is uniformly continuous on a *bounded* interval I, then their product is uniformly continuous on I. Theorems about the continuity of quotients need more restrictive hypotheses; we give one such theorem here and a stronger one in the next section.

Theorem 7.8. If the function g is continuous at c and $g(c) \neq 0$, then $1/g$ is continuous at c. As a consequence of this and the product theorem, if g and f are continuous at c and $g(c) \neq 0$, then f/g is continuous at c.

PROOF: As in Lemma 2, there is a positive number δ such that for x in $(c - \delta, c + \delta)$, and in the domain of f,

$$|f(x) - f(c)| < \tfrac{1}{2}|f(c)|$$

and hence $|f(x)| > \tfrac{1}{2}|f(c)|$.

For such x,

$$\left| \frac{1}{f(x)} - \frac{1}{f(c)} \right| = \left| \frac{f(x) - f(c)}{f(x)\,f(c)} \right| < \frac{2|f(x) - f(c)|}{|f(c)|^2}.$$

Given $\epsilon > 0$, let δ_ϵ be the smaller of the δ above and $\epsilon|f(c)|^2/2$. Then, for $|x - c| < \delta_\epsilon$ and x in the domain of f,

$$\left| \frac{1}{f(x)} - \frac{1}{f(c)} \right| < \epsilon. \qquad \blacksquare$$

§ 4. *Three Major Theorems*

None of the theorems of this chapter can be dismissed as unimportant, but the Intermediate Value Theorem and the three theorems of this section are outstandingly important. We state the three at the outset.

Theorem 7.9 [*Heine's Theorem*]. A real function continuous at each point of a *closed bounded* interval $[a, b]$ is uniformly continuous on $[a, b]$.

Theorem 7.10 [*The Extreme Value Theorem*]. Let f be a real function continuous at each point of a *closed bounded* interval $[a, b]$. Let m and M be respectively the glb and lub of $\{f(x)|a \leq x \leq b\}$. There are numbers x_1 and x_2 in $[a, b]$ such that $f(x_1) = m$ and $f(x_2) = M$.

Remark: By Theorem 7.9, f is uniformly continuous on $[a, b]$ and hence, by Theorem 7.5, bounded on $[a, b]$. Thus m and M exist. Theorems 7.10 and 7.7 [The Intermediate Value Theorem] together show that f maps $[a, b]$ onto $[m, M]$.

Theorem 7.11 [*Inverses*]. Let f be a *strictly monotone* mapping of an interval $[a, b]$ onto a set S. Then f is one-to-one and f^{-1} is a *continuous* mapping of S onto $[a, b]$, increasing or decreasing according as f is increasing or decreasing. If, furthermore, f is continuous on $[a, b]$, then f maps $[a, b]$ onto the interval $[f(a), f(b)]$ or $[f(b), f(a)]$.

PROOF OF THEOREM 7.9 [*Heine's Theorem*]: Let f be a real function continuous at each point of the closed interval $[a, b]$ and let ϵ be a positive number. We shall construct a partition p_ϵ such that the corresponding broken-line function B_ϵ differs from f by less than ϵ everywhere on $[a, b]$. To begin with we construct a strictly monotone sequence $x_0, x_1, \ldots$ converging to b, and then discard all but the first few terms.

Let $x_0 = a$. Since f is continuous at a, there are positive numbers δ such that

$$a \leq x < a + \delta \Rightarrow |f(x) - f(a)| < \frac{\epsilon}{2}.$$

Let δ_0 be the lub of the set of all such δ and set $x_1 = a + (\delta_0/2)$. The first segment of B_ϵ is from $(a, f(a))$ to $(x_1, f(x_1))$. For x between a and x_1,

$$|B_\epsilon(x) - f(a)| < |f(x_1) - f(a)| < \frac{\epsilon}{2},$$

and $|f(x) - f(a)| < \epsilon/2$, so that $|f(x) - B_\epsilon(x)| < \epsilon$. [A possible diagram is shown below.]

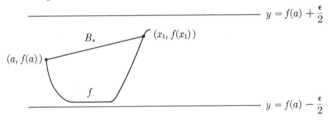

Our sequence is now defined recursively. Given a number x_n in (a, b) let δ_n be the lub of the set of positive δ such that

$$x_n \leq x < x_n + \delta \Rightarrow |f(x) - f(x_n)| < \frac{\epsilon}{2}.$$

We consider f only on the interval $[a, b]$, so that $x_n + \delta \leq b$. Then let $x_{n+1} = x_n + (\delta_n/2)$; x_{n+1} is larger than x_n but at most half-way from x_n to b.

The sequence $\{x_n\}$, being monotone increasing and bounded, converges to its least upper bound, say $c \leq b$. We want to show that, in fact, $c = b$. Suppose that $c < b$. Then since f is continuous at c, there is a positive number δ_c such that for any x in $(c - \delta_c, c + \delta_c)$,

$$|f(x) - f(c)| < \frac{\epsilon}{4}.$$

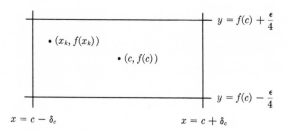

$$x = c - \delta_c \qquad\qquad\qquad x = c + \delta_c$$

Since the sequence converges to c, there is some positive integer k such that $x_k > c - \delta_c$. For any x in $[x_k, c + \delta_c)$,

$$|f(x) - f(c)| < \frac{\epsilon}{4} \quad \text{and} \quad |f(x_k) - f(c)| < \frac{\epsilon}{4}.$$

Thus for any x such that $x_k \leq x < c + \delta_c$,

$$|f(x) - f(x_k)| < \frac{\epsilon}{2}.$$

This means that the number δ_k, in our recursive definition of the sequence, is at least as big as $c + \delta_c - x_k$. Then $x_{k+1} = x_k + (\delta_k/2)$ is at least half-way from x_k to $c + \delta_c$. But this makes $x_{k+1} > c$, which is absurd, since c is an upper bound of $\{x_n\}$. [Details:

$$x_{k+1} \geq x_k + \tfrac{1}{2}(c + \delta_c - x_k) = \tfrac{1}{2}(x_k + c + \delta_c) > \tfrac{1}{2}(c - \delta_c + c + \delta_c) = c.]$$

Therefore, $c = b$ and our sequence converges to b. Since f is continuous at b, there is a positive number δ_b such that

$$b - \delta_b < x \leq b \Rightarrow |f(x) - f(b)| < \frac{\epsilon}{2}.$$

Let $n - 1$ be the smallest integer such that $x_{n-1} > b - \delta_b$. For the last segment of B_ϵ we take the segment from $(x_{n-1}, f(x_{n-1}))$ to $(b, f(b))$. By the same argument as for the interval $[a, x_1]$, over each interval of the partition, $|f(x) - B_\epsilon(x)| < \epsilon$. ∎

PROOF OF THEOREM 7.10 [*The Extreme Value Theorem*]: Let f be continuous at each point of $[a, b]$ and let m be the glb $\{f(x) | a \leq x \leq b\}$. Suppose that, for all x in $[a, b]$, $f(x) > m$. Then we define g on $[a, b]$ by

$$g(x) = f(x) - m,$$

and $g(x) > 0$ for all x in $[a, b]$. Also, g is continuous at each point of $[a, b]$, as it is the sum of f and a constant, each continuous on $[a, b]$.

By Theorem 7.8, $1/g$ is continuous at each point of $[a, b]$. Then, by Heine's Theorem, $1/g$ is uniformly continuous on $[a, b]$ and, by Theorem 7.5, $1/g$ is bounded on $[a, b]$. Since $g(x) > 0$ for all x in $[a, b]$, $1/g$ has a positive upper bound, say B. For all x in $[a, b]$, $1/g(x) \leq B$, or $g(x) \geq 1/B$, $f(x) - m \geq 1/B$, and finally: for all x in $[a, b]$, $f(x) \geq m + 1/B$, where $B > 0$. This contradicts the fact that m is the greatest lower bound of the range of f. Hence, after all, there must be some x_1 in $[a, b]$ with $f(x_1) = m$.

The proof that there is some x_2 in $[a, b]$ with $f(x_2) = M$ is essentially the same. If this were false the function $1/(M - f)$ would be bounded on $[a, b]$. ∎

As an example of Theorem 7.11, let $f(x) = x$ for $0 \le x < 1$ and let $f(x) = x + 1$ for $1 \le x \le 2$. Then f maps $[0, 2]$ onto the union of the intervals $[0, 1)$ and $[2, 3]$. On $[0, 1)$, $f^{-1}(x) = x$. On $[2, 3]$, $f^{-1}(x) = x - 1$. Thus f^{-1} is continuous on its domain. Also f is continuous on the subinterval $[1, 2]$ and maps it onto the interval $[2, 3]$.

PROOF OF THEOREM 7.11: As one of two cases, assume f strictly increasing on $[a, b]$. Then $a \le c < d \le b \Rightarrow f(c) < f(d)$, and f is seen to be one-to-one. Also, f^{-1} is strictly increasing on S, the image of $[a, b]$ under f, because, for $f(c)$ and $f(d)$ in S, $f^{-1}(f(c)) = c$ and $f^{-1}(f(d)) = d$, and $c < d$ iff $f(c) < f(d)$.

Now let $k = f(c)$ be in S and suppose c to be an interior point of $[a, b]$. Given $\epsilon' > 0$, let ϵ be positive and such that $\epsilon \le \epsilon'$, and also the interval $[c - \epsilon, c + \epsilon]$ is contained in $[a, b]$. Let $f(c - \epsilon) = k - \delta_1$ and $f(c + \epsilon) = k + \delta_2$. Since f is strictly increasing, both δ_1 and δ_2 are positive.

If x is in S and $k - \delta_1 < x < k + \delta_2$, then, because f^{-1} is strictly increasing on S, we have

$$f^{-1}(k - \delta_1) < f^{-1}(x) < f^{-1}(k + \delta_2),$$

or

$$c - \epsilon < f^{-1}(x) < c + \epsilon.$$

Since $\epsilon \le \epsilon'$, $|f^{-1}(x) - f^{-1}(k)| < \epsilon'$.

If k is $f(a)$ or $f(b)$, then suppression of one side of the inequalities above gives the proof that f^{-1} is continuous at k.

This completes the proof that f^{-1} is continuous on S. If, furthermore, f is continuous on $[a, b]$ then, as noted in the remark under the statement of the Extreme Value Theorem, f maps $[a, b]$ onto $[f(a), f(b)]$. ∎

The proof for f decreasing is essentially the same.

Remark: The geometric version of the theorem is compellingly self-evident. If f is strictly monotone, then f is one-to-one and has an inverse. The congruence $(x, y) \longrightarrow (y, x)$ maps the graph of f onto the graph of f^{-1}. If also f is continuous on $[a, b]$, then the graph of f over $[a, b]$ is a curve. Surely a congruence must map a curve onto a curve.

Applications to the Circular Functions

A periodic function is by definition a many-to-one correspondence of its domain to its range, and cannot have a composition inverse. For example, for any integer n, sin $x = 1/2$ if $x = \pi/6$, or $5\pi/6$, or $(\pi/6) + 2n\pi$, or $(5\pi/6) + 2n\pi$.

The restriction of the sine function to the interval $[-\pi/2, \pi/2]$ is called Sin. That is, the domain of Sin is $[-\pi/2, \pi/2]$ and for x in this interval Sin $x = \sin x$. The function Sin is strictly monotone increasing and continuous on its domain. By Theorem 7.11 it has a strictly increasing continuous inverse on $[-1, 1]$, called Sin^{-1} or Arc sin.

The cosine function is strictly decreasing and continuous on $[0, \pi]$. Its restriction to this interval is called Cos and has a strictly decreasing continuous inverse, Cos^{-1} or Arc cos, with domain $[-1, 1]$ and range $[0, \pi]$.

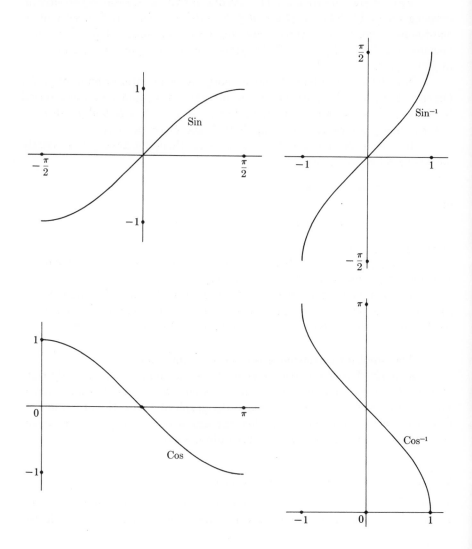

Four other functions defined in terms of sine and cosine are tangent (tan), cotangent (cot), secant (sec), and cosecant (csc), defined as follows:

$$\tan = \frac{\sin}{\cos}, \quad \cot = \frac{\cos}{\sin}, \quad \sec = \frac{1}{\cos}, \quad \csc = \frac{1}{\sin}.$$

For example the domain of the tangent function is the set of all x such that $\cos x \neq 0$, and for such x $\tan x = \sin x/\cos x$. By Theorem 7.8, tan is continuous on its domain, and by Heine's Theorem tan is uniformly continuous on any closed interval $[a, b]$ not containing a number x such that $\cos x = 0$—that is, not containing any odd multiple of $\pi/2$.

For all x with $\cos x \neq 0$,

$$\tan (-x) = \frac{\sin (-x)}{\cos (-x)} = \frac{-\sin x}{\cos x} = -\tan x.$$

For all x,

$$\sin(x + \pi) = \sin x \cos \pi + \cos x \sin \pi = -\sin x,$$

and

$$\cos (x + \pi) = \cos x \cos \pi - \sin x \sin \pi = -\cos x.$$

Thus, for all x in the domain of tan, $\tan (x + \pi) = \tan x$: tan is periodic with period π. On the interval $[0, \pi/2)$, sin and cos are both nonnegative, sin increasing and cos decreasing. Thus on $[0, \pi/2)$ tan is strictly increasing.

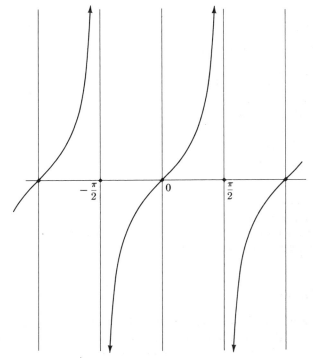

Partial graph of tan

The restriction of tan to the open interval $(-\pi/2, \pi/2)$ is called Tan and has an inverse, Tan^{-1} or Arc tan, continuous on $(-\infty, \infty)$.

Graph of Arc tan

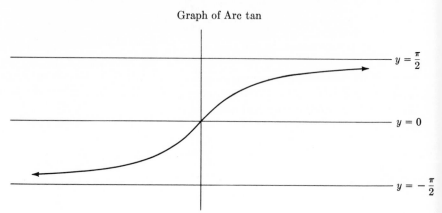

$y = \dfrac{\pi}{2}$

$y = 0$

$y = -\dfrac{\pi}{2}$

Exercises

1. Distinguish between the functions cot and $1/\tan$.

2. Prove that

$$1 + \tan^2 = \sec^2,$$

and

$$\cot^2 + 1 = \csc^2.$$

3. Prove that, with appropriate restrictions on x and y,

$$\tan(x + y) = \frac{\tan x + \tan y}{1 - \tan x \tan y}.$$

4. Sketch graphs of sec, csc, and cot.

5. Prove that if $\cos x \neq -1$,

$$\tan \frac{x}{2} = \frac{\sin x}{1 + \cos x}.$$

6. Sketch the graph of

$$y = \frac{1}{1 + \tan^2 x}$$

over a complete period.

7. Prove that the function $\tan \circ \tan$ is uniformly continuous on $[-\pi/4, \pi/4]$.

8. Sketch the graph of $y = \tan(\tan x)$.

§ 5. *Curves*

At the beginning of the chapter we confined the discussion to the question of the conditions that make the graph of a function acceptable as a curve. We have proved that a function continuous on an interval has the intermediate value property on that interval, is uniformly continuous on each closed bounded subinterval, and hence is uniformly well approximable by broken-line functions on each such subinterval. Thus our original definition is equivalent to

Definition 7.10. The graph of a real function f is a **curve** iff the domain of f is an interval and f is continuous at each point of its domain.

Curves other than graphs of real functions are described by parametric equations using continuous real functions to determine the coordinates of points on the curve. If each of two real functions f and g is continuous on an interval I, then the set of all points (x, y) such that, for some t in I, $x = f(t)$ and $y = g(t)$, is a curve. Put slightly differently, a curve in the plane is the image of an interval I under a mapping: $t \longrightarrow (f(t), g(t))$, where f and g are continuous on I. Similarly, a curve in $\mathfrak{R}^3$ is the image of an interval I under a mapping:

$$t \longrightarrow (f(t), g(t), h(t)),$$

where f, g, and h are real functions continuous on I.

Examples

1. For a positive number r, with the understanding that $0 \le t \le 2\pi$,

$$x = r \cos t \quad \text{and} \quad y = r \sin t$$

are parametric equations of the circle with radius r and center at the origin. The mapping of $[0, 2\pi]$ onto the circle is one-to-one except that the point $(1, 0)$ is the image of both 0 and 2π.

2. For $0 \le t \le 2\pi$,

$$x = \cos t \quad \text{and} \quad y = \sin t,$$

and for $2\pi \le t \le 4\pi$,

$$x = 2 - \cos t \quad \text{and} \quad y = \sin t.$$

This maps the interval $[0, 4\pi]$ onto a figure eight made up out of two circles: for $0 \le t \le 2\pi$, $x^2 + y^2 = 1$; for $2\pi \le t \le 4\pi$, $(x - 2)^2 + y^2 = 1$.

3. For $t \ge 0$,

$$x = \cos t, \qquad y = \sin t, \qquad z = t^2.$$

Each point on this curve is at distance 1 from the z-axis:

$$|(\cos t, \sin t, t^2) - (0, 0, t^2)| = 1.$$

The curve lies on a right circular cylinder of radius 1 around the z-axis.

4. Let a and b be positive numbers. With $0 \le t \le 2\pi$, the equations

$$x = a \cos t \quad \text{and} \quad y = b \sin t$$

are parametric equations of an ellipse. The point (x, y) is on the curve iff

$$\frac{x^2}{a^2} + \frac{y^2}{b^2} = 1.$$

Exercises

1. Give parametric equations for each of the following curves.

a. A parabolic arc from $(0, 0)$ to $(1, 1)$ along with the line segment from $(1, 1)$ to $(0, 0)$.

b. The triangular path with vertices at $(1, 2)$, $(3, 5)$, and $(7, -2)$.

c. The path of a particle which starts at $(1, 0)$, follows the upper half of the unit circle to $(0, 1)$, goes up the y-axis to $(0, 5)$, then goes straight to $(3, 3)$ and stops.

d. A spiral of the sort used to bind notebooks.

2. Let f and g be real functions continuous on the interval $[0, 1]$. Prove that for each $\epsilon > 0$ there is a number $\delta > 0$ such that, for s and t in $[0, 1]$,

$$|s - t| < \delta \Rightarrow |(f(s), g(s)) - (f(t), g(t))| < \epsilon.$$

3. If a and b are positive, the point $(0, b)$ is on each of

the line $y = b$,

the circle $x^2 + y^2 = b^2$,

the ellipse $b^2x^2 + a^2y^2 = a^2b^2$.

Prove that, if $b^2 < a^2$, the upper part of the ellipse is between the circle and the line over the intervals $(-b, 0)$ and $(0, b)$. Draw a diagram to illustrate.

4. Let f be a real function continuous on the interval $[a, b]$. For $x_1 < x_2$ in $[a, b]$, suppose $y_1 < f(x_1)$ and $y_2 > f(x_2)$. Prove that the segment from (x_1, y_1) to (x_2, y_2) intersects the graph of f. [*Hint:* The segment is the graph of a function, say L; consider $f - L$.]

§ 6. *Minkowski's ? Function*

The function to be considered is a strictly increasing continuous mapping of the interval $[0, 1]$ onto itself. Hermann Minkowski defined the function and discussed one of its interesting properties at the meeting of the International Congress of Mathematicians at Heidelberg in 1904. His presentation is given in the second volume (pages 50–51) of his collected works. More recently R. Salem ["Singular monotonic functions," *Trans. Amer. Math. Soc.*, **53**: 427–439 (1943)] has settled some questions about lines tangent to the graph of the function. The object of this section is to argue that any broken-line approximation to the graph of ? is necessarily, qualitatively, a grotesque misrepresentation of the curve.

We start by defining a sequence of domains D_n and on each domain a function G_n:

$$D_0 = \{\tfrac{0}{1}, \tfrac{1}{1}\},$$
$$D_1 = \{\tfrac{0}{1}, \tfrac{1}{2}, \tfrac{1}{1}\},$$
$$D_2 = \{\tfrac{0}{1}, \tfrac{1}{3}, \tfrac{1}{2}, \tfrac{2}{3}, \tfrac{1}{1}\},$$
$$D_3 = \{\tfrac{0}{1}, \tfrac{1}{4}, \tfrac{1}{3}, \tfrac{2}{5}, \tfrac{1}{2}, \tfrac{3}{5}, \tfrac{2}{3}, \tfrac{3}{4}, \tfrac{1}{1}\}.$$

In general, D_{n+1} is the union of D_n with the set of mediants of the intervals determined by adjacent numbers in D_n. It follows [see the discussion of Farey sections on pages 56–58] that the union of all the sets D_n is the set of rational numbers in the interval $[0, 1]$.

The functions G_n are defined as follows:

$$G_0(0) = 0, \quad G_0(1) = 1,$$
$$G_1(0) = 0, \quad G_1(\tfrac{1}{2}) = \tfrac{1}{2}, \quad G_1(1) = 1,$$
$$G_2(0) = 0, \quad G_2(\tfrac{1}{3}) = \tfrac{1}{4}, \quad G_2(\tfrac{1}{2}) = \tfrac{1}{2}, \quad G_2(\tfrac{2}{3}) = \tfrac{3}{4}, \quad G_2(1) = 1.$$

To get G_{n+1} from G_n this scheme is used. If a/b and c/d are adjacent in D_n, with $a/b < c/d$, then

$$G_{n+1}\left(\frac{a}{b}\right) = G_n\left(\frac{a}{b}\right), \quad G_{n+1}\left(\frac{a+c}{b+d}\right) = \frac{1}{2}\left[G_n\left(\frac{a}{b}\right) + G_n\left(\frac{c}{d}\right)\right],$$

$$G_{n+1}\left(\frac{c}{d}\right) = G_n\left(\frac{c}{d}\right).$$

In short, on D_n, G_{n+1} agrees with G_n; to each mediant in D_{n+1}, G_{n+1} assigns the average of the values of G_n at the end points surrounding the mediant.

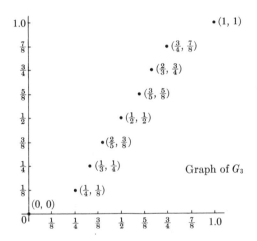

For real x and y, if $x < y$, then $x < (x + y)/2 < y$. From this we see that if G_n is strictly increasing on D_n, then G_{n+1} is strictly increasing on D_{n+1}. Each function G_n can be represented as a set of ordered pairs of rational numbers. In this representation we have G_n a subset of G_{n+1}, for each n. The union of all the functions G_n, where n is a nonnegative integer, we shall call G. As thus defined, G is a strictly increasing mapping of the set of rational numbers in $[0, 1]$ into itself. As Minkowski points out, the range of G contains 0 and 1 and all rational numbers in $(0, 1)$ of the form $a/2^k$, with a odd and k a positive integer.

Furthermore, G is uniformly continuous on its domain. Arguments for this assertion and some others are outlined in the exercises at the end of the section. It follows that G has a unique extension to a function con-

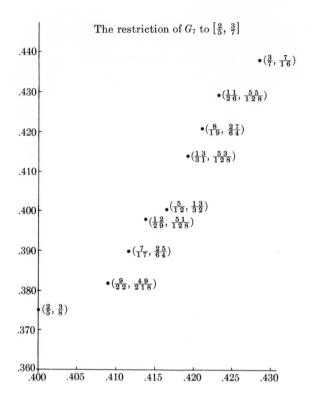

The restriction of G_7 to $[\frac{2}{5}, \frac{3}{7}]$

tinuous on the real interval $[0, 1]$. This extension of G is Minkowski's **?** Function. For rational x in $[0, 1]$, $?(x) = G(x)$. For irrational x in $(0, 1)$, $?(x)$ is the limit of the sequence $\{G(r_n)\}$ if $\{r_n\}$ is any rational sequence converging to x.

The segments joining the points of G_3 form a broken-line approximation to the graph of **?**. Each segment has a positive slope. For example, the segment from $(0, 0)$ to $(1/4, 1/8)$ has slope $1/2$. It is qualitatively a poor approximation to the graph of G near the origin because, for each positive integer n, $G(1/n) = 1/2^{n-1}$, and over the open interval $(0, 1/n)$ the graph of G is below the line $y = (n/2^{n-1})x$, which for large n has slope close to 0.

For another example consider the segment from $(2/5, 3/8)$ to $(1/2, 1/2)$, with slope $5/4$, as an approximation to G near $2/5$. The sequence of mediants $3/7, 5/12, 7/17, \ldots, m_k = (1 + 2k)/(2 + 5k), \ldots$ converges to $2/5$. For each positive integer k, $G(m_k) = (3/8) + (1/2^{k+3})$ and the segment from $(2/5, 3/8)$ to $(m_k, G(m_k))$ has slope $(10 + 25k)/2^{k+3}$, which is close to 0 for large k. A similar argument shows that if k is any rational number in $[0, 1]$, then a line through $(r, G(r))$ is a qualitatively bad approximation to the graph of G on a neighborhood of r unless it has slope 0. Since **?** is strictly increasing, each broken-line approximation is composed of segments with positive slopes, and is consequently qualitatively wrong at rational points.

Consider now the sequence $0/1, 1/1, 1/2, 2/3, 3/5, 5/8, \ldots$, where each term from $1/2$ on is the mediant between the two preceding ones. It is clear that the nth term r_n is the quotient f_n/f_{n+1} of successive Fibonacci numbers. It is well known that if α and β are the two roots of the quadratic equation $x^2 = x + 1$, then, for $n \geq 0$,

$$f_n = \frac{\alpha^n - \beta^n}{\alpha - \beta}.$$

This formula is not affected by interchanging α and β. For definiteness, assume $3/2 < \alpha < 2$ and $-1 < \beta < -1/2$. Then

$$r_n = \frac{f_n}{f_{n+1}} = \frac{\alpha^n - \beta^n}{\alpha^{n+1} - \beta^{n+1}} = \frac{1 - (\beta/\alpha)^n}{\alpha - \beta(\beta/\alpha)^n},$$

and the sequence converges to $1/\alpha$. It is easily established that $G(r_n) = \frac{2}{3} - \frac{2}{3}(-\frac{1}{2})^n$. Thus

$$? \left(\frac{1}{\alpha}\right) = \lim \{G(r_n)\} = \frac{2}{3}.$$

The point $(1/\alpha, 2/3)$ and a few of the points $(r_n, G(r_n))$ are shown in the figure.

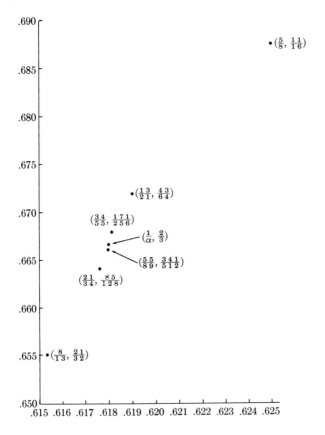

The diagram suggests that a line through $(1/\alpha, 2/3)$ and $(r_n, G(r_n))$ is steep for large n. In fact,

$$\frac{2/3 - G(r_n)}{1/\alpha - r_n} = \frac{2\alpha^2}{3(\alpha - \beta)}\left(\frac{\alpha}{-2\beta}\right)^n - \frac{2\alpha\beta}{3(\alpha - \beta)}\left(-\frac{1}{2}\right)^n.$$

Since $\alpha/-2\beta > 1$, the sequence of slopes is unbounded. It follows that no nonvertical line through $(1/\alpha, 2/3)$ can be a qualitatively good approximation to the graph of **?** over a neighborhood of $1/\alpha$.

Minkowski proved, relying on a theorem of Lagrange's, that iff x in $(0, 1)$ is a *quadratic irrationality* [an irrational root of a quadratic equation with rational coefficients], then **?**(x) is a rational number whose denominator is not a power of 2. The same theorem of Lagrange's can be used to show that the behavior of **?** at $1/\alpha$ is typical of its behavior at quadratic irrationalities, which are dense on the real line.

We have partly established that if a curve drawn with pencil is to be a qualitatively good approximation to the graph of **?**, then it must have, among others, these two properties: at each rational point it must look horizontal, and at each quadratic irrationality it must look vertical.

Exercises

1. For each fraction a/b in D_2, $b < 4$.
2. If each fraction in D_n has denominator less than 2^n, then each fraction in D_{n+1} has denominator less than 2^{n+1}.
3. For all n the length of each interval between adjacent fractions in D_n is greater than $1/4^n$.
4. For positive integers a and b, if $0 \leq a/b \leq 1$, then a/b is in D_{b-1}.
5. If x and y in $[0, 1]$ are rational and $|x - y| < 1/4^n$, then x and y are in the same interval or in adjacent intervals in D_n and $|G_n(x) - G_n(y)| < 1/2^{n-1}$.
6. G is uniformly continuous on the set of rational numbers in $[0, 1]$.
7. If $\{r_n\}$ is a Cauchy sequence of rational numbers in $[0, 1]$, then $\{G(r_n)\}$ is a Cauchy sequence and converges to some real x in $[0, 1]$.
8. If $\{r_n\}$ and $\{s_n\}$ are sequences of rational numbers in $[0, 1]$ and both converge to the same number x, then $\lim \{G(r_n)\} = \lim \{G(s_n)\}$.
9. For each x in $[0, 1]$ the function **?** is continuous at x.
10. The function **?** is strictly increasing on $[0, 1]$.
11. Let α and β be the roots of the equation $x^2 = x + 1$. Then $\alpha^2 = \alpha + 1$ and $\beta^2 = \beta + 1$. For each nonnegative integer n, set

$$g_n = \frac{\alpha^n - \beta^n}{\alpha - \beta}.$$

Prove that $g_0 = 0$, $g_1 = 1$, and, for all n, $g_{n+2} = g_{n+1} + g_n$.

12. Let a/b and c/d be adjacent fractions in some D_n. For k in $\mathbf{Z}^+$ let $r_k = (a + kc)/(b + kd)$. Prove that the sequence
$$\left\{ \frac{G(r_k) - G(c/d)}{r_k - c/d} \right\}$$
converges to 0.

13. Define a sequence x by: $x_0 = 2$, $x_1 = 5$, for $n \geq 0$, $x_{n+2} = 5x_{n+1} - 6x_n$. Prove that, because $2^2 = 5(2) - 6$ and $3^2 = 5(3) - 6$, $x_n = 2^n + 3^n$ for all n.

8

Integration Problems

This chapter is a collection of problems, each of which has a number for an answer. We shall treat them as isolated problems, but it will be clear that there is a common feature.

§ 1. A Distance Problem

Suppose we have a car with a clock and a speedometer which indicates speed but fails to record miles traveled. Can we use the car to determine the distance between towns A and B several hundred miles apart? Theoretically we might drive from A to B at a constant speed, say at exactly 60 mph, read the elapsed time from the clock and compute the distance. We shall rule this out by assuming there is no freeway from A to B and that it is impossible to make the trip at a constant speed.

Suppose the trip has actually been made in exactly 10 hours and that we have a film showing the clock and speedometer over the 10-hour interval, which can be assumed to be from 0 to 10. It should be possible, by watching the film, to partition this interval into subintervals, over each of which the speed does not vary by as much as 5 mph. Presumably some of these time intervals would have to be quite short: perhaps, for example, over the interval from 0 to 1/600 hours, we could say that the speed was at least 0 and not more than 5 mph. Others might be long: there might be a two-hour period during which the speed was at least 60 but not more than 65 mph.

We assume then that there is a partition $p = \{t_0, t_1, \ldots, t_n\}$ of $[0, 10]$ such that for each interval $[t_{i-1}, t_i]$ the speed is at least m_i but not more than M_i mph, and that $M_i - m_i \leq 5$ for each subinterval.

During the time from t_{i-1} to t_i the speed is at least m_i mph, and consequently the distance traveled is at least $m_i(t_i - t_{i-1})$ miles. Thus the distance from A to B along the route traveled is at least

$$m_1(t_1 - t_0) + m_2(t_2 - t_1) + \cdots + m_n(t_n - t_{n-1}) = \sum_{i=1}^{n} m_i(t_i - t_{i-1}) \text{ miles.}$$

This sum we shall call the *lower sum associated with the partition p* and denote it by $\underline{S}_p$.

Similarly the distance from A to B is at most

$$\sum_{i=1}^{n} M_i(t_i - t_{i-1}) = \overline{S}_p,$$

which we shall call the *upper sum associated with the partition p.*

Thus the distance from A to B, say L miles, is trapped between $\underline{S}_p$ and $\overline{S}_p$: $\underline{S}_p \leq L \leq \overline{S}_p$. But the difference between $\overline{S}_p$ and $\underline{S}_p$ is

$$\sum_{i=1}^{n} M_i(t_i - t_{i-1}) - \sum_{i=1}^{n} m_i(t_i - t_{i-1}) = \sum_{i=1}^{n} (M_i - m_i)(t_i - t_{i-1})$$

$$\leq \sum_{i=1}^{n} 5(t_i - t_{i-1})$$

$$= 5 \sum_{i=1}^{n} (t_i - t_{i-1}) = 50,$$

since the sum of the lengths of all the time intervals is 10.

Next suppose that by rerunning the film and watching very carefully we can find a partition $q = \{t_0, t_1, \ldots, t_k\}$ such that on each subinterval $[t_{i-1}, t_i]$ the speed varies by not more than 1 mph.

Again we let m_i and M_i be lower and upper bounds for the speed over the time from t_{i-1} to t_i, and we abbreviate the elapsed time $t_i - t_{i-1}$ to Δt_i.

$$\overline{S}_q = \sum_{i=1}^{k} M_i \, \Delta t_i,$$

and

$$\underline{S}_q = \sum_{i=1}^{k} m_i \, \Delta t_i.$$

As before, $\underline{S}_q \leq L \leq \overline{S}_q$, but

$$\overline{S}_q - \underline{S}_q = \sum_{i=1}^{k} (M_i - m_i) \, \Delta t_i \leq 10.$$

Perhaps we have already assumed more accuracy than actual speedometers and clocks permit, but we can idealize the problem. Assume a perfect speedometer, clock, and observer. In other words, assume the existence of a function f defined on the interval $[0, 10]$ such that, at time t, $0 \leq t \leq 10$, the speed, or velocity, is exactly $v = f(t)$ mph. Also assume f continuous on $[0, 10]$, and hence by Heine's Theorem uniformly continuous on $[0, 10]$.

Given $\epsilon > 0$, there is a partition $p_\epsilon = \{t_0, \ldots, t_n\}$ such that, if v_i and V_i are the smallest and largest values of f on the interval $[t_{i-1}, t_i]$, $V_i - v_i < \epsilon$. There are corresponding lower and upper sums $\underline{S}$ and $\overline{S}$ such that

$$\underline{S} = \sum_{i=1}^{n} v_i \, \Delta t_i \leq L \leq \overline{S} = \sum_{i=1}^{n} V_i \, \Delta t_i,$$

and

$$\overline{S} - \underline{S} = \sum_{i=1}^{n} (V_i - v_i) \, \Delta t_i$$

$$\leq \sum_{i=1}^{n} \epsilon \, \Delta t_i = 10\epsilon.$$

In this idealized version L can be trapped between lower sums and upper sums which differ by as little as we please. There are two standard notations for our answer. Since L is completely determined, via partitions and upper and lower sums, by the interval $[0, 10]$ and the function f, the simplest notation current in mathematics is

$$L = \int_0^{10} f.$$

A physicist, who needs to have constantly in mind certain *dimensions* [length, time, mass, and others], wants to be reminded that the sums defining the integral are of the form $\Sigma v_i \, \Delta t_i$, where v_i is a velocity and Δt_i a time, so that $v_i \, \Delta t_i$ is a distance. He prefers the notation established by Leibniz:

$$L = \int_0^{10} v \, dt.$$

§ 2. *An Area Problem*

For b, a positive number, what is the area, say $A(b)$, of the region of the plane bounded by the horizontal axis, the line $x = b$, and the graph of $y = x^2$? The diagram below is drawn as though $b < 1$, but this is not assumed.

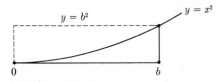

Since the region is contained in a rectangle of length b and height b^2, surely $0 < A(b) < b^3$.

To obtain better inequalities, consider a partition of the interval $[0, b]$. Over a subinterval $[x_{i-1}, x_i]$ the curve is strictly monotone increasing and is between, except at the end points, the lines $y = x_{i-1}^2$ and $y = x_i^2$.

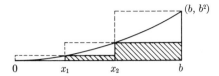

In the diagram above, $A(b)$ is larger than the sum of the areas of the two shaded rectangles, but is less than the sum of the areas of the three rectangles with partly dotted boundaries. Thus

$$x_1{}^2(x_2 - x_1) + x_2{}^2(b - x_2) < A(b),$$

and

$$A(b) < x_1{}^2(x_1 - 0) + x_2{}^2(x_2 - x_1) + b^2(b - x_2).$$

For each positive integer n, let p_n be the partition of $[0, b]$ into n sub-intervals each of length b/n. Setting $x_0 = 0$, $x_1 = b/n$, $x_2 = 2b/n, \ldots, x_n = nb/n = b$,

$$p_n = \{x_0, x_1, \ldots, x_n\}.$$

We define a *lower sum* $\underline{S}_n$ and an *upper sum* $\overline{S}_n$ by

$$\underline{S}_n = x_0{}^2(x_1 - x_0) + x_1{}^2(x_2 - x_1) + \cdots + x_{n-1}^2(x_n - x_{n-1})$$

$$= \sum_{i=1}^{n} x_{i-1}^2(x_i - x_{i-1})$$

and

$$\overline{S}_n = x_1{}^2(x_1 - x_0) + x_2{}^2(x_2 - x_1) + \cdots + x_n{}^2(x_n - x_{n-1})$$

$$= \sum_{i=1}^{n} x_i{}^2(x_i - x_{i-1}).$$

Each sum is a sum of areas of rectangles, chosen in such a way that intuitions about the area demand that

$$\underline{S}_n \le A(b) \le \overline{S}_n.$$

Furthermore, each is readily evaluated. Since

$$x_i = \frac{ib}{n} \qquad \text{and} \qquad x_i - x_{i-1} = \frac{b}{n},$$

we have

$$\overline{S}_n = \sum_{i=1}^{n} \frac{i^2 b^2}{n^2} \frac{b}{n}$$

$$= \frac{b^3}{n^3} \frac{n(n+1)(2n+1)}{6},$$

using a formula in Chapter 2 (page 25) for the sum of the squares of the first n positive integers.

Similarly,

$$\underline{S}_n = \sum_{i=1}^{n} \frac{(i-1)^2 b^2}{n^2} \frac{b}{n}$$

$$= \frac{b^3}{n^3} \frac{(n-1)n(2n-1)}{6}.$$

Writing the formulas for $\overline{S}_n$ and $\underline{S}_n$ in slightly different form, we have, for every positive integer n,

$$b^3 \left[\frac{1}{3} - \frac{1}{2n} + \frac{1}{6n^2} \right] \leq A(b) \leq b^3 \left[\frac{1}{3} + \frac{1}{2n} + \frac{1}{6n^2} \right].$$

From this we conclude that $A(b) = b^3/3$: the sequences $\{1/2n\}$ and $\{1/6n^2\}$ converge to 0; hence the sequences $\{\overline{S}_n\}$ and $\{\underline{S}_n\}$ both converge to $b^3/3$, and $A(b)$ is trapped between their nth terms for each n.

If $p = \{x_0, x_1, \ldots, x_n\}$ is any partition of $[0, b]$, and we write Δx_i for $x_i - x_{i-1}$, we have

$$\sum_{i=1}^{n} x_{i-1}^2 \Delta x_i \leq A(b) \leq \sum_{i=1}^{n} x_i^2 \Delta x_i.$$

Because the number $A(b)$ satisfies inequalities of this sort, it is, by a definition in the next chapter, the integral over the interval $[0, b]$ of the squaring function. Two standard notations are (1) if f is the squaring function,

$$\int_0^b f = \frac{b^3}{3},$$

and (2),

$$\int_0^b x^2 \, dx = \frac{b^3}{3}.$$

The sign $\int$ is an elongated S to remind one of *sum*; dx recalls Δx_i in the sums. The *variable of integration*, x, is strictly a dummy:

$$\int_0^3 x^2 \, dx = 9, \qquad \int_0^3 u^2 \, du = 9, \qquad \int_0^3 y^2 \, dy = 9.$$

Exercise

The region bounded by the x-axis, the line $x = 1$, and the line $y = x$ is a triangle which obviously has area $\frac{1}{2}$. Partition the interval $[0, 1]$ into n subintervals each of length $1/n$, calculate the sums of areas of rectangles above and below the graph of $y = x$, and verify that the same sort of process used to calculate $A(b)$ above will lead to the conclusion that this triangle has area $\frac{1}{2}$.

§ 3. *A Real Estate Problem*

A region north of a stinking swamp is being gradually built up with houses and a rule of thumb has developed by which the price of a lot is proportional to its area and to its distance from the swamp. There is a constant south wind and the distance from the swamp is measured straight north.

We assume that the northern edge of the swamp is along the parabola $y = -1 - x^2$ and thus that the distance of a point (x, y) from the swamp is $y + 1 + x^2$.

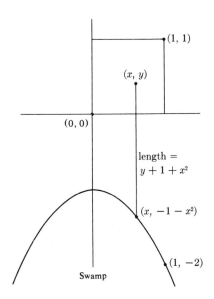

The lots sold so far have been small and quite far north and the question of the meaning of the distance of a lot from the swamp does not arise until a farmer wants to sell the square with vertices at $(0, 0)$ and $(1, 1)$ to a real estate agent.

The rule of thumb is that there is a constant K such that

$$\text{price} = K \cdot \text{area} \cdot \text{distance from swamp},$$

in which K has "dimensions" of money divided by area times distance. We assume distances measured in miles, areas in square miles, and money in a unit such that we can take $K = 1$ numerically.

The farmer says that the nearest point to the swamp on his farm, $(0, 0)$, is 1 mile away and the farthest point, $(1, 1)$, is 3 miles away. Thus he says the average distance is 2, the area is 1, and the price, possibly subject to a quantity discount, should be 2—that is, 2 large units of money.

The agent, after some reflection, draws a picture of the farm and of a parabola through it congruent to the edge of the swamp and at distance 2 from it.

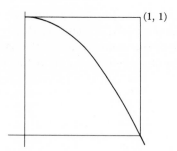

(1, 1)

He points out that clearly more than half the farm is less than 2 miles from the swamp and that the farmer's price is too high. The farmer has to admit that the agent's claim is not entirely implausible, although he still feels that the average distance should be fair to use. Finally they agree to submit the problem to the local arbitrator, a retired mathematician.

The arbitrator points out that the agent will probably partition [which, he explains, means subdivide] the farm into small lots, and suggests that they think about the price of each such lot. The agent quickly points out that there are something like 2500 building lots in a square mile and that it would be a formidable task to set a price for each and add them all up. But the arbitrator volunteers to do all the adding for no extra charge.

He suggests partitioning the farm into n^2 lots each of area $1/n^2$, for some positive integer n, by drawing lines $x = 1/n$, $x = 2/n$, ... , $x = (n-1)/n$, and $y = 1/n$, $y = 2/n$, ... , $y = (n-1)/n$, as well as the boundaries of the farm. A typical lot with boundaries as shown below might be called L_{ij}.

$\left(\dfrac{i}{n}, \dfrac{j}{n}\right)$

$y = \dfrac{j}{n}$

L_{ij}

$y = \dfrac{j-1}{n}$

$x = \dfrac{i-1}{n}$

$x = \dfrac{i}{n}$

The point of L_{ij} farthest north of the swamp is $(i/n, j/n)$ at distance $1 + (j/n) + (i/n)^2$. The closest point is $((i-1)/n, (j-1)/n)$, at distance $1 + (j-1)/n + ((i-1)/n)^2$. Let

$$H_{ij} = \frac{1}{n^2}\left(1 + \frac{j}{n} + \left(\frac{i}{n}\right)^2\right),$$

$$C_{ij} = \frac{1}{n^2}\left(1 + \frac{j-1}{n} + \left(\frac{i-1}{n}\right)^2\right).$$

Then certainly C_{ij} and H_{ij} are the cheapest possible and highest possible prices for L_{ij} and, if F_{ij} is the fair price for L_{ij}, $C_{ij} \leq F_{ij} \leq H_{ij}$.

Furthermore, the arbitrator points out, the difference between C_{ij} and H_{ij} is quite small if n is large:

$$H_{ij} - C_{ij} = \frac{1}{n^2}\left[\frac{1}{n} + \frac{2i}{n^2} - \frac{1}{n^2}\right]$$

$$< \frac{1}{n^2}\left[\frac{1}{n} + \frac{2i}{n^2}\right]$$

$$\leq \frac{1}{n^2}\left[\frac{1}{n} + \frac{2n}{n^2}\right] = \frac{3}{n^3}.$$

If we let F be the fair price for the farm, let $\bar{S}_n$ be the sum of all the H_{ij}, and let $\underline{S}_n$ be the sum of all the C_{ij}, then $\underline{S}_n \leq F \leq \bar{S}_n$.

Furthermore, since for each lot

$$H_{ij} - C_{ij} < \frac{3}{n^3},$$

we have

$$\bar{S}_n - \underline{S}_n < n^2 \frac{3}{n^3} = \frac{3}{n}.$$

From this it follows that, for each positive integer n,

$$\bar{S}_n - \frac{3}{n} < F \leq \bar{S}_n.$$

At this point the arbitrator does some calculation [shown later] and asserts that, for each positive integer n,

$$\bar{S}_n = \frac{11}{6} + \frac{1}{n} + \frac{1}{6n^2}.$$

Thus, for each positive integer n,

$$\frac{11}{6} - \frac{2}{n} + \frac{1}{6n^2} < F \leq \frac{11}{6} + \frac{1}{n} + \frac{1}{6n^2},$$

and

$$F = \frac{11}{6}.$$

In order to solve the problem—to find the fair price F—it was sufficient to partition the farmer's square, say S, into n^2 subsquares each of area $1/n^2$. Suppose we consider a more general partition of S effected by drawing lines $x = x_i$, with $0 \leq i \leq n$, and lines $y = y_j$, with $0 \leq j \leq m$, where each of $\{x_0, \ldots, x_n\}$ and $\{y_0, \ldots, y_m\}$ is a partition of $[0, 1]$. This partitions S into rectangles; a typical one, R_{ij}, is shown below.

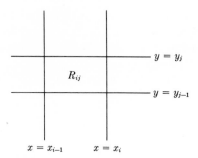

Writing Δx_i for $x_i - x_{i-1}$ and Δy_j for $y_j - y_{j-1}$, the area of R_{ij} is $\Delta x_i \, \Delta y_j$.

Let g be the function $g(x, y) = y + 1 + x^2$. If g_{ij} is the smallest and G_{ij} the largest value of g on R_{ij}, then the fair price F satisfies the inequality

$$\sum_{i=1}^{n} \sum_{j=1}^{m} g_{ij} \, \Delta x_i \, \Delta y_j \leq F \leq \sum_{i=1}^{n} \sum_{j=1}^{m} G_{ij} \, \Delta x_i \, \Delta y_j.$$

Because F satisfies such inequalities for any partition of S, F is the integral over S of the function g. Standard notations are:

$$F = \iint_S g, \qquad F = \int_0^1 \int_0^1 g, \qquad F = \int_0^1 \int_0^1 (y + 1 + x^2) \, dx \, dy.$$

The Arbitrator's Calculation

What is needed is the sum of all the upper estimates H_{ij}: $H_{11} + H_{12} + H_{21} + H_{13} + \cdots + H_{nn}$. The order in which they are added does not matter, but a systematic one is helpful. Suppose we set

$$H_1 = H_{11} + H_{12} + \cdots + H_{1n},$$

$$H_2 = H_{21} + H_{22} + \cdots + H_{2n},$$

$$H_n = H_{n1} + H_{n2} + \cdots + H_{nn}.$$

For each i, $H_i = \sum_{j=1}^{n} H_{ij}$ is a subtotal of a column, and $\bar{S}_n = \sum_{i=1}^{n} H_i$ is the sum of the subtotals:

$$H_i = \sum_{j=1}^{n} \frac{1}{n^2} \left(1 + \frac{j}{n} + \left(\frac{i}{n} \right)^2 \right)$$

$$= \frac{1}{n^2} \sum_{j=1}^{n} 1 + \frac{1}{n^3} \sum_{j=1}^{n} j + \frac{i^2}{n^4} \sum_{j=1}^{n} 1$$

$$= \frac{1}{n} + \frac{n(n+1)}{2n^3} + \frac{i^2}{n^3},$$

and

$$\sum_{i=1}^{n} H_i = n\frac{1}{n} + n\frac{n(n+1)}{2n^3} + \frac{1}{n^3}\sum_{i=1}^{n} i^2$$

$$= 1 + \frac{1}{2} + \frac{1}{2n} + \frac{1}{n^3}\frac{n(n+1)(2n+1)}{6}$$

$$= \frac{3}{2} + \frac{1}{2n} + \frac{1}{3} + \frac{1}{2n} + \frac{1}{6n^2} = \frac{11}{6} + \frac{1}{n} + \frac{1}{6n^2}.$$

§ 4. *Another Area Problem*

For positive numbers a and b, with $a < b$, let $Q[a, b]$ be the area of the region bounded by the x-axis, the lines $x = a$ and $x = b$, and the graph of $y = 1/x^2$.

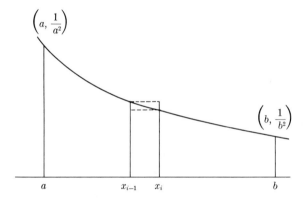

For p any partition of $[a, b]$, it is clear that the area under the curve over the interval $[x_{i-1}, x_i]$ is between that of two rectangles: one has base $x_i - x_{i-1}$ and height $1/x_i^2$; the other has base $x_i - x_{i-1}$ and height $1/x_{i-1}^2$.

Again, the number we want, $Q[a, b]$, is trapped between a lower sum and an upper sum. For $\{x_0, \ldots, x_n\}$ any partition of $[a, b]$,

$$\sum_{i=1}^{n} \frac{1}{x_i^2}(x_i - x_{i-1}) \le Q[a, b] \le \sum_{i=1}^{n} \frac{1}{x_{i-1}^2}(x_i - x_{i-1}).$$

Again, for any partition with each subinterval small enough, the upper sum and lower sum are close together. For example, let p_n be the partition of $[a, b]$ into n subintervals each of length $(b - a)/n$. The corresponding upper sum and lower sum are

$$\overline{S}_n = \frac{b-a}{n}\left[\frac{1}{a^2} + \frac{1}{x_1^2} + \frac{1}{x_2^2} + \cdots + \frac{1}{x_{n-1}^2}\right],$$

$$\underline{S}_n = \frac{b-a}{n}\left[\frac{1}{x_1^2} + \frac{1}{x_2^2} + \cdots + \frac{1}{x_{n-1}^2} + \frac{1}{b^2}\right].$$

Their difference is

$$\overline{S}_n - \underline{S}_n = \frac{b-a}{n}\left[\frac{1}{a^2} - \frac{1}{b^2}\right] = \frac{1}{n}\frac{(b-a)(b^2-a^2)}{a^2b^2}.$$

For all large enough n, $\overline{S}_n - \underline{S}_n$ is as small as one pleases, so either is a good approximation to $Q[a, b]$, which is between them.

We are unable to give a simpler formula for either $\overline{S}_n$ or $\underline{S}_n$ than the defining formulas above. But we can calculate the value of the function Q at the interval $[a, b]$ by a special device.

Claim: With $\overline{S}_n$ and $\underline{S}_n$ as defined above, for every positive integer n,

$$\underline{S}_n < \frac{1}{a} - \frac{1}{b} < \overline{S}_n.$$

This claim will be established below. Assuming its validity, we have not only

$$\underline{S}_n \le Q[a, b] \le \overline{S}_n,$$

but also, for any $\epsilon > 0$, $\overline{S}_n - \underline{S}_n < \epsilon$ for all large enough n.

Combining these, we have, for every $\epsilon > 0$,

$$\left| Q[a, b] - \left(\frac{1}{a} - \frac{1}{b}\right) \right| < \epsilon.$$

Therefore

$$Q[a, b] = \frac{1}{a} - \frac{1}{b}.$$

Thus, still assuming the validity of the claim made above, we have solved another problem. The area of the region of the plane above the interval $[a, b]$, with $0 < a < b$, and below the graph of $y = 1/x^2$, is $(1/a) - (1/b)$.

For $0 < a < b$, standard notations are (1) if $f(x) = 1/x^2$,

$$\int_a^b f = \frac{1}{a} - \frac{1}{b},$$

and (2),

$$\int_a^b \frac{1}{x^2}\,dx = \frac{1}{a} - \frac{1}{b}.$$

Also, for $0 < a < b$,

$$\int_a^b \frac{1}{t^2}\,dt = \frac{1}{a} - \frac{1}{b}, \quad \int_a^b \frac{1}{v^2}\,dv = \frac{1}{a} - \frac{1}{b}, \quad \text{and so forth.}$$

To establish the claim made above, let $p = \{x_0, \ldots, x_n\}$ be any partition of $[a, b]$. Since each number in p is positive, we have

$$x_{i-1}^2 < x_{i-1}x_i < x_i^2,$$

$$\frac{1}{x_i^2} < \frac{1}{x_{i-1}x_i} < \frac{1}{x_{i-1}^2},$$

$$\frac{x_i - x_{i-1}}{x_i^2} < \frac{x_i - x_{i-1}}{x_{i-1}x_i} < \frac{x_i - x_{i-1}}{x_{i-1}^2}.$$

Summing these inequalities,

$$\underline{S}(p) < S(p) < \overline{S}(p),$$

where
$$S(p) = \sum_{i=1}^{n} \frac{x_i - x_{i-1}}{x_{i-1}x_i}.$$
But
$$\frac{x_i - x_{i-1}}{x_{i-1}x_i} = \frac{1}{x_{i-1}} - \frac{1}{x_i},$$
and therefore
$$S(p) = \left(\frac{1}{a} - \frac{1}{x_1}\right) + \left(\frac{1}{x_1} - \frac{1}{x_2}\right) + \cdots + \left(\frac{1}{x_{n-1}} - \frac{1}{b}\right)$$
$$= \frac{1}{a} - \frac{1}{b}.$$

§ 5. *A Volume Problem*

Let f be the function on $\mathfrak{R}^2$ defined by
$$f(x, y) = 1 + y + x^2.$$
Let S be the square with diagonally opposite corners at $(0, 0)$ and $(1, 1)$. The graph of f is the set of all points $(x, y, 1 + y + x^2)$ in $\mathfrak{R}^3$. For (x, y) in S, $1 \le 1 + y + x^2 \le 3$ and the graph of f over S is a surface above the plane $z = 0$. What is the volume of the space bounded by the surface and the planes $z = 0$, $x = 0$, $x = 1$, $y = 0$, $y = 1$?

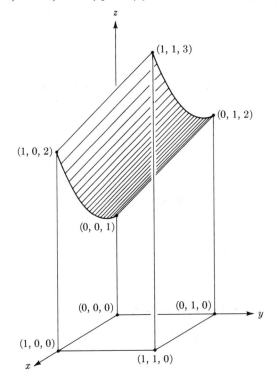

The region whose volume, V, we want, contains the cube obtained by replacing the surface by the plane $z = 1$, so surely $V \geq 1$. The region is contained in the rectangular solid obtained by replacing the surface by the plane $z = 3$, so surely $V \leq 3$.

Let p be a partition of S into n^2 squares by lines $x = x_i = i/n$ and $y = y_j = j/n$. Let V_{ij} be the volume of that part of our region over the square R_{ij}.

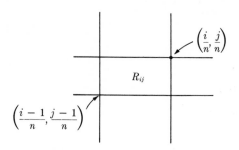

On R_{ij} the smallest value of f, the height of the lowest point on the surface, is

$$1 + \frac{j-1}{n} + \left(\frac{i-1}{n}\right)^2,$$

and the largest value of f is

$$1 + \frac{j}{n} + \left(\frac{i}{n}\right)^2.$$

Intuition demands that the definition of volume be such that

$$1 + \frac{j-1}{n} + \left(\frac{i-1}{n}\right)^2 \leq V_{ij} \leq 1 + \frac{j}{n} + \left(\frac{i}{n}\right)^2.$$

Intuition also demands that

$$V = \sum_{i=1}^{n} \sum_{j=1}^{n} V_{ij}.$$

Thus V satisfies the same inequalities as did the fair price F in the real estate problem. Therefore

$$V = \int_0^1 \int_0^1 (1 + y + x^2)\, dx\, dy = \frac{11}{6}.$$

§ 6. *Volume of a Solid of Revolution*

For $0 < a < b$, let R_{ab} be the region bounded by the x axis, the lines $x = a$ and $x = b$, and the graph of $y = 1/x$.

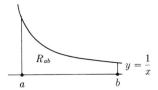

If R_{ab} is rotated around the x-axis it sweeps out what is known as a *solid of revolution*—the sort of solid one can readily make on a lathe. Let the volume of the solid be V_{ab}.

Let $p = \{x_0, \ldots, x_n\}$ be a partition of $[a, b]$. Let V_i be the volume of that part of the solid between planes perpendicular to the x-axis at x_{i-1} and x_i.

A rectangle of base width Δx and height h rotated around its base sweeps out a right circular cylinder of thickness Δx.

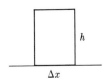

We assume the volume of such a cylinder is thickness times area of base, or $\pi h^2 \, \Delta x$.

Returning now to our partition, the piece with volume V_i is contained in a cylinder of volume

$$\pi \frac{1}{x_{i-1}^2} \Delta x_i$$

and contains a cylinder of volume

$$\pi \frac{1}{x_i^2} \Delta x_i.$$

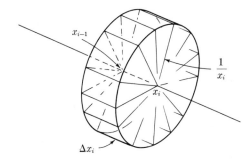

Thus, for any partition of $[a, b]$, we must have

$$\sum_{i=1}^{n} \pi \frac{1}{x_i^2} \Delta x_i \leq V_{ab} \leq \sum_{i=1}^{n} \pi \frac{1}{x_{i-1}^2} \Delta x_i.$$

These sums differ only by the factor π from those in § 4, and we conclude that

$$V_{ab} = \int_a^b \pi \frac{1}{x^2}\, dx = \pi\left(\frac{1}{a} - \frac{1}{b}\right).$$

§ 7. Newton's Problem

According to some historians, a principal motive for Newton's invention or discovery of the methods of calculus was his need to do a complicated problem in integration in order to apply his law of gravitation to the motion of the moon around the earth. It appears that he was held up for 20 years, partly because of the difficulty of the problem and partly because the observed data known at the time were none too accurate and therefore failed to confirm Newton's theoretical predictions.

Suppose, as did Newton, that any two "particles" of masses m and m' at a distance r apart exert on each other a gravitational force of magnitude

$$\frac{Gmm'}{r^2},$$

where G is a constant whose numerical value depends only on the units used for length, time, and mass. What then is the gravitational force between the earth and a particle in space?

One approach is to partition the earth into particles and add up estimates for the individual forces. Using the techniques developed by Newton, Leibniz, and their successors, we can solve the problem in minutes rather than years. But an ad hoc attack would be much too difficult.

Newton's result, which we use in the next problem, is that the force is as though the earth were a particle with all its mass at the center. That is, if M is the mass of the earth and r is the distance from the center of the earth to a particle of mass m located above the surface of the earth, the force exerted by the earth and particle on each other has magnitude GMm/r^2.

§ 8. A Rocket Problem

How much work is it to lift a payload of mass m from the surface of the earth to a height H above the center of the earth?

Here *work* has its technical definition from physics. Suppose an object moves a distance L in a straight line against a force which is at least $\underline{F}$ and at most $\overline{F}$: the work done, W, satisfies $\underline{F}L \le W \le \overline{F}L$. For a constant force, $\underline{F} = \overline{F}$ and the formula is

work = force times distance.

If we let R be the radius of the earth, we want to move our payload of mass m in a line from R to H against a force which is, when the load is at distance r from the center of the earth, GMm/r^2, where M is the mass of the earth.

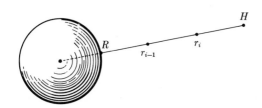

Let $p = \{r_0, \ldots, r_n\}$ be a partition of $[R, H]$ and let W_i be the work done to get the particle from r_{i-1} to r_i. We assume, as part of the definition of work, that if W is the work to get it from R to H, then $W = \sum_{i=1}^{n} W_i$.

We have then, for any partition of $[R, H]$,

$$\sum_{i=1}^{n} \frac{GMm}{r_i^2} (r_i - r_{i-1}) \leq W \leq \sum_{i=1}^{n} \frac{GMm}{r_{i-1}^2} (r_i - r_{i-1}).$$

The constant GMm can be factored out of both sums, and we have

$$GMm \sum_{i=1}^{n} \frac{r_i - r_{i-1}}{r_i^2} \leq W \leq GMm \sum_{i=1}^{n} \frac{r_i - r_{i-1}}{r_{i-1}^2}.$$

Apart from a notational difference, r instead of x, this problem is the same as that of § 4, and we conclude that

$$W = GMm \int_R^H \frac{1}{r^2} \, dr = GMm \left[\frac{1}{R} - \frac{1}{H} \right].$$

One obvious conclusion is that no matter how large H is, $W < GMm/R$.

The formula for W can be made somewhat more meaningful if we rewrite it as

$$W = \frac{GMm}{R^2} \left[R - \frac{R^2}{H} \right].$$

The factor GMm/R^2 is the gravitational force on the payload at the surface of the earth, which is the *weight* of the payload. If we set $H = nR$, $n > 1$, we have

$$W = (\text{weight of payload}) \, (R) \left(1 - \frac{1}{n} \right)$$

as the formula for the work needed to get the payload up to a height of n earth radii above the center of the earth.

Exercises on the Natural Logarithm

These are concerned with the area over an interval $[a, b]$, with $0 < a < b$, between the x-axis and the graph of $y = 1/x$. Let $A[a, b]$ be this area. If $p = \{x_0, \ldots, x_n\}$ is any partition of $[a, b]$, a diagram makes it clear that

$$\underline{S}(p) \leq A[a, b] \leq \overline{S}(p),$$

where

$$\overline{S}(p) = \sum_{i=1}^{n} \frac{1}{x_{i-1}} \Delta x_i,$$

$$\underline{S}(p) = \sum_{i=1}^{n} \frac{1}{x_i} \Delta x_i.$$

The set of all lower sums, $\{\underline{S}(p)|p$ is a partition of $[a, b]\}$, has an upper bound:

$$\underline{S}(p) \leq \sum_{i=1}^{n} \frac{1}{a} \Delta x_i = \frac{b - a}{a}.$$

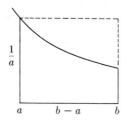

By the definition of area given in the next chapter, $A[a, b]$ is the least upper bound of the set of all lower sums, and also the greatest lower bound of the set of all upper sums.

1. Prove that $\frac{1}{2} < A[1, 2] < 1$.
2. Prove that $\frac{3}{5} < A[1, 2] < \frac{4}{5}$.
3. Prove that $\frac{3}{5} < A[\frac{1}{2}, 1] < \frac{4}{5}$.
4. For $b > 1$, prove that each lower sum for $A[1, b]$ is also a lower sum for $A[1/b, 1]$ and conversely. Hence, for $b > 1$, $A[1/b, 1] = A[1, b]$.
5. Prove that for any a and b, with $0 < a < b$, $A[2a, 2b] = A[a, b]$. [*Hint:* If $\{x_0, x_1, \ldots, x_n\}$ is a partition of $[a, b]$, $\{2x_0, 2x_1, \ldots, 2x_n\}$ is a partition of $[2a, 2b]$.]
6. Prove that, if $0 < a < b$ and $k > 0$, then $A[ka, kb] = A[a, b]$.
7. Draw a diagram making it clear that, if $0 < a < c < b$, then $A[a, c] + A[c, b] = A[a, b]$.
8. Let s and t be numbers both larger than 1. Prove that as a consequence of Exercises 6 and 7,

$$\begin{aligned} A[1, st] &= A[1, s] + A[s, st] \\ &= A[1, s] + A[1, t]. \end{aligned}$$

9. Define a function L on $[1, \infty)$ by

$$L(1) = 0,$$

and, for $t > 1$,

$$L(t) = A[1, t].$$

Prove that for $t \geq 1$ and $s \geq 1$, $L(st) = L(s) + L(t)$.

10. Prove that the function L is strictly monotone increasing on its domain.

11. Prove that for every positive integer n, $L(2^n) = nL(2)$. Prove that L is unbounded [the range of L has no upper bound].

12. Prove that L is uniformly continuous on $[1, \infty)$. [*Hints:* For $1 \leq x < t$,

$$L(t) - L(x) = A[1, t] - A[1, x]$$
$$= A[x, t],$$

by Exercise 7. Use the simplest possible upper sum to get an upper bound for $A(x, t)$.

13. Show that the properties of L, together with the result of Exercise 4, make it reasonable to extend the domain of L to the interval $(0, 1]$ by: for $0 < t < 1$,

$$L(t) = -A[t, 1] = -L\left(\frac{1}{t}\right).$$

In particular, prove that with this extension of L it is true that, for any two positive numbers x and y,

$$L(xy) = L(x) + L(y).$$

14. Prove that for any positive number x and any integer n,

$$L(x^n) = nL(x).$$

15. Prove that, for every positive integer n,

$$1 > L\left(1 + \frac{1}{n}\right)^n > \frac{n}{n+1}.$$

16. Prove that $L(e) = 1$, where

$$e = \lim\left\{\left(1 + \frac{1}{n}\right)^n\right\}.$$

Refer to Exercise 5 on page 94.

Hint: L is continuous at e. Given $\epsilon > 0$, there is some $\delta > 0$ such that

$$|x - e| < \delta \Longrightarrow |L(x) - L(e)| < \epsilon.$$

Since $\{(1 + (1/n))^n\}$ converges to e, there is some N such that

$$n > N \Longrightarrow \left|\left(1 + \frac{1}{n}\right)^n - e\right| < \delta.$$

9

Integration over Intervals

In the last chapter we considered several examples of the integral of a function over a subset of its domain. In each case we partitioned the region in question into subpieces. If we let "content" mean length in $\mathcal{R}^1$, area in $\mathcal{R}^2$, and volume in $\mathcal{R}^3$, the typical problem goes as follows. We want a number, say Q, determined by a bounded function f and a set S, a subset of the domain of f.

We partition S into n subpieces S_i and argue that Q is, for some geometric or physical or other reason, trapped between a lower sum and an upper sum associated with the partition p. The lower sum is of the form

$$\underline{S}(p) = \sum_{i=1}^{n} \text{(smallest value of } f \text{ on } S_i) \text{ (content of } S_i).$$

The upper sum is of the form

$$\overline{S}(p) = \sum_{i=1}^{n} \text{(largest value of } f \text{ on } S_i) \text{ (content of } S_i).$$

Although there are some exceptions, it is conceptually correct to say that Q is given by an integral iff, for every partition p of S,

$$\underline{S}(p) \leq Q \leq \overline{S}(p).$$

In this case Q is an upper bound for the set of all lower sums and a lower bound for the set of upper sums. If L is the least upper bound of the set of lower sums, $L \leq Q$. If G is the greatest lower bound of the set of upper sums, $Q \leq G$. Thus $L \leq Q \leq G$. With these abbreviations, the function f is integrable over S iff $L = G$. Then $Q = L = G$, and Q is the integral of f over S.

If S is an interval $[a, b]$, the integral of f over S is written as $\int_a^b f$ or $\int_a^b f(x)\, dx$ or $\int_a^b f(t)\, dt$ or some such notation.

If S is a region in the plane, the integral of f over S is written as $\iint_S f$, or, for example, $\iint_S f(x, y) \, dx \, dy$. The region S is typically defined by inequalities. If they are simple enough they can be given by some standard conventions. For example, $\int_0^1 \int_{x^2}^x f(x, y) \, dy \, dx$ means $\iint_S f$, where

$$S = \{(x, y) | 0 \le x \le 1 \quad \text{and} \quad x^2 \le y \le x\}.$$

Or, $\int_0^1 \int_3^5 f(x, y) \, dx \, dy$ means $\iint_S f$, where

$$S = \{(x, y) | 3 \le x \le 5 \quad \text{and} \quad 0 \le y \le 1\}.$$

For a triple integral, an integral of a real-valued function over a three-dimensional region S, we write something along the lines of $\iiint_S f$ or $\iiint_S f(P) \, dV$ or $\iiint_S f(x, y, z) \, dx \, dy \, dz$. Both dV and $dx \, dy \, dz$, as a reminder of $\Delta x \, \Delta y \, \Delta z$, recall the basic sums that define the integral: sums of the form $\Sigma f(P_i)$ (volume of S_i).

Although the concept of the integral of a bounded real-valued function over a bounded subset of its domain is no more complicated for two-dimensional or three-dimensional domains than it is for intervals, the techniques for evaluating double or triple integrals of specific functions are more complicated than, and ultimately depend on, techniques for evaluating integrals over intervals. For the remainder of this chapter we shall be concerned only with integrals of the type $\int_a^b f$.

§ 1. *Basic Theory*

Let f be a real function defined and bounded on an interval with end points a and b, with $a < b$. For notational convenience and only for this reason we assume the interval closed. Let $p = \{x_0, \ldots, x_n\}$ be a partition of $[a, b]$.

Since f is bounded on $[a, b]$, f is bounded on each subinterval $[x_{i-1}, x_i]$. Let m_i and M_i be respectively the greatest lower and least upper bounds of $\{f(x) | x_{i-1} \le x \le x_i\}$. [This notation is not fully adequate; when necessary we shall resort to the more cumbersome but adequate $m_i(f, p)$ and $M_i(f, p)$.]

If f is continuous on $[x_{i-1}, x_i]$ there are, by the Extreme Value Theorem, numbers s_i and t_i in $[x_{i-1}, x_i]$ such that $m_i = f(s_i)$ and $M_i = f(t_i)$. If f is monotone increasing on $[x_{i-1}, x_i]$, then $m_i = f(x_{i-1})$ and $M_i = f(x_i)$.

Since we are not assuming f either continuous or monotone, we cannot assert that m_i and M_i are the smallest and largest values of f on $[x_{i-1}, x_i]$.

But for many functions this will be the case, and for intuitive purposes it may be helpful to think of m_i and M_i in this way.

With the partition p we now associate an upper sum and a lower sum, defined by

$$\overline{S}(p) = \sum_{i=1}^{n} M_i(x_i - x_{i-1}) = \sum_{i=1}^{n} M_i \, \Delta x_i,$$

$$\underline{S}(p) = \sum_{i=1}^{n} m_i(x_i - x_{i-1}) = \sum_{i=1}^{n} m_i \, \Delta x_i.$$

If necessary, we resort to $\overline{S}(f, p)$ and $\underline{S}(f, p)$.

Let m and M be respectively the greatest lower and least upper bounds of $\{f(x) | a \le x \le b\}$. Then M is an upper bound of $\{f(x) | x_{i-1} \le x \le x_i\}$, so that $M_i \le M$. Similarly, $m \le m_i$. And, since $m_i \le M_i$, we have $m \le m_i \le M_i \le M$.

Now, for p any partition of $[a, b]$,

$$\overline{S}(p) = \sum_{i=1}^{n} M_i \, \Delta x_i \ge \sum_{i=1}^{n} m \, \Delta x_i = m(b - a),$$

$$\underline{S}(p) = \sum_{i=1}^{n} m_i \, \Delta x_i \le \sum_{i=1}^{n} M \, \Delta x_i = M(b - a).$$

These equations show that the set of all upper sums has a lower bound, $m(b - a)$, and the set of all lower sums has an upper bound, $M(b - a)$.

Definition 9.1. For f a real function defined and bounded on an interval $[a, b]$, the **lower integral** of f over $[a, b]$, $\underline{\int_a^b} f$, and the **upper integral** of f over $[a, b]$, $\overline{\int_a^b} f$, are defined by

$$\underline{\int_a^b} f = \text{lub } \{\text{lower sums}\},$$

$$\overline{\int_a^b} f = \text{glb } \{\text{upper sums}\}.$$

The two diagrams shown here may "collapse," as in Example 1 below. Although certainly $m(b - a) \le M(b - a)$, the two diagrams are separate and are not intended to compare the lower and upper integrals.

Examples

1. Let f be the constant function 2 on the interval $[a, b]$. For $p = \{x_0, \ldots, x_n\}$, any partition of $[a, b]$, $m_i = 2$ and $M_i = 2$ for each subinterval:

$$\underline{S}(p) = \sum_{i=1}^{n} 2\Delta x_i = 2(b - a) \quad \text{and} \quad \overline{S}(p) = 2(b - a).$$

The set of all lower sums is the set $\{2(b - a)\}$ and so is the set of all upper sums,

$$\underline{\int_a^b} 2 = 2(b - a) = \overline{\int_a^b} 2.$$

2. Let $f(1) = 10$ and, for all $x \neq 1$, $f(x) = 2$. Consider f over the interval $[0, 4]$. Let p be any partition of $[0, 4]$. For each subinterval, $m_i = 2$. Each lower sum becomes

$$\underline{S}(p) = \sum_{i=1}^{n} 2\,\Delta x_i = 2(4 - 0) = 8.$$

Thus $\underline{\int_0^4} f = 8$.

The set of upper sums is more interesting. Let $p = \{0, 4\}$ be the simplest partition: $M_1 = 10$ and $\overline{S}(p) = 10(4 - 0) = 40$. Let $q = \{0, 1, 4\}$. Then $M_1 = 10$ and $M_2 = 10$ and

$$\overline{S}(q) = 10(1 - 0) + 10(4 - 1) = 40.$$

Let $p' = \{0, x_1, x_2, 4\}$, where $0 < x_1 < 1 < x_2 < 4$. Then

$$\begin{aligned}
\overline{S}(p') &= 2(x_1 - 0) + 10(x_2 - x_1) + 2(4 - x_2) \\
&= 2[(x_1 - 0) + (x_2 - x_1) + (4 - x_2)] + 8(x_2 - x_1) \\
&= 8 + 8(x_2 - x_1).
\end{aligned}$$

Evidently we can choose x_1 and x_2 such that $\overline{S}(p')$ is any number larger than 8 but less than 40.

The set of all upper sums includes at least every number in the half-open interval $(8, 40]$. The greatest lower bound of the set of upper sums cannot be larger than 8, and we have

$$\underline{\int_0^4} f = 8, \qquad \overline{\int_0^4} f \leq 8.$$

Theorem 9.1 will establish that $\overline{\int_0^4} f = 8$.

3. For $1 \leq x \leq 2$, let $f(x) = 1$ if x is rational, but $f(x) = 5$ if x is irrational. For p any partition of $[1, 2]$ and for each subinterval $[x_{i-1}, x_i]$, $m_i = 1$ and $M_i = 5$. Thus

$$\underline{S}(p) = \sum_{i=1}^{n} 1\,\Delta x_i = 1,$$

$$\overline{S}(p) = \sum_{i=1}^{n} 5\,\Delta x_i = 5.$$

Thus $\underline{\int_0^1} f = 1$ and $\overline{\int_0^1} f = 5$.

Definition 9.2. Let p and p' be partitions of $[a, b]$. Then p' is a **refinement** of p if the set p is a subset of the set p'.

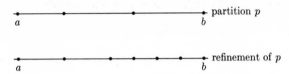

Lemma 1. If p' is a refinement of p, then $\underline{S}(p') \geq \underline{S}(p)$ and $\overline{S}(p') \leq \overline{S}(p)$.

One upper sum [lower sum] is "better" than another if the one is closer to the upper integral [lower integral] than is the other; Lemma 1 says that refinements tend to produce better sums.

PROOF: Let p be a partition and q a refinement having exactly one more point than p. If x_{j-1} and x_j are adjacent points of p, then let q have a point c between x_{j-1} and x_j.

Then the sums $\overline{S}(p)$ and $\overline{S}(q)$ are the same except that the term $M_j(x_j - x_{j-1})$ is replaced in $\overline{S}(q)$ by a sum of two terms,

$$M'_j(c - x_{j-1}) + M^*_j(x_j - c),$$

where M'_j is the lub of f on $[x_{j-1}, c]$ and M^*_j the lub of f on $[c, x_j]$.

Since M_j is the least upper bound of f on $[x_{j-1}, x_j]$, it is an upper bound of f on each of $[x_{j-1}, c]$ and $[c, x_j]$. Thus $M'_j \leq M_j$ and $M^*_j \leq M_j$, and

$$M'_j(c - x_{j-1}) + M^*_j(x_j - c) \leq M_j(c - x_{j-1}) + M_j(x_j - c)$$
$$= M_j(x_j - x_{j-1}).$$

This establishes that $\overline{S}(q) \leq S(p)$.

The argument for lower sums for a one-point refinement is very similar. Below is a picture of it.

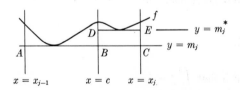

The refinement replaces AC by AB and DE.

Since every partition contains only finitely many points, any refinement can be obtained by a chain of one-point refinements, and Lemma 1 is established by mathematical induction. ∎

Exercises

1. Draw diagrams of Lemma 1 for f a positive function.
2. Verify Lemma 1 for $f(x) = -x$, with
$$p = \{1, 2, 3\} \quad \text{and} \quad p' = \{1, 1.3, 2, 2.4, 3\}.$$

Lemma 2. Let f be a real function bounded on $[a, b]$. If p and q are any two partitions of $[a, b]$, then $\underline{S}(q) \leq \overline{S}(p)$.

PROOF: Let p' be the common refinement of p and q; that is, p' consists of all points of p or q or both, or p' is the union of p and q.

By Lemma 1,

$$\overline{S}(p') \leq \overline{S}(p) \quad \text{and} \quad \underline{S}(p') \geq \underline{S}(q).$$

But $\underline{S}(p') \leq \overline{S}(p')$, so we have

$$\underline{S}(q) \leq \underline{S}(p') \leq \overline{S}(p') \leq \overline{S}(p). \quad \blacksquare$$

Theorem 9.1. Let f be a real function bounded on $[a, b]$. Then

$$\underline{\int_a^b} f \leq \overline{\int_a^b} f.$$

PROOF: Let q be any partition of $[a, b]$. By Lemma 2, $\underline{S}(q) \leq \overline{S}(p)$ for every partition p. Thus $\underline{S}(q)$ is a lower bound of the set of all upper sums. But $\overline{\int_a^b} f$ is the *greatest* lower bound of this set. Thus, for q any partition of $[a, b]$,

$$\underline{S}(q) \leq \overline{\int_a^b} f.$$

The last sentence proclaims that $\overline{\int_a^b} f$ is *an* upper bound of the set of all lower sums. Since $\underline{\int_a^b} f$ is the *least* upper bound of the set of lower sums,

$$\underline{\int_a^b} f \leq \overline{\int_a^b} f. \quad \blacksquare$$

Theorem 9.1 gives us a much sharper schematic picture.

lower sums $\qquad \underline{\int_a^b} f \qquad \overline{\int_a^b} f \qquad$ upper sums

The diagram may collapse, as in some examples above, but we can assert a little more than is pictured. For $\epsilon > 0$, $\overline{\int_a^b} f + \epsilon$ is not a lower bound for the set of upper sums, and there has to be an upper sum in the half-open interval $\left[\overline{\int_a^b} f, \overline{\int_a^b} f + \epsilon \right)$. Similarly, there must be a lower sum in the half-open interval $\left(\underline{\int_a^b} f - \epsilon, \underline{\int_a^b} f \right]$.

Theorem 9.2 [*Riemann's Necessary and Sufficient Condition for Integrability*]. Let f be a real function bounded on $[a, b]$. Then $\overline{\int_a^b} f = \underline{\int_a^b} f$ iff, for each $\epsilon > 0$, there is a partition p_ϵ of $[a, b]$ such that

$$\overline{S}(p_\epsilon) - \underline{S}(p_\epsilon) < \epsilon.$$

PROOF FOR *if:* For any partition p,

$$\underline{S}(p) \leq \underline{\int_a^b} f \leq \overline{\int_a^b} f \leq \overline{S}(p), \quad •$$

$$\overline{\int_a^b} f - \underline{\int_a^b} f \leq \overline{S}(p) - \underline{S}(p).$$

If, for each $\epsilon > 0$, there is a partition p_ϵ with $\overline{S}(p_\epsilon) - \underline{S}(p_\epsilon) < \epsilon$, then, for every $\epsilon > 0$,

$$0 \leq \overline{\int_a^b} f - \underline{\int_a^b} f < \epsilon,$$

from which $\overline{\int_a^b} f - \underline{\int_a^b} f = 0.$ ∎

PROOF FOR *only if:* If $\underline{\int_a^b} f = \overline{\int_a^b} f$, then, as noted above Theorem 9.2, there is a partition p such that $\underline{S}(p) > \underline{\int_a^b} f - \dfrac{\epsilon}{2}$ and a partition q such that $\overline{S}(q) < \overline{\int_a^b} f + \dfrac{\epsilon}{2}.$

Let p' be the common refinement of p and q. Then

$$\underline{S}(p') \geq \underline{S}(p) > \underline{\int_a^b} f - \frac{\epsilon}{2},$$

$$\overline{S}(p') \leq \overline{S}(q) < \overline{\int_a^b} f + \frac{\epsilon}{2}.$$

But $\underline{\int_a^b} f = \overline{\int_a^b} f$, so

$$\overline{S}(p') - \underline{S}(p') < \epsilon.$$ ∎

Definition 9.3. If $\underline{\int_a^b} f = \overline{\int_a^b} f$, f is said to be **integrable over** $[a, b]$; and $\int_a^b f$, the **integral of f over** $[a, b]$ is defined by

$$\int_a^b f = \underline{\int_a^b} f = \overline{\int_a^b} f.$$

Historical Remarks

The first man to do any integration problems was Archimedes, although he did not call them by that name. He found some areas and volumes by methods which now must be recognized as methods of calculating certain integrals. His proofs of his results were rigorous by Greek standards and, essentially, by current standards.

During the 17th century several English and French mathematicians—including Fermat, Descartes, and Newton's master Isaac Barrow—solved some isolated integration problems. Newton and Leibniz created techniques for handling large classes of such problems in an efficient way. Their followers in the 18th century applied these techniques with enormous success to many areas of geometry and physics. During this great period of development of applications of the techniques of calculus, almost no attention was paid to proofs or to careful definitions.

Although any 18th century mathematician had a feeling for what an integral was, and could compute a good many, it was not until the middle of the 19th century that the German mathematician Georg Riemann (1826–1866) gave a clear definition of $\int_a^b f$. Riemann did not use lower and upper integrals, which are a later conceptual simplification due to the French mathematician Darboux; but he defined the integral in essentially the way we have presented it here and established the essential content of Theorem 9.2.

To conclude this section we use Riemann's Condition to establish the integrability of a rather large class of functions.

Theorem 9.3. Let f be a real function bounded on an interval $[a, b]$.

1. If f is monotone on $[a, b]$, f is integrable over $[a, b]$.
2. If f is continuous on $[a, b]$, f is integrable over $[a, b]$.
3. If there is a partition p of $[a, b]$ such that, on each subinterval of p, f is either monotone or continuous, then f is integrable over $[a, b]$.

PROOFS: 1. Suppose f monotone decreasing on $[a, b]$. Let p_n be the partition of $[a, b]$ into n subintervals each of length $(b - a)/n$. Because f is monotone decreasing,

$$\overline{S}(p_n) = \sum_{i=1}^{n} f(x_{i-1}) \, \Delta x_i,$$

$$\underline{S}(p_n) = \sum_{i=1}^{n} f(x_i) \, \Delta x_i.$$

Thus

$$\overline{S}(p_n) - \underline{S}(p_n) = \sum_{i=1}^{n} [f(x_{i-1}) - f(x_i)] \, \Delta x_i.$$

But, for each i, $\Delta x_i = (b - a)/n$ and

$$\overline{S}(p_n) - \underline{S}(p_n) = \frac{b - a}{n} \sum_{i=1}^{n} [f(x_{i-1}) - f(x_i)].$$

The sum, $[f(a) - f(x_1)] + [f(x_1) - f(x_2)] + \cdots + [f(x_{n-1}) - f(b)]$, collapses, and

$$\overline{S}(p_n) - \underline{S}(p_n) = \frac{b - a}{n} [f(a) - f(b)].$$

Given $\epsilon > 0$, $\overline{S}(p_n) - \underline{S}(p_n) < \epsilon$ for large enough n and, by Theorem 9.2, $\underline{\int}_a^b f = \overline{\int}_a^b f$.

For f monotone increasing the proof is not essentially different. A picture of it is shown below: $\overline{S}(p_5) - \underline{S}(p_5)$ is geometrically the sum of the areas of the shaded rectangles, which can be fitted into a rectangle of height $f(b) - f(a)$ and base $(b - a)/5$.

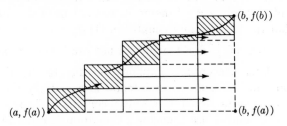

2. Suppose f continuous on $[a, b]$. By Heine's Theorem, f is uniformly continuous on $[a, b]$ and for any $\epsilon > 0$ there is some $\delta > 0$ such that

$$x, t \text{ in } [a, b] \text{ and } |x - t| < \delta \Rightarrow |f(x) - f(t)| < \frac{\epsilon}{b - a}.$$

Let p_ϵ be a partition of $[a, b]$ such that each subinterval is of length $< \delta$. On the subinterval $[x_{i-1}, x_i]$ there are, by The Extreme Value Theorem, s_i and t_i such that $m_i = f(s_i)$ and $M_i = f(t_i)$. Since $|s_i - t_i| < \delta$, $M_i - m_i < \frac{\epsilon}{b - a}$. Then

$$\overline{S}(p_\epsilon) = \sum_{i=1}^{n} M_i \Delta x_i,$$

$$\underline{S}(p_\epsilon) = \sum_{i=1}^{n} m_i \Delta x_i,$$

and their difference is

$$\overline{S}(p_\epsilon) - \underline{S}(p_\epsilon) = \sum_{i=1}^{n} (M_i - m_i) \Delta x_i$$

$$< \sum_{i=1}^{n} \frac{\epsilon}{b - a} \Delta x_i$$

$$= \frac{\epsilon}{b - a} (b - a) = \epsilon.$$

Hence, by Riemann's Condition, $\underline{\int}_a^b f = \overline{\int}_a^b f$.

3. Suppose $p = \{x_0, \ldots, x_n\}$ is a partition of $[a, b]$ and f, a function bounded on $[a, b]$, is either continuous or monotone on each subinterval $[x_{i-1}, x_i]$ of p. In the diagram below, f is monotone on $[a, x_1]$, continuous on $[x_1, x_2]$, and monotone on $[x_2, b]$.

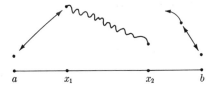

By parts (1) and (2) of this proof, f is integrable over each subinterval of p. By Riemann's Condition there is, for any $\epsilon > 0$, a partition $p_i(\epsilon)$ of $[x_{i-1}, x_i]$ with lower sum and upper sum differing by less than ϵ/n.

The union of these partitions of the subintervals of p is a partition p_ϵ of $[a, b]$ such that $\overline{S}(p_\epsilon) - \underline{S}(p_\epsilon) < \epsilon$.

By Riemann's Condition, f is integrable over $[a, b]$. ∎

§ 2. *Specific Formulas*

The final theorem of the last section, Theorem 9.3, not only guarantees the existence of many integrals but also shows that $\int_a^b f$ can be approximated with as much accuracy as we wish. Given $\epsilon > 0$, there is a partition p_ϵ such that $\overline{S}(p_\epsilon) - \underline{S}(p_\epsilon) < \epsilon$. Since the integral is between these sums, either sum differs from the integral by less than ϵ.

It is probably true that, except for textbook exercises, more integrals are calculated by approximations accurate to the required number of significant figures than by any other method. It is also true that numerical analysis—the art of efficient approximation—is a highly developed and interesting branch of mathematics. But we shall be concerned primarily with a few sorts of integrals which can be evaluated exactly.

There are two standard methods of calculating certain integrals exactly. One is to use a collection of techniques based on the *Fundamental Theorem of Calculus*; a later chapter gives a sample of these. The other is to find a sequence of sums converging to the integral, which is easy, and such that one can find the limit of the sequence, which is likely to be difficult.

In the last chapter we did establish, by considering particular sequences of sums, the following formulas, which follow a common pattern.

(1)   For every $b > 0$, $\quad \displaystyle\int_0^b x^2 \, dx = \frac{b^3}{3}.$

(2)   For $0 < a < b$, $\quad \displaystyle\int_a^b \frac{1}{x^2} \, dx = \frac{1}{a} - \frac{1}{b},$

or
$$\int_a^b x^{-2}\,dx = \frac{b^{-1}}{-1} - \frac{a^{-1}}{-1}.$$

The formulas below are proved in this section, some of them in exercises.

(3) For $0 \le a < b$, $\int_a^b \sqrt{x}\,dx = \frac{2}{3}(b\sqrt{b} - a\sqrt{a})$,

or

$$\int_a^b x^{1/2}\,dx = \frac{b^{3/2}}{\frac{3}{2}} - \frac{a^{3/2}}{\frac{3}{2}}$$

(4) For $a < b$, $\int_a^b 1 = b - a$,

or

$$\int_a^b x^0\,dx = \frac{b^1}{1} - \frac{a^1}{1}.$$

(5) For $a < b$, $\int_a^b x\,dx = \frac{b^2}{2} - \frac{a^2}{2}.$

We now state a theorem whose proof will be given later.

Theorem 9.4. If n is a nonnegative integer, then, for any real a and b,

$$\int_a^b x^n\,dx = \frac{b^{n+1}}{n+1} - \frac{a^{n+1}}{n+1}.$$

If n is a negative integer ≤ -2 and a and b are both positive or both negative,

$$\int_a^b x^n\,dx = \frac{b^{n+1}}{n+1} - \frac{a^{n+1}}{n+1}.$$

The two following theorems, which are proved here, extend greatly the usefulness of formulas (1) to (5) and Theorem 9.4.

Theorem 9.5. If each of the functions f and g is integrable over $[a, b]$, then $f + g$ is integrable over $[a, b]$ and

$$\int_a^b (f + g) = \int_a^b f + \int_a^b g.$$

Theorem 9.6. If the function f is integrable over $[a, b]$, then so is cf, for any constant c, and

$$\int_a^b cf = c \int_a^b f.$$

Typical Application: Evaluate

$$I = \int_0^1 [3u^2 + 5u - 7]\,du.$$

By Theorem 9.5,

$$I = \int_0^1 3u^2 \, du + \int_0^1 [5u - 7] \, du$$

$$= \int_0^1 3u^2 \, du + \int_0^1 5u \, du + \int_0^1 -7 du.$$

By Theorem 9.6,

$$I = 3 \int_0^1 u^2 \, du + 5 \int_0^1 u \, du + (-7) \int_0^1 1 du.$$

By formulas (1), (5), and (4),

$$I = 3 \cdot \tfrac{1}{3} + 5 \cdot \tfrac{1}{2} + -7 \cdot 1 = -\tfrac{7}{2}.$$

PROOF OF THEOREM 9.6 for $c \geq 0$: Let f be integrable over $[a, b]$, let c be a real number, and for x in $[a, b]$, $h(x) = cf(x)$. If $c = 0$, the theorem correctly asserts that $\int_a^b 0 = 0$.

If $c > 0$, the proof consists of two applications of Exercise 1 on page 63. For S a bounded set of real numbers and c a positive number, let $cS = \{cs | s \text{ in } S\}$. Then

$c(\text{glb } S) = \text{glb } (cS),$
$c(\text{lub } S) = \text{lub } (cS).$

On a subinterval $[x_{i-1}, x_i]$ of $[a, b]$ let $m_i(f)$, $M_i(f)$ and $m_i(h)$, $M_i(h)$ be the lubs and glbs of f and h. If $S = \{f(x) | x \text{ in } [x_{i-1}, x_i]\}$, then $cS = \{h(x) | x \text{ in } [x_{i-1}, x_i]\}$. Thus

$$m_i(h) = cm_i(f) \quad \text{and} \quad M_i(h) = cM_i(f).$$

It follows that if L is the set of all lower sums for $\int_a^b f$, then cL is the set of all lower sums for $\int_a^b cf$. Also, if U is the set of all upper sums for $\int_a^b f$, then cU is the set of all upper sums for $\int_a^b cf$.

Since $\overline{\int_a^b} f = \text{glb } U, c \overline{\int_a^b} f = \text{glb } cU$ and $\overline{\int_a^b} cf = c \overline{\int_a^b} f$. Similarly, $\underline{\int_a^b} cf = c \underline{\int_a^b} f$.

Since f is integrable, the lower and upper integrals for f are equal; hence so are those for cf, and $\int_a^b cf = c \int_a^b f$. ∎

Remarks: If $c < 0$, then $c = -|c|$ and

$$\int_a^b cf = \int_a^b -|c|f = \int_a^b |c|(-f).$$

If we establish that $\int_a^b -f = -\int_a^b f$, then from the proof above,

$$\int_a^b |c|(-f) = |c| \int_a^b -f = -|c| \int_a^b f = c \int_a^b f.$$

From $m_i \leq f(x) \leq M_i$ follows $-m_i \geq -f(x) \geq -M_i$. From this, for any partition p of $[a, b]$,

$$\underline{S}(p, f) = -\overline{S}(p, -f),$$
$$\overline{S}(p, f) = -\underline{S}(p, -f).$$

For example, let

$$f(x) = \begin{cases} 1, & \text{if } x \text{ is rational,} \\ 2, & \text{if } x \text{ is irrational,} \end{cases}$$

and let p be any partition of $[0, 1]$. Then

$$\overline{S}(p, f) = \sum_{i=1}^{n} 2\Delta x_i = 2,$$

$$\underline{S}(p, f) = \sum_{i=1}^{n} 1\Delta x_i = 1,$$

$$\overline{S}(p, -f) = \sum_{i=1}^{n} (-1)\Delta x_i = -1,$$

$$\underline{S}(p, -f) = \sum_{i=1}^{n} (-2)\Delta x_i = -2,$$

$$\int_0^1 -f = -2 = -\overline{\int_0^1} f,$$

$$\overline{\int_0^1} -f = -1 = -\int_0^1 f.$$

The example is typical: any lower sum for f is the negative of an upper sum for $-f$; any upper sum for f the negative of a lower sum for $-f$. Thus for any function f bounded on $[a, b]$,

$$\int_a^b -f = -\overline{\int_a^b} f,$$

$$\overline{\int_a^b} -f = -\int_a^b f.$$

For f integrable on $[a, b]$, $\int_a^b -f = -\int_a^b f$.

PROOF OF THEOREM 9.5:   First, for relaxation, suppose f and g both monotone increasing on $[a, b]$. Then $f + g$ is monotone increasing on $[a, b]$ and for $p = \{x_0, \ldots, x_n\}$ any partition of $[a, b]$,

$$\overline{S}(p, f) = \sum_{i=1}^{n} f(x_i)\, \Delta x_i,$$

$$\overline{S}(p, g) = \sum_{i=1}^{n} g(x_i)\, \Delta x_i,$$

$$\overline{S}(p, f + g) = \sum_{i=1}^{n} [f(x_i) + g(x_i)]\, \Delta x_i$$

$$= \overline{S}(p, f) + \overline{S}(p, g).$$

It follows immediately, from Exercise 2 on page 63 that

$$\overline{\int_a^b} [f + g] = \overline{\int_a^b} f + \overline{\int_a^b} g.$$

Similarly, $\underline{\int_a^b} [f + g] = \underline{\int_a^b} f + \underline{\int_a^b} g$ and the theorem is proved.

Now merely assume f and g integrable on $[a, b]$. For $[x_{i-1}, x_i]$ a sub-interval, consider the glbs $m_i(f)$, $m_i(g)$, and $m_i(f + g)$, and the lubs $M_i(f)$, $M_i(g)$, and $M_i(f + g)$. If f and g are not both monotone in the same sense, any example will show that it is very unlikely that $M_i(f + g) = M_i(f) + M_i(g)$.

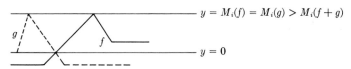

$$y = M_i(f) = M_i(g) > M_i(f + g)$$
$$y = 0$$

However, for x in $[x_{i-1}, x_i]$,
$$m_i(f) \leq f(x) \leq M_i(f),$$
$$m_i(g) \leq g(x) \leq M_i(g),$$
and
$$m_i(f) + m_i(g) \leq f(x) + g(x) \leq M_i(f) + M_i(g).$$
This shows that
$$m_i(f) + m_i(g) \leq m_i(f + g) \leq M_i(f + g) \leq M_i(f) + M_i(g).$$

For any partition $p = \{x_0, \ldots, x_n\}$, multiply the inequalities above by Δx_i and add to obtain
$$\underline{S}(p, f) + \underline{S}(p, g) \leq \underline{S}(p, f + g)$$
$$\leq \overline{S}(p, f + g) \leq \overline{S}(p, f) + \overline{S}(p, g).$$
Remembering the definition of lower and upper integrals, and that f and g are assumed integrable, we also have

$$\underline{S}(p, f) + \underline{S}(p, g) \leq \int_a^b f + \int_a^b g \leq \overline{S}(p, f) + \overline{S}(p, g),$$

$$\underline{S}(p, f + g) \leq \underline{\int_a^b} [f + g] \leq \overline{\int_a^b} [f + g] \leq \overline{S}(p, f + g).$$

For any $\epsilon > 0$ there is a partition p_ϵ such that

$$\overline{S}(p_\epsilon, f) - \underline{S}(p_\epsilon, f) < \frac{\epsilon}{2},$$

$$\overline{S}(p_\epsilon, g) - \underline{S}(p_\epsilon, g) < \frac{\epsilon}{2}.$$

These inequalities, for any $\epsilon > 0$, yield

$$\left| \underline{\int_a^b} [f + g] - \overline{\int_a^b} [f + g] \right| < \epsilon,$$

establishing that $f + g$ is integrable over $[a, b]$. They also yield

$$\left| \int_a^b f + \int_a^b g - \int_a^b [f + g] \right| < \epsilon,$$

establishing that $\int_a^b f + \int_a^b g = \int_a^b [f + g].$ ∎

Exercises

1. Use the theorems and formulas given to compute the integrals below.

a. $\int_2^5 x^2 \, dx.$

b. $\int_2^5 y^2 \, dy.$

c. $\int_2^3 (3x - 7)^2 \, dx.$

d. $\int_0^9 \sqrt{t} \, dt.$

e. $\int_0^1 (x + 5)^2 \, dx.$ [*Hint:* $(x + 5)^2 = x^2 + 10x + 25.$]

f. $\int_4^9 \sqrt{25t} \, dt.$ [*Hint:* $\sqrt{25} = 5.$]

g. $\frac{1}{25} \int_{100}^{225} \sqrt{x} \, dx.$

h. $\int_0^{25} \sqrt{7u} \, du.$

i. $\int_0^b (3x^7 + 2\sqrt{x} - 10) \, dx.$

j. Partition the interval $[4, 9]$ into 5 subintervals of length 1 and write down the upper sum for the integral in **f**.
   Partition $[100, 225]$ into 5 subintervals of length 25 and write down the upper sum for the integral in **g** above.

k. $\int_0^1 (x + 1)^3 \, dx.$ l. $\int_{-1}^1 \sqrt{x^2} \, dx.$ m. $\int_{-1}^1 x \, dx.$

2. a. Prove by computing one lower sum that $\int_1^2 (2x + 5)^{10} \, dx > 7^{10}.$

b. Prove by computing one upper sum that $\int_1^2 t^{10} \, dt < 2^{10}.$

c. Partition $[1, 2]$ into four subintervals of length $\frac{1}{4}$ and compute the corresponding upper sum for $\int_1^2 (2x + 5)^{10} \, dx.$

d. Partition $[7, 9]$ into four subintervals of length $\frac{1}{2}$ and compute the corresponding upper sum for $\int_7^9 t^{10} \, dt.$

3. a. Establish that, for $0 < b$, $\int_0^b \sqrt{x} \, dx = \frac{2}{3} b^{3/2}$ by using the following sequence of partitions. For each positive integer n, let q_n be

$$\left\{ 0, \frac{b}{n^2}, \frac{4b}{n^2}, \frac{9b}{n^2}, \ldots, \frac{n^2 b}{n^2} \right\}.$$

The interval $[(i-1)^2b/n^2, i^2b/n^2]$ has length $(2i-1)b/n^2 \leq (2n-1)b/n^2 < 2b/n$. Since the square root function is uniformly continuous on $[0, b]$, the proof of Riemann's Necessary and Sufficient Condition shows that the sequence $\{\overline{S}(q_n)\}$ of upper sums converges to $\int_0^b \sqrt{x}\,dx$.

b. Prove, without using Theorem 9.4, that for any interval $[a, b]$,

$$\int_a^b x\,dx = \frac{b^2}{2} - \frac{a^2}{2}.$$

Areas

If a bounded function f is positive over an interval $[a, b]$, intuition demands that the area between the axis and the graph of f, say $A(a, b)$, satisfies, for p any partition,

$$\underline{S}(p) \leq A(a, b) \leq \overline{S}(p).$$

Thus $A(a, b)$ is an upper bound for the set of lower sums and a lower bound for the set of upper sums. By the definition of lower and upper integrals,

$$\int_a^b f \leq A(a, b) \leq \overline{\int_a^b} f.$$

If f is integrable over $[a, b]$, then $A(a, b)$ has to be $\int_a^b f$, and we make this the basic definition of area. The basic definition leads naturally to some generalizations suggested by the following diagrams.

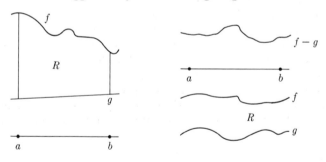

$$\text{Area of } R = \int_a^b f - \int_a^b g = \int_a^b (f - g)$$

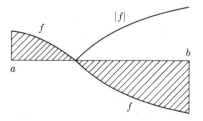

$$\text{Shaded area} = \int_a^b |f|$$

Definition 9.4. If each of the functions f and g is integrable over $[a, b]$, then the **area** of the region bounded by the lines $x = a$ and $x = b$ and the graphs of f and g is $\int_a^b |f - g|$. This holds in particular if $g = 0$, and defines the area of the region between the horizontal axis and the graph of f, for integrable f.

Remark: The hypothesis that f and g are integrable is an essential part of this definition. If $f(x) = 1$ for rational x but 2 for irrational x, then $\underline{\int_0^1} f = 1$ and $\overline{\int_0^1} f = 2$. The definition does not assign any area to the region

$$\{(x, y) | 0 \leq x \leq 1, 0 \leq y \leq f(x)\}.$$

If $f(x) = 1$ for rational x but -1 for irrational x, then $|f(x)| = 1$ for all x. Thus $|f|$ is integrable, but the definition above does not assign an area to the set of points between the horizontal axis and the graph of f, because f is not integrable.

As Exercise 2 below indicates, the integrability of f implies the integrability of $|f|$.

Exercises

1. Find the area of each region below.
   a. Over the interval $[-1, 1]$ between the graphs of $y = x^2$ and $y = 1$.
   b. Over the interval $[0, 1]$ between the graphs of $y = x$ and $y = x^2$.
   c. Over the interval $[0, 2]$ between the graphs of $y = x$ and $y = x^2$. [This really needs an additional theorem: find it in § 4 of this chapter.]
   d. The region between the graphs of $y = \sqrt{x}$ and $y = x^2/8$.
   e. The bounded region between the axis and the graph of $y = x^3 - x$.
2. Prove that if f is integrable over $[a, b]$, then so is $|f|$. [*Hints:* On a subinterval $[x_{i-1}, x_i]$ consider three cases: f nonnegative, f negative, f changes sign. In two cases,
   $$M_i(|f|) - m_i(|f|) = M_i(f) - m_i(f).$$
   In the third case,
   $$M_i(|f|) - m_i(|f|) < M_i(f) - m_i(f).$$
3. Draw a circle of radius r with center at the origin and fill in a picture of the following. For $-r \leq b \leq r$,
   $$\int_{-r}^b \sqrt{r^2 - x^2}\, dx = \frac{b}{2}\sqrt{r^2 - b^2} + \frac{r^2}{2}\left(\pi - \mathrm{Cos}^{-1}\frac{b}{r}\right).$$

Solids of Revolution

Suppose L is a line in the plane and C a curve such that C does not cross L and such that any line perpendicular to L intersects C in at most one point.

This amounts to saying that, if L is regarded as the horizontal axis of a co-ordinate system, then C is the graph of a continuous function which does not change sign over the interval in question.

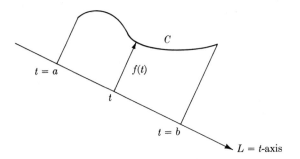

Rotation of the region between L and C around L generates a solid of revolution. Planes perpendicular to L slice the solid into pieces which, just as in § 6 of Chapter 8 [page 257], are trapped between cylinders.

Since there is a definition of volume which assigns volumes to solid regions much more general than solids of revolution, we are not really free to make a definition in this special case.

Assertion: The definition of volume is such that it can be proved that if V is the volume of a solid of revolution determined as above, then
$$V = \int_a^b \pi f^2.$$

Exercises

1. **a.** By rotating a semicircular region about a diameter, prove that the volume of a sphere of radius r is $\frac{4}{3}\pi r^3$.

   b. By rotating a triangle around one side, prove that a right circular cone of height h and base radius r has volume $\frac{1}{3}\pi r^2 h$.

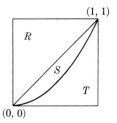

   c. The graphs of $y = x$ and $y = x^2$ split the unit square into three regions. Find the volumes of the solids obtained by the following rotations.

      (i) T around the x-axis.

      (ii) R around the y-axis.

     (iii) S around the x-axis.

     (iv) R around the x-axis.

2. a. Suppose two right circular cylinders of radius r intersect at right angles, with the axes also intersecting. To draw a satisfactory picture of the intersection, which is not a solid of revolution, is a well-known challenging problem in drawing. If we take the axes of the cylinders to be the x-axis and the y-axis, then, considered as solid cylinders, they have equations

$$y^2 + z^2 \leq r^2 \quad \text{and} \quad x^2 + z^2 \leq r^2.$$

Their intersection is the set of all (x, y, z) satisfying both inequalities. The intersection of the set with a plane, $z = h$, $-r \leq h \leq r$, is the set of all points (x, y, h) such that $|x| \leq \sqrt{r^2 - h^2}$ and $|y| \leq \sqrt{r^2 - h^2}$, a square of side $\sqrt{r^2 - h^2}$. Make a geometrically plausible argument that the volume of the intersection of the cylinders must be

$$\int_{-r}^{r} (r^2 - h^2) \, dh = \tfrac{4}{3} r^3.$$

If you have trouble deciphering the meaning of the integral, try it for $r = 2$ and $r = 5$. Or, if h is troublesome, make it $\int_{-r}^{r} (r^2 - z^2) \, dz$.

b. Define F as follows: for all real $x > 2$, $F(x) = \int_{2}^{x} t^2 \, dt$. Show that

$$\int_{3}^{5} F = \frac{5^4}{12} - \frac{3^4}{12} - \frac{16}{3}.$$

c. Define G as follows: for $0 < x < 1$, $G(x) = \int_{x^2}^{x} t \, dt$. Show that for $0 < u < 1$,

$$\int_{0}^{u} G = \frac{u^3}{6} - \frac{u^5}{10}.$$

d. Find $\int_{2}^{3} H$, where H is defined, for $x > 0$, by $H(x) = \int_{0}^{x} \left[\int_{u}^{2u} v^2 \, dv \right] du$. We could as well write

$$H(x) = \int_{0}^{x} \int_{u}^{2u} v^2 \, dv \, du,$$

$$H(x) = \int_{0}^{x} \int_{u}^{2u} y^2 \, dy \, du,$$

or

$$H(x) = \int_{0}^{x} \int_{s}^{2s} t^2 \, dt \, ds.$$

§ 3. *Averages*

Let f be a real function continuous on an interval $[a, b]$. Let m and M be the glb and lub of $\{f(x) | a \leq x \leq b\}$. The simplest partition gives

$$m(b - a) \leq \int_{a}^{b} f \leq M(b - a).$$

Unless f is constant, at least one of these inequalities is strict and there is some number k between m and M such that $\int_{a}^{b} f = k(b - a)$. By the

Extreme Value Theorem there are x_1 and x_2 in $[a, b]$ with $f(x_1) = m$ and $f(x_2) = M$. By the Intermediate Value Theorem there is at least one c between x_1 and x_2 such that $f(c) = k$. If f is constant, then, for any c in (a, b),

$$\int_a^b f = (b - a)f(c).$$

This establishes

Theorem 9.7 [*The First Mean Value Theorem for Integrals*]. If f is continuous on the closed interval $[a, b]$, there is at least one number c in (a, b) such that $\int_a^b f = (b - a)f(c)$.

In case f is continuous and nonnegative on $[a, b]$, an interpretation is that the area of the region between the axis and the graph of f is the same as the area of a rectangle with base length $b - a$ and height the mean value $f(c)$.

Corollary 1 to Theorem 9.7. If f is continuous on $[a, b]$ and positive on (a, b), then $\int_a^b f > 0$.

Corollary 2 to Theorem 9.7. If f and g are continuous on $[a, b]$ and $f(x) > g(x)$ for $a < x < b$, then $\int_a^b f > \int_a^b g$.

PROOFS: The proof of Corollary 1 from the theorem is immediate:
$$b - a > 0 \quad \text{and} \quad f(c) > 0.$$

Corollary 2 follows from Corollary 1: by hypothesis, $f - g$ is continuous on $[a, b]$ and positive on (a, b), and hence $\int_a^b [f - g] > 0$; but

$$\int_a^b [f - g] = \int_a^b f - \int_a^b g > 0,$$

giving Corollary 2. ∎

Later in this section we shall prove that, for $b > 0$, $\int_0^b \cos = \sin b$. In the next section we shall prove that, as a consequence of this and theorems of the next section, for all a and b,

$$\int_a^b \cos = \sin b - \sin a,$$

$$\int_a^b \sin = -\cos b + \cos a.$$

In particular, for $b > 0$, $\int_0^b \sin = -\cos b + 1$. We shall assume these integration formulas here because they give a fine application of Corollary 2, an application which produces tables of the sine and cosine functions.

For $x > 0$, $\cos x \le 1$. On the interval $(0, 2\pi)$, $\cos x < 1$. Since cos and the constant function 1 are continuous everywhere, then, at least for $0 < x \leq 2\pi$,

$$\int_0^x \cos < \int_0^x 1 \quad \text{and} \quad \sin x < x.$$

Of course, for $x \geq 2\pi$, $\sin x < x$. In fact we already knew that $\sin x < x$ for all $x > 0$.

Now let t be any positive number. Since, for $0 < x < t$, $\sin x < x$,

$$\int_0^t \sin x \, dx < \int_0^t x \, dx,$$

or

$$-\cos t + 1 < \frac{t^2}{2} \quad \text{and} \quad \cos t > 1 - \frac{t^2}{2}.$$

So far we have no new results. Indeed, our proof that $\int_0^b \cos = \sin b$ will depend on the basic inequalities for sin and cos derived geometrically from their definition.

Now, for $x > 0$,

$$\int_0^x \cos t \, dt > \int_0^x \left(1 - \frac{t^2}{2}\right) dt,$$

or

$$\sin x > x - \frac{x^3}{6}.$$

This inequality can immediately be integrated: for $t > 0$,

$$\int_0^t \sin x \, dx > \int_0^t \left(x - \frac{x^3}{6}\right) dx,$$

or

$$1 - \cos t > \frac{t^2}{2} - \frac{t^4}{24},$$

or

$$\cos t < 1 - \frac{t^2}{2} + \frac{t^4}{24}.$$

Integration of this gives, for $x > 0$,

$$\sin x < x - \frac{x^3}{6} + \frac{x^5}{120}.$$

As an informal exercise, establish that, for all $x > 0$,

$$x - \frac{x^3}{3!} + \frac{x^5}{5!} - \frac{x^7}{7!} < \sin x < x - \frac{x^3}{3!} + \frac{x^5}{5!} - \frac{x^7}{7!} + \frac{x^9}{9!}.$$

To know sin and cos everywhere, it is sufficient to know them on the interval $[0, \pi/4]$. Evidently we have a method for approximating sin and cos uniformly well by polynomials over this interval. For example, calculate sin (0.1) correct to seven decimal places.

Calculation of $\int_0^b \cos$, $b > 0$

Let $p_n = \{0, b/n, 2b/n, \ldots, (nb/n) = b\}$. Let

$$S_n = \sum_{i=1}^{n} \frac{b}{n} \cos\left(\frac{ib}{n}\right).$$

If $b \leq \pi$, then cos is monotone decreasing on $[0, b]$ and S_n is the lower sum. For $b > \pi$, S_n is unlikely to be either a lower or upper sum. But in any case, $\underline{S}(p_n) \leq S_n \leq \overline{S}(p_n)$. By the uniform continuity of cos on $[0, b]$ and the proof of Theorem 9.3, the sequence $\{S_n\}$ converges to $\int_0^b \cos$.

From

$$\sum_{i=1}^{n} \sin\frac{t}{2} \cos it = \frac{1}{2}\sum_{i=1}^{n}\left[\sin\left(i+\frac{1}{2}\right)t - \sin\left(i-\frac{1}{2}\right)t\right]$$

it follows that

$$\sum_{i=1}^{n} \cos(it) = -\frac{1}{2} + \frac{\sin(n+\frac{1}{2})t}{2\sin\frac{1}{2}t}.$$

For large enough n, $b/2n < \pi$ and $\sin b/2n \neq 0$. Thus, for all large n,

$$S_n = \frac{b}{n}\sum_{i=1}^{n}\cos\frac{ib}{n} = \frac{b}{n}\left[-\frac{1}{2} + \frac{\sin\left(n+\frac{1}{2}\right)\frac{b}{n}}{2\sin\frac{b}{2n}}\right].$$

The limit of $\{-b/2n\}$ is 0;

$$\sin\left(n+\frac{1}{2}\right)\frac{b}{n} = \sin\left(b + \frac{b}{2n}\right)$$

$$= \sin b \cos\frac{b}{2n} + \cos b \sin\frac{2b}{n}.$$

Thus

$$\lim\{S_n\} = \lim\left\{\frac{b}{n}\frac{\sin b \cos\frac{b}{2n}}{2\sin\frac{b}{2n}} + \frac{b}{n}\frac{\cos b \sin\frac{b}{2n}}{2\sin\frac{b}{2n}}\right\}$$

$$= \lim\left\{\frac{\frac{b}{2n}}{\sin\frac{b}{2n}}\sin b \cos\frac{b}{2n} + \frac{b}{2n}\cos b\right\}.$$

Since $\cos 0 = 1$ and $\cos$ is continuous at 0, $\lim \{\cos b/2n\} = 1$. Clearly, $\lim \{(b/2n) \cos b\} = 0$. By the Corollary to Theorem 6.14 [page 181], if $\{x_n\}$ is any sequence converging to 0, but no term of which is 0, then

$$\lim \left\{ \frac{\sin x_n}{x_n} \right\} = 1.$$

Also, by the theorem on the limit of a quotient,

$$\lim \left\{ \frac{x_n}{\sin x_n} \right\} = 1.$$

Since $\{b/2n\}$ converges to 0 but $b/2n \neq 0$ for all n, the preceding arguments yield

$$\lim \{S_n\} = \sin b.$$

Calculation of $\int_a^b \cos$ and $\int_a^b \sin$

These calculations rest on theorems from the next section. Each time we assert that something is "clear," we mean that it is (1) intuitively plausible, and (2) proved in the next section.

For $0 < a < b$, it is clear that

$$\int_0^b \cos = \int_0^a \cos + \int_a^b \cos.$$

Thus

$$\sin b = \sin a + \int_a^b \cos,$$

or

$$\int_a^b \cos = \sin b - \sin a.$$

For $a < 0$ it is clear that $\int_a^0 \cos = \int_0^{|a|} \cos$, because, for all x, $\cos(-x) = \cos x$.

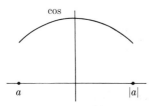

Thus, for $a < 0$,

$$\int_a^0 \cos = \int_0^{|a|} \cos = \sin |a| = \sin(-a) = -\sin a,$$

and

$$\int_a^0 \cos = -\sin a = \sin 0 - \sin a.$$

For $a < b < 0$, it is clear that

$$\int_a^b \cos + \int_b^0 \cos = \int_a^0 \cos$$

or

$$\int_a^b \cos + -\sin b = -\sin a,$$

and

$$\int_a^b \cos = \sin b - \sin a.$$

Similarly, for $a < 0 < b$, $\int_a^b \cos = \sin b - \sin a$.

If we recall the relation between the graphs of sin and cos given by: for all x, $\sin x = \cos (x - (\pi/2))$, it is clear that

$$\int_a^b \sin = \int_{a-(\pi/2)}^{b-(\pi/2)} \cos = \sin \left(b - \frac{\pi}{2} \right) - \sin \left(a - \frac{\pi}{2} \right)$$

$$= -\cos b + \cos a.$$

This calculation has been a digression from the consideration of average values, to which we now return. Theorem 9.7 [the First Mean Value Theorem for Integrals] asserts that, if the function f is continuous on $[a, b]$, then there is some c in (a, b) such that $\int_a^b f = (b - a)f(c)$. The number $f(c)$ is by definition the *mean* or *average* value of f on the interval $[a, b]$.

For a function f integrable but not necessarily continuous on an interval $[a, b]$, the *average value of f on $[a, b]$* is defined by

$$\text{average value of } f \text{ on } [a, b] = \frac{1}{b - a} \int_a^b f.$$

For example, if f is the step function which is 1 on $[0, 1]$ and 3 on $(1, 2]$, $\int_0^2 f = 4$ and the average value of f on $[0, 2]$ is 2. If f is also the constant 3 on $[2, 10]$, then $\int_0^{10} f = 28$ and the average value of f on $[0, 10]$ is 2.8.

Exercises

1. Find the average value of the following.
a. cos on the interval $[0, \pi]$.
b. cos on the interval $[0, \pi/2]$.
c. x^2 on $[a, b]$.
d. x on $[-1, 1]$.
e. $x - x^3$ on $[0, 1]$.
2. Find a number c between 1 and 3 such that

$$\int_1^3 (x + 2x^2)\, dx = 2(c + 2c^2).$$

3. **a.** For f and g, functions integrable over an interval $[a, b]$, prove that the average value of $f + g$ on $[a, b]$ is the sum of the average values of f and g.

   b. What can be said about the average value of $2f + 3g$?

In the last chapter we proved by a special device that, for $0 < a < b$,

$$\int_a^b \frac{1}{x^2}\, dx = \frac{1}{a} - \frac{1}{b}.$$

If p is a partition of $[a, b]$ and $[x_{i-1}, x_i] = [c, d]$, the typical subinterval, we noted that the contribution to the lower sum is $(d - c)/d^2$, the contribution to the upper sum is $(d - c)/c^2$, and that $(d - c)/dc = (1/d) - (1/c)$ is between these. This showed that, for every partition p,

$$\underline{S}(p) < \sum_{i=1}^{n} \left(\frac{1}{x_{i-1}} - \frac{1}{x_i}\right) = \frac{1}{a} - \frac{1}{b} < \overline{S}(p).$$

The choice of $1/cd$ as a convenient number between $1/c^2$ and $1/d^2$ was not accidental. The average value of $1/x^2$ on the interval $[c, d]$ is

$$\frac{1}{d - c} \int_c^d \frac{1}{x^2}\, dx = \frac{1}{d - c} \left(\frac{1}{c} - \frac{1}{d}\right) = \frac{1}{cd}.$$

A similar technique serves to integrate x^n for n any integer except -1.

For example, if $a < b$, we might conjecture on the basis of formulas we have derived that

$$\int_a^b x^3\, dx = \frac{b^4 - a^4}{4}.$$

If this conjecture is correct, then the average value of x^3 on $[a, b]$ is

$$\frac{b^4 - a^4}{4(b - a)} = \frac{b^3 + b^2 a + b a^2 + a^3}{4}.$$

Let $p = \{x_0, \ldots, x_n\}$ be a partition of $[a, b]$. Since the cubing function is strictly increasing, it is true that, for each subinterval,

$$x_{i-1}^3 < x_{i-1}^2 x_i < x_{i-1} x_i^2 < x_i^3,$$

$$x_{i-1}^3 < \frac{x_{i-1}^3 + x_{i-1}^2 x_i + x_{i-1} x_i^2 + x_i^3}{4} < x_i^3,$$

$$x_{i-1}^3 (x_i - x_{i-1}) < \frac{x_i^4 - x_{i-1}^4}{4} < x_i^3 (x_i - x_{i-1}),$$

$$\underline{S}(p) < \frac{b^4 - a^4}{4} < \overline{S}(p).$$

By definition of lower and upper integrals, then

$$\underline{\int_a^b} x^3\, dx \leq \frac{b^4 - a^4}{4} \leq \overline{\int_a^b} x^3\, dx.$$

But every monotone function is integrable, and thus

$$\int_a^b x^3 \, dx = \frac{b^4 - a^4}{4}.$$

To generalize this all that is needed is the observation that for any real numbers c and d and any positive integer n,

$$(d - c)(d^n + d^{n-1}c + \cdots + dc^{n-1} + c^n) = d^{n+1} - c^{n+1}.$$

This is readily proved by mathematical induction. Or, for $c \neq d \neq 0$, it can be derived from the formula for summing a geometric progression:

$$\sum_{i=0}^n d^{n-i}c^i = d^n \sum_{i=0}^n d^{-i}c^i$$

$$= d^n \sum_{i=0}^n \left(\frac{c}{d}\right)^i$$

$$= d^n \frac{1 - \left(\frac{c}{d}\right)^{n+1}}{1 - \frac{c}{d}}$$

$$= \frac{d^{n+1} - c^{n+1}}{d - c}.$$

Now let n be any positive integer and consider $\int_a^b x^n \, dx$. To have x^n monotone increasing on the interval whether n is even or odd, assume $0 \leq a < b$. Let $p = \{x_0, \ldots, x_m\}$ be a partition with $m \geq 2$, and $[c, d]$ the ith subinterval.

For $k = 0, 1, \ldots, n$, since $c^n \leq c^{n-k}d^k \leq d^n$, we have

$$c^n < \frac{1}{n+1} \sum_{k=0}^n c^{n-k}d^k \leq d^n,$$

$$(d - c)c^n < \frac{d^{n+1} - c^{n+1}}{n+1} \leq (d - c)d^n,$$

$$\sum_{i=1}^m x_{i-1}^n(x_i - x_{i-1}) < \sum_{i=1}^m \frac{x_i^{n+1} - x_{i-1}^{n+1}}{n+1} < \sum_{i=1}^m x_i^n(x_i - x_{i-1}),$$

$$\underline{S}(p) < \frac{b^{n+1} - a^{n+1}}{n+1} < \overline{S}(p),$$

and

$$\int_a^b x^n \, dx = \frac{b^{n+1} - a^{n+1}}{n+1}.$$

Exercises

1. For $0 < a < b$ or $a < b < 0$, the function $1/x^3 = x^{-3}$ is bounded and monotone on $[a, b]$, and hence integrable. Show that if the formula

$$\int_a^b x^{-3}\,dx = \frac{b^{-2}}{-2} - \frac{a^{-2}}{-2}$$

is correct, then the average value of $1/x^3$ on $[a, b]$ is $\frac{1}{2}[(1/a^2b) + (1/ab^2)]$.
Then prove that the formula is in fact correct.

2. In a similar way prove that, for $0 < a < b$ or $a < b < 0$,

$$\int_a^b x^{-4}\,dx = \frac{b^{-3}}{-3} - \frac{a^{-3}}{-3}.$$

§ 4. *Directed Integrals*

Theorem 9.8. Let f be a function bounded on an interval $[a, b]$
and c be a number in (a, b). If f is integrable over $[a, b]$, then f is
integrable over $[a, c]$ and over $[c, b]$ and

$$\int_a^b f = \int_a^c f + \int_c^b f.$$

Conversely, if f is integrable over $[a, c]$ and over $[c, b]$, then f is integrable over $[a, b]$ and the above equation holds.

PROOF: Assume f integrable over $[a, b]$. For $\epsilon > 0$ there is a parti-
tion p such that $\overline{S}(f, p) - \underline{S}(f, p) < \epsilon$. Let q be a refinement of p containing c.
Then q is the union of q_1, a partition of $[a, c]$, and q_2, a partition of $[c, b]$.

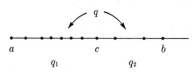

From the diagram above we can see that

(1) $\underline{S}(f, q) = \underline{S}(f, q_1) + \underline{S}(f, q_2),$

(2) $\overline{S}(f, q) = \overline{S}(f, q_1) + \overline{S}(f, q_2).$

Their difference is

$$\overline{S}(f, q) - \underline{S}(f, q) = \overline{S}(f, q_1) - \underline{S}(f, q_1) + \overline{S}(f, q_2) - \underline{S}(f, q_2).$$

Each of the nonnegative numbers $\overline{S}(f, q_1) - \underline{S}(f, q_1)$ and $\overline{S}(f, q_2) -$
$\underline{S}(f, q_2)$, whose sum is $< \epsilon$, must be $< \epsilon$. This establishes the integrability
of f over $[a, c]$ and $[c, b]$.

Since each of the three sums in Equation (1) differs from the corresponding integral by less than ϵ, for every $\epsilon > 0$, we have

$$\left| \int_a^b f - \left[\int_a^c f + \int_c^b f \right] \right| < 3\epsilon.$$

Conversely, if f is integrable over $[a, c]$ and over $[c, b]$, there are, for any $\epsilon > 0$, partitions q_1 of $[a, c]$ and q_2 of $[c, b]$ such that

$$\overline{S}(f, q_1) - \underline{S}(f, q_1) < \frac{\epsilon}{2},$$

$$\overline{S}(f, q_2) - \underline{S}(f, q_2) < \frac{\epsilon}{2}.$$

If q is the union of q_1 and q_2, then q is a partition of $[a, b]$ such that $\overline{S}(f, q) - \underline{S}(f, q) < \epsilon$.

This establishes the integrability of f over $[a, b]$. By the first part of the theorem,

$$\int_a^b f = \int_a^c f + \int_c^b f. \quad \blacksquare$$

Definition 9.5. For any number a in the domain of a real function f, $\int_a^a f = 0$.

If f is integrable over the interval $[a, b]$, then $\int_b^a f = -\int_a^b f$.

For example,

$$\int_3^2 x \, dx = -\int_2^3 x \, dx = -\left[\frac{3^2}{2} - \frac{2^2}{2}\right] = -\frac{5}{2}.$$

Remarks: Think of a directed interval from 3 to 2 and partition it, for example, according to the formula

$$x_i = 3 + i \frac{(2 - 3)}{n} = 3 - \frac{i}{n}.$$

Then

$$\sum_{i=1}^n f(x_i) \, \Delta x_i = \sum_{i=1}^n f\left(3 - \frac{i}{n}\right) \frac{-1}{n}$$

$$= -\frac{1}{n} \sum_{i=1}^n f\left(3 - \frac{i}{n}\right).$$

However,

$$f\left(3 - \frac{1}{n}\right) + f\left(3 - \frac{2}{n}\right) + \cdots + f\left(3 - \frac{n-1}{n}\right) + f(2)$$

$$= f(2) + f\left(2 + \frac{1}{n}\right) + \cdots + f\left(3 - \frac{2}{n}\right) + f\left(3 - \frac{1}{n}\right),$$

and

$$-\frac{1}{n} \sum_{i=1}^n f\left(3 - \frac{i}{n}\right) = -\frac{1}{n} \sum_{i=1}^n f\left(2 + \frac{i}{n}\right).$$

Thus, if we formally extend the idea of partitioning to a directed interval, we conclude that we want $\int_b^a f = -\int_a^b f$.

Theorem 9.9. If the function f is integrable over an interval containing a, b, and c, then, regardless of the order of these three numbers,

$$\int_a^c f + \int_c^b f = \int_a^b f$$

or, equivalently,

$$\int_a^b f - \int_a^c f = \int_c^b f.$$

The proof is by application of Theorem 9.8 and Definitions 9.5 to the various possible cases. We prove one case and leave the others to the reader.

$$\overline{\quad c \qquad\qquad\qquad a \qquad\qquad b \quad}$$

By Theorem 9.8,

$$\int_c^b f = \int_c^a f + \int_a^b f.$$

By Definition 9.5,

$$\int_c^a f = -\int_a^c f.$$

Thus

$$\int_c^b f = -\int_a^c f + \int_a^b f \quad\text{and}\quad \int_a^c f + \int_c^b f = \int_a^b f.$$

Typical Application: We have proved that for any positive number b, $\int_0^b x^2 \, dx = b^3/3$. Thus, if a and b are positive,

$$\int_0^b x^2 \, dx = \frac{b^3}{3} \quad\text{and}\quad \int_0^a x^2 \, dx = \frac{a^3}{3}.$$

By the theorem,

$$\int_a^b x^2 \, dx = \int_0^b x^2 \, dx - \int_0^a x^2 \, dx = \frac{b^3}{3} - \frac{a^3}{3}.$$

Remark: The Mean Value Theorem for Integrals in the last section asserts that if f is continuous on the interval $[a, b]$ there is some number c in the open interval (a, b) such that $\int_a^b f = (b - a)f(c)$.

If a is larger than b and f is continuous on $[b, a]$, then

$$\int_a^b f = -\int_b^a f,$$

and $\int_b^a f = (a - b)f(c)$ for some c between b and a by the above Mean

Value Theorem. Then

$$\int_a^b f = -\int_b^a f = -(a - b)f(c) = (b - a)f(c).$$

Thus the original theorem can be extended to

Corollary to Theorem 9.9. If the function f is continuous on an interval containing numbers a and b, with $a \neq b$, then there is a number c strictly between a and b such that $\int_a^b f = (b - a)f(c)$.

A Substitution Formula

The formula is actually a formula for integrating compositions of a special type. Integration of sums of functions works beautifully: the integral of the sum is the sum of the integrals, and that's that. Theorems about the integral of a product or composition of two functions are rare and very valuable. The only one we have so far requires one factor to be constant:

$$\int_a^b cf = c \int_a^b f.$$

The formula in this section concerns integrating a composition $f \circ g$ in the very special case that $g(x) = mx + k$, for some $m \neq 0$. We state the theorem in three forms, all equivalent. The proof is given in two parts.

Theorem 9.10. Let g be the function $g(x) = mx + k$, with $m \neq 0$. If f is integrable over $[g(a), g(b)]$, then

$$\int_a^b f \circ g = \frac{1}{m} \int_{g(a)}^{g(b)} f,$$

$$\int_a^b f(mx + k)\, dx = \frac{1}{m} \int_{ma+k}^{mb+k} f(t)\, dt,$$

or

$$\int_a^b f(mx + k)m\, dx = \int_{ma+k}^{mb+k} f(t)\, dt.$$

Examples

1. Find $I = \int_0^1 (2x + 3)^2\, dx$.

a. First solution:

$$I = \int_0^1 (4x^2 + 12x + 9)\, dx$$

$$= \tfrac{4}{3} + 6 + 9.$$

b. Second solution: $I = \int_0^1 f \circ g$, where $g(x) = 2x + 3$ and $f(x) = x^2$. By Theorem 9.10,

$$I = \frac{1}{2} \int_{g(0)}^{g(1)} f = \frac{1}{2} \int_3^5 x^2 \, dx = \frac{1}{2} \left[\frac{5^3}{3} - \frac{3^3}{3} \right].$$

2. $\displaystyle \int_1^2 (x + 7) \, dx = \int_8^9 t \, dt = \frac{9^2}{2} - \frac{8^2}{2}.$

PROOF OF THEOREM 9.10 FOR $m > 0$: With $m > 0$, let $g(x) = mx + k$ for all x. Then g is strictly monotone increasing and maps an interval $[a, b]$ one-to-one onto the interval $[g(a), g(b)]$. Let f be a function integrable over $[g(a), g(b)]$, and let $p = \{t_0, \ldots, t_n\}$ be a partition of $[g(a), g(b)]$.

For each number t in $[g(a), g(b)]$, let x be the number in $[a, b]$ such that $g(x) = t$. In particular,

$$t_0 = g(a) = g(x_0),$$
$$\ldots$$
$$t_{i-1} = g(x_{i-1}),$$
$$t_i = g(x_i),$$
$$\ldots$$
$$t_n = g(b) = g(x_n).$$

The partition p of $[g(a), g(b)]$ induces a partition $q = \{x_0, \ldots, x_n\}$ of $[a, b]$. Conversely, if $\{y_0, \ldots, y_n\}$ is any partition of $[a, b]$, then $\{g(y_0), \ldots, g(y_n)\}$ is a partition of $[g(a), g(b)]$.

Now set $h = f \circ g$ and consider the lower sums $\underline{S}(p, f)$ and $\underline{S}(q, h)$. The number $m_i(f)$ is the glb of the set

$$\{f(t)|t_{i-1} \le t \le t_i\} = \{f(g(x))|x_{i-1} \le x \le x_i\}$$
$$= \{h(x)|x_{i-1} \le x \le x_i\}.$$

Thus $m_i(f)$, the glb for f over the interval $[g(x_{i-1}), g(x_i)]$, is also $m_i(h)$, the glb of $h = f \circ g$ over $[x_{i-1}, x_i]$:

$$\underline{S}(p, f) = \sum_{i=1}^n m_i(f) \, \Delta t_i$$
$$= \sum_{i=1}^n m_i(h) \, \Delta t_i.$$

However,

$$\Delta t_i = t_i - t_{i-1}$$
$$= g(x_i) - g(x_{i-1})$$
$$= mx_i + k - [mx_{i-1} + k]$$
$$= m(x_i - x_{i-1})$$
$$= m \, \Delta x_i.$$

Thus

$$\underline{S}(p, f) = \sum_{i=1}^{n} m_i(h) \, \Delta t_i$$

$$= \sum_{i=1}^{n} m_i(h) m \, \Delta x_i$$

$$= m \sum_{i=1}^{n} m_i(h) \, \Delta x_i$$

$$= m\underline{S}(q, h).$$

The conclusion is that each lower sum for $\int_{g(a)}^{g(b)} f$ is m times the corresponding lower sum for $\int_a^b f \circ g$, and hence that

$$\underline{\int}_{g(a)}^{g(b)} f = m \underline{\int}_a^b f \circ g.$$

Exactly the same argument applies to the upper integrals and we conclude that, if f is integrable over $[g(a), g(b)]$, then

$$\int_a^b f \circ g = \frac{1}{m} \int_{g(a)}^{g(b)} f. \qquad \blacksquare$$

The crucial step was $\Delta t_i = m \, \Delta x_i$. This is where the particular form of g, $g(x) = mx + k$, makes the theorem work; g is a similarity of $[a, b]$ to $[g(a), g(b)]$, stretching or shrinking all subintervals by the same factor m.

The various statements of the theorem are equivalent because we can multiply or divide both sides by m and also have m inside or outside the integral, as we wish.

Examples

1. $\int_2^5 (3x + 7)^5 \, dx = \frac{1}{3} \int_2^5 (3x + 7)^5 3 \, dx \ \| \ \frac{1}{3} \int_{13}^{22} t^5 \, dt.$

2. Since, for all x, $\sin x = \cos (x - (\pi/2))$,

$$\int_a^b \sin x \, dx = \int_a^b \cos \left(x - \frac{\pi}{2} \right) dx = \int_{a-(\pi/2)}^{b-(\pi/2)} \cos t \, dt.$$

PROOF OF THEOREM 9.10 FOR $m < 0$: First consider $g(x) = -x$. The theorem says that

$$\int_a^b f(-x) \, dx = \frac{1}{-1} \int_{-a}^{-b} f(t) \, dt = - \int_{-a}^{-b} f(t) \, dt,$$

or $\int_a^b f(-x) \, dx = \int_{-b}^{-a} f(t) \, dt$. The diagram at the top of the next page, in which $h(x) = f(-x)$, makes this look right.

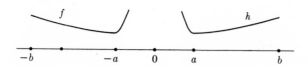

If $\{x_0, \ldots, x_n\}$ is any partition of $[a, b]$, then $\{-x_n, \ldots, -x_0\}$ is a partition of $[-b, -a]$. For each positive integer n, let p_n be the partition of $[a, b]$ into n subintervals each of length $L_n = (b - a)/n$ and q_n the partition of $[-b, -a]$ into n subintervals of length L_n.

The upper sum is

$$\overline{S}(q_n, f) = L_n \sum_{i=1}^{n} M_i(f),$$

where $M_i(f)$ is the lub of the set

$$\{f(x)|-b + (i - 1)L_n \le x \le -b + iL_n\}$$
$$= \{f(-x)|b - iL_n \le x \le b - (i - 1)L_n\}.$$

But, since $b - a = nL_n$,

$$b = a + nL_n,$$

and

$$b - iL_n = a + (n - i)L_n = x_{n-i}.$$

Similarly,

$$b - (i - 1)L_n = x_{n-i+1}.$$

Remembering that $f(-x) = h(x)$, we have $M_i(f) = M_{n-i+1}(h)$, and

$$\overline{S}(q_n, f) = L_n \sum_{i=1}^{n} M_{n-i+1}(h)$$

$$= L_n \sum_{i=1}^{n} M_i(h)$$

$$= \overline{S}(p_n, h).$$

The lower sums can be treated similarly and we have the essentials of a proof that, if f is integrable over $[-b, -a]$, then

$$\int_a^b f(-x)\, dx = \int_{-b}^{-a} f.$$

Now let m be any negative number and let $g(x) = mx + k$. Since m is negative, $m = -|m|$ and $g(x) = -(|m|x - k)$. Set $g_1(x) = -x$ and $g_2(x) = |m|x - k$. By the associativity of composition, $f \circ g = (f \circ g_1) \circ g_2$ and we can use what is already proved to obtain

$$\int_a^b f \circ g = \int_a^b [f \circ g_1](|m|x - k)\, dx$$

$$= \frac{1}{|m|} \int_{-ma-k}^{-mb-k} [f \circ g_1](t)\, dt$$

$$= \frac{-1}{m} \int_{-ma-k}^{-mb-k} f(-t)\, dt$$

$$= \frac{-1}{m} \int_{mb+k}^{ma+k} f$$

$$= \frac{1}{m} \int_{ma+k}^{mb+k} f \qquad \blacksquare$$

Remark: The two parts of the proof of Theorem 9.10 have assumed $a < b$. But the theorem also holds for $a > b$:

$$\int_a^b f(mx + k)m\, dx = -\int_b^a f(mx + k)m\, dx$$

$$= -\int_{mb+k}^{ma+k} f(t)\, dt$$

$$= \int_{ma+k}^{mb+k} f(t)\, dt.$$

Exercises

Apply Theorem 9.10 to evaluate the following integrals.

1. $\int_2^3 (3x - 6)^{10}\, dx.$

2. $\int_1^9 2\sqrt{2x + 7}\, dx.$

3. $\int_0^1 \frac{1}{x^2 + 6x + 9}\, dx.$

4. $\int_{-1}^1 (x - 1)^5\, dx.$

5. $\int_0^{\pi/2} \sin 4x\, dx.$

6. $\int_0^{\pi} \sin\left(\frac{x}{2}\right) dx.$

7. $\int_0^{\pi} \cos^2.$ [*Hint:* $\cos^2 x = \frac{1}{2} + \frac{1}{2}\cos 2x.$]

8. $\int_0^{\pi/4} \cos^2.$

9. $\int_0^{\pi/4} \sin^2.$

10. $\int_0^{\pi/2} \sin x \cos x\, dx.$ [*Hint:* $\sin 2x = 2\sin x \cos x.$]

11. $\int_0^{\pi/2} \cos^4.$ [*Hint:* $\cos^4 = (\cos^2)^2.$]

12. $\int_0^1 (-10x + 9)^5\, dx.$

13. $\int_1^2 \sqrt{2x - 7}\, dx.$

Even and Odd Functions

If a real function f has the property that, for every x in the domain of f, $-x$ is also in the domain and $f(-x) = f(x)$, then f is *even*. The prototype even functions are x^2, x^4, x^6, . . . , or powers with even exponents; the cosine function is also even.

If, for every x in the domain of f, $-x$ is also in the domain and $f(-x) = -f(x)$, then f is *odd*. Examples are x, x^3, x^5, and the sine function.

Suppose an even function E is integrable over an interval $[a, b]$. Then the interval $[-b, -a]$ is also in the domain of E and, using the fact that $E(-x) = E(x)$ together with Theorem 9.10,

$$\int_a^b E(x)\,dx = \int_a^b E(-x)\,dx = -\int_{-a}^{-b} E(t)\,dt = \int_{-b}^{-a} E(t)\,dt.$$

Also,

$$\int_b^a E = -\int_a^b E = -\int_{-b}^{-a} E = \int_{-a}^{-b} E.$$

Thus for any a and b in the domain of an even integrable function E, $\int_a^b E = \int_{-b}^{-a} E.$

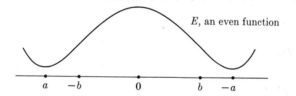

E, an even function

If Q is an odd integrable function, then, for any a and b in the domain of Q,

$$\int_a^b Q = \int_a^b Q(x)\,dx = -\int_a^b -Q(x)\,dx$$

$$= -\int_a^b Q(-x)\,dx$$

$$= -\left(-\int_{-a}^{-b} Q(t)\,dt\right)$$

$$= -\int_{-b}^{-a} Q.$$

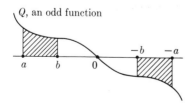

Q, an odd function

In the graph above, $\int_a^b Q$ is the area of a region and $\int_{-b}^{-a} Q$ is the negative of the area of a congruent region.

For n a positive integer we proved that, for $0 \le a < b$,

$$\int_a^b x^n \, dx = \frac{b^{n+1} - a^{n+1}}{n + 1}.$$

We can now readily extend the formula to negative intervals by considering separately even and odd exponents.

With $0 \le a < b$,

$$\int_{-b}^{-a} x^{2n} \, dx = \int_a^b x^{2n} \, dx = \frac{b^{2n+1} - a^{2n+1}}{2n + 1}$$

$$= \frac{-(-b)^{2n+1} + (-a)^{2n+1}}{2n + 1}$$

$$= \frac{(-a)^{2n+1} - (-b)^{2n+1}}{2n + 1},$$

and

$$\int_{-b}^{-a} x^{2n-1} \, dx = -\int_a^b x^{2n-1} \, dx$$

$$= \frac{-b^{2n} + a^{2n}}{2n}$$

$$= \frac{(-a)^{2n} - (-b)^{2n}}{2n}.$$

Thus the formula for $\int_a^b x^n \, dx$ holds for a and b nonnegative and for a and b nonpositive. If $a < 0 < b$, or $b < 0 < a$,

$$\int_a^b x^n \, dx = \int_a^0 x^n \, dx + \int_0^b x^n \, dx$$

$$= -\frac{a^{n+1}}{n + 1} + \frac{b^{n+1}}{n + 1}$$

$$= \frac{b^{n+1} - a^{n+1}}{n + 1}.$$

Exercises

In these exercises, assume for simplicity that all nonspecific functions concerned are defined and integrable on every bounded interval.

1. Prove that the sum of two even functions is even and the sum of two odd functions is odd.

2. Prove that, if E is even and Q is odd, then $E + Q$ is neither even nor odd unless one function is 0.

3. What can be said about the product of two even functions? two odd functions? an even function and an odd function?

4. Prove that, if E is even, $\int_{-b}^{0} E = \int_{0}^{b} E$, and also that $\int_{-b}^{b} E = 2 \int_{0}^{b} E$.

5. If Q is odd, prove that $\int_{-b}^{b} Q = 0$.

6. Evaluate $\int_{-1}^{1} \sin^3 (2x) \cos^8 (6x) \, dx$.

7. Use the results of Exercises 4 and 5 to calculate each integral below.

a. $\int_{-1}^{1} (x^3 + x^2) \, dx$.

b. $\int_{-5}^{5} (x^3 \cos 2x + 3 + x^4) \, dx$.

c. $\int_{-2}^{2} (3x^3 + 4x^2 - 7x + 2) \, dx$.

§ 5. *The Logarithm and Exponential Functions*

The *natural logarithm*, ln, is the function called L at the end of the last chapter. We can now give a briefer treatment.

Definition 9.6.   For each $x > 0$,

$$\ln x = \int_{1}^{x} \frac{1}{t} \, dt.$$

The integrand, the reciprocal function, is both continuous and monotone on $(0, \infty)$; either guarantees the existence of the integral. Since the integrand is positive, ln is strictly monotone increasing on $(0, \infty)$; from this and $\ln 1 = 0$, we see that $\ln x$ is negative for $0 < x < 1$, positive for $x > 1$.

We want to prove that ln is continuous on its domain, but it is just as easy to prove the more general

Theorem 9.11.   Let f be a function defined on an interval I and integrable on each subinterval $[a, b]$. Let a be in I and define a function F_a, for each x in I, by

$$F_a(x) = \int_{a}^{x} f.$$

Then F_a is continuous on its domain.

PROOF: Let c be in I. By hypothesis f is bounded on any closed subinterval containing c; let $M > 0$ be an upper bound for $|f|$ on such a subinterval S. Then, for x in S,

$$\begin{aligned}
|F_a(x) - F_a(c)| &= \left| \int_{a}^{x} f - \int_{a}^{c} f \right| \\
&= \left| \int_{c}^{x} f \right| \\
&\leq |x - c| M \\
&< \epsilon, \quad \text{if} \quad |x - c| < \frac{\epsilon}{M}. \quad \blacksquare
\end{aligned}$$

This theorem shows that integration provides a way to produce new functions guaranteed to be continuous. This section can be regarded as a study of one example, ln, drawn from a very large class of possible examples.

Theorem 9.12. For all positive x and y, $\ln (xy) = \ln x + \ln y$.

PROOF: For $x > 0$ and $y > 0$,

$$\ln (xy) = \int_1^{xy} \frac{1}{t} \, dt$$

$$= \int_1^x \frac{1}{t} \, dt + \int_x^{xy} \frac{1}{t} \, dt$$

$$= \ln x + \int_1^y \frac{1}{t} \, dt \qquad \text{by Theorem 9.10}$$

$$= \ln x + \ln y. \qquad \blacksquare$$

Corollary to Theorem 9.12. For each $x > 0$, $\ln (1/x) = -\ln x$, and, for each integer n, $\ln x^n = n \ln x$.

PROOF: Since $(1/x)x = 1$, $\ln (1/x) + \ln x = \ln 1 = 0$; $\ln (x^0) = \ln 1 = 0 \ln x$. For $n = -1$, 0, or 1, $\ln x^n = n \ln x$. Mathematical induction and Theorem 9.12 extends this to all integers. $\qquad \blacksquare$

Theorem 9.13. The function ln is a strictly increasing continuous one-to-one mapping of the set of positive real numbers onto the set of all real numbers.

PROOF: We have already established that ln is strictly monotone [and hence one-to-one] and continuous. Since

$$\ln 2 = \int_1^2 \frac{1}{t} \, dt > \int_1^2 \frac{1}{2} \, dt = \frac{1}{2},$$

the Corollary to Theorem 9.12 gives: for every positive integer n, $\ln 2^n > n/2$ and $\ln 2^{-n} < -n/2$. Thus the range of ln has neither an upper bound nor a lower bound. For each real k there is some integer n such that $-n/2 < k < n/2$; by the continuity of ln and the Intermediate Value Theorem there is some c between 2^{-n} and 2^n such that $\ln c = k$. $\qquad \blacksquare$

Theorem 9.14. If

$$e = \lim \left\{ \left(1 + \frac{1}{n} \right)^n \right\},$$

then $\ln e = 1$.

PROOF: For each positive integer n,

$$\ln \left(1 + \frac{1}{n} \right)^n = n \ln \left(1 + \frac{1}{n} \right) = n \int_1^{1+(1/n)} \frac{1}{t} \, dt.$$

If

$$1 < t < 1 + \frac{1}{n},$$

then

$$\frac{n}{n+1} < \frac{1}{t} < 1.$$

From this we see that

$$n \int_{1}^{1+(1/n)} \frac{n}{n+1} < n \int_{1}^{1+(1/n)} \frac{1}{t}\, dt < n \int_{1}^{1+(1/n)} 1,$$

or

$$\frac{n}{n+1} < \ln\left(1 + \frac{1}{n}\right)^{n} < 1,$$

and the sequence $\{\ln (1 + (1/n))^n\}$ converges to 1.

But $\{(1 + (1/n))^n\}$ converges to e, and ln is continuous at e. By Theorem 9.15, $\{\ln (1 + (1/n))^n\}$ converges to ln e.   ∎

Theorem 9.15. Let $\{x_n\}$ be a real sequence converging to c. If f is a real function whose domain includes each x_n in the sequence and f is continuous at c, then $\{f(x_n)\}$ converges to $f(c)$.

PROOF: Given $\epsilon > 0$, there is some $\delta > 0$ such that

$$x \text{ in dom } f \quad\text{and}\quad |x - c| < \delta \Rightarrow |f(x) - f(c)| < \epsilon.$$

By hypothesis, each x_n in the sequence is in the domain of f. And, since $\lim \{x_n\} = c$ and $\delta > 0$, there is some N such that, for $n > N$,

$$|x_n - c| < \delta,$$

and hence $|f(x_n) - f(c)| < \epsilon$.   ∎

Theorems 9.13 and 9.12 jointly imply that ln is an isomorphism of the multiplicative group of the positive real numbers to the additive group of all real numbers. One application of ln, formerly important, is to replace long multiplications by comparatively short additions: for positive x, y, z, $xyz = \ln^{-1} (\ln x + \ln y + \ln z)$. The continuity of the function makes tables of logarithms useful: if L_x and L_y are good approximations to ln x and ln y, then $L_x + L_y$ is a good approximation to ln (xy). Following are a very small table of approximations and a partial graph of ln.

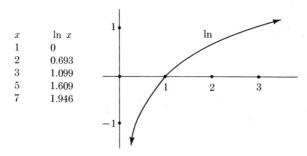

x	ln x
1	0
2	0.693
3	1.099
5	1.609
7	1.946

Exercises

1. Extend the table above to each composite integer from 4 to 20.
2. Find reasonably good approximations to $\ln(11)$, $\ln(13)$, $\ln(17)$, $\ln(19)$. Note that, for example,

$$\ln(11) = \ln(10) + \int_{10}^{11} \frac{1}{t}\, dt \quad \text{and} \quad \ln(12) = \ln(11) + \int_{11}^{12} \frac{1}{t}\, dt.$$

3. For each positive integer n, let $H(n)$ be the sum of the reciprocals of the first n integers:

$$H(n) = 1 + \frac{1}{2} + \cdots + \frac{1}{n}.$$

Prove that

$$\ln(n+1) < H(n) < \ln(n) + 1.$$

Give an estimate for $\dfrac{1}{1{,}000} + \dfrac{1}{1{,}001} + \cdots + \dfrac{1}{1{,}000{,}000}$.

4. For each positive integer k, over the open interval $(k, k+1)$, the graph of $y = 1/x$ is below the segment joining the points $(k, 1/k)$ and $(k+1, 1/(k+1))$. Show from this that

$$\int_{k}^{k+1} \frac{1}{t}\, dt < \frac{1}{k+1} + \frac{1}{2}\left(\frac{1}{k} - \frac{1}{k+1}\right).$$

Then, by adding such inequalities, prove that, for each positive integer n,

$$\ln n < H(n) + \frac{1}{2} - \frac{1}{2n}.$$

5. Since $(\sqrt[5]{3})^5 = 3$, the Corollary to Theorem 9.12 implies that $\ln \sqrt[5]{3} = \frac{1}{5} \ln 3$, which is nearly 0.2. Find approximately the number x such that $\int_{1}^{x} (1/t)\, dt = 0.2$.

Since the natural logarithm is strictly monotone, it has a composition inverse, called *the exponential function*, abbreviated as exp. By Theorems 9.13 and 7.11 [page 230], we have

Theorem 9.16. Setting $\exp = \ln^{-1}$, exp is a strictly increasing, continuous one-to-one mapping of the set of all real numbers onto the set of positive real numbers.

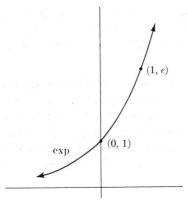

For any real x and y we have

$$\ln (\exp x \exp y) = \ln (\exp x) + \ln (\exp y)$$
$$= x + y$$
$$= \ln (\exp (x + y)).$$

Since ln is one-to-one, this proves

Theorem 9.17.   For all real x and y, $\exp x \exp y = \exp (x + y)$.

Theorem 9.18.   For every integer n, $\exp n = e^n$, and, if $n \neq 0$,

$$\exp \frac{1}{n} = e^{1/n}.$$

PROOF: The statement $\exp n = e^n$ is equivalent to $n = \ln e^n$, which is true by the Corollary to Theorem 9.12, since $\ln e = 1$.

For n an integer $\neq 0$, $e^{1/n}$ is by definition the positive number x such that $x^n = e$. This last equation, with $x > 0$, is equivalent to $n \ln x = \ln e = 1$ and to $\ln x = 1/n$. But this is equivalent to $\exp 1/n = x = e^{1/n}$.   ∎

Definition 9.7.
(1)   For every real a, $e^a = \exp a$.
(2)   For every real a and every positive x,

$$x^a = e^{a \ln x} = \exp (a \ln x).$$

For example, $5^{\sqrt{2}} = e^{\sqrt{2} \ln 5} = \exp (\sqrt{2} \ln 5)$, or equivalently, $\ln 5^{\sqrt{2}} = \sqrt{2} \ln 5$.

As another example, $\sqrt{2}^5 = e^{5 \ln \sqrt{2}} = e^{(5/2) \ln 2}$.

Theorem 9.19.   For all real a and b and all positive x and y,

$$(xy)^a = x^a y^a, \qquad x^a x^b = x^{a+b}, \qquad (x^a)^b = x^{ab}.$$

The proof is left to the reader.

Theorem 9.20.   For $b > 0$ but $b \neq 1$, let $f(x) = b^x$ for all real x; f is a continuous one-to-one mapping of the set of all real numbers onto the set of positive real numbers. If $b > 1$, f is strictly increasing; if $b < 1$, f is strictly decreasing.

PROOF: For all x, $f(x) = e^{x \ln b} = \exp (x \ln b)$. Thus f is the composition $\exp \circ g$, where $g(x) = x(\ln b)$ for all real x. Since $b \neq 1$, g is a continuous one-to-one mapping of $\mathfrak{R}$ onto $\mathfrak{R}$, increasing if $\ln b > 0$ [that is, if $b > 1$], but decreasing if $\ln b < 0$ [that is, if $b < 1$]. Since $\exp$ is a continuous, strictly increasing mapping of $\mathfrak{R}$ onto the set of positive real numbers, the composition $\exp \circ g$ has the properties asserted by the theorem.   ∎

Definition 9.8. For $b > 0$ but $b \neq 1$ the function $\log_b$, **the loga-rithm to the base** b, is the inverse of the mapping: $x \longrightarrow b^x$. That is, for $y > 0$, $\log_b y = x$ if and only if $b^x = y$.

Theorem 9.21. For $b > 0$ but $b \neq 1$, and for all $a > 0$,

$$\log_b (a) = \frac{\ln a}{\ln b}.$$

In particular, $\log_e = \ln$.

PROOF: For a and b positive, but $b \neq 1$,

$$b^{\ln a / \ln b} = (e^{\ln b})^{\ln a / \ln b} = e^{\ln a} = a. \qquad \blacksquare$$

Exercises

1. Sketch graphs of $y = 2^x$ and of $y = (\frac{1}{3})^x$.
2. Prove Theorem 9.19. [*Hint:* Prove first that $e^a e^b = e^{a+b}$ and $(e^a)^b = e^{ab}$.]
3. Use Theorem 9.21 and your approximate table of $\ln n$ for small positive integers n to construct a table of approximations to $\log_{10} n$.
4. Sketch graphs of $\log_{10}$, $\log_{1/2}$, and $\log_{1.01}$.
5. Sketch graphs of $\ln \circ \sin$ and $\sin \circ \ln$.
6. Sketch a graph of $y = \ln |x|$, $x \neq 0$.
7. Sketch a graph of $y = \ln|\ln|x||$, and of $y = \ln (\ln x)$.
8. For any $x > 0$, the sequence $\left\{ \dfrac{\ln x}{n} \right\}$ converges to 0. Use Theorem 9.15 to deduce that $\{\sqrt[n]{x}\}$ converges to 1.

10
Differentiation

§ 1. *Basic Concepts*

The historical motivation for the topic of this chapter is the consideration of two questions, one geometrical and the other physical. (1) How does one define and find the tangent line to a curve at a point on it? (2) What is meant by, and how does one calculate, the instantaneous velocity of a moving particle? For example, if a car starts from rest and accelerates along a straight level road, what does it mean to say that exactly 6.2832 seconds after starting it is going exactly $30\sqrt{2}$ miles per hour?

Consider intuitively a curve in space in the shape of a stretched conical coil spring. If $\mathbf{p}$ is a point on the curve, it is clear that there are many lines through $\mathbf{p}$ which do not meet the curve elsewhere, but only one of these seems tangent to the curve at $\mathbf{p}$. No arc of the curve lies in a plane and it is not clear what "radius to $\mathbf{p}$" might mean, and given a radius to $\mathbf{p}$ there are many lines through $\mathbf{p}$ perpendicular to the radius. In short, the two simple properties that characterize the tangent to a circle at a point on it do not seem relevant to this space curve.

Nor are the two properties relevant to all plane curves. In the diagram at left below, the line is tangent to the curve even though it also intersects the curve at other points. In the diagram at right there are many lines through $\mathbf{p}$ not intersecting the curve elsewhere, but none of them is considered tangent

to the curve at **p**. [There is a *left-hand tangent* and also a *right-hand tangent*, but no unique tangent.]

We can employ an intuitive concept that will lead to a successful formulation: if a curve has a tangent at a point, then the curve should hug the tangent closely [almost merge with the tangent] over a small neighborhood of the point. Put the other way around, the tangent should be an excellent approximation to the curve over a sufficiently small stretch.

Here and for most of the chapter we consider only plane curves which are graphs of functions. Before stating the basic definition, however, we introduce the usual notation. Suppose a continuous function f does have a non-vertical tangent at each point of its graph. Each of these tangents has a slope and thus there is derived from f a new function, labeled f' and called the *derivative* of f, such that, for each c in the domain of f, $f'(c)$ is the slope of the tangent to the graph of f at $(c, f(c))$. The notation is essentially that of Newton, although he used a dot rather than a prime.

The accompanying diagram is based on these notions: two intersecting lines do not hug each other, but diverge sharply; if a curve is to hug a tangent line, it must diverge sharply from other lines.

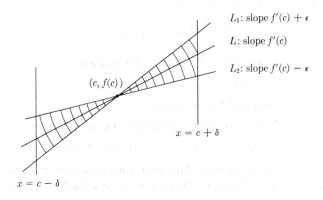

L_1: slope $f'(c) + \epsilon$

L: slope $f'(c)$

L_2: slope $f'(c) - \epsilon$

$(c, f(c))$

$x = c + \delta$

$x = c - \delta$

If L is tangent to the graph of f at $(c, f(c))$, then for each $\epsilon > 0$ there must be some $\delta > 0$ such that the graph of f is in the shaded regions between L_1 and L_2 over each of the intervals $(c - \delta, c)$ and $(c, c + \delta)$.

The inequalities corresponding to the graph are the following.

1. For $c < x < c + \delta$,
$$f(c) + (x - c)(f'(c) - \epsilon) < f(x) < f(c) + (x - c)(f'(c) + \epsilon).$$

2. For $c - \delta < x < c$,
$$f(c) + (x - c)(f'(c) - \epsilon) > f(x) > f(c) + (x - c)(f'(c) + \epsilon).$$

These can be rewritten as follows.

1'. For $c < x < c + \delta$,
$$(x - c)(f'(c) - \epsilon) < f(x) - f(c) < (x - c)(f'(c) + \epsilon).$$

2′. For $c - \delta < x < c$,

$$(x - c)(f'(c) - \epsilon) > f(x) - f(c) > (x - c)(f'(c) + \epsilon).$$

Divide through by $x - c$ in both 1′ and 2′, remembering that $x - c > 0$ in 1′ but < 0 in 2′. Then, for all x such that either $c < x < c + \delta$ or $c - \delta < x < c$,

$$f'(c) - \epsilon < \frac{f(x) - f(c)}{x - c} < f'(c) + \epsilon,$$

or

$$\left| \frac{f(x) - f(c)}{x - c} - f'(c) \right| < \epsilon.$$

The condition that x be in one of the open intervals $(c - \delta, c)$ or $(c, c + \delta)$ can be abbreviated to $0 < |x - c| < \delta$. Thus the definition below is the analytic formulation of the geometric intuition.

Definitions 10.1. The real function f is **differentiable** at c in its domain provided there is a number, called $f'(c)$, such that for each $\epsilon > 0$ there is some $\delta > 0$ such that

$$0 < |x - c| < \delta \Rightarrow \left| \frac{f(x) - f(c)}{x - c} - f'(c) \right| < \epsilon.$$

If f is differentiable at c, then the line with equation

$$y = f(c) + (x - c)f'(c)$$

is **tangent** to the graph of f at $(c, f(c))$.

Remarks: 1. The inequality in the definition is equivalent to

$$0 < |x - c| < \delta \Rightarrow |f(x) - (f(c) + (x - c)f'(c))| < \epsilon |x - c|.$$

One can approximate f by the tangent line, and, for any $\epsilon > 0$, the error in this approximation to $f(x)$ will be less than $\epsilon |x - c|$, provided $|x - c|$ is less than the δ corresponding to ϵ.

2. The definition is usually abbreviated to

$$\lim_{x \to c} \frac{f(x) - f(c)}{x - c} = f'(c).$$

§ 3 contains some useful theory of limits. In this section and the next we consider only very simple examples and theorems which require no such theory.

3. For f to be differentiable at c, each point of some open interval $(c - \delta, c + \delta)$ must be in the domain of f.

4. The basic picture shows that if f is differentiable at c, then for each $\epsilon > 0$ the graph of f is confined to a sort of double scissors centered at $(c, f(c))$. For f to be continuous at c, for each $\epsilon > 0$ the graph of f need only be confined to a rectangle centered at $(c, f(c))$.

Since a scissors can be boxed up but a rectangle cannot be put into such a scissors, the pictures suggest that differentiability should imply continuity, but not conversely.

Suppose now a function f differentiable at c. For $\epsilon = 1$ the definition guarantees the existence of some $\delta_1 > 0$ such that

$$0 < |x - c| < \delta_1 \Rightarrow \left| \frac{f(x) - f(c)}{x - c} - f'(c) \right| < 1.$$

From the last inequality follow

$$|f(x) - f(c) - (x - c)f'(c)| < |x - c|$$

and

$$|f(x) - f(c)| < |x - c|[1 + |f'(c)|].$$

Setting $k = 1 + |f'(c)|$, we have

$$0 < |x - c| < \delta_1 \Rightarrow |f(x) - f(c)| < k|x - c|.$$

If $x = c$, then $f(x) = f(c)$ and $|f(x) - f(c)| = k|x - c|$. This establishes the following lemma.

Lemma. If the function f is differentiable at c, then there are positive numbers δ_1 and k such that

$$|x - c| < \delta_1 \Rightarrow |f(x) - f(c)| \leq k|x - c|.$$

Theorem 10.1. If the function f is differentiable at c, then f is continuous at c.

PROOF: By the lemma there are positive δ_1 and k such that, if $|x - c| < \delta_1$, then $|f(x) - f(c)| \leq k|x - c|$. Given $\epsilon > 0$, let δ_ϵ be the smaller of δ_1 and ϵ/k. Then

$$|x - c| < \delta_\epsilon \Rightarrow |f(x) - f(c)| \leq k|x - c|$$

$$< k\frac{\epsilon}{k} = \epsilon. \qquad \blacksquare$$

Examples

1. Suppose the graph of f is a nonvertical line: $f(x) = mx + b$ for all x. This line has slope m and the tangent to it at a point $(c, mc + b)$ should be the line itself. Thus we should have $f'(c) = m$ for all c. In fact, for $0 < |x - c|$—that is, for $x \neq c$—we have

$$\left| \frac{f(x) - f(c)}{x - c} - m \right| = \left| \frac{mx + b - mc - b}{x - c} - m \right| = 0 < \epsilon$$

for any positive ϵ.

Two special cases are of interest. Taking $m = 0$ makes f a constant and $f'(c) = 0$ for all c. Thus the derivative of any constant function is the constant function 0. Taking $m = 1$ and $b = 0$ makes f the identity function: the derivative of the identity function is the constant function 1.

2. Let f be the squaring function. The graph of f is the parabola $y = x^2$, and geometric intuition says that the tangent to this curve at (a, a^2) is the line through (a, a^2) which does not intersect the parabola elsewhere.

The line of slope m through (a, a^2) has the equation $y = a^2 + m(x - a)$. Intersecting this with $y = x^2$ gives

$$x^2 = a^2 + m(x - a),$$

or

$$(x - a)(x + a - m) = 0.$$

The line intersects the parabola at (a, a^2) and also at $(m - a, (m - a)^2)$; these points are different unless $m - a = a$ or $m = 2a$. Thus we conjecture that, if $f(x) = x^2$ for all x, then, for all a, $f'(a) = 2a$.

In fact, for $0 < |x - a|$,

$$\left| \frac{x^2 - a^2}{x - a} - 2a \right| = |x + a - 2a| = |x - a|.$$

Thus, given $\epsilon > 0$,

$$0 < |x - a| < \epsilon \Longrightarrow \left| \frac{x^2 - a^2}{x - a} - 2a \right| < \epsilon.$$

3. If $f(x) = x^3$ for all x, then $f'(c) = 3c^2$ for all c; equivalently, $f'(x) = 3x^2$ for all x.

This is easily seen as follows: for $x \neq c$,

$$\frac{x^3 - c^3}{x - c} = x^2 + xc + c^2.$$

Let P be the polynomial defined, for *all* x, by $P(x) = x^2 + xc + c^2$; P is continuous everywhere, in particular at c. Thus for each $\epsilon > 0$ there is some $\delta > 0$ such that

$$|x - c| < \delta \Longrightarrow |P(x) - P(c)| < \epsilon.$$

Now, with ϵ and δ as above, suppose $0 < |x - c| < \delta$. Since $0 < |x - c|$, $x \neq c$, and

$$\frac{f(x) - f(c)}{x - c} = P(x).$$

Since $|x - c| < \delta$, $|P(x) - P(c)| < \epsilon$. Thus

$$0 < |x - c| < \delta \Longrightarrow \left| \frac{f(x) - f(c)}{x - c} - P(c) \right| < \epsilon,$$

which proves that $f'(c) = P(c) = 3c^2$.

4. If $f(x) = \sqrt{x}$ for $x \geq 0$, then $f'(c) = 1/2\sqrt{c}$ for all $c > 0$.

To see this, observe that if $c > 0$ and $|x - c| < c$, then $0 < x$, and $\sqrt{x}$ exists. If, furthermore, $x \neq c$, then

$$\frac{\sqrt{x} - \sqrt{c}}{x - c} = \frac{1}{\sqrt{x} + \sqrt{c}}.$$

Define F, for all $x > 0$, by

$$F(x) = \frac{1}{\sqrt{x} + \sqrt{c}}.$$

Then F is continuous at c and, just as in Example 3, we now obtain

$$f'(c) = F(c) = \frac{1}{2\sqrt{c}}.$$

5. The natural logarithm is differentiable on its domain and, for each $c > 0$, $\ln'(c) = 1/c$. For $x > 0$, $x \neq c$,

$$\ln x - \ln c = \int_1^x \frac{1}{t}\,dt - \int_1^c \frac{1}{t}\,dt$$

$$= \int_c^x \frac{1}{t}\,dt.$$

By the Mean Value Theorem for integrals of continuous functions there is some number c_x between c and x such that

$$\int_c^x \frac{1}{t}\,dt = (x - c)\frac{1}{c_x}.$$

Thus we have

$$\frac{\ln x - \ln c}{x - c} = \frac{x - c}{x - c}\frac{1}{c_x} = \frac{1}{c_x},$$

and

$$\left| \frac{\ln x - \ln c}{x - c} - \frac{1}{c} \right| = \left| \frac{1}{c_x} - \frac{1}{c} \right|.$$

Since c_x is between c and x,

$$\left| \frac{1}{c_x} - \frac{1}{c} \right| < \left| \frac{1}{x} - \frac{1}{c} \right|.$$

By the continuity of the reciprocal function there is, given $\epsilon > 0$, some $\delta > 0$ such that

$$|x - c| < \delta \Longrightarrow \left| \frac{1}{x} - \frac{1}{c} \right| < \epsilon.$$

6. The absolute value function [abs], although continuous everywhere, is not differentiable at 0.

To see this, note that, for any $\delta > 0$,

$$-\delta < x < 0 \Longrightarrow \frac{|x|}{x} = -1 \quad \text{and} \quad 0 < x < \delta \Longrightarrow \frac{|x|}{x} = 1.$$

If the function were differentiable at 0 and $\text{abs}'(0) = m$, then corresponding to $1 > 0$ there would be some $\delta > 0$ such that

$$0 < |x - 0| < \delta \Longrightarrow \left| \frac{|x| - |0|}{x - 0} - m \right| < 1,$$

or

$$0 < |x| < \delta \Longrightarrow \left| \frac{|x|}{x} - m \right| < 1.$$

Setting $x = \delta/2$ gives $|1 - m| < 1$ and $0 < m < 2$. Setting $x = -\delta/2$ gives $|-1 - m| < 1$ and $-2 < m < 0$. The assumed differentiability leads to a contradiction.

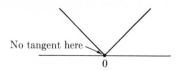

No tangent here

0

We were led to the difference quotient $(f(x) - f(c))/(x - c)$ by formulating the conditions ensuring that the graph of f hug its tangent line at $(c, f(c))$. This quotient has a direct geometric interpretation, as in the diagram below.

$(x, f(x))$

$(c, f(c))$

The difference quotient is the slope of a "secant" line through $(c, f(c))$ and $(x, f(x))$. The 18th century formulation was this: the tangent line at $(c, f(c))$ is the limiting position of the secant line as $(x, f(x))$ approaches $(c, f(c))$ along the curve. This has considerable intuitive appeal: you make "x approach c" [someone has said that x does this by slithering along the axis]; this causes $(x, f(x))$ to slither along the curve and causes the secant line to rotate or wobble toward coincidence with the tangent line at $(c, f(c))$. During the 19th century it was found necessary to replace all such dynamic descriptions by the ultimately clearer definitions now used.

The velocity problem in physics leads immediately to difference quotients. Consider a classical particle constrained to be always on a line, which we take to be the real line. At each time t, a classical particle is at some particular point, so that there is automatically a function f giving the position of the particle at each t.

Suppose distance is measured in feet and time in seconds. At time t_1 seconds the particle is at $f(t_1)$ feet from 0 on the line. At another time t seconds it is at $f(t)$ feet from 0. Over a time interval of length $t - t_1$ seconds the particle has changed its position by $f(t) - f(t_1)$ feet. By definition, the *average velocity* of the particle over the time interval is $(f(t) - f(t_1))/(t - t_1)$ feet/second. The *instantaneous velocity* at time t_1 is $f'(t_1)$ feet/second if f is differentiable at t_1; if f is not differentiable at t_1, the particle fails to have an instantaneous velocity at t_1.

The examples above have calculated the derivatives of a few familiar functions, and the exercises at the end of the section will give a few more derivatives. The next two theorems greatly extend the usefulness of these few results.

Theorem 10.2. If each of the functions f and g is differentiable at c, then so is $f + g$, and

$$(f + g)'(c) = f'(c) + g'(c).$$

That is, the formula $(f + g)' = f' + g'$ holds on the intersection of the domains of f' and g'.

PROOF: If each function is differentiable at c, the domain of each includes an open interval containing c. The intersection of these is an open interval containing c which is included in the domain of $f + g$. For x in this interval, but $x \neq c$, we can form the difference quotient

$$\frac{(f + g)(x) - (f + g)(c)}{x - c} = \frac{f(x) - f(c)}{x - c} + \frac{g(x) - g(c)}{x - c}.$$

From this,

$$\left| \frac{(f + g)(x) - (f + g)(c)}{x - c} - (f'(c) + g'(c)) \right|$$

$$\leq \left| \frac{f(x) - f(c)}{x - c} - f'(c) \right| + \left| \frac{g(x) - g(c)}{x - c} - g'(c) \right|.$$

Given $\epsilon > 0$, there is some $\delta_1 > 0$ such that for $0 < |x - c| < \delta_1$ the first term above is $< \epsilon/2$, and there is some $\delta_2 > 0$ such that for $0 < |x - c| < \delta_2$ the second term is $< \epsilon/2$. For $0 < |x - c| < \min \{\delta_1, \delta_2\}$, both these inequalities hold, completing the proof. ∎

If f is a real function and k a real number, we can regard the product kf either as the product of the constant function k and the function f, or as a scalar multiple of f defined by: for x in the domain of f, $(kf)(x) = kf(x)$.

Theorem 10.3. Let f be a real function and $g = kf$ a scalar multiple of f. Then the domain of g' includes the domain of f' and, for each c in the domain of f', $g'(c) = kf'(c)$.

Remark: If $k \neq 0$, then $f = k^{-1}g$ and by the theorem the domain of f' includes the domain of g'. Thus, for $k \neq 0$, f' and $(kf)'$ have the same domain. But of course $0f$ is the constant function 0 on the domain of f and is differentiable there even if f is not.

PROOF: For x in the domain of f, but $x \neq c$,

$$\left| \frac{g(x) - g(c)}{x - c} - kf'(c) \right| = \left| \frac{kf(x) - kf(c)}{x - c} - kf'(c) \right|$$

$$= |k| \left| \frac{f(x) - f(c)}{x - c} - f'(c) \right|.$$

If $k = 0$, this displayed expression is $< \epsilon$ for every $\epsilon > 0$. If $k \neq 0$, this is $< \epsilon$ provided that

$$\left| \frac{f(x) - f(c)}{x - c} - f'(c) \right| < \frac{\epsilon}{|k|},$$

but by hypothesis there is some $\delta > 0$ such that the last inequality holds for all x with $0 < |x - c| < \delta$.   ∎

Algebraic Summary

Let S be the set of all functions differentiable on (at each point of) some open interval I. Theorems 10.2 and 10.3 show that S is closed under addition and scalar multiplication. It is clear that $(S; +)$ is a commutative group, with the constant function 0 on I being the identity element. [If f is in S, then by Theorem 10.3 so is $-f$, with $k = -1$.] It is also clear that the scalar product has the usual algebraic properties. In short, the set of all functions differentiable on some given interval forms a linear space over the real numbers.

Theorems 10.2 and 10.3 have even more specific content. Let D, the *differentiating operator*, be defined by: for each differentiable function f, $Df = f'$. Let f and g be in S, the set of functions differentiable on a given open interval I. By Theorem 10.2,

$$D(f + g) = Df + Dg.$$

By Theorem 10.3, for every real k,

$$D(kf) = kDf.$$

Thus D is a linear operator on S.

One useful conclusion from this is that, knowing the derivatives of a few functions, we can immediately give the derivative of any linear combination of them.

Examples

1. Let $F(x) = 7x^2 + \ln x^3$ for $x > 0$. Exploiting the fact that $\ln x^3 = 3 \ln x$, we have

   $$F = 7f + 3 \ln,$$

   where $f(x) = x^2$.
   By Theorems 10.2 and 10.3,

   $$F' = 7f' + 3 \ln'.$$

   From the examples worked out, for all $x > 0$,

   $$F'(x) = 14x + \frac{3}{x}.$$

2. Let $G(x) = 5x^3 - 2x + 7$ for all x. From the previous examples and the linearity of the differentiating operator, for all x,

   $$G'(x) = 5(3x^2) - 2(1) + 0 = 15x^2 - 2.$$

Exercises

1. Use Theorems 10.2 and 10.3 and the derivatives given in this section to write down the formula for the derivative of each function below. In each case specify the domain.

a. $f(x) = 3x^3 - 9x^2 + 17$.
b. $g(x) = \ln (5x)$. [*Hint:* $\ln (5x) = \ln 5 + \ln x$, if $x > 0$.]
c. $h(x) = (5x)^3 = 125x^3$.
d. $j(x) = x + \ln x$.
e. $k(x) = (3x)^2 + \sqrt{9x}$.
2. Let $F(x) = x^2 + 3x$. Prove directly from the definition that, for all c, $F'(c) = 2c + 3$.
3. Let $R(x) = 1/x$, with $x \neq 0$. Prove that, for all $c \neq 0$, $R'(c) = -1/c^2$.

Consider the following problem from elementary physics. A particle is moving along the real line in such a way that at each time t in some time interval it has velocity $6t$ feet/second, and at time 0 the particle's position is known to be x_0 feet from the origin. Where is the particle at the end of 5 seconds? 7 seconds?

If we let $f(t)$ be the position at time t, then we are given

$$f(0) = x_0 \quad \text{and} \quad f'(t) = 6t$$

for all t in the interval. For definiteness, assume the time interval is $(-10, 10)$.

We want to find all functions f satisfying (1) the *initial condition* $f(0) = x_0$, and (2) the *differential equation* $f'(t) = 6t$, for $-10 < t < 10$.

Physical intuition suggests that the given initial position and the velocity should determine the position.

Previous examples suggest functions satisfying the differential equation. Consider two instances.

If $f_1(t) = 3t^2 + 8$, for t in $(-10, 10)$, then $f'_1(t) = 6t$, for t in $(-10, 10)$.

If $f_2(t) = 3t^2 + x_0$, for t in $(-10, 10)$, then $f'_2(t) = 6t$, for t in $(-10, 10)$, and also $f_2(0) = x_0$.

If the problem has a unique solution, then f_2 *is* the solution and we know where the particle is at each time in $(-10, 10)$. If there are other solutions, then we need more information.

To generalize a little, let I be an open interval and S be the set of all functions differentiable on I. By Theorems 10.2 and 10.3, for functions f and g in S, $f'(x) = g'(x)$ for each x in I iff $(f - g)'(x) = 0$ for each x in I.

More briefly, since the differentiating operator D is a linear operator on S, $Df = Dg$ iff $D(f - g) = 0$. The kernel of D, restricting D to S, is the set of functions h in S such that Dh is the 0 function in S. Functions f and g in S have the same derivative iff $f - g$ is in the kernel of D.

Each constant function on I is in the kernel of D. Geometrically, each horizontal line has at each point a tangent [itself] with slope 0. Given that the graph of a function f has a horizontal tangent at each point, can f be anything but a horizontal line?

Theorem 10.4 [*The Kernel of D*]. If the function f has derivative 0 on an open interval I, then f is constant on I.

PROOF: Suppose the theorem is false. Then there is some function f, with $f'(x) = 0$ for each x in an open interval I; but for some a and b in I, with $a < b$, $f(a) \neq f(b)$. If $f(a) > f(b)$, then $-f(a) < -f(b)$.

Let g be f, if $f(a) < f(b)$; otherwise, $-f$. If the theorem is false we have a function g such that $g'(x) = 0$ for each x in I; for some a and b in I, $a < b$ and $g(a) < g(b)$. We shall show that the existence of such a function leads to a contradiction.

Assume g as above and let L be the line through $(a, g(a))$ and $(b, g(b))$, and with positive slope, say m.

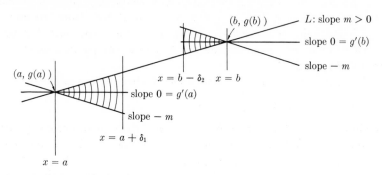

Apply the basic diagram [page 305] of the inequality defining $g'(a)$ at $(a, g(a))$, and look at the right half. Since $m > 0$ and $g'(a) = 0$, there is some $\delta_1 > 0$ such that, for $a < x < a + \delta_1$, the point $(x, g(x))$ is in the shaded region and thus strictly below L.

Similarly, applying the picture at $(b, g(b))$, for $b - \delta_2 < x < b$, $(x, g(x))$ is strictly above L.

Let A be the set of those x in (a, b) for which $(x, g(x))$ is below L: x is in A iff $g(x) < L(x)$.

Then A is not empty because each number in the interval $(a, a + \delta_1)$ is in A. Each number in the interval $(b - \delta_2, b)$ is an upper bound for A.

Let c be in the interval (a, b); then $g'(c) = 0$. The diagrams below indicate, and the inequalities they illustrate prove, that (1) if $g(c) < L(c)$, then c is not an upper bound of A; and (2) if $g(c) \geq L(c)$, then c is not the least upper bound of A.

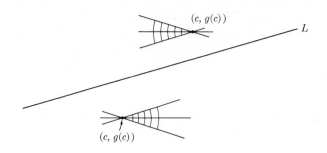

Conclusion: If Theorem 10.4 is false, then A is a nonempty bounded subset of $\mathfrak{R}$ with no least upper bound.   ∎

Corollary to Theorem 10.4.   If $f' = g'$ on an interval I, then f and g differ by a constant on I: there is some number k such that, for all x in I, $f(x) = g(x) + k$.

Exercises

1. If the position of a classical particle confined to a line is determined by a differentiable function f, then, as above, its velocity at time t is $f'(t)$. Assuming the function f' is itself differentiable and has a derivative f'' [read f *double-prime* or *the second derivative of f*], then by definition the *acceleration* at time t is $f''(t)$.

   Suppose that on an interval $(-a, a)$ f'' is constant; say $f''(t) = g$ for all t in $(-a, a)$. Also suppose that $f'(0) = v_0$ and $f(0) = x_0$.

   Prove that, for all t in $(-a, a)$, (a) $f'(t) = gt + v_0$, and (b) $f(t) = \frac{1}{2}gt^2 + v_0t + x_0$.

2. If $g'(x) = x + (1/x)$ for all $x > 0$ and $g(1) = 3$, what is $g(8)$? [*Hint:* First prove that there is some number c such that $g(x) = (x^2/2) + \ln x + c$ for all $x > 0$.]

§ 2. *Applications to Sketching Curves*

Suppose a function f differentiable on an interval I, and furthermore suppose $f'(c) > 0$ for each c in I. Then for each c in I the tangent to the graph of f at $(c, f(c))$ has positive slope. Intuition insists that f must be strictly monotone increasing on I. This sort of result is the objective of this section. We begin with some definitions.

Definition 10.2.   Let the domain of a real function f include an interval I. For c an interior point of I, f is **strictly increasing at c** if there is some $\delta > 0$ such that

$$c - \delta < x < c \Rightarrow f(x) < f(c),$$
$$c < x < c + \delta \Rightarrow f(c) < f(x).$$

If c is an end point of the domain of f, then f is strictly increasing at c if the appropriate one of these two inequalities holds. Similarly, f is **strictly decreasing at c** if there is some $\delta > 0$ such that

$$c - \delta < x < c \Rightarrow f(x) > f(c),$$
$$c < x < c + \delta \Rightarrow f(c) > f(x).$$

Again, for c an end point, only one of these inequalities must hold.

Definitions 10.3. Let the domain of a real function f include an interval I and let c be in I. Then f has a **relative maximum at c** if there is some $\delta > 0$ such that

$$x \text{ in dom } f \text{ and } |x - c| < \delta \Rightarrow f(x) \leq f(c).$$

Also, f has a **relative minimum at c** if there is some $\delta > 0$ such that

$$x \text{ in dom } f \text{ and } |x - c| < \delta \Rightarrow f(x) \geq f(c).$$

Dom $f = [a, b]$

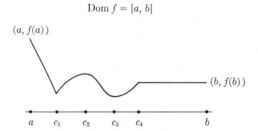

The function has a relative maximum at a, c_2, and every point of the closed interval $[c_4, b]$. The function has a relative minimum at c_1, c_3, and each point of the half-open interval $(c_4, b]$. It is strictly decreasing at each point of the half-open interval $[a, c_1)$ and at each point of the open interval (c_2, c_3).

Theorem 10.5. If a real function f is strictly increasing (decreasing) at each point of an interval I, then f is strictly monotone increasing (decreasing) on I.

PROOF: The proof is outlined in Exercise 5 below.

Theorem 10.6. Let the domain of a real function f include an interval I and let c be an interior point of I. If f is differentiable at c and $f'(c) > 0$, then f is strictly increasing at c; if $f'(c) < 0$, then f is strictly decreasing at c.

PROOF: Suppose $f'(c) > 0$. There is some $\delta > 0$ such that

$$0 < |x - c| < \delta \Rightarrow \left| \frac{f(x) - f(c)}{x - c} - f'(c) \right| < \frac{1}{2} f'(c).$$

For x in $(c - \delta, c)$ or in $(c, c + \delta)$,

$$\frac{f(x) - f(c)}{x - c} > \frac{1}{2} f'(c) > 0.$$

Thus, for all such x, $f(x) - f(c)$ has the same sign as has $x - c$. For $c < x < c + \delta$, $f(x) > f(c)$, and for $c - \delta < x < c$, $f(x) < f(c)$.

If $f'(c) < 0$, then there is some $\delta > 0$ such that

$$0 < |x - c| < \delta \Rightarrow \left| \frac{f(x) - f(c)}{x - c} - f'(c) \right| < -\frac{1}{2} f'(c).$$

It follows that the difference quotient is negative for x in $(c - \delta, c)$ or in $(c, c + \delta)$. ∎

If c is an interior point of the domain of a function f and f is strictly increasing or strictly decreasing at c, then in any open interval containing c there are x with $f(x) > f(c)$ and also x with $f(x) < c$. A function cannot have a relative maximum or minimum at an interior point at which it is strictly increasing or strictly decreasing. These observations, together with Theorem 10.6, prove

Theorem 10.7. Let a real function f be defined on an interval I. For c in I, f can have a relative maximum or minimum at c only if (1) c is an end point of I, or (2) c is an interior point and $f'(c) = 0$, or (3) c is an interior point and f is not differentiable at c.

Examples

1. Let $f(x) = x^3$ for all real x. Then $f'(x) = 3x^2$ for all real x. The domain of f has no end points, and there is no c at which f is not differentiable. Thus f can have a maximum or minimum at c only if $f'(c) = 0$—that is, if $c = 0$. But f is strictly increasing at 0:
$$x < 0 < t \Rightarrow x^3 < 0^3 < t^3.$$
The graph of $y = x^3$ is tangent to the x-axis at the origin but crosses its tangent there.

2. Let $g(x) = x - \ln x$, for $x > 0$. Then $g'(x) = 1 - (1/x)$, for $x > 0$. On the open interval $(0, 1)$ g' is negative and g strictly decreasing. On the open interval $(1, \infty)$ g' is positive and g strictly increasing. The graph below shows a few points $(x, g(x))$ and a piece of the tangent to the graph at each point.

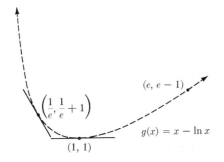

$(e, e - 1)$

$\left(\dfrac{1}{e}, \dfrac{1}{e} + 1\right)$

$g(x) = x - \ln x$

$(1, 1)$

By the next theorem, g has a minimum at 1: for all positive $x \neq 1$, $x - \ln x > 1$. The formula for g' makes it clear that for large x, $g'(x)$ is nearly 1, and for x close to 0, $|g'(x)|$ is large. The curve should be as the dotted curve suggests.

Theorem 10.8. If a function f is strictly monotone on an interval (b, c) or (c, d), and continuous at c, then f is also strictly monotone on $(b, c]$ or $[c, d)$.

PROOF: Assume f strictly increasing on the open interval (b, c) and continuous at c. We want to prove that, for all x in (b, c), $f(x) < f(c)$. If there is some x_1 in (b, c) with $f(x_1) \geq f(c)$, then, for any x_2 such that $x_1 < x_2 < c$, $f(x_2) > f(c)$. And, for every x in (x_2, c), $f(x) > f(x_2)$, so that

$$|f(x) - f(c)| > f(x_2) - f(c).$$

Setting $\epsilon = f(x_2) - f(c) > 0$, we see that there is no $\delta > 0$ such that

$$x \text{ in dom } f \text{ and } |x - c| < \delta \Rightarrow |f(x) - f(c)| < \epsilon.$$

This contradicts the assumed continuity of f at c, and we must conclude that, for all x_1 in (b, c), $f(x_1) < f(c)$. The other cases are proved in a very similar way.   ∎

Since the differentiability of f at c implies the continuity of f at c we have as a corollary

Theorem 10.9.   Let f be differentiable on an interval and suppose $f'(c) = 0$ for some interior point c. If f' is positive on an interval (b, c) but negative on an interval (c, d), then f has a relative maximum at c. If f' is negative on an interval (b, c) but positive on an interval (c, d), then f has a relative minimum at c.

Exercises

1. Let $f(x) = x^3 - 3x - 1$ for all x. Prove that f is strictly increasing on $(-\infty, -1)$ and $(1, \infty)$, strictly decreasing on $(-1, 1)$, and has a relative maximum at -1 and a relative minimum at 1. Plot a few points on the graph of f and indicate the slope of the tangent at each. Then sketch a respectable graph.

2. For $x > 0$ let $f(x) = x + (1/x)$. By Exercise 3 [page 313], $f'(x) = 1 - 1/x^2$ for all $x > 0$.

   a. Use the result above to prove that f has a minimum at 1, and sketch the graph of f.

   b. Prove without using the derivative that $x + (1/x) \geq 2$ for all $x > 0$. [*Hint:* What is $(x + (1/x))^2$?]

3. For $x > 0$, find the maximum value of $\ln x^2 - x = 2 \ln x - x$.

4. For real a, b, c, let $g(x) = x^3 + ax^2 + bx + c$ for all real x. Prove that g can have at most one maximum and at most one minimum. [*Hint:* First establish that either $g'(x) > 0$ for all x, or else $g'(x_1) = 0$ for only one x_1, or else there are x_1 and x_2, $x_1 < x_2$, such that $g'(x_1) = g'(x_2) = 0$, $g'(x) < 0$ for $x_1 < x < x_2$, and $g'(x) > 0$ for x not in the interval $[x_1, x_2]$.]

5. Assume a function f strictly increasing at each point of an interval I. Suppose a and b in I, with $a < b$. A proof that $f(a) < f(b)$ is a proof of Theorem 10.5. Let B be the set of x in $(a, b]$ such that $f(a) < f(x)$; b is an upper bound for B and, since f is strictly increasing at a, each x in some interval $(a, a + \delta)$ is in B. Let c be the least upper bound of B and prove that c is in B and that it is not possible to have $c < b$.

§ 3. *Limits*

If the domain of a real function f is an open interval and c is a number in the interval, then the difference quotient

$$\frac{f(x) - f(c)}{x - c} = F(x)$$

is defined for all $x \neq c$ in the domain of f. The domain of F is the union of two open intervals, obtained by deleting c from the domain of f.

Such domains occur naturally in other contexts. For example, $(x - 1)^2/\ln x$ is defined for x in the union of the open intervals $(0, 1)$ and $(1, \infty)$. We cannot set $x = 1$ in this formula, but we can investigate the behavior of the function for x close to 1.

Definition 10.4. For c in $\mathfrak{R}$, a **punctured neighborhood of** c is any union of two open intervals (a, c) and (c, b).

Remarks: 1. For $\delta > 0$, the set of x such that $0 < |x - c| < \delta$ is the union of the open intervals $(c - \delta, c)$ and $(c, c + \delta)$, and is a punctured neighborhood of c. Every punctured neighborhood of c includes subneighborhoods of this sort.

2. If the function f is differentiable at c, then the difference quotient $(f(x) - f(c))/(x - c)$ is defined for all x in some punctured neighborhood of c.

3. The intersection of two punctured neighborhoods of c is a punctured neighborhood of c.

Definition 10.5. If the domain of the real function F contains a punctured neighborhood of the number c, then each of $\lim_{c} F = L$ and $\lim_{x \to c} F(x) = L$ means that for each $\epsilon > 0$ there exists some $\delta > 0$ such that

$$0 < |x - c| < \delta \Rightarrow |F(x) - L| < \epsilon.$$

Or crudely, in words, for all x close enough to c, but different from c, $F(x)$ is very close to L.

As an example, let $F(x) = \sin x/x$ for $x \neq 0$. The domain of F contains a punctured neighborhood of 0. From Theorem 6.14 [page 180], for $0 < |x| < 1$,

$$1 - \frac{x^2}{2} < \frac{\sin x}{x} < 1 \quad \text{and} \quad \left|\frac{\sin x}{x} - 1\right| < \frac{x^2}{2} < |x|.$$

Given $\epsilon > 0$, let δ be the smaller of ϵ and 1. Then

$$0 < |x| < \delta \Rightarrow \left|\frac{\sin x}{x} - 1\right| < \epsilon.$$

Hence $\lim_{x \to 0} (\sin x/x) = 1$, or $\lim_{0} F = 1$.

For $c \neq 0$ this function F is continuous at c. Therefore for each $\epsilon > 0$ there is some $\delta_\epsilon > 0$ such that

$|x - c| < \delta_\epsilon$ and x in dom $F \Rightarrow |F(x) - F(c)| < \epsilon.$

Since every number except 0 is in the domain of F,

$|x - c| < |c| \Rightarrow x$ in dom $F.$

Hence, if δ is the smaller of $|c|$ and δ_ϵ above,

$|x - c| < \delta \Rightarrow |F(x) - F(c)| < \epsilon,$

and trivially from this,

$0 < |x - c| < \delta \Rightarrow |F(x) - F(c)| < \epsilon.$

We have shown that, for $c \neq 0$, $\lim\limits_{c} F = F(c)$, or

$$\lim_{x \to c} \frac{\sin x}{x} = \frac{\sin c}{c}.$$

Theorem 10.10. Let the number c be in an open interval contained in the domain of a real function F. Then F is continuous at c iff $\lim\limits_{c} F = F(c)$.

Note: By hypothesis, c is in the domain of F and also the domain of F contains a punctured neighborhood of c.

PROOF FOR *if:* Suppose $\lim\limits_{c} F = F(c)$. Then for each $\epsilon > 0$ there is $\delta > 0$ such that

$0 < |x - c| < \delta \Rightarrow |F(x) - F(c)| < \epsilon.$

But $x = c \Rightarrow |F(x) - F(c)| = 0 < \epsilon$, so

$|x - c| < \delta \Rightarrow |F(x) - F(c)| < \epsilon,$

and F is continuous at c. ∎

PROOF FOR *only if:* Suppose F continuous at c. Then for each $\epsilon > 0$ there is $\delta > 0$ such that

$|x - c| < \delta$ and x in dom $F \Rightarrow |F(x) - F(c)| < \epsilon.$

Let δ_1 be $\leq \delta$ above and also small enough so that the domain of F includes the interval $(c - \delta_1, c + \delta_1)$. Then $0 < |x - c| < \delta_1$ implies both x in dom F and $|x - c| < \delta$. Thus for each $\epsilon > 0$ there is some $\delta_1 > 0$ such that

$0 < |x - c| < \delta_1 \Rightarrow |F(x) - F(c)| < \epsilon,$

and hence $\lim\limits_{c} F = F(c)$. ∎

Remark: If the real function f is differentiable at c, then by Theorem 10.1 [page 307] f is continuous at c and, by Theorem 10.10, $\lim\limits_{x \to c} f(x) = f(c)$.

Theorems 10.11 [*The Limit Theorems*]. If F and G are real functions and $\lim\limits_{c} F = L$ and $\lim\limits_{c} G = M$, then

(1) $\lim\limits_{c} (F + G) = L + M$,

(2) $\lim\limits_{c} (F - G) = L - M$,

(3) $\lim\limits_{c} (FG) = LM$,

(4)   if $M \neq 0$, $\lim\limits_{c} \dfrac{F}{G} = \dfrac{L}{M}$.

The proof is very similar to that of the analogous theorem about limits of sequences and to that of the theorem on the continuity of the sum and product of continuous functions. We leave the details to the reader, but point out the following:

1. Since the intersection of two punctured neighborhoods of c is a punctured neighborhood of c, each of $F + G$, $F - G$, and FG is defined on a punctured neighborhood of c.

2. If $\lim\limits_{c} F = L$, then F is bounded on some punctured neighborhood of c: for some $\delta > 0$,

$$0 < |x - c| < \delta \Rightarrow |F(x) - L| < 1 \Rightarrow |F(x)| < 1 + |L|.$$

3. If $\lim\limits_{c} G = M \neq 0$, then, for some $\delta > 0$,

$$0 < |x - c| < \delta \Rightarrow |G(x) - M| < \tfrac{1}{2}|M| \Rightarrow |G(x)| > \tfrac{1}{2}|M|.$$

Exercises

1. Let $G(0) = 5$ and, for $x \neq 0$, $G(x) = \sin x / x$. Prove that $\lim\limits_{x \to 0} G(x) = 1$.

2. Prove that

$$\lim_{x \to 1} \frac{x^2 - 1}{x^2 + x - 2} = \frac{2}{3}.$$

3. Let f be a real function defined for all real x. Prove that the statements

$$0 < |x - 3| < \frac{1}{2} \Rightarrow \left| \frac{f(x) - f(3)}{x - 3} - 2 \right| < 1$$

and

$$0 < |h| < \frac{1}{2} \Rightarrow \left| \frac{f(3 + h) - f(3)}{h} - 2 \right| < 1$$

are equivalent.

4. Prove that the real function f is differentiable at c iff

$$\lim_{h \to 0} \frac{f(c + h) - f(c)}{h} = f'(c).$$

§ 4. *Differentiation Formulas*

An *elementary function* is a function which can be built from the constants, the identity function, the sine, and the natural logarithm by a finite number of additions, subtractions, multiplications, divisions, compositions, restrictions of domains, and taking composition inverses.

For example, temporarily let I be the identity function on the real numbers and J its restriction to the nonnegative real numbers: $J(x) = x$ for $x \geq 0$. Then both I^2 and J^2 are elementary; J^2 is strictly monotone and its inverse is the square root function. Since $|x| = \sqrt{x^2}$ for all real x, the absolute value function is elementary. Exp is elementary because $\exp = \ln^{-1}$. Since $\cos x = \sin(x + (\pi/2))$ for all real x, cos is a composition of elementary functions and therefore elementary. So, for example, is

$$g(x) = \ln(\sin(x^5 + e^{\tan x} + \sec x)).$$

We have already established that the derivative of any constant is 0, that the derivative of the identity function is 1, and that, for $x > 0$, $\ln'(x) = 1/x$.

Theorem 10.12. For all real x, $\sin'(x) = \cos x$; that is, $\sin' = \cos$.

PROOF: We have established that $\lim_{x\to 0} (\sin x/x) = 1 = \cos 0$. Thus we have $\sin'(0) = \cos 0$.

For all x with $0 < |x| < \pi$,

$$\frac{\cos x - 1}{x} = \frac{\cos x - 1}{x} \frac{\cos x + 1}{\cos x + 1}$$

$$= -\frac{\sin^2 x}{x(\cos x + 1)}$$

$$= \frac{\sin x}{x} \frac{-\sin x}{\cos x + 1}.$$

From the Theorems 10.11 and the continuity of sin and cos,

$$\lim_{x\to 0} \frac{\cos x - 1}{x} = \lim_{x\to 0} \frac{\sin x}{x} \lim_{x\to 0} \frac{-\sin x}{\cos x + 1}$$

$$= 1\left(\frac{0}{2}\right) = 0.$$

Now, if this limit exists, for any real c,

$$\sin'(c) = \lim_{h\to 0} \frac{\sin(c + h) - \sin c}{h}.$$

For real c and $h \neq 0$,

$$\frac{\sin(c + h) - \sin c}{h} = \frac{\sin c \cos h + \cos c \sin h - \sin c}{h}$$

$$= \sin c \frac{\cos h - 1}{h} + \cos c \frac{\sin h}{h}.$$

Since

$$\lim_{h \to 0} \frac{\cos h - 1}{h} = 0 \quad \text{and} \quad \lim_{h \to 0} \frac{\sin h}{h} = 1,$$

by Theorems 10.11 we have $\sin'(c) = \cos c$. ∎

ALTERNATIVE PROOF: For all real x and c, with $x \neq c$,

$$\sin x - \sin c = \int_0^x \cos - \int_0^c \cos$$

$$= \int_c^x \cos$$

$$= (x - c) \cos c_x$$

for some c_x between c and x.

Thus, for $x \neq c$,

$$\frac{\sin x - \sin c}{x - c} - \cos c = \cos c_x - \cos c,$$

for some c_x between c and x. But

$$|\cos c_x - \cos c| \leq |c_x - c| < |x - c|.$$

[The key inequality was established in the proof that sin and cos are continuous on $\mathfrak{R}$.]

Clearly now, for each real c and $\epsilon > 0$,

$$0 < |x - c| < \epsilon \Rightarrow \left| \frac{\sin x - \sin c}{x - c} - \cos c \right| < \epsilon. \quad ∎$$

Thus each of the basic elementary functions is differentiable on its domain. By the linearity of D, sums, differences, and scalar multiples of differentiable functions are differentiable. The three theorems below give explicit formulas for differentiating products, compositions, and inverses. For g any real function except the 0 function, $1/g = R \circ g$, where $R(x) = 1/x$ for $x \neq 0$; we have seen that $R'(x) = -1/x^2$ for $x \neq 0$. The upshot is that by using formulas obtained so far and the three theorems below, we can write down immediately the derivative of any given elementary function. We shall state and illustrate all three before proving any.

Theorem 10.13 [*The Product Formula*]. If each of the real functions f and g is differentiable at c, then so is the product fg, and

$$(fg)'(c) = f'(c)g(c) + f(c)g'(c).$$

The formula $(fg)' = f'g + fg'$ holds on the intersection of the domains of f' and g'.

Theorem 10.14 [*The Chain Rule*].   If the real function g is differentiable at c and the real function f is differentiable at $g(c)$, then the composition $f \circ g$ is differentiable at c, and

$$(f \circ g)'(c) = f'(g(c))g'(c).$$

Theorem 10.15 [*Differentiation of Inverses*].   Let g be a real function differentiable at c and strictly monotone on an open interval containing c, so that the restriction of g to this interval has an inverse g^{-1}. If $g'(c) \neq 0$, then g^{-1} is differentiable at $g(c)$, and

$$(g^{-1})'(g(c)) = \frac{1}{g'(c)}.$$

Remark: Theorem 10.15 could be put this way. Let f and g be mutually inverse functions, with $g(c) = k$ and $f(k) = c$. If g is differentiable at c and $g'(c) \neq 0$, then f is differentiable at k and $f'(k) = 1/g'(c)$.

Examples

1. For all real x, set $f_2(x) = x^2$ and $f_4(x) = x^4$. From a previous example, $f'_2(x) = 2x$ for all x.

   Since $f_4 = f_2 f_2$, for all real x the product formula gives

   $$f'_4(x) = f'_2(x)f_2(x) + f_2(x)f'_2(x)$$
   $$= 2f'_2(x)f_2(x)$$
   $$= 2 \cdot 2x \cdot x^2 = 4x^3.$$

   Since also $f_4 = f_2 \circ f_2$, for all real x the Chain Rule gives

   $$f'_4(x) = f'_2(f_2(x)) \cdot f'_2(x)$$
   $$= 2f_2(x) \cdot 2x$$
   $$= 2x^2 \cdot 2x = 4x^3.$$

2. Let $h(x) = \ln x^2$ for $x \neq 0$. Since $\ln x^2 = 2 \ln x$, $h'(x) = 2 \ln' x = 2/x$. Alternatively, h is the composition $\ln \circ f_2$. By the Chain Rule,

   $$h'(x) = \ln' (f_2(x)) \cdot f'_2(x)$$

   $$= \frac{1}{x^2} \cdot 2x$$

   for all x for which both factors are defined—that is, for all $x \neq 0$.

3. Let $F(x) = \sin (\ln (x^2 + 2x + 10))$. Set

   $$g(x) = x^2 + 2x + 10 = (x + 1)^2 + 9 > 0$$

   for all x. For each real x, $g(x)$ is in the domain of $\ln$ and $\ln (g(x))$ is in the domain of $\sin$. Thus the domain of F is $\Re$, and $F = \sin \circ (\ln \circ g)$. By the Chain Rule,

   $$F'(x) = \sin' ([\ln \circ g](x)) \cdot [\ln \circ g]'(x)$$
   $$= \sin' (\ln (g(x))) \cdot \ln' (g(x)) \cdot g'(x)$$

   for all x. By previous results,

   $$f'(x) = \cos (\ln (x^2 + 2x + 10)) \cdot \frac{1}{x^2 + 2x + 10} \cdot (2x + 2).$$

4. From the last chapter's discussion of the logarithm and exponential functions, for all real x, $\exp x > 0$ and $\ln(\exp x) = x$. That is, $\ln \circ \exp$ is the identity function on $\mathcal{R}$. Hence $\ln \circ \exp$ is differentiable and, for every real x, $[\ln \circ \exp]'(x) = 1$.

Also, for each real x, $\ln$ is differentiable at $\exp x$ and $\ln'(\exp x) = 1/\exp x$.

Now assume that for some x the exponential function is differentiable at x. For such x the chain rule gives

$$1 = [\ln \circ \exp]'(x) = \ln'(\exp x) \cdot \exp'(x)$$

$$= \frac{1}{\exp x} \cdot \exp'(x).$$

Thus, by the Chain Rule, if $\exp$ is differentiable at x, then $\exp'(x) = \exp x$.

Now in Theorem 10.15 put $g = \ln$ and $g^{-1} = \exp$. For real x, let c be the positive number such that $x = \ln c$. According to the theorem, $\exp$ is differentiable at $x = \ln c$, and

$$\exp'(x) = \exp'(\ln c) = \frac{1}{\ln'(c)} = \frac{1}{\dfrac{1}{c}} = c = \exp x.$$

From Theorem 10.15 and properties of the logarithm, the exponential function is its own derivative.

Exercises

1. Let $F(x) = 1/x^2$ for $x \neq 0$. With f_2 the squaring function and R the reciprocal function,

$$F = R \circ f_2 = f_2 \circ R = RR.$$

Give three different derivations of $F'(x) = -2x^{-3}$ for $x \neq 0$.

2. Set

$$G(x) = \frac{1}{3x - 5} = R(3x - 5),$$

for $x \neq \frac{5}{3}$. Prove that, for $x \neq \frac{5}{3}$,

$$G'(x) = \frac{-3}{(3x - 5)^2}.$$

3. Find the derivative of H: $H(x) = (x^2 + 5x)/(3x - 5)$, for $x \neq \frac{5}{3}$.

4. For $x \neq \frac{5}{3}$, let

$$f(x) = \sin^2\left(\frac{1}{3x - 5}\right).$$

Note that $f = f_2 \circ \sin \circ G$, and write down the formula for f'.

5. If $g(x) = \ln(\sin x^2)$, for $0 < x < \pi^{1/2}$, prove that, for $0 < x < \pi^{1/2}$,

$$g'(x) = 2x \frac{\cos x^2}{\sin x^2}.$$

PROOF OF THEOREM 10.13 [*The Product Formula*]: Assume real functions f and g both differentiable at c. The domain of each function includes an open interval around c and hence the product fg is defined on an open interval around c.

For x in the domain of fg, but $x \neq c$,

$$\frac{[fg](x) - [fg](c)}{x - c} = \frac{f(x)g(x) - f(c)g(c)}{x - c}$$

$$= f(x)\frac{g(x) - g(c)}{x - c} + \frac{f(x) - f(c)}{x - c}g(c).$$

Since f is differentiable at c, $\lim_{x \to c} f(x) = f(c)$, by the Remark after Theorem 10.10.

By hypothesis,

$$\lim_{x \to c}\frac{g(x) - g(c)}{x - c} = g'(c) \quad \text{and} \quad \lim_{x \to c}\frac{f(x) - f(c)}{x - c} = f'(c).$$

Also, $\lim_{x \to c} g(c) = g(c)$. [Define G, for all x, by $G(x) = g(c)$. Then G is constant and $\lim_c G = g(c)$.]

By the limit theorems and the definition of $(fg)'(c)$,

$$(fg)'(c) = f(c)g'(c) + f'(c)g(c). \qquad \blacksquare$$

PROOF OF THEOREM 10.14 [*The Chain Rule*]:   We are to prove that if g is differentiable at c and f is differentiable at $g(c)$, then $f \circ g$ is differentiable at c and

$$[f \circ g]'(c) = f'(g(c))g'(c).$$

In particular, if $g'(c) = 0$ and f is differentiable at $g(c)$, we must prove that also $[f \circ g]'(c) = 0$: that is, that

$$\lim_{x \to c}\frac{f(g(x)) - f(g(c))}{x - c} = 0.$$

The differentiability of f at $g(c)$ implies, by the Lemma on page 307, the existence of positive k and δ_1 such that

(1) $|g(x) - g(c)| < \delta_1 \Rightarrow |f(g(x)) - f(g(c))| \leq k|g(x) - g(c)|.$

Since $g'(c) = 0$, if $\epsilon > 0$ there is some $\delta_\epsilon > 0$ such that

$$0 < |x - c| < \delta_\epsilon \Rightarrow \left|\frac{g(x) - g(c)}{x - c}\right| < \frac{\epsilon}{k},$$

or

(2) $0 < |x - c| < \delta_\epsilon \Rightarrow |g(x) - g(c)| < \frac{\epsilon}{k}|x - c|.$

Now, for x such that $0 < |x - c| < \min\{\delta_\epsilon, \delta_1 k/\epsilon\}$, we have

$$|g(x) - g(c)| < \frac{\epsilon}{k}|x - c| < \frac{\epsilon}{k}\frac{\delta_1 k}{\epsilon} = \delta_1,$$

so that, by (1),

$$|f(g(x)) - f(g(c))| \leq k|g(x) - g(c)|.$$

But also, by (2),

$$|g(x) - g(c)| < \frac{\epsilon}{k}|x - c|,$$

so that

$$|f(g(x)) - f(g(c))| < \epsilon|x - c|.$$

We have established that for each $\epsilon > 0$ there is some $\delta > 0$ such that

$$0 < |x - c| < \delta \Rightarrow \left| \frac{f(g(x)) - f(g(c))}{x - c} \right| < \epsilon.$$

This completes the proof of the Chain Rule in the special case $g'(c) = 0$. If $g'(c) \neq 0$, either $g'(c) > 0$ and g is strictly increasing at c, or $g'(c) < 0$ and g is strictly decreasing at c. In either case, for all x in some punctured neighborhood of c, $g(x) \neq g(c)$, and there is some $\delta > 0$ such that, if $0 < |x - c| < \delta$, then

$$\frac{f(g(x)) - f(g(c))}{x - c} = \frac{f(g(x)) - f(g(c))}{g(x) - g(c)} \cdot \frac{g(x) - g(c)}{x - c}.$$

This equation makes the Chain Rule virtually self-evident. By definition of $g'(c)$,

$$\lim_{x \to c} \frac{g(x) - g(c)}{x - c} = g'(c).$$

Because of the theorem on the limit of a product we need only prove that

$$\lim_{x \to c} \frac{f(g(x)) - f(g(c))}{g(x) - g(c)} = f'(g(c)).$$

This is intuitively clear on the ground that, if x is close to c, then $g(x)$ is close to $g(c)$ and consequently the quotient above is close to $f'(g(c))$.

In fact, given $\epsilon > 0$, the differentiability of f at $g(c)$ ensures the existence of some $\delta_\epsilon > 0$ such that

$$0 < |u - g(c)| < \delta_\epsilon \Rightarrow \left| \frac{f(u) - f(g(c))}{u - g(c)} - f'(g(c)) \right| < \epsilon.$$

Since g is differentiable at c, g is continuous at c, and there is some $p_\epsilon > 0$ such that

$$|x - c| < p_\epsilon \Rightarrow |g(x) - g(c)| < \delta_\epsilon.$$

Let $q_\epsilon = \min \{p_\epsilon, \delta\}$. If $0 < |x - c| < q_\epsilon$, then $g(x) \neq g(c)$, but $|g(x) - g(c)| < \delta_\epsilon$, and consequently

$$\left| \frac{f(g(x)) - f(g(c))}{g(x) - g(c)} - f'(g(c)) \right| < \epsilon. \qquad \blacksquare$$

PROOF OF THEOREM 10.15: If the real function g is strictly monotone on an open interval I, then g has a composition inverse g^{-1}, and $g^{-1} \circ g$ is the identity function on I. For notational convenience set $f = g^{-1}$, so that $f \circ g$ is the identity function on I; it follows that $f \circ g$ is differentiable on I and, for x in I, $[f \circ g]'(x) = 1$.

Suppose now that, for some c in I, g is differentiable at c, and let $b = g(c)$ so that $f(b) = c$. If also f is differentiable at $b = g(c)$, the Chain Rule gives

$$1 = [f \circ g]'(c) = f'(g(c)) \cdot g'(c)$$
$$= f'(b) \cdot g'(c).$$

Two conclusions follow:

1. If $g'(c) = 0$, then f is not differentiable at b because there is no number $f'(b)$ such that $1 = f'(b) \cdot 0$.

2. If $g'(c) \neq 0$ then $f'(b) = 1/g'(c)$.

We want to prove that, if $g'(c) \neq 0$, then $f = g^{-1}$ *is* differentiable at $b = g(c)$ and that consequently $f'(b) = 1/g'(c)$.

From the chapter on continuity, f is continuous at b because g, being differentiable at c, is continuous at c. Consider the difference quotient $(f(x) - f(b))/(x - b)$ for x in a punctured neighborhood of b. Now $f(b) = c$, and if we set $f(x) = t$, then, as $f = g^{-1}$, $x = g(t)$. For each x in a punctured neighborhood of b, there is one and only one t in the image of this punctured neighborhood under f such that

$$\frac{f(x) - f(b)}{x - b} = \frac{t - c}{g(t) - g(c)}.$$

By hypothesis,

$$\lim_{t \to c} \frac{g(t) - g(c)}{t - c} = g'(c) \neq 0.$$

By the limit theorems,

$$\lim_{t \to c} \frac{t - c}{g(t) - g(c)} = \frac{1}{g'(c)}.$$

Thus, given $\epsilon > 0$, there is $\delta_\epsilon > 0$ such that

$$0 < |t - c| < \delta_\epsilon \Longrightarrow \left| \frac{t - c}{g(t) - g(c)} - \frac{1}{g'(c)} \right| < \epsilon.$$

In other words,

$$0 < |f(x) - f(b)| < \delta_\epsilon \Longrightarrow \left| \frac{f(x) - f(b)}{x - b} - \frac{1}{g'(c)} \right| < \epsilon.$$

Since f is continuous at b and strictly monotone, for each $\delta_\epsilon > 0$ there is some $p_\epsilon > 0$ such that

$$0 < |x - b| < p_\epsilon \Longrightarrow 0 < |f(x) - f(b)| < \delta_\epsilon,$$

and hence

$$\left| \frac{f(x) - f(b)}{x - b} - \frac{1}{g'(c)} \right| < \epsilon. \qquad ∎$$

Summary of Formulas

In examples throughout this chapter we have so far established, among others, the following differentiation formulas.

1. For $x > 0$, $\ln'(x) = 1/x$.
2. For all real x, $\sin'(x) = \cos x$ and $\cos'(x) = -\sin x$.
3. For all real x, $\exp'(x) = \exp x$.
4. For $n = 0, 1, 2, 3, -1$, if $f_n(x) = x^n$ for $x \neq 0$, then $f'_n(x) = nx^{n-1}$

for $x \neq 0$.

5. If $f_{1/2}(x) = \sqrt{x} = x^{1/2}$ for $x \geq 0$, then, for $x > 0$,

$$f'_{1/2}(x) = \frac{1}{2\sqrt{x}} = \frac{1}{2} x^{-1/2}.$$

From these and the preceding theorems we can derive formulas for the derivative of any elementary function.

Examples

1. With abs $x = |x|$ for all real x, we have seen that abs is not differentiable at 0. But

$$\text{abs } x = \sqrt{x^2} = f_{1/2}(x^2) = [f_{1/2} \circ f_2](x).$$

By the Chain Rule, for $x \neq 0$,

$$\text{abs}'(x) = f'_{1/2}(f_2(x))f'_2(x)$$

$$= \frac{1}{2\sqrt{x^2}} \cdot 2x = \frac{x}{\sqrt{x^2}} = \frac{x}{|x|}.$$

2. For real x, let $f(x) = \sin^3 x = f_3(\sin x) = [f_3 \circ \sin](x)$. Then

$$f'(x) = f'_3(\sin x) \sin'(x) = 3 \sin^2 x \cos x.$$

3. For $x \neq 0$, let $f(x) = \ln |x| = [\ln \circ \text{abs}](x)$. Then, for $x \neq 0$,

$$f'(x) = \ln'(\text{abs } x) \text{ abs}'(x) = \frac{1}{|x|} \cdot \frac{x}{|x|} = \frac{x}{x^2} = \frac{1}{x}.$$

4. For all real x, let

$$f(x) = e^{\sin x} = \exp(\sin x) = [\exp \circ \sin](x).$$

Then for all real x, $f'(x) = \exp'(\sin x) \sin' x = \exp(\sin x) \cos x = e^{\sin x} \cos x$.

5. Recall that Sin is the restriction of the sine function to the interval $[-\pi/2, \pi/2]$. For $-\pi/2 < x < \pi/2$,

$$\text{Sin}'(x) = \sin'(x) = \cos x > 0.$$

Thus Sin is strictly increasing on $(-\pi/2, \pi/2)$. Also, Sin is continuous at

$\pi/2$ and $-\pi/2$, so that, by Theorem 10.8, Sin is strictly increasing on $[-\pi/2, \pi/2]$ and is a one-to-one mapping of $[-\pi/2, \pi/2]$ onto $[-1, 1]$.

It follows that Sin has an inverse, Sin^{-1} or Arc sin, a one-to-one mapping of $[-1, 1]$ onto $[-\pi/2, \pi/2]$. By Theorem 10.15, Arc sin is differentiable on $(-1, 1)$, and, for $-1 < x < 1$,

$$\text{Arc sin}' \ (x) = \frac{1}{\sin' \ (\text{Arc sin } x)} = \frac{1}{\cos \ (\text{Arc sin } x)}.$$

Now $\cos^2 (\text{Arc sin } x) = 1 - \sin^2 (\text{Arc sin } x) = 1 - x^2$, and Arc sin x is in $(-\pi/2, \pi/2)$, an interval on which the cosine function is positive and $\sqrt{\cos^2} = \cos$. Therefore, for $-1 < x < 1$,

$$\text{Arc sin}' \ (x) = \frac{1}{\sqrt{1 - x^2}}.$$

Exercises

The functions tangent, cotangent, secant, and cosecant are defined on page 235.
1. Prove the following.
a. $\sec' = \sec \tan$.
b. $\csc' = -\csc \cot$.
c. $\tan' = 1 + \tan^2 = \sec^2$.
d. $\cot' = -\csc^2 = -1 - \cot^2$.
2. If Tan is the restriction of tan to the interval $(-\pi/2, \pi/2)$, prove that Tan is a strictly increasing differentiable one-to-one mapping of $(-\pi/2, \pi/2)$ onto $\Re$. Then prove that $\text{Tan}^{-1} = \text{Arc tan}$ is a strictly increasing differentiable one-to-one mapping of $\Re$ onto $(-\pi/2, \pi/2)$, and that, for all real x,

$$\text{Arc tan}' \ (x) = \frac{1}{1 + x^2}.$$

3. Cos is the restriction of the cosine function to the interval $[0, \pi]$. Prove that Cos is a strictly decreasing one-to-one mapping of $[0, \pi]$ onto $[-1, 1]$. Let Arc cos $= \text{Cos}^{-1}$ and prove that, for $-1 < x < 1$,

$$\text{Arc cos}' \ (x) = \frac{-1}{\sqrt{1 - x^2}}.$$

4. Sketch graphs of Arc sin, Arc cos, and Arc tan.
5. For each integer n, let $f_n(x) = x^n$ for $x \neq 0$, and also for $x = 0$ if this makes sense. Prove that, for all n in Z and all $x \neq 0$, $f'_n(x) = nx^{n-1}$.
6. For $x > 0$ and any real α, recall that x^α is defined to be $e^{\alpha \ln x} = \exp (\alpha \ln x)$. For each real α, define $f_\alpha(x) = x^\alpha$ for $x > 0$, and prove that, for $x > 0$, $f'_\alpha(x) = \alpha x^{\alpha-1}$.
7. Let g be a real function differentiable on an interval I. Prove the following.
a. If $f(x) = e^{g(x)}$, then $f'(x) = e^{g(x)}g'(x)$ for all x in I.
b. If $H(x) = g^{17}(x) = (g(x))^{17}$, then, for all x in I, $H'(x) = 17g^{16}(x)g'(x)$.
c. If $F(x) = \ln (|g(x)|)$, for those x in I such that $g(x) \neq 0$, then $F'(x) = g'(x)/g(x)$ for those x in I such that $g(x) \neq 0$.
d. If $G(x) = \sin^5 (g(x))$, then $G'(x) = 5 \sin^4 (g(x)) \cos (g(x))g'(x)$ for all x in I.
8. Sketch graphs of the curves described below. In each case locate any maxima or minima as precisely as possible.

a. $y = \sin(x^2)$, for $-2 \le x \le 2$.
b. $y = \sin^2 x$, for $-1 \le x \le 2\pi$.
c. $y = \ln|x|$, for $x \ne 0$.
d. $y = x \sin x$, for $-\pi \le x \le 3\pi$.
e. $y = \sin(\tan x)$, for $-\pi/4 \le x < \pi/2$.
f. $y = \text{Arc}\tan(2x - 3)$.

9. If $F(x) = x \ln x$, with $x > 0$, what is $F'(x)$? Find all functions G such that, for all $x > 0$, $G'(x) = \ln x$.

10. If $H(x) = xe^x$ for all real x, what is $H'(x)$? Find all functions f such that $f'(x) = xe^x$ for all x.

11. Find a function F such that $F'(x) = x^2 e^x$.

12. Each formula below defines, on at least one open interval, an elementary function. Write down a formula for the derivative of each.

a. $\text{Arc}\tan(5x^2 + 7x - 3)$.

b. $\dfrac{x^3 - 18x}{x^2 + 7}$.

c. $\ln((x + 3)(x - 5))$.

d. $\ln|\sec x + \tan x|$.

e. $e^{x^2 \sin(5x+7)}$.

f. $\cos(e^x + \cot(x^2 + \sin x))$.

g. $\dfrac{\sin x + e^{x^2}}{1 + \tan x}$.

h. $e^{x^2-5} \sin^3(x + \ln x)$.

i. $\sin^{17}(\cos^5 e^x)$.

j. $(\sin^{17} x) \cos^5 e^x$.

k. $\sqrt{3 + x^2 + \sin 5x}$.

l. $\ln((x^2 + 5)^2(x^3 + 3x)^5(x^2 + 1)^{-3})$. [*Hint:* $\ln(A^2 B^3) = 2 \ln A + 3 \ln B$.]

m. $e^{5 \ln x}$.

n. $x^3 e^{5x}$.

o. $\text{Arc}\sin \dfrac{1}{1 + x^2}$.

p. $\sin 2x - 2 \sin x \cos x$.

q. $\ln(x^4 + x^2 + 1)$.

r. e^{e^x}.

s. $\exp(3 \ln(5 \exp x))$.

t. $\tan(3 \,\text{Arc}\tan x)$.

u. $\sin^3(\sin x)$.

v. $\ln|\cos x|$.

§ 5. *Examples of Differentiable Functions*

The purpose of this section is to give some examples of differentiable functions with mildly unpleasant or surprising features. The first two examples are smoothed versions of the functions called a squeezed sawtooth or a tapered sawtooth function in the chapter on continuity.

Examples

1. Let $h(0) = 0$ and, for $x \neq 0$, $h(x) = \sin \pi/x$. Except perhaps at 0, h is differentiable and, for $x \neq 0$,

$$h'(x) = -\frac{\pi}{x^2} \cos \frac{\pi}{x}.$$

For each integer $n \neq 0$, $h(1/n) = \sin n\pi = 0$, and

$$h\left(\frac{1}{n + \frac{1}{2}}\right) = \sin (n + \tfrac{1}{2})\pi = \cos n\pi = (-1)^n.$$

In any open interval $(0, b)$ there are infinitely many x with $h(x) = -1$, and infinitely many t with $h(t) = 1$. Thus h is not uniformly continuous on any open interval $(0, b)$, and h cannot be continuous at 0 no matter how $h(0)$ is defined or redefined.

2. For all x let $f(x) = xh(x)$, with h as in Example 1. For $x \neq 0$,

$$f'(x) = xh'(x) + h(x) = -\frac{\pi}{x} \cos \frac{\pi}{x} + \sin \frac{\pi}{x}.$$

Now f is continuous at 0 because, for $x \neq 0$, $|f(x)| \leq |x|$, so that $\lim_{x \to 0} f(x) = 0 = f(0)$.

But f is not differentiable at 0 because the difference quotient,

$$\frac{f(x) - f(0)}{x - 0} = \frac{xh(x)}{x} = h(x),$$

and $\lim_{x \to 0} H(x)$ does not exist.

Not only is $|f(x)| \leq |x|$ for all x, but $f(x) = x$ if $h(x) = 1$, and $f(x) = -x$ if $h(x) = -1$. If $h(x) = \sin \pi/x = 1$ or -1, then $\cos \pi/x = 0$ and $h'(x) = 0$. From $f'(x) = xh'(x) + h(x)$, if $f(x) = x \neq 0$, then $f'(x) = 1$; if $f(x) = -x \neq 0$, then $f'(x) = -1$.

The graph of f is confined between the lines $y = x$ and $y = -x$, and is tangent to each at infinitely many points.

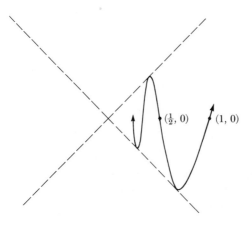

If we think of a secant line through $(0, f(0)) = (0, 0)$ and $(x, f(x))$, then as $x \longrightarrow 0$ the secant line wobbles up and down, taking on every slope between -1 and 1 infinitely often.

3. Let $g(x) = x^2 h(x)$ for all x. For $x \neq 0$,

$$g'(x) = x^2 h'(x) + 2x h(x) = -\pi \cos \frac{\pi}{x} + 2x \sin \frac{\pi}{x}.$$

In any open interval $(0, b)$ or $(-b, 0)$ there are infinitely many x with $\sin \pi/x = 0$ and $\cos \pi/x = 1$, and also infinitely many x with $\sin \pi/x = 0$ and $\cos \pi/x = -1$. Thus, in any punctured neighborhood of 0, g' assumes every value between $-\pi$ and π infinitely often. As a consequence, $\lim_{x \to 0} g'(x)$ does not exist.

However, g is differentiable at 0. For $x \neq 0$,

$$\frac{g(x) - g(0)}{x - 0} = \frac{g(x)}{x} = x \sin \frac{\pi}{x} = f(x),$$

and $\lim_{x \to 0} f(x) = 0$. Thus $g'(0) = 0$, although $\lim_{x \to 0} g'(x)$ does not exist. The derivative g' is defined for all x, but is not continuous at 0.

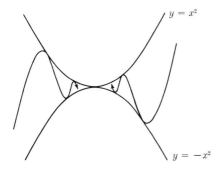

$y = x^2$

$y = -x^2$

Although the slope of the graph of g oscillates rapidly between $-\pi$ and π on any punctured neighborhood of 0, nevertheless $g'(0) = 0$: somehow "at 0" the graph of g is mashed flat between the two parabolas.

Note that if F is any function differentiable at 0, then, by the chain rule, $F \circ g$ is differentiable at 0, and $[F \circ g]'(0) = 0$. But in any punctured neighborhood of 0 there are infinitely many x with $g(x) = g(0)$, and we cannot have

$$\frac{F(g(x)) - F(g(0))}{x - 0} = \frac{F(g(x)) - F(g(0))}{g(x) - g(0)} \frac{g(x) - g(0)}{x - 0}.$$

This example shows that in the proof of the chain rule it is necessary to give special consideration to the possibility that $g'(c) = 0$.

4. With g as in Example 3, let $G(x) = x + g(x)$ for all x. Then $G'(x) = 1 + g'(x)$ for all x. In particular, $G'(0) = 1$, and hence G is strictly increasing at 0. But in any interval containing 0 there are infinitely many x with $G'(x) = 1 - \pi < 0$. At each such x, G is strictly decreasing. Thus G is not monotone on any interval containing 0.

As an *exercise*, try to sketch some indication of the graph of G over an interval containing 0.

Of course, G' is not continuous at 0, because g' is not continuous at 0. If a function H has a derivative H' continuous at 0, and $H'(0) > 0$, then necessarily $H'(x) > 0$ for all x in some open interval containing 0, and H is strictly monotone increasing on this interval.

§ 6. *Tangents to Curves*

In the last section of Chapter 7 is a brief discussion of curves in $\mathfrak{R}^2$ or $\mathfrak{R}^3$ as images of intervals in $\mathfrak{R}^1$ under continuous mappings. Here we consider briefly the question of tangents to such a curve.

Let X, Y, Z be three real functions, each continuous on an interval I. For t in I let $F(t) = (X(t), Y(t), Z(t))$ in $\mathfrak{R}^3$. The range of F is a curve C in $\mathfrak{R}^3$, by definition. If $Z(t) = 0$ for all t in I, then the curve is entirely in the plane $z = 0$, which we can identify with $\mathfrak{R}^2$.

For c in I the curve defined above may or may not have a tangent line at $F(c)$. Let L be a line through the point $F(c)$. For $0 < \theta < \pi/2$ let K_θ be the cone which is the union of all lines L' through $F(c)$ such that the smaller angle between L and L' has radian measure θ.

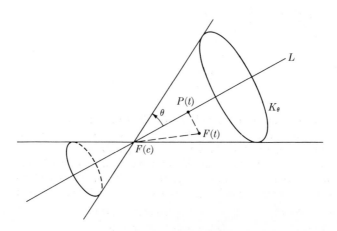

In the graph above, $F(t)$ is a point on the curve and $P(t)$ is the unique corresponding point on L such that the triangle $F(c)$, $P(t)$, $F(t)$ has a right angle at $P(t)$. [If $F(t)$ is on L, $P(t) = F(t)$.]

Definition 10.6. With notation as above, the line L is **tangent** to the curve C at $F(c)$ iff for each θ in the interval $(0, \pi/2)$ there is some $\delta > 0$ such that, if $0 < |t - c| < \delta$, then $F(t)$ is in the interior of the cone K_θ.

Remark: The analytic formulation is

$$0 < |t - c| < \delta \Rightarrow \frac{|P(t) - F(t)|}{|P(t) - F(c)|} < \tan \theta.$$

For $0 < \theta < \frac{\pi}{2}$, $\theta < \tan \theta$, and consequently it suffices to prove that

$$\frac{|P(t) - F(t)|}{|P(t) - F(c)|} < \theta.$$

Definition 10.7. If the three real functions X, Y, Z have derivatives X', Y', Z', each continuous on an open interval I, and furthermore, for each t in I, at least one of $X'(t)$, $Y'(t)$, $Z'(t)$ is different from 0, then the mapping F: for t in I,

$$F(t) = (X(t), Y(t), Z(t))$$

is **smooth**, and the range of F is a **smooth curve**.

Theorem 10.16. Let $F: t \longrightarrow (X(t), Y(t), Z(t))$ be a smooth mapping of an open interval I onto a smooth curve C. For c in I, the line L through $F(c)$ and $F(c) + (X'(c), Y'(c), Z'(c))$ is tangent to C at $F(c)$.

PROOF: 1. Since F is smooth, $(X'(c), Y'(c), Z'(c)) \neq (0, 0, 0)$, and the line L is determined.

2. For convenience set $Q = (X'(c), Y'(c), Z'(c))$, and set $k = |Q| > 0$. For all real t, set $L(t) = F(c) + (t - c)Q$. Then, for all t, $L(t)$ is on the line L. In particular, $L(c) = F(c)$ and $L(c + 1) = F(c) + Q$. And, for all t,

$$|L(t) - F(c)| = |t - c| \, |Q| = k|t - c|.$$

3. Given $\epsilon > 0$, there are positive numbers δ_1, δ_2, δ_3 such that

$$0 < |t - c| < \delta_1 \Rightarrow |X(t) - X(c) - (t - c)X'(c)| < \epsilon|t - c|,$$
$$0 < |t - c| < \delta_2 \Rightarrow |Y(t) - Y(c) - (t - c)Y'(c)| < \epsilon|t - c|,$$
$$0 < |t - c| < \delta_3 \Rightarrow |Z(t) - Z(c) - (t - c)Z'(c)| < \epsilon|t - c|.$$

Let $\delta = \min \{\delta_1, \delta_2, \delta_3\}$, and for all t such that $0 < |t - c| < \delta$ we have

$$|F(t) - L(t)|^2 < 3\epsilon^2|t - c|^2,$$
$$|F(t) - L(t)| < \epsilon\sqrt{3}|t - c|.$$

4. Given θ with $0 < \theta < \pi/2$ we want to prove there is some $p > 0$ such that for all t in I, with $0 < |t - c| < p$, $F(t)$ is in the interior of the cone K_θ.

Rather than compute the quotient $\dfrac{|P(t) - F(t)|}{|P(t) - F(c)|}$ exactly, we estimate both the numerator and denominator.

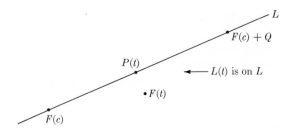

Let

$$\epsilon = \min\left\{\frac{k}{2\sqrt{3}}, \frac{k\theta}{2\sqrt{3}}\right\},$$

where $k = |Q|$, as above. Let $\delta > 0$ be such that $0 < |t - c| < \delta$ implies $|F(t) - L(t)| < \epsilon\sqrt{3}|t - c|$. Then

$$|L(t) - F(c)| = k|t - c| \leq |P(t) - F(c)| + |F(t) - L(t)|,$$

and

$$
\begin{aligned}
|P(t) - F(c)| &\geq k|t - c| - |F(t) - L(t)| \\
&> k|t - c| - \epsilon\sqrt{3}|t - c| \\
&\geq k|t - c| - \tfrac{1}{2}k|t - c| \\
&= \tfrac{1}{2}k|t - c|.
\end{aligned}
$$

Also, since $L(t)$ is on L,

$$
\begin{aligned}
|F(t) - P(t)| &\leq |F(t) - L(t)| \\
&< \epsilon\sqrt{3}|t - c| \\
&\leq \tfrac{1}{2}k\theta|t - c|.
\end{aligned}
$$

Thus, for $0 < |t - c| < \delta$,

$$\frac{|F(t) - P(t)|}{|P(t) - F(c)|} < \frac{\tfrac{1}{2}k\theta|t - c|}{\tfrac{1}{2}k|t - c|} = \theta,$$

and, by the Remark after Definition 10.6, $F(t)$ is in the cone K_θ. ∎

By letting $Z(t) = 0$ for all t in I and identifying $(X(t), Y(t), 0)$ with $(X(t), Y(t))$, we have

Theorem 10.17. Let $F: t \longrightarrow (X(t), Y(t))$, be a smooth mapping of an open interval I onto a smooth curve C in $\mathfrak{R}^2$. [X' and Y' are continuous on I, and for no t in I are $X'(t)$ and $Y'(t)$, both 0.] Then for c in I the line L through $F(c)$ and $F(c) + (X'(c), Y'(c))$ is tangent to C at $F(c)$.

If F is a mapping of an open interval I into $\mathfrak{R}^3$, then for t and c in I, with $t \neq c$, $F(t) - F(c)$ is a point in $\mathfrak{R}^3$, and can be multiplied by the scalar $1/(t - c)$:

$$\frac{F(t) - F(c)}{t - c} = \left(\frac{X(t) - X(c)}{t - c}, \frac{Y(t) - Y(c)}{t - c}, \frac{Z(t) - Z(c)}{t - c} \right).$$

Because the absolute value function on $\mathfrak{R}^3$ has the essential properties of the absolute value function on $\mathfrak{R}$, we can define $\displaystyle\lim_{t \to c} \frac{F(t) - F(c)}{t - c}$. If we do this, and if X, Y, and Z are differentiable at c, it follows that

$$\lim_{t \to c} \frac{F(t) - F(c)}{t - c} = (X'(c), Y'(c), Z'(c)).$$

If F is a smooth mapping of an open interval I into $\mathfrak{R}^3$ or $\mathfrak{R}^2$, we shall write $F'(t)$ for $(X'(t), Y'(t), Z'(t))$, or $(X'(t), Y'(t))$. Such a function F is often called a vector-valued function with a vector-valued derivative.

Examples

1. For all real t let $F(t) = (t, t^2) = (X(t), Y(t))$. Then X' and Y' are everywhere continuous and

   $$(X'(t), Y'(t)) = (1, 2t) \neq (0, 0).$$

   Thus F is a smooth mapping of $\mathfrak{R}$ onto the parabola $y = x^2$, which is therefore a smooth curve. The tangent at (c, c^2) is, by Theorem 10.17, the line through (c, c^2) and $(c + 1, c^2 + 2c)$, having slope $2c$, in accord with previous results.

2. For real t let $F(t) = (a \cos t, b \sin t)$, where a and b are positive real numbers. Then F maps $\mathfrak{R}$ many-to-one onto the ellipse $(x^2/a^2) + (y^2/b^2) = 1$. The tangent at $F(t)$ is the line through $F(t)$ and $F(t) + F'(t)$, where $F'(t) = (-a \sin t, b \cos t)$. This line is vertical if $\sin t = 0$. Otherwise it has slope $-b \cos t/a \sin t$.

3. For real t let $F(t) = (t^2, t^4, t^3 - t - 1)$. Then

   $$F'(t) = (2t, 4t^3, 3t^2 - 1) \neq (0, 0, 0)$$

   for any t. Thus F is a smooth mapping of $\mathfrak{R}$ into $\mathfrak{R}^3$; $F(1) = (1, 1, -1)$, and $F(-1) = (1, 1, -1)$. If $F(t) = (1, 1, -1)$, then $t = 1$ or -1; $(1, 1, -1)$ is a *double point* on the curve.

   The tangent to the curve at $(1, 1, -1)$ considered as $F(1)$ is the line through $(1, 1, -1)$ and

   $$(1, 1, -1) + F'(1) = (3, 5, 1).$$

   The tangent to the curve at $(1, 1, -1)$ considered as $F(-1)$ is the line through $(1, 1, -1)$, and

   $$(1, 1, -1) + F'(-1) = (-1, -3, 1).$$

   Thus there are two different tangents at $(1, 1, -1)$.

   A two-dimensional analogue is shown below.

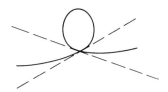

4. For real t let $F(t) = (t^3, t^6)$; F is a one-to-one mapping of $\mathcal{R}$ onto the parabola $y = x^2$. For all t, $F'(t) = (3t^2, 6t^5)$, and $F'(0) = (0, 0)$. Thus F is not smooth, and the tangent to the parabola at the origin is not determined by F.

The parabola is a smooth curve, because the mapping $t \longrightarrow (t, t^2)$ is smooth. The function F in this example is an unsmooth parametrization of a smooth curve.

Theorem 10.18. Let $F: t \longrightarrow (X(t), Y(t))$ be a smooth mapping of an interval I into $\mathcal{R}^2$. If, for some c in I, $X'(c) \neq 0$, then, by the continuity of X', $X'(t)$ has the same sign as $X'(c)$ for all t in some open interval J containing c. The set of all points $(X(t), Y(t))$, for t in J, is the graph of a real function g. This function g is differentiable at $X(t)$ for each t in J, and

$$g'(X(t)) = \frac{Y'(t)}{X'(t)}.$$

PROOF: Since X' is either strictly positive or else strictly negative on J, X is strictly monotone on J and has an inverse X^{-1}. Then, for t in J,

$$Y(t) = Y(X^{-1}(X(t))) = g(X(t)),$$

where $g = Y \circ X^{-1}$.

By the chain rule and the theorem on the derivatives of inverses,

$$g'(X(t)) = Y'(X^{-1}(X(t)))(X^{-1})'(X(t))$$

$$= Y'(t) \frac{1}{X'(t)}. \quad \blacksquare$$

Remark: If $X'(t) \neq 0$, the line through $(X(t), Y(t))$ and $(X(t), Y(t)) + (X'(t), Y'(t))$ has slope $Y'(t)/X'(t)$. Thus the tangents to the graph of the function g as determined by Theorem 10.16 include all the tangents determined by g'. Theorem 10.16 may also provide vertical tangents at end points of the domain of g.

For example, for real t let $F(t) = (\cos t, \sin t)$. For $0 < t < \pi$,

$$\sin t = \sqrt{1 - \cos^2 t} = g(\cos t).$$

For such t,

$$\frac{\sin'(t)}{\cos'(t)} = \frac{\cos t}{-\sin t}.$$

And, if $x = \cos t$,

$$g'(x) = \frac{-x}{\sqrt{1 - x^2}} = \frac{-\cos t}{\sin t} = \frac{\sin'(t)}{\cos'(t)}.$$

For $\pi < t < 2\pi$, $\sin t = -\sqrt{1 - \cos^2 t} = h(\cos t)$. For such t,

$$\frac{\sin'(t)}{\cos'(t)} = \frac{\cos t}{-\sin t}.$$

And, if $x = \cos t$,

$$h'(x) = \frac{x}{\sqrt{1 - x^2}} = \frac{\cos t}{-\sin t} = \frac{\sin'(t)}{\cos'(t)}.$$

Exercises

1. Sketch the graph of the plane curve with parametric equations $x = t - t^3$, $y = t^2$. In particular, locate all vertical tangents and horizontal tangents.

  [In the language of this section, the curve is the range of F: for all real t, $F(t) = (t - t^3, t^2)$.]

2. The set of all (x, y) in R^2 such that $x^3 + y^3 = 2xy$ is a *folium* [leaf] *of Descartes*. Obviously $(0, 0)$ and $(1, 1)$ are points of the curve; other points are not easily found. If we look for the intersection of the folium with the line $y = mx$, we are led to

$$x = \frac{2m}{1 + m^3}, \qquad y = \frac{2m^2}{1 + m^3}.$$

  For $m \neq -1$, set

$$F(m) = \left(\frac{2m}{1 + m^3}, \frac{2m^2}{1 + m^3} \right).$$

  By considering separately the intervals $(-1, \infty)$ and $(-\infty, -1)$, deduce that the folium looks something like the following.

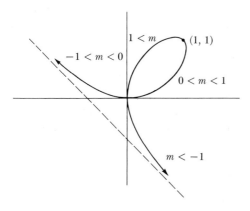

3. For $a > 0$ the set of (x, y) such that $y^2 = x^3/(2a - x)$ is a *cissoid* [ivy; that is, vinelike] *of Diocles*. Establish that this cissoid looks something like the following graph.

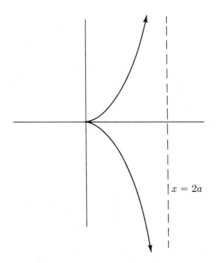

$x = 2a$

Hint: Either

$$y = \left(\frac{x^3}{2a - x}\right)^{1/2} \quad \text{or} \quad y = -\left(\frac{x^3}{2a - x}\right)^{1/2}.$$

4. For $a > 0$ the set of (x, y) such that $x^2 y = 4a^2(2a - y)$ is a *witch of Agnesi*. Establish that the witch looks something like the following.

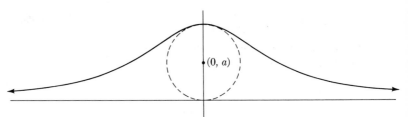

$(0, a)$

5. For $a > 0$ the set of (x, y) such that, for some real t,

$$x = a(t - \sin t) \quad \text{and} \quad y = a(1 - \cos t)$$

is a *cycloid*. Prove that the graph of a cycloid is the union of infinitely many congruent arches and has a vertical tangent at $(2n\pi, 0)$ for each integer n.

6. Let $F: t \longrightarrow (X(t), Y(t), Z(t))$ be a mapping of an interval I into $\Re^3$. Then F is continuous at c in I iff for each $\epsilon > 0$ there is some $\delta > 0$ such that

$$t \text{ in } I \text{ and } |t - c| < \delta \Rightarrow |F(t) - F(c)| < \epsilon.$$

Prove that F is continuous at c iff each of X, Y, Z is continuous at c.

7. Let F be a mapping of an interval I into $\Re^2$ or $\Re^3$ such that both F and its derivative F' are smooth. The second condition implies that F'' is continuous and that, for t in I, $F''(t) \neq (0, 0)$ or $(0, 0, 0)$.

For t in I let $\mathbf{F}(t)$, $\mathbf{F}'(t)$, $\mathbf{F}''(t)$ be respectively the vector from the origin to $F(t)$; the vector from $F(t)$ to $F(t) + F'(t)$; the vector from $F'(t)$ to $F'(t) + F''(t)$. If I is regarded as a time interval and F is physically reasonable, these three vectors are respectively the position vector, velocity vector, and acceleration vector of a classical particle which, at time t, is at the point $F(t)$. Note that the velocity vector is along the tangent to the curve which is the path of the particle; its length at t, $|F'(t)|$, is the *speed* at t.

a. For $r > 0$ let $F(t) = (r \cos t, r \sin t)$ for all t. Regarding the range of F as the path of a particle, prove that the speed is constant and that the acceleration vector is always directed toward the origin.

b. For positive a and b, discuss the velocity, speed, and acceleration of a particle which, at time t, is at $(a \cos t, b \sin t)$.

c. Discuss the motion of a particle which at time t is at $(\sin t, 2 \sin t, 3 \sin t)$.

8. From Chapter 5, if L is a line through the origin in $\Re^n$, each point of $\Re^n$ is a unique sum of a point on L and a point of the orthogonal complement of L. Use a translation to establish that the acceleration vector [Exercise 7] is uniquely the sum of a component along the tangent and a component orthogonal to the tangent. Do this specifically for parts **a**, **b**, **c** of Exercise 7.

9. For $g > 0$ discuss the motion of a particle which at time t is at $(\cos t, \sin t, -(g/2)t^2)$. Also discuss the motion of a particle which at time t is at $(t \cos t, t \sin t, -(g/2)t^2)$.

§ 7. *The Leibnitz Notation*

If f is (the graph of) a differentiable real function, we can let x and y be the restrictions of the usual coordinate variables to the curve f. Then for any (p, q) on f we have

$$x(p, q) = p,$$
$$y(p, q) = q = f(p) = f(x(p, q)).$$

Thus, with the understanding that the coordinate mappings x and y are restricted to f, we have $y = f \circ x$.

Now define a *slope variable* m on f by: for (p, q) on f,

$$m(p, q) = f'(p) = f'(x(p, q)).$$

This definition of m as a variable gives $m = f' \circ x$.

There is no upper bound to the number of geometrical and physical variables that can be defined this way. For example, suppose the curve f above to be the range of a smooth mapping $F: t \longrightarrow (X(t), Y(t))$. Furthermore, assume that X' and Y' are positive on some interval I.

Regard the curve f as the path of a particle, and, in addition to the variables x, y, and m defined above, consider the following. The time variable t: $t(p, q)$ = the time when the particle is at $(p, q) = F^{-1}(p, q)$. The *first velocity component* is v_x:

$$v_x(p, q) = X'(F^{-1}(p, q)).$$

If we further assume the existence of the second derivatives X'' and Y'', there is also an acceleration variable a:

$$a(p, q) = F''(F^{-1}(p, q)).$$

We have now several variables, each a mapping of the curve f into $\mathcal{R}$, related or connected in pairs by real functions. The functions X and Y are assumed to have positive derivatives and therefore to be strictly increasing and to have strictly increasing differentiable inverses. From $f = Y \circ X^{-1}$, f is strictly increasing and $f^{-1} = X \circ Y^{-1}$.

The Leibnitz notation has the great advantage of making applications of the chain rule and other theorems to functions such as those above look natural and obvious. Given two variables u and w and a differentiable function G such that $u = G \circ w$, define du/dw to mean $G' \circ w$.

Examples

1. Above we have $y = f \circ x$ and $x = f^{-1} \circ y$. Set $dy/dx = f' \circ x$ and $dx/dy = (f^{-1})' \circ y$. For each point (p, q) on f,

$$(f^{-1})'(q) = \frac{1}{f'(p)},$$

by the theorem on derivatives of inverses. Thus, for all (p, q) in the domain of the variables dy/dx and dx/dy,

$$\frac{dx}{dy}(p, q) = (f^{-1})'(y(p, q))$$

$$= (f^{-1})'(q) = \frac{1}{f'(p)}$$

$$= \frac{1}{f'(x(p, q))}$$

$$= \frac{1}{\dfrac{dy}{dx}(p, q)}.$$

Leibnitz's version of Theorem 10.14:

$$\frac{dx}{dy} = \frac{1}{\dfrac{dy}{dx}}.$$

2. Above we have $y = f \circ x$ and $x = X \circ t$. In the Leibnitz notation,

$$\frac{dy}{dx} = f' \circ x \qquad \text{and} \qquad \frac{dx}{dt} = X' \circ t.$$

We also have $y = (f \circ X) \circ t$, and therefore $dy/dt = (f \circ X)' \circ t$. By the Chain Rule, $(f \circ X)' = (f' \circ X)X'$. Thus

$$\frac{dy}{dt} = [(f' \circ X)X'] \circ t$$

$$= (f' \circ X \circ t)(X' \circ t).$$

Since $X \circ t = x$,

$$\frac{dy}{dt} = (f' \circ x)(X' \circ t) = \frac{dy}{dx}\frac{dx}{dt}.$$

Leibnitz's version of the chain rule:

$$\frac{dy}{dt} = \frac{dy}{dx}\frac{dx}{dt}.$$

3. For (p, q) on f, the slope at (p, q) is $f'(p)$. Also, if c is the number such that $F(c) = (p, q)$ [that is, if $c = t(p, q)$], then by Theorem 10.18 the slope is $Y'(c)/X'(c)$. Using the variables defined above and the Leibnitz notation, we have

$$m = \frac{dy}{dx} = \frac{\dfrac{dy}{dt}}{\dfrac{dx}{dt}}.$$

4. Let P be the *position variable* on the range of F. That is, let $P = F \circ t$ be the identity function on the curve f. Then $v = F' \circ t = dP/dt$, and

$$a = F'' \circ t = \frac{dv}{dt} = \frac{d}{dt}\frac{dP}{dt} = \frac{d^2P}{dt^2}.$$

More generally, if u and w are variables and there is a twice-differentiable real function g such that $u = g \circ w$, then the standard Leibnitz notation is

$$\frac{du}{dw} = g' \circ w, \qquad \frac{d^2u}{dw^2} = g'' \circ w.$$

Remarks: 1. The notation was developed long before any precise notion of what a function or a variable is. Usually one sees $u = f(w)$ rather than $u = f \circ w$.

2. Above we displayed the differentiable functions relating the variables explicitly in order to explain the use of the notation. Once you learn the usage there is no need to do this.

If $y = \sin^3 x$, then $dy/dx = 3 \sin^2 x \cos x$. Or set $\sin x = t$; then $y = t^3$ and $dy/dt = 3t^2$, and

$$\frac{dy}{dx} = \frac{dy}{dt}\frac{dt}{dx} = 3t^2 \cos x = 3 \sin^2 x \cos x.$$

If $x = \pi/4$, then $y = \sqrt{2}/4$ and $dy/dx = 3\sqrt{2}/4$. The last sentence is an abbreviation for: if $\mathbf{p}$ is a point on the underlying curve such that $x(\mathbf{p}) = \pi/4$, then $y(\mathbf{p}) = \sqrt{2}/4$ and $(dy/dx)(\mathbf{p}) = 3\sqrt{2}/4$. The domain of the variables x, y, dy/dx is, in this paragraph, the set of points (a, b) such that $b = \sin^3 a$. We cannot write $y(\pi/4)$ without introducing a confusing ambiguity.

Consider the following. For (a, b) in $\mathfrak{R}^2$ and $(a, b) \neq (0, 0)$ we have said [page 172] that r and θ are polar coordinates of (a, b) if $r = \sqrt{a^2 + b^2}$ and θ is any real number such that $\cos \theta = a/r$ and $\sin \theta = b/r$. To have polar coordinate mappings r and θ defined on $\mathfrak{R}^2 - \{(0, 0)\}$ it is necessary to restrict θ; for example, insist on $0 \leq \theta(a, b) < 2\pi$, for all $(a, b) \neq (0, 0)$.

It is more interesting in some contexts to put no restriction on θ or on r. For any real r and θ, $(r \cos \theta, r \sin \theta)$ is in $\mathfrak{R}^2$, and $|(r \cos \theta, r \sin \theta)| = |r|$. For $r > 0$ this point has polar coordinates r and θ. If $r < 0$, $|r|$ and $\theta + \pi$ are polar coordinates as previously defined.

Let f be a real function with a continuous derivative on an open interval I. The mapping $\theta \longrightarrow (f(\theta) \cos \theta, f(\theta) \sin \theta)$ maps I onto a curve which is said to have the *polar equation* $r = f(\theta)$.

As an example, for $a > 0$ the curve with polar equation $r = a\theta$ is a *spiral of Archimedes*. For all real θ, set $F(\theta) = (a\theta \cos \theta, a\theta \sin \theta)$. Then

$$F'(\theta) = a(\cos \theta - \theta \sin \theta, \sin \theta + \theta \cos \theta) \neq (0, 0).$$

On the spiral we have $x = a\theta \cos \theta$, $y = a\theta \sin \theta$; therefore

$$\frac{dx}{d\theta} = a(\cos \theta - \theta \sin \theta) \quad \text{and} \quad \frac{dy}{d\theta} = a(\sin \theta + \theta \cos \theta),$$

and, unless $dx/d\theta = 0$,

$$\frac{dy}{dx} = \frac{\dfrac{dy}{d\theta}}{\dfrac{dx}{d\theta}}.$$

Exercises

1. With notation as above, let C be the curve with polar equation $r = f(\theta)$. [Less idiomatically, but correctly, $r = f \circ \theta$.] Establish that, on C,

$$\frac{dx}{d\theta} = -r \sin \theta + \cos \theta \frac{dr}{d\theta}, \qquad \frac{dy}{d\theta} = r \cos \theta + \sin \theta \frac{dr}{d\theta},$$

and, at points where the denominator is not 0,

$$\frac{dy}{dx} = \frac{r \cos \theta + \sin \theta \dfrac{dr}{d\theta}}{-r \sin \theta + \cos \theta \dfrac{dr}{d\theta}}.$$

2. For each curve given below in polar coordinates, compute $dx/d\theta$, $dy/d\theta$, and dy/dx. Then sketch a graph of the curve.
a. $r = 5$.
b. $r = \theta$.
c. $r = \sin 3\theta$.
d. For some real k and positive e, $r = e|r \cos \theta - k|$. [*Hint:* On the plane the variable $|x - k|$ measures distance from the line $x = k$.]
e. $r = \sin 2\theta$.
f. $r = 3 \sec \theta$.
g. $r = \sin 4\theta$.

3. For a particle moving on the real line, two basic variables are the time variable t and the position variable x. With appropriate assumptions about differentiability, there are the velocity variable $v = dx/dt$ and the acceleration variable $a = dv/dt = d^2x/dt^2$. What additional assumptions, if any, are needed for $a = (dv/dx)(dx/dt) = v(dv/dx)$? The essentials appear in the special case $x = k \sin t$.

11

The Central Theorems of Calculus and Some Applications

§ 1. *The Mean Value Theorem*

Theorem 11.1 [*The Mean Value Theorem*]. If the real function f is differentiable on the open interval (a, b) and continuous at a and b, then there is at least one c in (a, b) such that

$$\frac{f(b) - f(a)}{b - a} = f'(c).$$

Theorem 11.2 [*Rolle's Theorem*]. If the real function f is differentiable on the open interval (a, b) and continuous at a and b, and furthermore $f(a) = f(b) = 0$, then there is at least one c in (a, b) with $f'(c) = 0$.

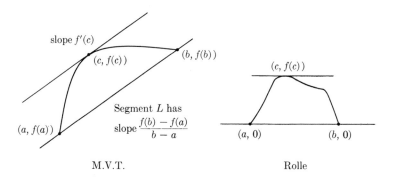

M.V.T.   Rolle

Rolle's Theorem is a special case of the Mean Value Theorem, stated by Michel Rolle in the late 17th century, before calculus could really be said to exist. Its geometric plausibility is compelling: if $f(a) = f(b)$ and the graph of f has a tangent at each point, then there must somewhere be a horizontal tangent.

PROOF OF ROLLE'S THEOREM: Since differentiability implies continuity, the hypotheses ensure that f is continuous on the closed interval $[a, b]$. The major theorems about functions continuous on closed intervals imply that f is bounded on $[a, b]$ and that, if m and M are respectively the glb and lub of $\{f(x)|a \le x \le b\}$, there are x_1 and x_2 in $[a, b]$ such that $f(x_1) = m$ and $f(x_2) = M$.

If $m = M$, then f is constant on $[a, b]$ and $f'(c) = 0$ for each c in (a, b).

If $m < M$, we may have $f(a) = f(b) = m$ or $f(a) = f(b) = M$, but not both. Hence at least one of the extreme values m and M is attained at an interior point c: either for some c in (a, b), $f(c) = m$, or for some c in (a, b), $f(c) = M$. In either case, $f'(c) = 0$.   ∎

PROOF OF THE MEAN VALUE THEOREM: The graph above at left suggests that, if $(c, f(c))$ is as far as possible from the segment L, then the tangent at $(c, f(c))$ is parallel to L. The graph below suggests that maximizing the perpendicular distance from L to f is equivalent to maximizing the vertical distance from L to f.

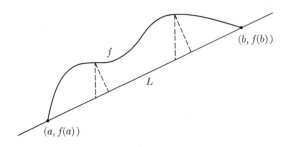

Motivated by this, for x in $[a, b]$ set

$$L(x) = f(a) + \frac{f(b) - f(a)}{b - a} (x - a),$$

and set $V(x) = f(x) - L(x)$.

The graph of L is the segment from $(a, f(a))$ to $(b, f(b))$, of slope $(f(b) - f(a))/(b - a)$. For $a < x < b$,

$$L'(x) = \frac{f(b) - f(a)}{b - a}.$$

Since both f and L are differentiable on (a, b) and continuous at a and b, V is differentiable on (a, b) and continuous at a and b. Furthermore, $V(a) = V(b) = 0$.

By Rolle's Theorem, there is some c in the open interval (a, b), with $V'(c) = 0$. But $V'(c) = f'(c) - L'(c)$, and

$$f'(c) = L'(c) = \frac{f(b) - f(a)}{b - a}.$$ ∎

Corollary to the Mean Value Theorem. If the real function f is differentiable on an open interval I and a and b are in I, with $a \neq b$, then

$$\frac{f(b) - f(a)}{b - a} = f'(c)$$

for some c between a and b.

PROOF: Since f is differentiable on I, f is continuous at a and b and differentiable on (a, b) or (b, a), as the case may be.

Since

$$\frac{f(b) - f(a)}{b - a} = \frac{f(a) - f(b)}{a - b},$$

the Mean Value Theorem gives the result regardless of the order of a and b. ∎

Sample Application: Suppose a real function f is continuous at a and b and that $f'(x) > 0$ for all x in the open interval (a, b). Then, by several theorems in the last chapter, f is strictly increasing on the closed interval $[a, b]$.

This can be proved immediately from the Mean Value Theorem and its corollary. Suppose $a \leq x_1 < x_2 \leq b$. Then, for some c between x_1 and x_2,

$$\frac{f(x_2) - f(x_1)}{x_2 - x_1} = f'(c),$$

and $f(x_2) = f(x_1) + (x_2 - x_1)f'(c)$. Since both $x_2 - x_1 > 0$ and $f'(c) > 0$, $f(x_2) > f(x_1)$.

The next theorem is interesting because it implies that if a derivative fails to be continuous at some point of its domain, then the discontinuity must be quite complicated. In particular, a step function cannot be a derivative and neither can the function shown below.

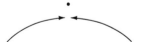

Theorem 11.3. If the real function f is differentiable on an open interval I, then its derivative f' has the intermediate value property on I.

PROOF: Let a and b be in I, with $a < b$ and $f'(a) \neq f'(b)$. We must prove that, if k is between $f'(a)$ and $f'(b)$, then there is some c between a and b with $f'(c) = k$.

Define two functions F and G on the closed interval $[a, b]$ as follows:

$$F(a) = f'(a) \qquad \text{and} \qquad G(b) = f'(b).$$

For $a < x \leq b$,

$$F(x) = \frac{f(x) - f(a)}{x - a},$$

and for $a \leq x < b$,

$$G(x) = \frac{f(x) - f(b)}{x - b}.$$

Then F is continuous on the half-open interval $(a, b]$ because it is a quotient of continuous functions, and F is continuous at a because $\lim_{x \to a} F(x) = f'(a) = F(a)$. Similarly, G is continuous on $[a, b]$.

By the Intermediate Value Theorem for continuous functions, every number between

$$F(a) = f'(a) \quad \text{and} \quad F(b) = \frac{f(b) - f(a)}{b - a}$$

is in the range of F. And every number between

$$G(a) = \frac{f(b) - f(a)}{b - a} \qquad \text{and} \qquad G(b) = f'(b)$$

is in the range of G.

Therefore, if k is between $f'(a)$ and $f'(b)$, either there is some d in (a, b) with $F(d) = k$, or there is some d' in (a, b) with $G(d') = k$; both may be the case.

However,

$$F(d) = \frac{f(d) - f(a)}{d - a} = f'(c_1)$$

for some c_1 in (a, d), by the Mean Value Theorem, and

$$G(d') = \frac{f(d') - f(b)}{d' - b} = f'(c_2)$$

for some c_2 in (d', b), by the Mean Value Theorem. In either case, $k = f'(c)$ for some c in (a, b). ∎

Exercises

1. For $f(x) = x^2 + x$, find all c between 1 and 3 such that $f(3) - f(1) = 2f'(c)$.
2. Prove that if f has a second derivative f'', and f'' is positive on an interval (a, b), then there is at most one c in (a, b) such that

   $$f(b) - f(a) = (b - a)f'(c).$$

3. Use Rolle's Theorem and mathematical induction to prove that a polynomial equation of degree n cannot have more than n real roots.
4. Use the Mean Value Theorem to find an approximation to $\sqrt{101}$. [*Hint:* Consider $\sqrt{101} - \sqrt{100}$.]
5. Find an approximation to $\sqrt[3]{1002}$.

§ 2. *The Fundamental Theorem of Calculus*

Many mathematicians from the time of Archimedes to the 17th century succeeded in solving isolated problems in geometry or physics by ad hoc attacks which in effect calculated certain integrals and derivatives. However, it is Newton (1642–1727) and Leibnitz (1646–1716) who are credited with discovering and making explicit the relation between integration and differentiation. There were disputes among their followers as to which man deserved the more credit. Current opinion is that they independently and more or less simultaneously penetrated to the heart of what many of their contemporaries or immediate predecessors were struggling with. Newton said that if he had seen far it was because he stood on the shoulders of giants. No one person can be regarded as the author of the two assertions which comprise the theorem of this section.

Theorem 11.4 [*The Fundamental Theorem of Calculus*]. 1. If a and b are numbers in an interval over which the derivative F' is integrable, then

$$\int_a^b F' = F(b) - F(a).$$

2. Let the real function f be continuous on an open interval I. For a in I, define the function F_a by: for x in I, $F_a(x) = \int_a^x f$. Then F_a is differentiable, and, on I, $F'_a = f$.

Corollary to Theorem 11.4. If a and b are in an interval on which the function f is continuous, then there are functions F such that $F' = f$; for any such F,

$$\int_a^b f = F(b) - F(a).$$

PROOFS: Assume $\int_a^b F'$ exists. If $\int_a^b F' = F(b) - F(a)$, then

$$\int_b^a F' = -\int_a^b F' = F(a) - F(b).$$

Trivially, $\int_a^a F' = 0 = F(a) - F(a)$. To prove statement 1, then, we can assume $a < b$ and $\int_a^b F'$ exists.

Let $p = \{x_0, \ldots, x_n\}$ be a partition of $[a, b]$. If, for example, $n = 3$,

$$F(b) - F(a) = F(x_3) - F(x_0)$$
$$= F(x_1) - F(x_0) + F(x_2) - F(x_1) + F(x_3) - F(x_2).$$

Similarly, for any n,

(1) $$F(b) - F(a) = \sum_{i=1}^n [F(x_i) - F(x_{i-1})].$$

By the Mean Value Theorem, for each i there is some c_i in the open interval (x_{i-1}, x_i) such that

(2) $F(x_i) - F(x_{i-1}) = [x_i - x_{i-1}]F'(c_i).$

Let $\underline{S}(p)$ and $\overline{S}(p)$ be the lower and upper sums associated with the partition p and $\int_a^b F'$. By Equations (1) and (2),

$\underline{S}(p) \leq F(b) - F(a) \leq \overline{S}(p).$

From the definition and assumed existence of the integral,

$\underline{S}(p) \leq \int_a^b F' \leq \overline{S}(p).$

Therefore, for every partition p,

$$\left| F(b) - F(a) - \int_a^b F' \right| \leq \overline{S}(p) - \underline{S}(p).$$

By the theorem on the necessary and sufficient condition for the existence of the integral, for each $\epsilon > 0$ there is a partition p_ϵ with $\overline{S}(p_\epsilon) - \underline{S}(p_\epsilon) < \epsilon$. Consequently, for every $\epsilon > 0$,

$$\left| F(b) - F(a) - \int_a^b F' \right| < \epsilon.$$

To prove statement 2, assume f continuous on an open interval I, and, for a and x in I, set $F_a(x) = \int_a^x f$. For any c and x in I, with $x \neq c$,

$$F_a(x) - F_a(c) = \int_a^x f - \int_a^c f = \int_c^x f = (x - c)f(c_x),$$

for some c_x between c and x, by the Mean Value Theorem for integrals of continuous functions.

By the continuity of f at c,

$$\lim_{x \to c} \frac{F_a(x) - F_a(c)}{x - c} = f(c). \qquad \blacksquare$$

A principal and immediate application of the Fundamental Theorem is that it turns every formula for a derivative into a formula for an integral.

Examples

1. Consider $\int_0^1 xe^{x^2}\, dx$. If $F(x) = e^{x^2}$, then $F'(x) = 2xe^{x^2}$. Thus

$$\int_0^1 xe^{x^2}\, dx = \frac{1}{2}\int_0^1 2xe^{x^2}\, dx = \frac{1}{2}\int_0^1 F'$$

$$= \frac{1}{2}[F(1) - F(0)] = \frac{1}{2}[e - 1].$$

2. $\displaystyle\int_0^{\pi/2} \sin^2 \cos = \int_0^{\pi} F', \text{ if } F = \frac{1}{3}\sin^3;$

$\displaystyle\int_0^{\pi/2} \sin^2 \cos = \frac{1}{3}\sin^3 \frac{\pi}{2} - \frac{1}{3}\sin^3 0 = \frac{1}{3}.$

3. Let f be continuous on $\mathfrak{R}$ and $F' = f$. For any numbers, a, b, m, k,

$$\int_{ma+k}^{mb+k} f = F(mb + k) - F(ma + k).$$

Now consider $\displaystyle\int_a^b f(mx + k)m\,dx$. If $G(x) = F(mx + k)$, then

$G'(x) = mF'(mx + k) = mf(mx + k).$

By the Fundamental Theorem,

$$\int_a^b f(mx + k)m\,dx = \int_a^b G' = G(b) - G(a)$$
$$= F(mb + k) - F(ma + k).$$

Our previous proof that $\displaystyle\int_a^b f(mx + k)m\,dx = \int_{ma+k}^{mb+k} f$ was considerably longer.

4. Let f be continuous on $\mathfrak{R}$ and $F' = f$. For x in $\mathfrak{R}$ set $G(x) = \displaystyle\int_0^{x^3} f$. By the Fundamental Theorem, $G(x) = F(x^3) - F(0)$. For all x,

$G'(x) = F'(x^3)3x^2 = 3x^2 f(x).$

In particular, if $G(x) = \displaystyle\int_0^{x^3} t\sin^2 t\,dt$, then

$G'(x) = 3x^2 x \sin^2 x = 3x^3 \sin^2 x.$

We need to know that there is a function F such that $F'(t) = t\sin^2 t$, but for this problem we need not know anything else about F.

Exercises

1. Use the Fundamental Theorem to evaluate each integral below.

a. $\displaystyle\int_0^b \cos.$

b. $\displaystyle\int_0^b x^3\,dx.$

c. $\displaystyle\int_0^1 e^x\,dx.$

d. $\displaystyle\int_5^{10} \frac{1}{x-3}\,dx.$

e. $\displaystyle\int_5^{10} \frac{3}{x-3}\,dx.$

f. $\displaystyle\int_0^1 \frac{2u}{1+u^2}\,du.$

g. $\displaystyle\int_{-3}^{-1} \frac{u}{1+u^2}\,du.$

h. $\displaystyle\int_0^\pi \cos \frac{t}{10}\, dt.$

i. $\displaystyle\int_1^4 \sqrt{x}\, dx.$

j. $\displaystyle\int_1^4 \frac{1}{\sqrt{x}}\, dx.$

2. If $f(0) = 1$ and $f(t) = \sin t/t$ for $t \neq 0$, f is continuous on $\mathcal{R}$. Define G on $\mathcal{R}$ by

$$G(x) = \int_x^{x^2} \frac{\sin t}{t}\, dt = \int_x^{x^2} f.$$

Prove that, for all x,

$$G'(x) = 2xf(x^2) - f(x).$$

Sketch the graph of G over the interval $[-\sqrt{\pi}, \sqrt{\pi}]$. Without using the derivative, explain why, from the definition of G, it is obvious that $G(x)$ is negative for $0 < x < 1$.

The symbol $\int$ has three empty spots. If two of them are filled, we get a symbol which is a natural name for a function. For example, for $a < b$, let $C[a, b]$ be the set of all real functions continuous on the interval $[a, b]$. Then $C[a, b]$ is closed under addition and under multiplication by scalars, and is a linear space over $\mathcal{R}$.

Let $\int_a^b$ be the mapping which assigns to each function f in $C[a, b]$ the number $\int_a^b f$ in $\mathcal{R}$. For f and g in $C[a, b]$ and k in $\mathcal{R}$, $\int_a^b (f + g) = \int_a^b f + \int_a^b g$, and $\int_a^b kf = k \int_a^b f$. That is, $\int_a^b$ is a linear operator mapping $C[a, b]$ into $\mathcal{R}$.

Alternatively, let I be an open interval and a a number in I, and let $C(I)$ be the set of all real functions continuous on I. For f in $C(I)$, consider the symbol $\int_a f$. This is a rather natural name for the function which assigns to x in I the number $\int_a^x f$. That is, $\int_a f$ is a natural name for the function called F_a in the Fundamental Theorem.

For example, $\int_0 \cos = \sin$. For all x, $\int_0^x \cos = \sin x$. And $\int_{\pi/2} \cos = \sin - 1$. For all x, $\int_{\pi/2}^x \cos = \sin x - 1$.

With a and I as above, for each f in $C(I)$, $\int_a f$ is a function which is also in $C(I)$. Thus we can now give a meaning to $\int_a$. Namely, $\int_a$ is the mapping which assigns to each function f in $C(I)$ the function $\int_a f$ in $C(I)$. Thus $\int_a$ is a mapping of $C(I)$ into $C(I)$.

If I is an open interval, then $C(I)$ is a linear space over $\mathfrak{R}$. And, for any a in I, $\int_a$ is a *linear* operator mapping $C(I)$ into $C(I)$.

The linearity is easily proved. For x in I and f and g in $C(I)$,

$$\int_a^x [f + g] = \int_a^x f + \int_a^x g.$$

Since this equation holds for all x in I,

$$\int_a [f + g] = \int_a f + \int_a g.$$

Similarly, for any scalar k, $\int_a kf = k \int_a f$.

With I and a as above, let $C'(I)$ be the set of all real functions which have continuous derivatives on I. Let D be the differentiating operator restricted to $C'(I)$: for F in $C'(I)$, $DF = F'$ in $C(I)$.

Statement 2 of the Fundamental Theorem asserts that, for each a in I and each f in $C(I)$, $D \int_a f = f$. For each a in I, $D \circ \int_a$ is the identity map on $C(I)$, and $\int_a$ is a right inverse for a restriction of D.

We know from the theorem on the kernel of D that, if $DF = DG$ on I, then $F - G$ is constant on I. Hence it must be that for a and b in I the functions $\int_a f$ and $\int_b f$ must differ by a constant. In fact, for x in I,

$$\int_a^x f - \int_b^x f = \int_a^b f,$$

and $\int_a f - \int_b f$ is the constant $\int_a^b f$.

Statement 1 of the Fundamental Theorem implies that, if F is in $C'(I)$, then, for x in I,

$$\int_a^x DF = F(x) - F(a).$$

Thus $\int_a DF = F$ iff $F(a) = 0$.

Everything now fits together quite neatly. Let I be an open interval and a a number in I. Let $C(I)$ be the set of functions continuous on I. Let $C'_a(I)$ be the set of functions F such that F has a continuous derivative on I, *and* $F(a) = 0$. Let D be the differentiating operator restricted to $C'_a(I)$.

If F and G are in $C'_a(I)$ and $DF = DG$, then $F - G$ is constant. But $F(a) - G(a) = 0$; thus, with D restricted to $C'_a(I)$, $DF = DG$ implies $F = G$, and D is a one-to-one mapping of $C'_a(I)$ into $C(I)$.

For f in $C(I)$, $\int_a f$ is in $C'_a(I)$ because (1) by the Fundamental Theorem, $\int_a f$ has a continuous derivative on I; (2) $\int_a f$ maps a to $\int_a^a f = 0$. And, since $D \int_a f = f$, D is a one-to-one mapping of $C'_a(I)$ onto $C(I)$.

Finally with D restricted to $C'_a(I)$, $\int_a$ is both the right inverse and the left inverse of D.

The Fundamental Theorem is slightly stronger than the content of the last paragraph, because the hypothesis for $\int_a^b F' = F(b) - F(a)$ is merely the existence of the integral rather than the continuity of F'. But the last paragraph, in its context, summarizes the algebraic essence of the Fundamental Theorem.

Exercises

1. For b, a number in an open interval I, give a reasonable meaning to $\int^b$ and discuss the properties of $\int^b$.

2. For a in an open interval I, let $K'_a(I)$ be the set of functions F such that F' is continuous on I and $F'(a) = 3$. Point out ways in which K'_a is significantly similar to, or different from, the set $C'_a(I)$ defined in the text.

3. Let S and T be sets of functions. For f and g in T let $f \equiv g$ modulo S mean $f - g$ is in S. Under what circumstances is congruence modulo S an equivalence relation in T?

§ 3. *Two Differential Equations*

The title dates from the time when a derivative was known as a "differential coefficient." Differential equations are equations involving functions and their derivatives. Some typical problems are these.

1. Find all real functions f such that
$$f'' - 3f' + 2f = \sin.$$

2. Find all real functions f such that, for all x,
$$x^2 f'(x) + \sin x\, f(x) = e^x \qquad \text{and} \qquad f(0) = 1.$$

3. Find all real functions f such that, for all x,
$$f'(x) = e^{-x^2} \qquad \text{and} \qquad f(0) = 0.$$

4. Find all real functions h such that, for all x,
$$h'(x) = x \qquad \text{and} \qquad h(0) = 0.$$

Examples 3 and 4 are, from one point of view, very similar. Given a continuous function g, one is asked to find functions f such that $f' = g$ and, for some numbers x_0 and y_0, $f(x_0) = y_0$.

Such a problem has, on an interval containing x_0, a unique solution. For x in an interval on which g is continuous, let $f(x) = \int_{x_0}^x g + y_0$. Then

$f' = g$, and $f(x_0) = 0 + y_0 = y_0$. If $F' = g$, then $F - f$ is a constant; if also $F(x_0) = y_0$, the constant is 0 and $F = f$. Thus the respective solutions to Examples 3 and 4 are

$$f(x) = \int_0^x e^{-t^2}\, dt \quad \text{and} \quad h(x) = \int_0^x t\, dt.$$

In one sense these two formulas completely solve the associated problems. In another sense we are still left with two "puzzle problems." Is h an elementary function? Is f an elementary function?

For h the puzzle is very easy: for all x, $h(x) = x^2/2$. For f the puzzle is not easy: we state without proof that there is no elementary function f such that $f'(x) = e^{x^2}$ for all x. Just as the equation $\ln x = \int_0^x (1/t)\, dt$ defines the natural logarithm, so does the equation $f(x) = \int_0^x e^{-t^2}\, dt$ define f as a new function which can be studied, tabulated, graphed, and so on. [See Exercises 1 and 2 below.]

One of the two problems to be considered in detail in this section is to find the *eigenfunctions* or *characteristic functions* of the linear operator D. Here f is a characteristic function of D if, for some real $\lambda \neq 0$, $Df = \lambda f$.

Since the exponential function is its own derivative, exp is a characteristic function of D corresponding to the characteristic value $1: D \exp = 1 \exp$. More generally, for each real λ let $\exp_\lambda (x) = e^{\lambda x}$, for all real x. Then $D \exp_\lambda = \lambda \exp_\lambda$, and $\exp_\lambda$ is a characteristic function belonging to λ.

Since D is one of the basic linear operators, it is mathematically reasonable to single out this problem as an important one. It is also important in studying theoretical models for growths of populations. Here "population" refers to a large but finite set of a reasonably homogeneous nature. For example, the people living in Ohio, or the rats in New York City, or the bacteria in a test tube, or the liquid assets of Mr. Manybucks.

Let $P(t)$ be the size of the population at time t. If Δt is neither too small nor too large, it seems a reasonable assumption that $P(t + \Delta t) - P(t)$, the change in the population over the time interval Δt, should be proportional to Δt and proportional to $P(t)$.

Suppose, for example, the population of a city is currently 1,000,000 and is increasing at the rate of about 1,000 people per month. It is reasonable to assume that the average rate of increase is also about 250 per week or 12,000 per year. But similar assumptions about the change in population per century or per second are less plausible for centuries, and probably untestable for seconds. This is the argument for the change being proportional to Δt for Δt reasonable in size. The argument for proportionality to $P(t)$ is also plausible. Suppose the population of our city increases to 1,100,000. If this does not in itself produce any appreciable change in living conditions, then one would expect the population to be increasing at about 1,100 people per month. A 10% increase in the population should—other things being equal—produce a 10% increase in the monthly number of births, deaths, and other arrivals and departures.

At this point in the discussion a philosopher might raise the question of whether there is an exact instant at which a foetus becomes a person, or a person becomes a corpse, or a cell divides into two cells. An affirmative answer leads to a model in which the population-counting function is a step function. A scientist or applied mathematician, if he is looking for a theoretical model that predicts the size of a large population which can never be counted exactly at any instant, goes to the opposite extreme and assumes the existence of a differentiable function P such that at time t the population is likely to be approximately $P(t)$.

He is then led, from the discussion above, to the hypothesis that there is some constant λ depending on the particular population such that, for each t in some interval and for all Δt, he has

$$P(t + \Delta t) - P(t) = \lambda P(t)\, \Delta t + E(t, \Delta t),$$

where, for each t, $\lim_{\Delta t \to 0} E(t, \Delta t)/\Delta t = 0$.

From this immediately follows $P'(t) = \lambda P(t)$. Or, in Leibnitz's notation, $dP/dt = \lambda P$. The theory of this differential equation is easily worked out once we have

> **Theorem 11.5.** Let λ be a real number and I an open interval. If the function f has the property that, for all t in I, $f'(t) = \lambda f(t)$, then either $f(t) = 0$ for all t in L, or $f(t) > 0$ for all t in I, or $f(t) < 0$ for all t in I.

PROOF: First we show that the assumption that there are a and c in I, with $f(a) \neq 0$ but $f(c) = 0$, leads to a contradiction. The hypothesis that f is differentiable on I implies that f is continuous on I. Thus if $f(a) \neq 0$, a is in an open interval J such that, for t in J, $f(t)$ has the same sign as $f(a)$.

Suppose now $f(c) = 0$ for some c in I, and, as one of two possibilities, assume $a < c$. Let S be the set of d in I such that, for t in the half-open interval $[a, d)$, $f(t)$ has the same sign as $f(a)$. Then S is not empty because any d in J with $d > a$ is in S. Also, S has c as an upper bound: let b be the least upper bound of S.

By continuity, both $f(b) > 0$ and $f(b) < 0$ contradict the definition of b, and we must have $f(b) = 0$.

For t in the half-open interval $[a, b)$, $|f(t)| > 0$. By the Intermediate Value Theorem, for each number k in the half-open interval $(0, |f(a)|]$ there is some t in $[a, b)$ with $|f(t)| = k$.

For t in $[a, b)$ set $g(t) = \ln |f(t)|$. Since ln is unbounded on $(0, |f(a)|]$, g is unbounded on $[a, b)$.

However, g is differentiable on (a, b). In fact, for t in (a, b),

$$g'(t) = \frac{f'(t)}{f(t)} = \lambda.$$

We have come to the absurd result that g, whose graph is a finite line segment of slope λ, is unbounded. For a nongeometric contradiction, the Mean Value Theorem provides a bound: for t in (a, b), $g(t) - g(a) = (t - a)g'(t_a)$, and

$$|g(t)| < |g(a) + \lambda(b - a)| \leq |g(a)| + |\lambda|(b - a).$$

We conclude then that, if there is some a in I with $f(a) \neq 0$, then, for each t in I, $f(t) \neq 0$. If there were b in I with $f(b)$ of opposite sign to $f(a)$, then there would be some c between a and b with $f(c) = 0$. This proves that, if f is positive [negative] at one point in I, then f is positive [negative] at every point in I. ∎

Theorem 11.6. Let λ be a real number and I an open interval. If the function f has the property that, for all t in I, $f'(t) = \lambda f(t)$, then there is a constant c such that $f(t) = ce^{\lambda t}$ for all t in I.

PROOF: 1. The constant function 0 satisfies the differential equation, and $0 = 0e^{\lambda t}$ for all t in I.

2. If f satisfies the differential equation and is not the 0 function, then, by Theorem 11.5, f is either strictly positive or strictly negative on I.

Set $g = \ln |f|$ and we have $g' = f'/f = \lambda$ on I. Consequently there is some constant k such that $g(t) = \lambda t + k$ for all t in I. It follows from this and $g = \ln |f|$ that $|f(t)| = e^{\lambda t + k} = e^k e^{\lambda t}$ for all t in I. Since f cannot change sign on I, either $f(t) = e^k e^{\lambda t}$ for all t in I, or $f(t) = -e^k e^{\lambda t}$ for all t in I. ∎

Corollary to Theorem 11.6. If $f'(t) = \lambda f(t)$ for all t, and $f(t_0) = c_0$, then, for all t, $f(t) = c_0 e^{\lambda(t - t_0)}$.

PROOF: Set $g(t) = f(t + t_0)$. Then, for all t,

$$g'(t) = f'(t + t_0) = \lambda f(t + t_0) = \lambda g(t).$$

By Theorem 11.6, there is a constant c such that, for all t, $g(t) = ce^{\lambda t}$. From the last equation, $c = g(0)$; from the definition of g, $g(0) = f(t_0) = c_0$. Thus, for all t, $g(t) = c_0 e^{\lambda t}$. And, for all t,

$$f(t) = g(t - t_0) = c_0 e^{\lambda(t - t_0)}. \quad ∎$$

Remark: For application to problems of population growth there is no need to insist on using e as a base. For $\lambda \neq 0$ we can, for example, set $\lambda = k \ln 10$. Then

$$e^{\lambda t} = e^{(k \ln 10)t} = (e^{\ln 10})^{kt} = 10^{kt}.$$

This might be more convenient in some applications. To a banker the natural base is $1 + r$, where r is the going interest rate. An initial capital of \$$A_0$ collects \$$rA_0$ interest in one year. Unless a profligate spends the interest, the capital is now \$$A_1 =$ \$$A_0(1 + r)$. It is easily verified that if the interest is always reinvested, then for any positive integer n the capital after n years is \$$A_n$, where $A_n = A_0(1 + r)^n$. This of course assumes a stable economy with a constant interest rate.

The problem of finding the characteristic functions of D is closely associated with another problem. For real λ we can consider $D - \lambda$ as an operator defined by: for differentiable f, $(D - \lambda)f = f' - \lambda f$. For example, $(D - 3)\sin = \cos - 3\sin$.

For I an open interval, the restriction of $D - \lambda$ to $C'(I)$ is a linear operator on $C'(I)$, and its kernel is the set of functions f in $C'(I)$ such that $(D - \lambda)f$ is the 0 function on I. Thus the kernel of $D - \lambda$ is the set of characteristic functions of D corresponding to the characteristic value λ. From Theorem 11.6, the kernel of $D - \lambda$ is the set of all scalar multiples of $\exp_\lambda$: $t \longrightarrow e^{\lambda t}$.

Example

Solve the differential equation

$$\frac{dy}{dx} - 5y = e^x.$$

If $y = f(x)$ or $y = f \circ x$, the equation is satisfied iff $f' - 5f = \exp$ or $(D - 5)f = \exp$.

By inspection, $(D - 5)(-\frac{1}{4}\exp) = -\frac{1}{4}\exp + \frac{5}{4}\exp = \exp$.

The kernel of $D - 5$ is the set of scalar multiples of $\exp_5$.

In Leibnitz's notation, which reads more smoothly here, one particular solution is

$$y_p = -\tfrac{1}{4}e^x.$$

The kernel is the set of all functions ce^{5x} for constant c. Then y is a solution of the equation iff, for some constant c,

$$y = -\tfrac{1}{4}e^x + ce^{5x}.$$

Exercises

1. For each positive integer n, set $I_n = \int_{-n}^0 e^{-t^2}\,dt$.

a. Prove that the sequence $\{I_n\}$ is monotone increasing and bounded. [*Hint for boundedness:* For $n > 1$, $\int_{-n}^{-1} e^{-t^2}\,dt < \int_{-n}^{-1} e^{-t}\,dt$.]

b. Let B be the least upper bound of the sequence above. Prove that for $\epsilon > 0$ there is a positive integer n_ϵ such that, if $x < -n_\epsilon$, then

$$\left| \int_x^0 e^{-t^2}\,dt - B \right| < \epsilon.$$

2. The number B of Exercise 1 is, by definition, $\int_{-\infty}^0 e^{-t^2}\,dt$. Let F be defined by: for all x,

$$F(x) = \frac{1}{2B} \int_{-\infty}^x e^{-t^2}\,dt.$$

It is known that $2B = \sqrt{\pi}$, and this function F is a tabulated function of importance in statistics. If $f(x) = \int_0^x e^{-t^2}\,dt$, give f in terms of F.

3. Give the complete solution of each differential equation below.

a. $\dfrac{dy}{dx} + 6y = 0.$

b. $\dfrac{dy}{dx} + 6y = e^{2x}.$

c. $\dfrac{dy}{dx} + 6y = \sin x.$

d. $\dfrac{dy}{dx} + 6y = x.$

e. $\dfrac{dy}{dx} + 6y = e^{-6x}.$ [*Hint:* For appropriate k, kxe^{-6x} is a solution.]

f. $\dfrac{dy}{dx} + 6y = x + \sin x + e^{2x}.$

g. $\dfrac{dy}{dx} + 6y = e^{5x}.$

h. $\dfrac{dy}{dx} + 6y = \cos 5x.$

i. $\dfrac{dy}{dx} + 6y = x^2.$

4. Suppose a piece of matter to be decaying, or shrinking, in such a way that at time t its mass is given by $M(t) = M_0 10^{-0.01t}$, where time is measured in years. If $10^{-0.3} = \frac{1}{2}$, which is approximately correct, then $M(30) = \frac{1}{2}M_0$. Show that over any stretch of 30 years the mass decreases by a factor of $\frac{1}{2}$. The *half-life* of the piece of matter is 30 years.

5. If the going yearly interest rate on savings deposits is r, a bank anxious to build up deposits may decide to compound interest quarterly. This changes the annual growth factor from $1 + r$ to $(1 + (r/4))^4 > 1 + r$. A competing bank may decide to compound monthly, or even weekly or daily. The ultimate is to compound continuously, which means to replace $1 + r$ by $\lim \{(1 + (r/n))^n\}$. Show that the limit is e^r. [*Hint:* Start by considering the sequence $\{n \ln (1 + (r/n))\}$.

  Numerical Note: $(1.01)^4 = 1.0406$, and $e^{.04} = 1.0408$, correct to 5 significant figures. Thus \$1,000 in a savings bank for a year at 4% will collect interest of \$40 with no compounding, \$40.60 with quarterly compounding, and \$40.80 if the interest is compounded continuously. The difference hardly seems enough to make one change banks.

  However, \$1,000 left in the bank for 25 years at 4% will grow to about \$2,666 if the interest is compounded yearly, but to about \$2,705 if the interest is compounded quarterly.

  The final two Exercises constitute a short course on Victorian ethics and finance.

6. Assume stable families A and B living in a no-income-tax and no-inheritance-tax economy assumed to be stable for many years to come. Assume each family has \$10,000 it does not need to spend and that a prudent investor can count on a 6% annual return. Family A decides to spend its \$600 a year income from the capital on luxuries. Family B decides to reinvest all income from the capital. Under these assumptions family A will always have \$10,000 capital and \$600 a year income for luxuries. Since

$$2.01 < (1.06)^{12} < 2.02,$$

B's capital will double every 12 years, or slightly less, and, let us say, quadruple every generation.

How many generations does it take to get B's income from the capital (all to be reinvested, of course) up to \$10,000 a year? How many additional generations to get the income up to \$10,000 a week? \$10,000 an hour?

7. Suppose a spendthrift family spends all its current income and 5% of its capital every year. What is the half-life of the family capital?

The general ordinary linear second-order differential equation is

(1) $$a(t) \frac{dx^2}{dt^2} + b(t) \frac{dx}{dt} + c(t)x = F(t),$$

where the functions a, b, c, F are continuous on some interval. The problem is to find functions f such that, if $x = f \circ t$, then the equation holds. This means finding f such that

(2) $$af'' + bf' + cf = F.$$

Equation (1), or its equivalent (2), is of great importance in parts of classical mechanics and in parts of the theory of electricity. In mechanics t is the time variable, x a position variable, and the coefficients have physical units such that (1) equates two forces. The simplest case is $m(d^2x/dt^2) = F(t)$, where m is mass.

We shall consider the equation only for constant a, b, c. If $a = 0$ but $b \neq 0$, Equation (2) reduces to

$$\left(D + \frac{c}{b}\right)f = \frac{F}{b},$$

which has already been discussed. For $a \neq 0$ we can divide through by a, rename the resulting coefficients, and consider

(2') $$f'' + bf' + cf = F,$$

which we rewrite in the form

(3) $$(D^2 + bD + c)f = F.$$

Here D^2 means $D \circ D$, and in this section we shall write compositions of operators as products. The sum and product (composition) of linear operators is linear, and $L = D^2 + bD + c$ is a linear operator on $C''(I)$, the set of functions with continuous second derivatives on an open interval I.

The attack on (3) is now clear. We need to find the kernel of L and also find one function f such that $Lf = F$.

Example

Consider $(D^2 + 3D + 2)f = \sin$. It is reasonable to guess that there is a solution of the form $a \sin + b \cos$; then

$$(D^2 + 3D + 2)(a \sin + b \cos) = (a - 3b) \sin + (3a + b) \cos,$$

and we want $3a + b = 0$ and $a - 3b = 1$: one solution to the equation is $\frac{1}{10} \sin - \frac{3}{10} \cos$.

Now for the kernel. If D were a number we would have

$$D^2 + 3D + 2 = (D + 1)(D + 2) = (D + 2)(D + 1).$$

For any twice-differentiable function f,

$$\begin{aligned}(D + 1)(D + 2)f &= (D + 1)(f' + 2f)\\ &= f'' + 2f' + f' + 2f\\ &= (D^2 + 3D + 2)f.\end{aligned}$$

Similarly, $(D + 2)(D + 1) = D^2 + 3D + 2$.

Because there are no standard names for functions such as $x \longrightarrow e^{3x}$ or $t \longrightarrow \sin 5t$, we shall use a modified Liebnitz-like notation with a subscript on D. Agree, for example, that

$$D_x(e^{3x} + x^2) = 3e^{3x} + 2x,$$

and $D_t \sin 8t = 8 \cos 8t$. We shall also use "the function e^{3x}" as an abbreviation for "the function mapping x to e^{3x} for all real x."

Now, $(D_x + 1)e^{-x} = 0$, and

$$(D_x + 2)(D_x + 1)e^{-x} = (D_x + 2)0 = 0.$$

Also, $(D_x + 1)(D_x + 2)e^{-2x} = (D_x + 1)0 = 0$.

The kernel of a linear operator is a linear space, and every linear combination of functions in the kernel is in the kernel. Thus the kernel of $D_x^2 + 3D_x + 2$ includes the set of all $c_1e^{-x} + c_2e^{-2x}$ for constants c_1 and c_2. We shall shortly prove that this set *is* the kernel. It follows that y is a solution of $(D_x^2 + 3D_x + 2)y = \sin x$ iff

$$y = \tfrac{1}{10} \sin x - \tfrac{3}{10} \cos x + c_1e^{-x} + c_2e^{-2x},$$

for constants c_1 and c_2. ∎

For λ_1 and λ_2 any real numbers it is easy to demonstrate that

$$(D - \lambda_1)(D - \lambda_2) = D^2 - (\lambda_1 + \lambda_2)D + \lambda_1\lambda_2 = (D - \lambda_2)(D - \lambda_1).$$

This implies that the method of the example above can be applied to many equations. The reason our discussion is confined to operators with constant coefficients is that this method does not apply to operators with nonconstant coefficients. For example, the three linear operators $D^2 - \sin^2$, $(D + \sin)(D - \sin)$, and $(D - \sin)(D + \sin)$ are all different. Since "multiplication" is really composition, this is not surprising.

Theorem 11.7. Let $L = D_x^2 + bD_x + c$, where b and c are real numbers. If L can be factored into

$$L = (D_x - \lambda_1)(D_x - \lambda_2),$$

for real λ_1 and λ_2, then, if $\lambda_1 \neq \lambda_2$, the kernel of L is the set of all linear combinations of $e^{\lambda_1 x}$ and $e^{\lambda_2 x}$, and if $\lambda_1 = \lambda_2 = \lambda$, the kernel of L is the set of all linear combinations of $e^{\lambda x}$ and $xe^{\lambda x}$.

PROOF: If $\lambda_1 \neq \lambda_2$, then, just as in the example above, $L(e^{\lambda_1 x}) = 0$ because $(D_x - \lambda_1)e^{\lambda_1 x} = 0$, and $L(e^{\lambda_2 x}) = 0$ because $(D_x - \lambda_2)e^{\lambda_2 x} = 0$.

If $L = (D_x - \lambda)^2$, then $L(e^{\lambda x}) = 0$, as above, and

$$L(xe^{\lambda x}) = (D_x - \lambda)(e^{\lambda x} + \lambda xe^{\lambda x} - \lambda xe^{\lambda x}) = (D_x - \lambda)e^{\lambda x} = 0.$$

We have proved that the kernel of L includes the sets stipulated by the theorem.

If f is any function such that $(D_x - \lambda_1)(D_x - \lambda_2)f(x) = 0$, set $g(x) = (D_x - \lambda_2)f(x)$. Then $(D_x - \lambda_1)g(x) = 0$. This is a previously solved problem: by Theorem 11.6, $g(x) = ce^{\lambda_1 x}$ for some constant c.

We must now find all f such that $(D_x - \lambda_2)f(x) = ce^{\lambda_1 x}$. Unless $\lambda_2 = \lambda_1$, this is also a previously solved problem. The kernel of $D_x - \lambda_2$ is the set of all scalar multiples of $e^{\lambda_2 x}$. A solution of $(D_x - \lambda_2)f(x) = ce^{\lambda_1 x}$ is

$$f(x) = \frac{1}{\lambda_1 - \lambda_2} ce^{\lambda_1 x}.$$

If $\lambda_1 = \lambda_2 = \lambda$, then as above, f must be a solution of $(D_x - \lambda)f(x) = ce^{\lambda x}$. This equation implies

$$e^{-\lambda x}(D_x - \lambda)f(x) = c.$$

Now, for any differentiable function f,

$$\begin{aligned} D_x(e^{-\lambda x}f(x)) &= -\lambda e^{-\lambda x}f(x) + e^{-\lambda x}f'(x) \\ &= e^{-\lambda x}(f'(x) - \lambda f(x)) \\ &= e^{-\lambda x}(D_x - \lambda)f(x). \end{aligned}$$

Returning to our solution f, we have $D_x(e^{-\lambda x}f(x)) = c$. From this, there is some constant k such that

$$e^{-\lambda x}f(x) = cx + k,$$

and

$$f(x) = cxe^{\lambda x} + ke^{\lambda x},$$

which completes the proof that each function in the kernel of $(D - \lambda)^2$ is a linear combination of $e^{\lambda x}$ and $xe^{\lambda x}$. ∎

Exercises

1. Find all solutions of each equation below.
   a. $(D_x^2 + 2D_x - 3)f(x) = 0$.
   b. $(D_x^2 + 2D_x - 3)f(x) = x^2$. [*Hint:* Try $f(x) = ax^2 + bx + c$ for a particular solution.]
   c. $(D_x^2 + 2D_x - 3)f(x) = e^{2x}$.
   d. $(D_x^2 + 2D_x - 3)f(x) = x^2 + e^{2x}$.
   e. $(D_x^2 + 2D_x - 3)f(x) = \sin 5x$.
   f. $(D_x^2 + 2D_x - 3)f(x) = e^x$. [*Hint:* If f is a solution, then $(D - 1)(D + 3)f =$

exp, and $(D - 1)^2(D + 3)f = 0$. If $(D - 1)^2(D + 3) = (D + 3)(D - 1)^2$ then Theorem 11.7 gives a solution.]

2. Find all solutions of each equation below.

a. $(D_x{}^2 - 6D_x + 9)f(x) = 0$.

b. $(D_x{}^2 - 6D_x + 9)f(x) = 3x$.

c. $(D_x{}^2 - 6D_x + 9)f(x) = e^{2x}$.

d. $(D_x{}^2 - 6D_x + 9)f(x) = \sin 2x$.

e. $(D_x{}^2 - 6D_x + 9)f(x) = e^{3x}$.

f. $(D_x{}^2 - 6D_x + 9)f(x) = 6x + 5e^{2x} + 7 \sin 2x$.

3. a. Prove that every linear combination of sin and cos is in the kernel of $D^2 + 1$.

b. Find many solutions of $(D_x{}^2 + 1)f(x) = e^{3x}$.

4. Let $L = D_x{}^2 + 4D_x + 13 = (D_x + 2)^2 + 9$. Prove that both $e^{-2x} \cos 3x$ and $e^{-2x} \sin 3x$ are in the kernel of L.

Factor L formally [without attaching any meaning to the factors] into $(D_x - \lambda_1)(D_x - \lambda_2)$, where λ_1 and λ_2 are complex numbers. Using the definition

$$e^{\alpha + i\beta} = e^\alpha(\cos \beta + i \sin \beta),$$

show that both $e^{-2x} \cos 3x$ and $e^{-2x} \sin 3x$ are linear combinations, with complex coefficients, of $e^{\lambda_1 x}$ and $e^{\lambda_2 x}$.

5. Prove that, if $L = (D_x - \alpha)^2 + \beta^2$, where α and β are real and $\beta \neq 0$, then every linear combination of $e^{\alpha x} \cos \beta x$ and $e^{\alpha x} \sin \beta x$ is in the kernel of L.

Theorem 11.8. If $L = (D_x - \alpha)^2 + \beta^2$, where α and β are real and $\beta \neq 0$, then the kernel of L is the set of all linear combinations of $e^{\alpha x} \cos \beta x$ and $e^{\alpha x} \sin \beta x$.

Part of the proof is left to the reader in Exercise 5 above. The other part follows easily from

Theorem 11.9. Let $L = D^2 + bD + c$, for real b and c. The kernel of L is a linear space over $\mathcal{R}$ of dimension 2. That is, the kernel contains two linearly independent functions; any three functions in the kernel are linearly dependent.

PROOF THAT THE DIMENSION IS ≥ 2: There are three cases: either $L = (D - \lambda_1)(D - \lambda_2)$ for real λ_1 and $\lambda_2 \neq \lambda_1$; or $L = (D - \lambda)^2$ for real λ; or $L = (D - \alpha)^2 + \beta^2$ for real α and β, with $\beta \neq 0$.

The statement that the functions $e^{\lambda_1 x}$ and $e^{\lambda_2 x}$ are linearly independent, if $\lambda_1 \neq \lambda_2$, is by definition equivalent to the statement that, if $c_1 e^{\lambda_1 x} + c_2 e^{\lambda_2 x} = 0$ for all x, then $c_1 = c_2 = 0$. This is obviously true. For example, setting $x = 0$ gives $c_1 + c_2 = 0$, and setting $x = 1$ gives $c_1 e^{\lambda_1} + c_2 e^{\lambda_2} = 0$. With $\lambda_1 \neq \lambda_2$, these equations imply that $c_1 = c_2 = 0$.

The proof that $e^{\lambda x}$ and $xe^{\lambda x}$ are linearly independent is even easier, as is the proof that $e^{\alpha x} \cos \beta x$ and $e^{\alpha x} \sin \beta x$ are linearly independent if $\beta \neq 0$.

PROOF THAT THE DIMENSION IS ≤ 2: Theorem 11.7 proves this for $L = (D - \lambda_1)(D - \lambda_2)$ or $L = (D - \lambda)^2$. The case $L = (D - \alpha)^2 + \beta^2$ is more difficult and we shall take a circuitous but interesting route.

Definition 11.1. For functions f and g both differentiable on some interval, the *Wronskian* of f and g is

$$w = fg' - f'g = \begin{vmatrix} f & g \\ f' & g' \end{vmatrix}.$$

Note: J. Hoene-Wronski (Polish, 1778–1853) was a minor literary and philosophical figure in Paris. The Wronskian is what survives of his three-volume *Messianisme ou Réforme Absolue du savoir humain*. [On the spine of Prof. A. J. Kempner's copy of the book the reformulation is "absolue, et par consequent finale."]

Theorem 11.10. If f and g are in the kernel of $D^2 + bD + c$ and $w = fg' - f'g$, then $w' = -bw$.

PROOF: The proof is straightforward: differentiate w and use the hypothesis that $f'' = -bf' - cf$ and $g'' = -bg' - cg$. ∎

The significance is that, from Theorem 11.5, either w is the 0 function or else $w(x) \neq 0$ for all x in the domain.

Theorem 11.11. If F is in the kernel of $D^2 + bD + c$ and $F(0) = F'(0) = 0$, then F is the 0 function.

PROOF: If the kernel contains a function g with $g(x) = e^{\lambda x}$ for some real λ, consider the Wronskian $w = Fg' - F'g$. Since $w(0) = 0$, $w(x) = 0$ for all x. Now $w(x) = F(x)\lambda e^{\lambda x} - F'(x)e^{\lambda x}$. From $w(x) = 0$ for all x follows $F' = \lambda F$. By Theorem 11.5, F is the 0 function because $F(0) = 0$.

If the kernel does not contain $e^{\lambda x}$ for real λ, then the kernel does contain both $G(x) = e^{\alpha x} \cos \beta x$ and $H(x) = e^{\alpha x} \sin \beta x$ for some real α and β, with $\beta \neq 0$. The Wronskians of F and G, and F and H are both the 0 function, as above. Computing them gives, for all x,

$$F(x)[\alpha \cos \beta x - \beta \sin \beta x] - F'(x) \cos \beta x = 0$$

and

$$F(x)[\alpha \sin \beta x + \beta \cos \beta x] - F'(x) \sin \beta x = 0.$$

Multiply the upper equation by $\cos \beta x$, the lower equation by $\sin \beta x$, and add to obtain $F' = \alpha F$. As before, F is the 0 function. ∎

We can now complete the proof of Theorem 11.9. For $L = (D - \alpha)^2 + \beta^2$, with $\beta \neq 0$, let $f(x) = e^{\alpha x} \cos \beta x$ and $g(x) = e^{\alpha x} \sin \beta x$. For h in the kernel of L, set $F = c_1 f + c_2 g - h$.

Then F, as a linear combination of functions in the kernel of L, is in the kernel:

$$F(0) = c_1 f(0) + c_2 g(0) - h(0),$$

and

$$F'(0) = c_1 f'(0) + c_2 g'(0) - h'(0).$$

The equations

$$c_1 f(0) + c_2 g(0) = h(0), \qquad c_1 f'(0) + c_2 g'(0) = h'(0)$$

are solvable uniquely for c_1 and c_2 because

$$f(0)g'(0) - f'(0)g(0) \neq 0.$$

Choosing this c_1 and c_2 makes $F(0) = F'(0) = 0$, and, by Theorem 11.11, F is the 0 function. This makes h a linear combination of f and g. ∎

Exercises

1. Let K be the kernel of $D^2 + bD + c$. Prove that, if f and g are linearly independent functions in K, then the mapping

$$(c_1, c_2) \longrightarrow c_1 f + c_2 g$$

is an algebraic isomorphism of $(\Re^2; +, \text{scalar product})$ to $(K; +, \text{scalar product})$.

2. Prove that, if differentiable functions f and g are linearly dependent over an open interval I, then their Wronskian is 0 on I.

3. Let $f(x) = x^2$ for all x, $g(x) = -x^2$ for $x \leq 0$, and $g(x) = x^2$ for $x \geq 0$. Prove that the Wronskian of f and g is 0 on $\Re$, but that f and g are linearly independent over the interval $(-1, 1)$. This is a well-known counterexample to a notoriously false doctrine proclaimed in many once well-known texts.

4. If K is the kernel of $D^2 + bD + c$ and c_0 and c_1 are real numbers, prove that there is one and only one function f in K with $f(0) = c_0$ and $f'(0) = c_1$.

5. The kernel of $D^2 - 1$ contains e^x and e^{-x}. It also contains the *hyperbolic cosine* and *hyperbolic sine* functions, defined by

$$\cosh x = \frac{e^x + e^{-x}}{2}, \qquad \sinh x = \frac{e^x - e^{-x}}{2}.$$

Investigate the derivatives and second derivatives of sinh and cosh. Also investigate functions such as $\sinh^2 + \cosh^2$, $\cosh^2 - \sinh^2$, $2 \sinh \cosh$, $\tanh = \sinh/\cosh$.

§ 4. *Two Techniques of Integration*

By the Fundamental Theorem, each differentiation formula can be turned into an integration formula. The integration formulas corresponding to the product rule and the chain rule are, as one might guess, very useful.

If f and g have continuous derivatives on an interval containing a and b, then from

$$(fg)' = f'g + fg'$$

follows

$$\int_a^b (fg)' = \int_a^b f'g + \int_a^b fg'$$

and, by the Fundamental Theorem,

$$f(b)g(b) - f(a)g(a) = \int_a^b f'g + \int_a^b fg'.$$

Integration by Parts. If f and g have continuous derivatives on an interval containing a and b, then

$$\int_a^b fg' = f(b)g(b) - f(a)g(a) - \int_a^b f'g.$$

We use this as follows. To try to evaluate $\int_a^b F$ we may be able to factor F into a product fg', where g' is a derivative from which g is recognizable. Then the formula replaces the problem of finding $\int_a^b fg'$, by the presumably different and possibly easier problem of finding $\int_a^b f'g$.

Example

Find $\int_0^\pi x \sin x \, dx$. The natural factors are x and $\sin x$. Setting $f(x) = \sin x$ and $g'(x) = x$ replaces the original problem by $\int_0^\pi (x^2/2) \cos x \, dx$, which is no improvement.

Setting $f(x) = x$ and $g'(x) = \sin x$ gives, with $g(x) = -\cos x$,

$$\int_0^\pi x \sin x \, dx = -\pi \cos \pi + 0 \cos 0 - \int_0^\pi - \cos x \, dx$$

$$= \pi + \sin \pi - \sin 0 = \pi.$$

Exercises

1. $\displaystyle\int_0^\pi \frac{x^2}{2} \cos x \, dx.$

2. $\displaystyle\int_0^{\pi/2} \sin x \cos x \, dx.$

3. $\displaystyle\int_0^1 x^2 e^{3x} \, dx.$

4. $\displaystyle\int_a^b e^{\alpha x} \sin \beta x \, dx.$

[*Hint for Exercise* 4. One integration by parts leads to $k \int_a^b e^{\alpha x} \cos \beta x \, dx$. Integrate this by parts to get an equation solvable for the original integral. What restrictions on α and β are needed?]

The problems above are typical applications to specific problems. In the next section there is a more general application of integration by parts. We turn now to the translation of the chain rule into an integral formula.

Integration by Substitution. If f is continuous on an interval containing a and b and if g' is continuous on an interval containing α and β, and furthermore $g(\alpha) = a$ and $g(\beta) = b$, then

$$\int_a^b f = \int_\alpha^\beta (f \circ g)g'.$$

PROOF: Let F be a function such that $F' = f$. Then $\int_a^b f = F(b) - F(a)$. Let $G = F \circ g$, so that

$$G' = (F' \circ g)g' = (f \circ g)g'.$$

Then

$$\int_\alpha^\beta (f \circ g)g' = G(\beta) - G(\alpha)$$

$$= F(g(\beta)) - F(g(\alpha))$$

$$= F(b) - F(a) = \int_a^b f. \qquad \blacksquare$$

Examples

1. If we know that Arc $\tan' x = 1/(1 + x^2)$, then we know that

$$\int_0^b \frac{1}{1 + x^2}\, dx = \text{Arc} \tan b.$$

If we don't know this, the integral is a candidate for substitution. The formula says that

$$\int_0^b \frac{1}{1 + x^2}\, dx = \int_\alpha^\beta \frac{g'}{1 + g^2}$$

provided g' is continuous and $g(\alpha) = 0$ and $g(\beta) = b$. For instance, if $-1 \le b \le 1$ and $\sin \beta = b$, then

$$\int_0^b \frac{1}{1 + x^2}\, dx = \int_0^\beta \frac{\cos}{1 + \sin^2}.$$

If we can now find a function whose derivative is $\cos/(1 + \sin^2)$, the problem is solved.

We might try $g(t) = t^3$, $g'(t) = 3t^2$, to get

$$\int_0^b \frac{1}{1 + x^2}\, dx = \int_0^{b^{\frac{1}{3}}} \frac{3t^2}{1 + t^6}\, dt.$$

We could go on forever making substitutions at random. What is wanted is a function g such that $g'/(1 + g^2)$ is recognizable as a derivative. The best possible choice is tan:

$$\frac{\tan'}{1 + \tan^2} = \frac{1 + \tan^2}{1 + \tan^2} = 1.$$

Then

$$\int_0^b \frac{1}{1+x^2}\,dx = \int_0^{\text{Arc tan } b} 1 = \text{Arc tan } b.$$

2. Computation of $\int_1^2 (x+1)\sqrt{x+3}\,dx$.

If $x + 3 = t^2$, then $x = t^2 - 3 = g(t)$. Since $g(2) = 1$, $g(\sqrt{5}) = 2$, and g' is continuous,

$$\int_1^2 (x+1)\sqrt{x+3}\,dx = \int_2^{\sqrt{5}} (t^2 - 2)\sqrt{t^2}\,2t\,dt,$$

which is readily evaluated.

If the formula is written in the form

$$\int_a^b f(x)\,dx = \int_\alpha^\beta f(g(t))g'(t)\,dt,$$

we can easily remember

for x, substitute $g(t)$,

for dx, substitute $g'(t)\,dt$.

It is possible, but it is a difficult and sophisticated affair, to define differentials in such a way that $dx = g'(t)\,dt$ becomes meaningful and true. It is much easier to regard it as a convenient mnemonic device, compatible with $dx/dt = g'(t)$.

There are standard substitutions which handle some integrals that occur often in applications. This chapter is not designed to teach the reader to evaluate all the usual integrals and we shall limit the topic to a few more examples and problems.

Expressions of the form $a^2 - b^2x^2$, $a^2 + b^2x^2$, and $b^2x^2 - a^2$ can be made into perfect squares by trigonometric substitutions. If $x = (a/b)\sin t$, then

$$a^2 - b^2x^2 = a^2(1 - \sin^2 t) = a^2 \cos^2 t.$$

The other two forms exploit $1 + \tan^2 = \sec^2$ and $\sec^2 - 1 = \tan^2$.

Sometimes a substitution suggests itself naturally. If we don't see that

$$\int_0^1 \frac{e^x}{1+e^x}\,dx = \ln(1+e) - \ln 2,$$

the natural substitution is $x = \ln t$, so that $e^x = t$. This gives $\int_1^e \frac{1}{1+t}\,dt$.

Exercises

Evaluate each of the following.

1. $\int_{-r}^r \sqrt{r^2 - x^2}\,dx$.

2. $\int_0^1 (x^2 + 5)\sqrt{x + 1}\, dx.$

3. $\int_0^b \dfrac{dx}{1 + 9x^2}.$

4. $\int_1^5 \dfrac{dx}{1 - 9x^2}.$ $\left[Hint: \text{ for } x \neq \pm \tfrac{1}{3}, \right.$

$\left. \dfrac{1}{1 - 3x} + \dfrac{1}{1 + 3x} = \dfrac{2}{1 - 9x^2}. \right]$

5. $\int_0^\pi \sin^5 t \cos t\, dt.$

6. $\int_0^\pi \sin^5.$ [*Hint:* $\sin^5 = \sin^4 \sin = (1 - \cos^2)^2 \sin.$]

7. $\int_0^\pi \sin^4.$ [*Hint:*

$\cos 2x = \cos^2 x - \sin^2 x = 1 - 2\sin^2 x,$

for all x, and $\sin^2 x = (1 - \cos 2x)/2.$

8. $\int_0^b \dfrac{1}{\sqrt{1 - x^2}}\, dx,$ where $-1 < b < 1.$

9. Let f be a function continuous on the closed interval $[a, b]$. Corresponding to each partition of $[a, b]$ there is a broken-line approximation to f. This broken-line function has a length, the sum of the lengths of the segments. If the set of all lengths of broken-line approximations has an upper bound, which is by no means guaranteed, the least upper bound is by definition the arc length of the graph of f.

Use the Mean Value Theorem to prove that, if f has a continuous derivative on $[a, b]$, then the arc length is given by $\int_a^b \sqrt{1 + (f')^2}.$

10. Find the arc length of the parabola $y = x^2$ over an interval $[0, b]$. *Remark:* Integrating $\sec^3$ is something of a puzzle; it can be done by various combinations of integration by parts, identities, and good luck. Checks on the answer, say $L(b)$, are possible. For $b > 0$, a picture makes it clear that

$\sqrt{b^2 + b^4} < L(b) < b + b^2.$

11. Evaluate $\int_1^b \ln$ (a) by using integration by parts with $g' = 1$, and (b) by using the natural substitution.

12. For any m, n, and x,

$\sin mx \sin nx = \tfrac{1}{2} \cos (m - n)x - \tfrac{1}{2} \cos (m + n)x.$

Prove that if m and n are integers, then

if $m \neq n$, $\quad \displaystyle\int_0^\pi \sin mx \sin nx\, dx = 0,$

if $m \neq 0$, $\quad \displaystyle\int_0^\pi \sin^2 mx\, dx = \dfrac{\pi}{2}.$

13. Investigate $\displaystyle\int_0^{2\pi} \cos mx \cos nx\, dx$ for integers m and n.

§ 5. *Taylor Polynomials*

The basic idea of the calculus of derivatives, put geometrically, is that if f is differentiable at a, then the line

$$y = f(a) + (x - a)f'(a)$$

is tangent to the graph of f at $(a, f(a))$, and consequently $f(a) + (x - a)f'(a)$ is a good approximation to $f(x)$, for x close enough to a. Put more algebraically, it is that the difference function $f(x) - f(a)$ is well-approximated, on an interval around a, by the linear mapping $x - a \longrightarrow (x - a)f'(a)$.

The purpose of this section is to investigate in some detail the error in this approximation. The theorems demand that any function f considered have at least a second derivative f'' continuous on some interval, and preferably continuous kth derivatives $f^{(k)}$ for each positive integer k. The basic formula is given below; others follow by routine integrations by parts and estimations of integrals.

> **Theorem 11.12.** If the real function f has a second derivative f'' continuous on an open interval I containing a, then, for each x in I,
>
> $$f(x) = f(a) + (x - a)f'(a) + \int_a^x (x - t)f''(t)\, dt.$$

This is readily proved by an integration by parts, differentiating the first factor and integrating f''. It is more interesting to derive the formula than to verify it.

PROOF: For x in I, set $T(x) = f(a) + (x - a)f'(a)$, and define an *error term* or *remainder term* $R(x)$ by $f(x) = T(x) + R(x)$. This gives

$$R(x) = f(x) - f(a) - (x - a)f'(a)$$

$$= \int_a^x f' - (x - a)f'(a).$$

If to $R(x)$ we add $0 = (x - x)f'(x)$, we obtain

$$R(x) = \int_a^x f' + (x - x)f'(x) - (x - a)f'(a).$$

The last two terms suggest an integral: regarding x as fixed, define a function H by: for t in I, $H(t) = (x - t)f'(t)$. Then

$$(x - x)f'(x) - (x - a)f'(a) = H(x) - H(a)$$

$$= \int_a^x H'.$$

We then have

$$R(x) = \int_a^x f' + \int_a^x H' = \int_a^x (f' + H').$$

Moreover, for t in I,

$$f'(t) + H'(t) = f'(t) - f'(t) + (x - t)f''(t),$$

which establishes Theorem 11.12. ∎

Now assume that f has a third derivative continuous on I and apply integration by parts to $\int_a^x (x - t)f''(t)\, dt$, integrating the first factor and differentiating f'':

$$\int_a^x (x - t)f''(t)\, dt = \frac{(x - a)^2}{2} f''(a) + \int_a^x \frac{(x - t)^2}{2} f'''(t)\, dt.$$

This suggests an immediate generalization. If f has a continuous $(k + 1)$st derivative $f^{(k+1)}$ on I, then integration by parts establishes that, for a and x in I,

$$\int_a^x \frac{(x - t)^{k-1}}{(k - 1)!} f^{(k)}(t)\, dt = \frac{(x - a)^k}{k!} f^{(k)}(a) + \int_a^x \frac{(x - t)^k}{k!} f^{(k+1)}(t)\, dt.$$

With Theorem 11.12 as our starting place, and using the essentials of the inductive argument given above, we have

Theorem 11.13. If the real function f has an $(n + 1)$st derivative continuous on an open interval I containing a, then, for each x in I, $f(x) = T_n(x) + R_n(x)$, where

$$T_n(x) = f(a) + \sum_{k=1}^n \frac{f^{(k)}(a)}{k!} (x - a)^k,$$

$$R_n(x) = \int_a^x \frac{(x - t)^n}{n!} f^{(n+1)}(t)\, dt.$$

The polynomial T_n is called the *Taylor polynomial of order n for f* around a [after Brook Taylor, English mathematician, 1685–1731]. The degree of the polynomial is n unless $f^{(n)}(a) = 0$.

If the function f has derivatives of order n for all n, then the sequence $\{T_n(x)\}$ will converge to $f(x)$ iff the sequence $\{R_n(x)\}$ converges to 0.

Examples

1. Let $f(x) = x^3 + x^2 + 1$ and $a = 2$. Since $f^{(4)} = 0$, the Taylor polynomial $T_3 = f$. Since $f(2) = 13$, $f'(2) = 16$, $f''(2) = 14$, and $f'''(2) = 6$,

   $$x^3 + x^2 + 1 = 13 + 16(x - 2) + 7(x - 2)^2 + (x - 2)^3,$$

   for all x.
2. Let $f(x) = e^x$ and $a = 0$. Since $\exp^{(n)}(x) = \exp x$ for all n and x, and $\exp^{(n)}(0) = 1$ for all n, for all real x and each positive integer n,

   $$e^x = 1 + \sum_{k=1}^n \frac{x^k}{k!} + \int_0^x \frac{(x - t)^n}{n!} e^t\, dt.$$

We consider the remainder term first for $x > 0$, say $0 < x \leq b$. The integrand is positive on the interval $[0, x]$ and

$$0 < \int_0^x \frac{(x - t)^n}{n!} e^t \, dt < e^b \int_0^x \frac{(x - t)^n}{n!} \, dt$$

$$= e^b \frac{x^{n+1}}{(n + 1)!} \leq \frac{e^b b^{n+1}}{(n + 1)!}.$$

In particular, for $0 < x \leq 1$,

$$e^x = 1 + \sum_{k=1}^n \frac{x^k}{k!} + R_n(x),$$

where $0 < R_n(x) < e/(n + 1)!$.

Setting $n = 4$, for example, for $0 < x \leq 1$,

$$e^x = 1 + x + \frac{x^2}{2} + \frac{x^3}{6} + \frac{x^4}{24} + R_4(x),$$

where $0 < R_4(x) < e/120 < 1/40$.

For $x < 0$ and t in the open interval $(x, 0)$, $e^t < 1$ and $x - t < 0$, so that $(x - t)^n$ is strictly positive or negative according as n is even or odd. For $x < 0$, then, an easy estimate is

$$|R_n(x)| = \left| \int_0^x \frac{(x - t)^n}{n!} e^t \, dt \right| < \frac{|x|^{n+1}}{(n + 1)!}.$$

3. Let $f(x) = \sin x$ and $a = 0$. For every nonnegative integer k,

$$\sin^{(2k)}(0) = 0 \quad \text{and} \quad \sin^{(2k+1)}(0) = (-1)^k.$$

[Convention: $f^{(0)} = f$.]

For $n \geq 0$ and all real x, set

$$S_n(x) = \sum_{k=0}^n (-1)^k \frac{x^{2k+1}}{(2k + 1)!}$$

$$= x - \frac{x^3}{3!} + \cdots + (-1)^n \frac{x^{2n+1}}{(2n + 1)!}.$$

This makes S_n the Taylor polynomial of order $2n + 1$ and also [since $\sin^{(2n+2)}(0) = 0$] the Taylor polynomial of order $2n + 2$, for sine around 0. Theorem 11.13 then gives

$$\sin x = S_n(x) + \int_0^x \frac{(x - t)^{2n+2}}{(2n + 2)!} \sin^{(2n+3)}(t) \, dt.$$

To estimate the integral, simply ignore the favorable fact that the integrand may change sign, bound $|\pm \sin t|$ by 1, and obtain

$$|\sin x - S_n(x)| < \frac{|x|^{2n+3}}{(2n + 3)!}.$$

These polynomial approximations to the sine function are the same polynomials obtained in Chapter 9, § 3, by repeated integrations of the inequality

$$1 - \frac{x^2}{2} \leq \cos x \leq 1.$$

Similarly, the previously given polynomial approximations to cosine are the Taylor polynomials for cosine around 0.

For $n \geq 0$ and all real x, set

$$C_n(x) = \sum_{k=0}^{n} (-1)^k \frac{x^{2k}}{(2k)!}$$

$$= 1 - \frac{x^2}{2} + \cdots + (-1)^n \frac{x^{2n}}{(2n)!}.$$

Theorem 11.13 confirms the previous result that, for all x,

$$|\cos x - C_n(x)| < \frac{|x|^{2n+2}}{(2n+2)!}.$$

Exercises

1. Let $f(x) = x^3 - 1$ for all x. Since $f^{(4)} = 0$, the Taylor expansion of order 3 in powers of $(x - a)$ is exact for any a. Give the expansion in powers of $(x - 1)$, $(x + 1)$, x.

2. With T_n as in Theorem 11.13, prove that, for $0 \leq k \leq n$,
$$T_n^{(k)}(a) = f^{(k)}(a).$$

3. Let f be a function with at least a fourth derivative at a. Let
$$P(x) = c_0 + c_1(x - a) + c_2(x - a)^2 + c_3(x - a)^3 + c_4(x - a)^4.$$
Prove that $P(a) = f(a)$, $P'(a) = f'(a)$, $\ldots$, and $P^{(4)}(a) = f^{(4)}(a)$ iff P is the Taylor polynomial of order 4 for f around a.

4. Let $f(x) = \sin 2x$. Find the Taylor polynomial of order 5 for f around 0.

5. For real c, and a real function f with an $(n + 1)$st derivative continuous on an interval around a, let $g(x) = f(cx)$. Discuss the relation between the Taylor expansions of f and g.

6. **a.** Prove that the Taylor expansion of the natural logarithm in powers of $x - 1$, for $x > 0$, is
$$\ln x = \sum_{k=1}^{n} \frac{(-1)^{k-1}}{k} (x - 1)^k + R_n(x),$$
where
$$R_n(x) = \int_1^x \frac{(-1)^n (x - t)^n}{t^{n+1}} \, dt.$$

b. Over the interval $(0, 3]$, sketch graphs of
$$y = \ln x \quad \text{and} \quad y = (x - 1) - \frac{(x - 1)^2}{2} + \frac{(x - 1)^3}{3}.$$

c. If $\frac{2}{3} \leq x \leq \frac{4}{3}$, and t is between 1 and x, then $0 < |x - t|^n < (\frac{1}{3})^n$. Prove that on the interval $[\frac{2}{3}, \frac{4}{3}]$ the sequence of Taylor polynomials for $\ln$ converges to $\ln$.

d. In part **a**, set $x = 1 + h$ and deduce that, for $h > -1$,
$$\ln(1 + h) = \sum_{k=1}^{n} \frac{(-1)^{k-1}}{k} h^k + \int_1^{1+h} \frac{(-1)^n (1 + h - t)^n}{t^{n+1}} \, dt.$$

7. For n a positive integer and $x \neq -1$,

$$\frac{1}{1+x} = 1 - x + x^2 - + \cdots + (-1)^{n-1}x^{n-1} + \frac{(-x)^n}{1+x}.$$

a. Prove that, if $|x| \leq b < 1$, then

$$\lim_{n \to \infty} \frac{b^n}{1+b} = 0 = \lim_{n \to \infty} \frac{b^n}{1-b},$$

and, for $n \geq 1$,

$$\left| \frac{(-x)^n}{1+x} \right| \leq \frac{b^n}{1-b}.$$

b. If $-b \leq h \leq b < 1$, then for each $\epsilon > 0$ there is some N_ϵ such that, for $n > N_\epsilon$,

$$\int_1^{1+h} \frac{1}{1+x}\, dx$$

differs by less than ϵ from

$$\int_1^{1+h} \sum_{k=0}^{n-1} (-1)^k x^k\, dx = \sum_{k=1}^{n} \frac{(-1)^{k-1}}{k} h^k.$$

This is an indirect but easy way of establishing that, for $-1 < h < 1$,

$$\ln(1+h) = h - \frac{h^2}{2} + \frac{h^3}{3} + \cdots + (-1)^{n-1}\frac{h^n}{n} + R_n(h),$$

where $\lim_{n \to \infty} R_n(h) = 0$.

c. Prove that the result of (b) also holds for $h = 1$, giving

$$\ln 2 = 1 - \tfrac{1}{2} + \tfrac{1}{3} - \tfrac{1}{4} + \tfrac{1}{5} - + \cdots.$$

8. Work out Taylor expansions for Arc tan x in powers of x (a) by computing derivatives, and (b) by replacing x by x^2 in the discussion in Exercise 7.

9. Approximate $\int_0^1 \sqrt{x} \sin x\, dx$ by approximating $\sin x$ by $x - (x^3/6)$. How large is the possible error? How large is the possible error if $\sin x$ is approximated by

$$x - (x^3/6) + (x^5/120)?$$

10. a. Give the Taylor polynomial of order 5 for the tangent function around 0.
b. Compare the above with the result of dividing

$$x - \frac{x^3}{6} + \frac{x^5}{120} \qquad \text{by} \qquad 1 - \frac{x^2}{2} + \frac{x^4}{24}.$$

11. Write $x^3 - x - 1$ as a polynomial in $(x - \tfrac{4}{3})$. Then find an approximate solution of the equation $x^3 - x - 1 = 0$.

12. Let T_n be the Taylor polynomial of order n for f around a. Prove that T'_n is the Taylor polynomial of order $n - 1$ for f' around a.

The examples and exercises above illustrate two usual types of behavior. The sequence of Taylor polynomials $T_n(x)$ may converge to $f(x)$ for all x, as do those for the exponential, sine, and cosine functions. Or, as is the case with the expansions for $\ln x$ in powers of $x - 1$, the sequence of polynomials may converge for x in some open interval $(a - h, a + h)$, but diverge for $|x - a| > h$.

The classical example of a third sort of behavior is the function g defined on $\Re$ by $g(0) = 0$; for $x \neq 0$, $g(x) = e^{-1/x^2}$. It can be shown that g has derivatives of all orders, and that $g^{(k)}(0) = 0$ for all k. Each Taylor polynomial for $g(x)$ in powers of x is the 0 function, and the sequence fails to converge to $g(x)$ except for $x = 0$.

If a real function has a Taylor expansion convergent on some interval, it may lead to interesting and useful extensions of the function.

For example, the expression $x - (x^3/6) + (x^5/120)$ is meaningful if x is a square matrix instead of a real number. So also is $1 - (x^2/2) + (x^4/24)$, provided we interpret 1 to mean the identity matrix.

For real x, let

$$E_n(x) = 1 + \sum_{k=1}^{n} \frac{x^k}{k!}.$$

From Example 2 above, the sequence $\{E_n(x)\}$ converges to e^x for each real x.

For $A = \begin{pmatrix} 1 & 1 \\ 0 & 1 \end{pmatrix}$, let

$$E_n(A) = \begin{pmatrix} 1 & 0 \\ 0 & 1 \end{pmatrix} + \sum_{k=1}^{n} \frac{1}{k!} A^k.$$

Then, for example,

$$E_3(A) = \begin{pmatrix} 1 & 0 \\ 0 & 1 \end{pmatrix} + \begin{pmatrix} 1 & 1 \\ 0 & 1 \end{pmatrix} + \frac{1}{2} \begin{pmatrix} 1 & 2 \\ 0 & 1 \end{pmatrix} + \frac{1}{6} \begin{pmatrix} 1 & 3 \\ 0 & 1 \end{pmatrix}$$

$$= \begin{pmatrix} E_3(1) & E_2(1) \\ 0 & E_3(1) \end{pmatrix}.$$

An easy induction establishes that, for all n,

$$E_n(A) = \begin{pmatrix} E_n(1) & E_{n-1}(1) \\ 0 & E_n(1) \end{pmatrix}.$$

Any reasonable definition of the "distance between" two matrices will now lead to

$$\lim_{n \to \infty} E_n(A) = \begin{pmatrix} e & e \\ 0 & e \end{pmatrix}.$$

Since the symbol $\exp \begin{pmatrix} 1 & 1 \\ 0 & 1 \end{pmatrix}$ has not yet been given a meaning, we are free to make the definition

$$\exp \begin{pmatrix} 1 & 1 \\ 0 & 1 \end{pmatrix} = \begin{pmatrix} e & e \\ 0 & e \end{pmatrix}.$$

Rather than explore further the possibility of defining an exponential function mapping matrices to matrices, we consider complex numbers. If z

is any complex number and 1 is understood to mean $(1, 0) = 1 + 0i$, then the definition

$$E_n(z) = 1 + \sum_{k=1}^{n} \frac{z^k}{k!}$$

makes sense.

For example, setting $z = it$, for real t, we have

$$E_5(it) = 1 + it + \frac{(it)^2}{2} + \frac{(it)^3}{6} + \frac{(it)^4}{24} + \frac{(it)^5}{120}$$

$$= 1 - \frac{t^2}{2} + \frac{t^4}{24} + i\left(t - \frac{t^3}{6} + \frac{t^5}{120}\right)$$

$$= C_2(t) + iS_2(t),$$

where C_2 and S_2 are the Taylor polynomials of order 5 for cosine and sine around 0.

Similarly, for any positive integer n and any real t,

$$E_{2n+1}(it) = C_n(t) + iS_n(t).$$

The real sequences $\{C_n(t)\}$ and $\{S_n(t)\}$ converge to $\cos t$ and $\sin t$. Given $\epsilon > 0$, there is N_ϵ such that, for $n > N_\epsilon$,

$$|C_n(t) - \cos t| < \epsilon \quad \text{and} \quad |S_n(t) - \sin t| < \epsilon.$$

The distance between two complex numbers has been defined, and, for $n > N_\epsilon$, we have

$$|C_n(t) + iS_n(t) - (\cos t + i \sin t)| < \epsilon\sqrt{2}.$$

We have established that, using the natural definition of convergence, for each real t the complex sequence $\{E_n(it)\}$ converges to $\cos t + i \sin t$. This is a sufficient justification for the definition made in Chapter 6 [page 175]: for real t,

$$e^{it} = \cos t + i \sin t.$$

In the earlier chapter we pointed out the naturalness of extending this to a definition of e^z for all complex z by

$$e^{x+iy} = e^x e^{iy} = e^x(\cos y + i \sin y).$$

We can now point to more evidence for the inevitability of this definition: for all real x and y, the complex sequence $\{E_n(x + iy)\}$ converges to $e^x(\cos y + i \sin y)$. [See Exercises.]

We have arrived at the threshold of a large subject, the theory of analytic functions of a complex variable, and at a natural end point for this text. Each elementary function, as well as many other real functions, can be extended, by means of Taylor expansions, to a function with a complex domain and range. There is an extensive theory of differentiation and integration of analytic complex functions—too extensive to be treated even sketchily here. For the interested reader, *Dienes* [9] and *Knopp* [10] are two classic texts.

Elementary Exercises on Power Series

Given a sequence $\{c_n\}$, $n = 0, 1, \ldots$, of real or complex numbers we can, for any complex z, consider the following sequence of partial sums:

$$P_0(z) = c_0 = c_0 z^0,$$

$$P_1(z) = c_0 + c_1 z,$$

$$P_n(z) = \sum_{k=0}^{n} c_k z^k.$$

In case $z = 0$, $c_0 0^0$ is to mean c_0.

If the sequence $\{P_n(z)\}$ converges, say to $P(z)$, then we say that the *power series* $\sum_{k=0}^{\infty} c_k z^k$ converges to $P(z)$. If the sequence of partial sums fails to converge, then we say that the power series $\sum_{k=0}^{\infty} c_k z^k$ diverges. No new idea has been introduced here, only some new language.

The definition of Cauchy sequence is the same for complex sequences as for real sequences. The complex sequence $\{z_n\}$ is a Cauchy sequence iff for each $\epsilon > 0$ there is some N such that $|z_n - z_m| < \epsilon$ for all n and $m > N$.

1. Let $\{z_n\} = \{x_n + iy_n\}$ be a complex sequence. Prove that $\{z_n\}$ is a Cauchy sequence iff both the real sequences $\{x_n\}$ and $\{y_n\}$ are Cauchy sequences.

2. Prove that a complex sequence $\{z_n\}$ converges iff it is a Cauchy sequence.

3. Let $\{c_n\}$ be a sequence of real nonnegative numbers. Assume that for some positive real p the power series $\sum_{k=0}^{\infty} c_k p^k$ converges. Note that since each term $c_k p^k$ is nonnegative, the sequence of partial sums, $\left\{ \sum_{k=0}^{n} c_k p^k \right\}$, is monotone increasing, and converges iff it is bounded.

Prove that if z is any real or complex number, with $|z| < p$, then $\sum_{k=0}^{\infty} c_k z^k$ converges. $\Big[$*Hint:* For $m > n$,

$$\left| \sum_{k=0}^{m} c_k z^k - \sum_{k=0}^{n} c_k z^k \right| = \left| \sum_{k=n+1}^{m} c_k z^k \right| < \sum_{k=n+1}^{m} c_k p^k. \Big]$$

4. With $\{c_n\}$ as in Exercise 3, assume that for some positive real q the power series $\sum_{k=0}^{\infty} c_k q^k$ diverges. Prove that, if $x > q$, then $\sum_{k=0}^{\infty} c_k x^k$ diverges.

5. If $\{u_n\}$ is a sequence of real or complex numbers, the series $\sum_{k=0}^{\infty} u_k$ *converges absolutely* in case $\sum_{k=0}^{\infty} |u_k|$ converges—that is, in case the sequence of partial

sums $\sum_{k=0}^{n} |u_k|$ converges. Prove that, if $\sum_{k=0}^{\infty} u_k$ converges absolutely, then $\sum_{k=0}^{\infty} u_k$ converges. $\left[Hint: \right.$

$$\left| \sum_{k=n+1}^{m} u_k \right| \le \sum_{k=n+1}^{m} |u_k|. \Big]$$

6. Prove that, if $\{c_n\}$ is a sequence of real or complex numbers and, for some complex $z_0 \ne 0$, $\sum_{k=0}^{\infty} |c_k| \, |z_0|^k$ converges, then $\sum_{k=0}^{\infty} c_k z^k$ converges for every complex z with $|z| < |z_0|$.

7. With $\{c_n\}$ as in Exercise 6, prove that, if for some complex w the series $\sum_{k=0}^{\infty} c_k w^k$ diverges, than $\sum_{k=0}^{\infty} c_k z^k$ diverges for all complex z with $|z| > |w|$. [*Hint:* See Exercise 6.]

8. Use Exercise 6 and the fact that the Taylor expansion of e^x in powers of x converges for all real x to prove that $\sum_{k=0}^{\infty} z^k/k!$ converges for all complex z.

9. Prove that, for all real x, $\sum_{k=0}^{\infty} x^{2k+1}/(2k+1)!$ converges to

$$\sinh x = \frac{e^x - e^{-x}}{2}.$$

10. Use Exercises 9 and 6 to prove that

$$\sum_{k=0}^{\infty} (-1)^k z^{2k+1}/(2k+1)!$$

converges for all complex z.

11. Prove that $\sum_{k=0}^{\infty} (-1)^k z^{2k}/(2k)!$ converges for all complex z.

12. Extend the domain of hyperbolic sine to the complex plane by the definition: for all complex z,

$$\sinh z = \sum_{k=0}^{\infty} \frac{z^{2k+1}}{(2k+1)!}.$$

For complex w, what is $\sinh(iw)$?

13. For real x, $\sum_{k=0}^{\infty} (-1)^k x^{2k+1}/(2k+1)$ converges to Arc tan x if $|x| < 1$, but diverges if $|x| > 1$. Use this, together with Exercises 6 and 7, to establish that $\sum_{k=0}^{\infty} (-1)^k z^{2k+1}/(2k+1)$ converges for all complex z with $|z| < 1$, but diverges for all complex z with $|z| > 1$.

14. Prove that $\sum_{k=0}^{\infty} k! z^k$ diverges for all real $z > 0$, and therefore for all complex $z \ne 0$.

We can generalize from Exercises 6–14 and say that a complex power series

$\sum\limits_{k=0}^{\infty} c_k(z - \alpha)^k$ may converge for all z, diverge for all $z \neq \alpha$, or have a positive *radius of convergence* r. The last possibility means that the series converges for all z with $|z - \alpha| < r$, but diverges for all z with $|z - \alpha| > r$.

Additional Miscellaneous Exercises

1. Let P be a polynomial of degree n with complex coefficients. Prove that, if $P(k)$ is an integer for each integer k with $0 \leq k \leq n$, then $P(x)$ is an integer for every integer x. Does it follow that the coefficients of P must be real? rational? integers?

2. Let P be a polynomial of degree 2 with real coefficients. For any real a and b,

$$P(b) - P(a) = (b - a)P'\left(\frac{a + b}{2}\right).$$

If $a < b$, then the average value of P' on the interval $[a, b]$ is

$$\frac{1}{b - a} \int_a^b P' = P'\left(\frac{a + b}{2}\right).$$

Say that a real function F "has the midpoint property" if the average value of F on each interval $[a, b]$ is $F((a + b)/2)$. A function F has the midpoint property iff $F + c$ has this property for every constant c. Discuss the set of functions F such that F has the midpoint property and $F(0) = 0$. [*Hint:* For every positive x, $1/2x \int_{-x}^{x} F = F(0)$ and $F(x) = 1/2x \int_0^{2x} F$. Functions given by integrals have pleasant properties.]

3. The formula for integration by parts replaces the problem of computing $\int_a^b fg'$ by the presumably different problem of computing $\int_a^b f'g$. Under what circumstances is the presumably different problem in fact not essentially different?

4. *Newton's Method* for finding successive approximations to a real zero of a differentiable function is based on the diagram below: $f(\alpha) = 0$, and x_1, x_2, x_3 are the first three approximations to α. The formula based on the diagram is

$$x_{n+1} = x_n - \frac{f(x_n)}{f'(x_n)}.$$

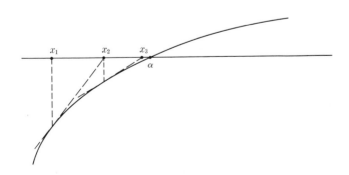

A tentative rule of thumb says that if all goes well each approximation can be expected to have about twice as many significant digits as the previous one.

a. Apply Newton's Method to find approximations to (i) the real root of $x^3 - x - 1 = 0$, and (ii) the smallest positive solution of $\sin x = x/2$.

b. As the diagram below suggests, all may not go well. Discuss conditions that guarantee convergence and methods for estimating the errors. Note that a positive lower bound for $\{|f'(c)|| c$ in a neighborhood of $\alpha\}$ will, via the Mean Value Theorem, allow us to estimate $|x - \alpha|$ in terms of $|f(x) - f(\alpha)| = |f(x)|$.

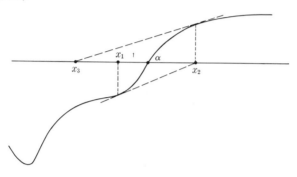

5. If $w_0 = 1$ and

$$w_n = w_{n-1} + \frac{(-1)^n i^{3n}}{\cdot \ 3n}$$

for $n \geq 1$, what does the sequence converge to?

6. Prove that e is irrational. [*Hint:* See the last pages of Chapter 4.]

7. Consider the arithmetic progression $0, d, 2d, 3d, \ldots$ and the geometric progression $1, r, r^2, r^3, \ldots$, where we assume $d > 0, r > 0$, and $r \neq 1$.

Is there a base b such that $\log_b r^n = nd$ for $n = 0, 1, 2, \ldots$? Assume that r is very close to 1; say $1 < r^{2000} < 4$. Furthermore, assume you have a table giving r^k to four significant figures for $1 \leq k \leq 2000$. Can the table be used for converting multiplication problems into addition problems? Need the base be specified? [When Napier first constructed logarithms he had no notion of a base. The Napierian logarithm of x is $10^7 \ln (10^7/x)$, but Napier did not know this.]

8. Let S be the following set of functions. A real function F is in S iff on the interval $[0, 1]$ F can be uniformly well approximated by polynomials with positive coefficients. [This is intended to mean any polynomial with no negative coefficient and at least one positive coefficient.]

a. Is the 0 function in S?

b. Is S closed under addition?

c. Are there any functions in S which are not polynomials?

d. If F is in S, can $F(x)$ be negative for any x in $[0, 1]$?

e. Can a function in S have a discontinuity in $[0, 1]$?

Selected References

1. J. L. Synge, *Science—Sense and Nonsense*, Jonathan Cape, London, 1951.
2. E. T. Bell, *Men of Mathematics*, Simon and Schuster, New York, 1937.
3. Leon Henkin, *On Mathematical Induction*, American Mathematical Monthly, 67, Providence, 1960, pp. 323–338.
4. Leon W. Cohen and Gertrude Ehrlich, *The Structure of the Real Number System*, Van Nostrand, New York, 1963.
5. E. Landau, *Foundations of Analysis*, Chelsea, 1951.
6. J. B. Roberts, *The Real Number System in an Algebraic Setting*, W. H. Freeman and Company, San Francisco and London, 1962.
7. H. A. Thurston, *The Number System*, Interscience, New York, 1956.
8. Richard Dedekind, *Essays on the Theory of Numbers*, Open Court, La Salle, Ill., 1924.
9. P. Dienes, *The Taylor Series*, Oxford University Press, Clarendon, 1931.
10. Konrad Knopp, *Theory and Application of Infinite Series*, Blackie & Son, Glasgow, 1928.

Answers or Comments for Selected Exercises

Pages 12–13

1. {2}   {4}   {6}   {2, 4}   {2, 6}   {4, 6}   {2, 4, 6}   ∅.

7. 3^9.

11. $x = 5$ and $y = 3$ or $x = 3$ and $y = 5$.

13. No, because for example $3 * 2 = 6$.   Yes.
    $1 * 0 = 0 = 1 * 3$ but $0 \neq 3$.

Page 24 *Example*

Suppose $k(k + 1)(k + 2) = 6m$.

Then $(k + 1)(k + 2)(k + 3)$
$$\begin{aligned}
&= k(k + 1)(k + 2) + 3(k + 1)(k + 2) \\
&= 6m + 3k(k + 1) + 6(k + 1) \\
&= 6(m + k + 1) + 3(k(k + 1)) \\
&= 6(m + k + 1) + 3(2p) \qquad \text{[By Theorem 2.18]} \\
&= 6(m + k + 1 + p).
\end{aligned}$$

Pages 25–26

3. $F(n) = n(n - 1)(n - 2) \cdots (n - (n - 1)) = n!$.

7. S_5 is empty.

13. 5, 8, 55.

Page 32

5. First show that $0 * x = 0$ for each x in $\mathfrak{N}$, by letting $M_0 = \{y \text{ in } \mathfrak{N} | 0 * y = 0\}$.
   Clearly 0 is in M_0. For k in M_0, $0 * (k + 1) = (0 * k) + 0 = 0$, so $M_0 = \mathfrak{N}$.
      Now let $M_x = \{y \text{ in } \mathfrak{N} | x * y = y * x\}$. 0 is in M_x from above. Let k be in M_x.
   Then $x * (k + 1) = (x * k) + x = (k * x) + x = (k + 1) * x$, by Problem 4
   above. Hence $M_x = \mathfrak{N}$.

Page 35

1. 19, 58, 1, 1.

Pages 35–36

1. Let $T = \{n \text{ in } \mathfrak{N} | t^n > n\}$. 0 is in T, since $t^0 = 1 > 0$, and 1 is in T since $t^1 = t > 1$. Let $k \geq 1$ be in T; then

$$
\begin{aligned}
t^{k+1} = t^k \cdot t &> kt \\
&\geq 2k = k + k \\
&\geq k + 1.
\end{aligned}
$$

Page 44 *Theorem 3.12*

If there is some x in $\mathfrak{R}$ with $a + x = b$, then

$$
\begin{aligned}
-a + b &= -a + (a + x) \\
&= (-a + a) + x \qquad\qquad \text{[By associativity]} \\
&= 0 + x \\
&= x.
\end{aligned}
$$

Thus the only possible such x is $-a + b$. In fact, $a + (-a + b) = (a + -a) + b = 0 + b = b$.

Page 44 *Theorem 3.14*

The proof can be adapted from that of Theorem 3.12.

Pages 54–55

1. If $x - 3 \geq 0$, then $0 \leq x - 3 = |x - 3| < 0.2$, so $3 \leq x < 3.2$.
   If $x - 3 < 0$, then $0 < |x - 3| = 3 - x < 0.2$, so $-0.2 < x - 3 < 0$, or $2.8 < x < 3$.
   Both inequalities together say $2.8 < x < 3.2$. Conversely, suppose $2.8 < x < 3.2$. Then $-0.2 < x - 3 < 0.2$, and multiplying by -1, we also have $-0.2 < 3 - x < 0.2$, so in any case $|x - 3| < 0.2$.

3. First suppose that x is in one of the defined subintervals; that is, for some k with $1 \leq k \leq n$,

$$
a + (k - 1)\frac{(b - a)}{n} \leq x \leq a + k\frac{(b - a)}{n}.
$$

Since $1 \leq k$,

$$
a \leq a + (k - 1)\frac{(b - a)}{n} \leq x.
$$

Since $k \leq n$,

$$
a + k\frac{(b - a)}{n} \leq a + (b - a) = b.
$$

Hence $a \leq x \leq b$, so x is in $[a, b]$.

Now suppose that x is in $[a, b]$, so $a \leq x \leq b$. By the Archimedian property and the Least Integer Principle, there is some integer $k \geq 1$ such that

$$
(k - 1)\frac{(b - a)}{n} \leq x - a < k\frac{(b - a)}{n}.
$$

If $n < k$, then $n - 1 < k - 1$, so

$$
(n - 1)\frac{(b - a)}{n} < (k - 1)\frac{(b - a)}{n} \leq x - a
$$

or

$$b - a < x - a + \frac{b - a}{n},$$

and thus

$$b < x + \frac{b - a}{n},$$

which contradicts $x \le b$. Hence $1 \le k \le n$.

Page 58

3. $\frac{97}{76}, \frac{60}{47}, \frac{83}{65}, \frac{106}{83}$.

Page 61

1. $49 < 55 < 64$, so if $x^2 = 55$, then

$$7^2 < x^2 < (7 + 1)^2 \qquad \text{or} \qquad 7 < x < 7 + 1.$$

By Theorem 3.47, if x is rational it must be an integer, but there is no integer between 7 and $7 + 1$. Hence 55 has no rational square root.

7. Assume $pq = rst$. Then p divides rst. Either $p = r$, or p and r are relatively prime. If $p = r$, then $q = st$, which is impossible since q is prime. Therefore p and r must be relatively prime, and by Theorem 3.46, p divides st.

By the same reasoning, since p divides st it must divide t. But t is prime, so p must be 1 or t. It cannot be 1, because 1 is not a prime. It cannot be t, because then $q = rs$, which is impossible since q is prime. Therefore the assumption that $pq = rst$ leads to a contradiction.

Pages 63–64

5. By Exercise 3 above, lub $S \le$ lub T.
   By Exercise 4 above, lub $T \le$ lub S.
   Hence lub $S =$ lub T.

7. $\sqrt{2}$ is irrational because $1 < \sqrt{2} < 2$ and there is no integer between 1 and 2. [See Theorem 3.47.] If $(p/q)\sqrt{2} = a/b$ for integers a and b, $p \ne 0$, $q \ne 0$, $b \ne 0$, then $\sqrt{2} = aq/bp$, which contradicts the fact that $\sqrt{2}$ is irrational. Now for $a < b$, consider the interval $(a/\sqrt{2}, b/\sqrt{2})$. By the preceding exercise, there is some rational p/q such that $a/\sqrt{2} < p/q < b/\sqrt{2}$. But then $a < (p/q)\sqrt{2} < b$. Hence $\sqrt{2}\mathbb{Q}$ is dense in $\mathfrak{R}$.

Page 67

5. For $n = 1$ the equality is $3f(1) = 3f(1)$. If for some positive integer n,

$$\sum_{k=1}^{n} 3f(k) = 3 \sum_{k=1}^{n} f(k),$$

then

$$\sum_{k=1}^{n+1} 3f(k) = \sum_{k=1}^{n} 3f(k) + 3f(n + 1) = 3 \sum_{k=1}^{n} f(k) + 3f(n + 1)$$

$$= 3 \left(\sum_{k=1}^{n} f(k) + f(n + 1) \right) = 3 \sum_{k=1}^{n+1} f(k).$$

7. From Exercises 4 and 5, $\sum\limits_{k=1}^{n} 2k = n(n+1)$, and $\sum\limits_{k=1}^{m-1} 2k = (m-1)m$. Thus

$$\sum_{k=m}^{n} 2k = n(n+1) - (m-1)m.$$

Page 69

1. $\sum\limits_{k=0}^{100} \binom{100}{2k} = 2^{99}$.

5. $(1 + -1)^{101} = 0$.

Page 71

1. $Q_1(x) = x^2 - 2x + 5$, and $r_1 = -5$.

3. $Q_2(x) = x^2 - x + 5$, and $r_2 = 0$.

Page 73

$$|(x_3/y_3) - \sqrt{7}| = \frac{1}{765(2024 + 765\sqrt{7})} < \frac{1}{3{,}000{,}000}.$$

Page 74

1. $x_3 = \frac{127}{48}$, and $x_3^2 - 7 = (\frac{1}{48})^2$.

3. Replacing 28 by $27 = 3^3$ leads to

$$x_8^2 - 7 < 3^{-317} < 10^{-105},$$

since $3^3 > 10$.

Pages 74–75

1. Ten-elevenths of the proof is very easy. The other eleventh points out that if a and b are rational numbers not both 0, then $a^2 - 7b^2 \neq 0$, and

$$(a + b\sqrt{7})^{-1} = (a/(a^2 - 7b^2)) - (b\sqrt{7}/(a^2 - 7b^2)).$$

2b. Clearly $\bar{\alpha} = c + d\sqrt{7}$ iff $\alpha = c - d\sqrt{7}$, and the conjugate maps $Q(\sqrt{7})$ one-to-one onto itself. One must now prove that, for all α and β in the field, $\overline{\alpha + \beta} = \bar{\alpha} + \bar{\beta}$ and $\overline{\alpha\beta} = \bar{\alpha}\bar{\beta}$.

3a. Page 73 displays many units.

3d, e. Since $Z(\sqrt{7})$ is closed under addition, Part e follows easily from Part d: If $0 < \alpha < \epsilon$, then the set $\{n\alpha | n \text{ in } Z\}$ is spaced apart on the line by $<\epsilon$. Part d follows from Part c if one finds a unit β with $0 < \beta < 1$.

Page 75

6. The unpleasant but useful conclusion from $x^2 - y^2 = a$ and $x^2 + y^2 = \sqrt{a^2 + b^2}$ is that $2x^2 = a + \sqrt{a^2 + b^2}$ and $2y^2 = -a + \sqrt{a^2 + b^2}$. The resulting x's and y's have to be paired so that $2xy = b$.

Page 78

2. Let S be the nonempty set of reals with lower bound s. Then $-S$, the nonempty set of additive inverses of the elements of S, has an upper bound $-s$ by Ex. 1 above. $-S$ therefore has a lub b and $b \leq -s$. From this $-b$ is a lower bound of S and $-b \geq s$, so $-b$ is the glb of S.

4. Let n be odd. Note that for $z < 0$, $z^n < 0$ since $z^n = z^{2k+1} = (z^k)^2 z < 0$. Now suppose $x < y < 0$, so $0 < -y < -x$ and by Exercise 3, $(-y)^n < (-x)^n$. This is equivalent to $(-1)y^n < (-1)x^n$, hence $x^n < y^n$. Now suppose $x < 0 < y$. Then since $x^n < 0$, clearly $x^n < y^n$.

Let n be even, so that $(-1)^n = (-1)^{2k} = (-1^k)^2 > 0$. Suppose $x < y < 0$. Then $0 < -y < -x$, so $(-y)^n < (-x)^n$, or $(-1)^n y^n < (-1)^n y^n$, hence $y^n < x^n$.

5. Suppose $x < y$. Assume $[y] < [x]$. Since $[y]$ and $[x]$ are integers, $[y] + 1 \leq [x]$. But then $y < [y] + 1 \leq [x] \leq x$, or $y < x$, which is a contradiction. Hence $[x] \leq [y]$.

$2.1 < 2.2$, but $[2.1] = 2 = [2.2]$, hence the function is not strictly monotone.

Page 79

3. $f(x) = \begin{cases} 1, & 0 \leq x < 1, \\ 0, & x = 1. \end{cases}$

$g(x) = \begin{cases} 2, & 0 \leq x < 1, \\ 3, & x = 1. \end{cases}$

$h(x) = \begin{cases} 2, & 0 \leq x < 1, \\ 4, & x = 1. \end{cases}$

Pages 80–81

1. $[f \circ g](x) = x^2$, x in $\mathcal{R}$.
   $[g \circ f](x) = x^2$, $x \geq 0$.
   $[g \circ h](x) = x^2 - 1$, $x \geq 1$.
   $[h \circ g](x) = \sqrt{x^4 - 1}$, $x \geq 1$.
   $[f \circ h](x) = \sqrt{x^2 - 1}$, $x \geq 1$.
3. $[F \circ F](x) = x$, $x \neq 0$.

Pages 83–84

3b. Since $(g_2 + g_3)(1) = 2 > 1$, $g_2 + g_3$ is not in S. The supposition that S is not closed under multiplication is absurd. If f and g are in S and x in $[0, 1]$, then $(fg)(x) = f(x)g(x)$ in $[0, 1]$, and S is closed under multiplication.

Page 85

1. Why the 16? Well, it's convenient to have D_n positive so that $|D_n| = D_n$.

Pages 87–88

1.

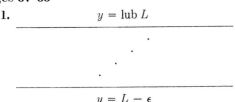

$$y = \mathrm{lub}\ L$$

$$y = L - \epsilon$$

Dots eventually get above $L - \epsilon$ and can't go back down.

2. Those in Parts a, b, c, e, and f.

5. Note that $\left|\dfrac{3n^2 + 5}{n^2} - 3\right| = \dfrac{5}{n^2}$ for all n in Z^+.

6. Prove that Theorem 4.4 applies.

Pages 93–94

1a. 5.

1b. It does not converge: see the lemma at the bottom of page 89.

1f. 0.

2. Modify the proof of Theorem 4.4, principally by replacing "$n > N_\epsilon$" by "$n > \max\ \{10^{10},\ N_\epsilon\}$." Intuitively, note that the first 10^{10} terms of a sequence are not relevant to convergence questions.

Pages 96–97

3. This is difficult. Clearly $1 - \frac{1}{2} + \frac{1}{3}$ differs from the limit by less than $\frac{1}{4}$. Similarly, the sum of the first 99 terms is off by less than 0.01, but in computing this sum as a decimal it would be hard to hold the total rounding-off error to 0.01. See page 374, Ex. 7.

4. $10! > 3,000,000$.

Page 108

1c. radius 1; center $(0, 0)$.

1d. radius $\sqrt{101}/2$; center $(-1, 5)$.

1e. radius $\sqrt{11}/2$; center $(-\frac{1}{2}, \frac{3}{2}, -1)$.

5. Since

$$d_3(F(t) - F(s)) = |t - s|\sqrt{a_1{}^2 + a_2{}^2 + a_3{}^2},$$

the scale factor is 1 iff $\sqrt{a_1{}^2 + a_2{}^2 + a_3{}^2} = 1$ and $\mathbf{a}$ is on the unit sphere.

Pages 111–112

4. An equation of the image of C is

$$(x - 1)^2 + 2(y - 3)^2 + 3(z + 2)^2 = 6.$$

7a. A circle of radius 5, center at $(2, 3)$.

7c. All of $\Re^2$ except the closed disc of radius 1 around $(-1, 1)$.

Pages 115–116

3. $|S(t) - S(u)| = |\mathbf{a} + t(\mathbf{b} - \mathbf{a}) - [\mathbf{a} + u(\mathbf{b} - \mathbf{a})]| = |t(\mathbf{b} - \mathbf{a}) - u(\mathbf{b} - \mathbf{a})|$
$= |(t - u)(\mathbf{b} - \mathbf{a})| = |t - u|\ |\mathbf{b} - \mathbf{a}|.$

4. $S(t) = \mathbf{a} + \dfrac{t}{|\mathbf{b} - \mathbf{a}|}(\mathbf{b} - \mathbf{a})$.

6. The system $(U; \circ)$ is isomorphic to $(\Re^+; \cdot)$.

Pages 119–120

1. The symbols displayed in parts **a, c, g, i, j** are undefined. Those in parts **b, d, e, k** give real numbers, and the rest points.

Pages 132–133

  2. Let $T_\mathbf{c}$ be the translation mapping $\mathbf{a}$ to $r\mathbf{a}$. Then $T_\mathbf{c}\mathbf{a} = \mathbf{a} + \mathbf{c} = r\mathbf{a}$ or $\mathbf{c} = r\mathbf{a} - \mathbf{a}$.

    Now let $\mathbf{x}$ be a point of $\mathbf{ab}$. Then $\mathbf{x} = \mathbf{a} + t(\mathbf{b} - \mathbf{a})$ for some real t. Now,

$$T_\mathbf{c}(\mathbf{x}) = \mathbf{a} + t(\mathbf{b} - \mathbf{a}) + r\mathbf{a} - \mathbf{a} = r\mathbf{a} + t(\mathbf{b} - \mathbf{a}).$$

    But $t = rs$ for some real s, so

$$\begin{aligned}T_\mathbf{c}(\mathbf{x}) &= r\mathbf{a} + sr(\mathbf{b} - \mathbf{a}) \\ &= r\mathbf{a} + s(r\mathbf{b} - r\mathbf{a}).\end{aligned}$$

    Hence $T_\mathbf{c}(\mathbf{x})$ is on $(r\mathbf{a})(r\mathbf{b})$.

  7. Adding $(2, -3)$ to each vertex gives $(0, 0)$, $(1, 1)$, $(2, 4)$, $(1, 3)$, which are vertices of a parallelogram because $(1, 1) + (1, 3) = (2, 4)$. The area is 2.

 12. Since det $(\mathbf{a}, \times\mathbf{a}) = a_1{}^2 + a_2{}^2 > 0$, the angle is counterclockwise by Definition 5.18.

 13. If $a_1 = 0$ the equation implies that $b_2 = 0$ and $\mathbf{b} = -\dfrac{b_1}{a_2}(-a_2, 0)$. If $a_1 \neq 0$

    then $b_1 = -a_2 b_2 / a_1$ and $\mathbf{b} = \dfrac{b_2}{a_1}(-a_2, a_1)$.

 17. Since $\langle \mathbf{a}, \mathbf{p} \rangle = 0$, we have $p_1 + p_2 + p_3 = 0$. Since $\langle \mathbf{b}, \mathbf{p} \rangle = 0$, we have also $2p_1 - p_2 + 3p_3 = 0$. It follows that $p_1 = -\frac{4}{3}p_3$ and $p_2 = \frac{1}{3}p_3$. Let $p_3 = c$. Then $p = (-\frac{4}{3}c, \frac{1}{3}c, c) = -\frac{1}{3}c(\mathbf{a} \times \mathbf{b})$.

 19. Suppose $\mathbf{a}'$ and $\mathbf{b}'$ are in the range of F. Then for some $\mathbf{a}$ and $\mathbf{b}$, $\mathbf{a}' = F(\mathbf{a})$ and $\mathbf{b}' = F(\mathbf{b})$. But then

$$\mathbf{a}' + \mathbf{b}' = F(\mathbf{a}) + F(\mathbf{b}) = F(\mathbf{a} + \mathbf{b}),$$

    and $\mathbf{a}' + \mathbf{b}'$ is in the range of F. Also, for any scalar c,

$$c\mathbf{a}' = cF(\mathbf{a})\ F(c\mathbf{a}),$$

    so the range is also closed under scalar multiplication.

 24. See Exercise 17: K_F is the line through $(0, 0, 0)$ and $(-4, 1, 3)$.

Page 137

  2. The point (x, y, z) is a solution iff for some real t, $(x, y, z) = (-1, 0, 1) + t(-4, 1, 3)$. The set of solutions is the line through $(-1, 0, 1)$ and $(-5, 1, 4)$.

  3. There are no solutions.

  7. If $d - bc = 0$ there are no solutions unless $k_2 = ck_1$, in which case $(k_1 - by, y)$ is a solution for each real y.

Pages 142–143

  3. The line is

$$\begin{aligned}\{t(5, 2) &+ (1 - t)(5, 8)|t \text{ real}\} \\ &= \{(5, 8 - 6t)|t \text{ real}\} = \{(x, y)|x = 1\}.\end{aligned}$$

Pages 144–145

  3. The point $\mathbf{a}$ must be (a, a) or $(a, -a)$ for some $a \neq 0$.

Page 146

  2. $x' = \dfrac{3x + y + 7z}{\sqrt{59}}$,

$$y' = \frac{2x + y - z}{\sqrt{6}},$$

$$z' = \frac{-8x + 17y + z}{\sqrt{354}}.$$

Page 154

1. $AB = \begin{pmatrix} -17 & 4 \\ -13 & 3 \end{pmatrix}.$ $CA = \begin{pmatrix} -1 + 5k & -k \\ 5 & -1 \end{pmatrix}.$

3. See answer to next exercise for method.

4. The matrix I corresponds to $\mathbf{I}$, the identity map on $\mathfrak{R}^2$. For $\mathbf{A}$ any linear transformation in $\mathfrak{R}^2$ we have $\mathbf{I} \circ \mathbf{A} = \mathbf{A} \circ \mathbf{I} = \mathbf{A}$. If A is the matrix corresponding to $\mathbf{A}$ then, from Definition 6.2, $IA = AI = A$.

Page 158

5. $\begin{pmatrix} 1 & 2 \\ 2 & 4 \end{pmatrix} \begin{pmatrix} x \\ y \end{pmatrix} = \begin{pmatrix} 0 \\ 0 \end{pmatrix}$ iff $x + 2y = 0$. The kernel of $\mathbf{A}$ is the line through $(0, 0)$ and $(-2, 1)$.

6. $\begin{pmatrix} x \\ y \end{pmatrix}$ is a solution iff $(x, y) = (1, 1) + \mathbf{k}$, where $\mathbf{k}$ is in the kernel of $\mathbf{A}$.

Pages 162–163

4. If the rotation is through x degrees, then there will be integers n and m such that $nx = 360 \, m$ iff x is rational.

9. $(\mathfrak{R}^2; +)$ to itself.

Pages 165–166

7a. Using the formula for roots of a quadratic equation, note that $b^2 - 4ac < 0$.

7b. For any real a, ϵ can be $\begin{pmatrix} a & a^2 - 4a + 5 \\ -1 & 4 - a \end{pmatrix}.$

7c. $\epsilon = 2 \pm i$.

Pages 171–174

13. If $\epsilon = W(2m\pi/n)$ for integers m and n, then $\epsilon^n = 1^*$, and ϵ generates a finite subgroup as in Exercises 11 and 12 above.

19. For the graph, see page 235.

20. If $\tan s \tan t = 1$, then $\sin s \sin t = \cos s \cos t$ and, from the addition theorems, $\cos (s + t) = 0$.

Page 181

4. Given $\epsilon > 0$, the hypotheses imply there is some N such that, for $n > N$, $0 < |t_n| < \min \{\epsilon, \pi/2\}$. For such n, Theorem 6.14 gives $\left| \frac{\sin t_n}{t_n} - 1 \right| < t_n^2/2 < |t_n| < \epsilon$.

Pages 185–186

4. The eigenvalue is 1 and the eigenvectors are $(x, 0)$ for $x \neq 0$.

6. A reflection in the line $x = -2y$ composed with a dilation by 5.

11. The basic formula is $T_{(5,7)} \circ \mathbf{R}_{\pi/6} \circ T_{(-5,-7)}$.

16. If $a^2 + b^2 = 1$, there is a line of fixed points if (h, k) is a scalar multiple of $(a - 1, b)$, but no fixed point otherwise. If $a^2 + b^2 \neq 1$, there is a unique fixed point.

Page 194

32a. A spiral on the surface of a cylinder of radius 1.

32c. The plane through $(0, 0, 0)$, $(1, 1, 2)$, and $(1, -1, 1)$.

32e. The sphere of radius 3 around $(0, 0, 0)$.

Page 218

4. Suppose $0 < c < x < d$. The segment from $(c, 1/c)$ to $(d, 1/d)$ has the equation $y = (1/c) - (x - c/dc)$. Now

$$\left[\frac{1}{c} - \frac{x - c}{dc}\right] - \frac{1}{x} = \frac{x - c}{cx} - \frac{x - c}{cd}.$$

But $cdx > 0$, so multiplying this last expression by cdx, we get $d(x - c) - x(x - c)$. That this is positive follows from $c < x < d$.

Pages 222–223

4. The mapping $g{:}x \longrightarrow 1/x$ is uniformly continuous on $[a, \infty)$ and therefore uniformly continuous on the range of f, which is a subset of this interval. By Theorem 7.6 the mapping $g \circ f{:}x \longrightarrow 1/f(x)$ is uniformly continuous on I.

Page 229

2. If $f(x) = x^3 - \sin x$, then $f(0) = 0$. Also, $f(\frac{1}{2}) = \frac{1}{8} - \sin(\frac{1}{2}) < 0$, but $f(1) = 1 - \sin 1 > 0$. For at least one x_1 between $\frac{1}{2}$ and 1, $f(x_1) = 0$ and $f(-x_1) = 0$.

Page 236

1. One distinction is that $\cot(\pi/2) = 0$, but $\pi/2$ is not in the domain of $1/\tan$ because it is not in the domain of $\tan$.

8. If x_1 is the smallest positive number with $\tan x_1 = \pi/2$, then x_1 is roughly 1 and over the interval $(-x_1, x_1)$ the graph of $\tan \circ \tan$ resembles that of $\tan$ over $(-\pi/2, \pi/2)$. Tan $(1.37) > 4.9 > 3\pi/2$. With x_2 almost 1.37, and $\tan x_2 = 3\pi/2$, over the interval (x_1, x_2) the graph is another unbounded curve. Then $\tan x_3 = 5\pi/2$, where $1.44 < x_3 < 1.45$, giving another unbounded curve. The graph of $\tan \circ \tan$ over the interval $[0, \pi/2)$ consists of infinitely many unbounded monotone curves.

Page 276

1b. 39.   **1c.** 1.   **1d.** 18.

1j. $5\sqrt{5} + 5\sqrt{6} + 5\sqrt{7} + 5\sqrt{8} + 5\sqrt{9}$.   **1l.** 1.   **1m.** 0.

2a. Let $p = \{1, \frac{3}{2}, 2\}$. Then

$$\int_1^2 (2x + 5)^{10} \, dx \geq S(p, f) = \frac{7^{10} + 8^{10}}{2} > \frac{7^{10} + 7^{10}}{2} = 7^{10}.$$

2b. Let $p = \{1, \frac{3}{2}, 2\}$.

2c. $\overline{S}(p, f) = \dfrac{(\frac{15}{2})^{10} + 8^{10} + (\frac{17}{2})^{10} + 9^{10}}{4}$.

2d. $\overline{S}(p, f) = \dfrac{(\frac{15}{2})^{10} + 8^{10} + (\frac{17}{2})^{10} + 9^{10}}{2}$.

Page 278
1a. $\frac{4}{3}$.　　　**1b.** $\frac{1}{6}$.　　　**1c.** 1.　　　**1d.** $\frac{8}{3}$.　　　**1e.** $\frac{1}{2}$.

Pages 279–280
1c. (i) $\pi/5$.　　　(ii) $\pi/3$.　　　(iii) $\frac{2}{15}\pi$.　　　(iv) $\frac{2}{3}\pi$.

Pages 285–286
1a. 0.　　　**1b.** $2/\pi$.　　　**1c.** $\dfrac{b^3 - a^3}{3(b - a)} = \dfrac{b^2 + ba + a^2}{3}$.

1d. 0.　　　**1e.** $\frac{1}{4}$.

Page 295
1. $\displaystyle\int_2^3 (3x - 6)^{10}\, dx = \frac{1}{3}\int_0^3 t^{10}\, dt = \frac{1}{3}\cdot\frac{3^{11}}{11} = \frac{3^{10}}{11}$.

3. $\displaystyle\int_0^1 \frac{1}{x^2 + 6x + 9}\, dx = \int_3^4 \frac{1}{t^2}\, dt = \frac{1}{12}$.

5. 0.　　　**7.** $\pi/2$.　　　**9.** $\pi/8 - \frac{1}{4}$.

Page 301
2. Answers should be consistent with the following, each correct to four significant figures:

$\ln 11 = 2.398$　　　$\ln 13 = 2.565$　　　$\ln 17 = 2.833$　　　$\ln 19 = 2.944$.

Pages 312–313
1a. $f'(x) = 9x^2 - 18x$, for all real x.
1b. $g'(x) = 1/x$, for $x > 0$.
1c. $h'(x) = 375x^2$, for all real x.
1d. $j'(x) = 1 + (1/x)$, for $x > 0$.
1e. $k'(x) = 18x + \frac{3}{2}\sqrt{x}$, for $x > 0$.
3. For $c \neq 0$ and $0 < |x - c| < |c|/2$,

$$\left|\frac{(1/x) - (1/c)}{x - c} - \left(-\frac{1}{c^2}\right)\right| = \left|-\frac{1}{cx} + \frac{1}{c^2}\right| = \frac{|x - c|}{c^2|x|} < \frac{2}{|c|^3}|x - c|.$$

Given $\epsilon > 0$, if $\delta = \min\{|c|/2,\ \epsilon|c|\frac{3}{2}\}$ and $0 < |x - c| < \delta$, then

$$\left|\frac{R(x) - R(c)}{x - c} - \frac{-1}{c^2}\right| < \epsilon.$$

Page 321
4. This is essentially Exercise 3 with $(3, 2, 1, \frac{1}{2})$ replaced by $(c, f'(c), \epsilon, \delta)$.

Page 325
4. $f'(x) = 2\sin\left(\dfrac{1}{3x - 5}\right)\cos\left(\dfrac{1}{3x - 5}\right)\left(\dfrac{-3}{(3x - 5)^2}\right)$

$$= \frac{-6}{(3x-5)^2} \sin\left(\frac{1}{3x-5}\right) \cos\left(\frac{1}{3x-5}\right).$$

Pages 330–331

1a. $\sec' = \left(\dfrac{1}{\cos}\right)' = -\dfrac{1}{\cos^2}(-\sin) = \dfrac{1}{\cos}\left(\dfrac{\sin}{\cos}\right) = \sec\tan.$

1c. $\tan' = \left[(\sin)\left(\dfrac{1}{\cos}\right)\right]' = \sin\left(\dfrac{\sin}{\cos}\right) + \cos\left(\dfrac{1}{\cos}\right) = \tan^2 + 1 = \sec^2.$

2. $\mathrm{Tan}'(x) = \sec^2(x) > 0$, so Tan is increasing.

$$\mathrm{Arc\ tan}'(x) = \frac{1}{\tan(\mathrm{Arc\ tan}(x))} = \frac{1}{\sec^2(\mathrm{Arc\ tan}(x))}$$

$$= \frac{1}{\tan^2(\mathrm{Arc\ tan}(x)) + 1} = \frac{1}{1 + x^2}.$$

11. $F(x) = x^2 e^x - 2xe^x + 2e^x.$

12a. $\dfrac{10x + 7}{1 + (5x^2 + 7x - 3)^2}.$

12c. $\dfrac{2x - 2}{(x + 3)(x - 5)}.$

12d. $\sec x.$

12e. $e^{x^2 \sin(5x+7)}[5x^2 \cos(5x + 7) + 2x \sin(5x + 7)].$

12h. $2xe^{x^2-5} \sin^3(x + \ln x) + e^{x^2-5}\,3\sin^2(x + \ln x)\cos(x + \ln x)(1 + (1/x)).$

12 j. $17\sin^{16} x \cos x \cos^5 e^x - 5(\sin^{17} x)(\cos^4 e^x)(\sin e^x)e^x.$

12p. $0.$

12r. $e^x e^{e^x}.$

12v. $-\tan x.$

Pages 339–341

1. Horizontal tangent at $(0, 0)$, vertical tangents at $(\pm 2\sqrt{3}/9, \tfrac{1}{3})$. The tangents at the double point $(0, 1)$ have slopes 1 and -1.

6. Suppose F is continuous at c, and let $\epsilon > 0$. There is δ such that $|t - c| < \delta \Rightarrow 0 < |F(t) - F(c)| < \epsilon$. But

$$|F(t) - F(c)| = \sqrt{[X(t) - X(c)]^2 + [Y(t) - Y(c)]^2 + [Z(t) - Z(c)]^2},$$

so we have

$$0 < [X(t) - X(c)]^2 + [Y(t) - Y(c)]^2 + [Z(t) - Z(c)]^2 < \epsilon^2.$$

Thus

$$[X(t) - X(c)]^2 < \epsilon^2$$

or

$$|X(t) - X(c)| < \epsilon.$$

Similarly for Y and Z. Hence X, Y, and Z are continuous at c. The converse is straightforward.

Page 344

2a. $dx/d\theta = -5\sin\theta$; $dy/d\theta = 5\cos\theta$; $dy/dx = -\cot\theta$. The graph is a circle.

2b. $dx/d\theta = -\theta \sin \theta + \cos \theta$; $dy/d\theta = \theta \cos \theta + \sin \theta$;

$$\frac{dy}{dx} = \frac{\theta \cos \theta + \sin \theta}{-\theta \sin \theta + \cos \theta}.$$

2d. This is the general polar equation of a conic. Try various e and k.

2e. $dx/d\theta = -\sin 2\theta \sin \theta + 2 \cos 2\theta \cos \theta$; $dy/d\theta = \sin 2\theta \cos \theta + 2 \cos 2\theta \sin \theta$;

$$\frac{dy}{dx} = \frac{\sin 2\theta \cos \theta + 2 \cos 2\theta \sin \theta}{-\sin 2\theta \sin \theta + 2 \cos 2\theta \cos \theta}.$$

2f. $dx/d\theta = 0$; $dy/d\theta = 3 \sec^2 \theta$. dy/dx does not exist. The line $x = 3$.

Page 348

1. $c = 2$.

5. $\sqrt[3]{1002} - \sqrt[3]{1000} = \dfrac{2}{3\sqrt[3]{c^2}}$ for some c between 1000 and 1002. Then

$$10 < \sqrt[3]{1002} = \frac{2}{3\sqrt[3]{c^2}} + 10 < \frac{2}{300} + 10 = 10.006.$$

Pages 351–352

1c. $e - 1$.

1d. $\ln \left(\frac{7}{2}\right)$.

1f. $\ln 2$.

2. The last statement is obvious because, for $0 < x < 1$, $x^2 < x$, and the integrand is positive on the interval $[x^2, x]$.

Page 354

3. The most general answer is pretty boring. For each f in T, $f - f$ must be in S. For f and g in T, if $f - g$ is in S, so must $g - f$ be. Similarly one must assure transitivity. The pleasantest situation is to have T be a group under addition and S a proper subgroup. For example, T could be the set of all real functions continuous on $[0, 1]$ and S the set of all polynomials over $[0, 1]$.

Pages 358–360

2. From $f' = 2BF'$ we have $f - 2BF$ is constant. From $f(0) = 0$ and $F(0) = \frac{1}{2}$, $f = 2BF + \frac{1}{2}$.

3a. $y = ce^{-6x}$.

3c. $y = ce^{-6x} + \left(\frac{6}{37}\right) \sin x + \left(-\frac{1}{37}\right) \cos x$.

3d. Guessing y_p to be of the form $ax + b$ gives $y_p = x/6 - \frac{1}{36}$. The kernel is still ce^{-6x}.

3f. Notice parts d, c, and b.

Pages 362–363

1a. $y = c_1 e^x + c_2 e^{-3x}$.

1c. One solution is $e^{2x}/5$.

2. For the kernel see Theorem 11.7; the answer is easily checked. Particular solutions can be found by trial and error as in 1.

Pages 368–369

2. Letting $x + 1 = t^2$ leads to $\int_1^{\sqrt{2}} (t^5 - 2t^3 + 6t)2t \, dt$.

Letting $x + 1 = u$ leads to $\int_1^2 (u^{5/2} - 2u^{3/2} + 6u^{1/2}) \, du$.

6. $\frac{4}{3}$.

9. The segment from $(x_{k-1}, f(x_{k-1}))$ to $(x_k, f(x_k))$ has length

$$[(f(x_k) - f(x_{k-1}))^2 + (x_k - x_{k-1})^2]^{1/2}.$$

M.V.T. produces some t_k between x_{k-1} and x_k with $f(x_k) - f(x_{k-1}) = (x_k - x_{k-1})f'(t_k)$. Thus the length of the broken line is

$$\sum_{k=1}^{n} \sqrt{1 + [f'(t_k)]^2}(x_k - x_{k-1}),$$

which is between the lower and upper sums for the partition and $\int_a^b \sqrt{1 + (f')^2}$.

Continuity of f' guarantees the existence of the integral. Given $\epsilon > 0$, usual rituals produce a partition p such that the length of the broken line is almost the arc length, and a partition q with lower and upper sums close to the integral. The common refinement finishes up.

Pages 373–374

4. $2x - \dfrac{(2x)^3}{3} + \dfrac{(2x)^5}{120}$.

8. For $|x| < 1$,

$$\text{Arc tan } x = \sum_{k=0}^{\infty} (-1)^k x^{2k+1}/(2k + 1).$$

11. From $f(x) = \frac{1}{9} + (x - \frac{4}{3})(\frac{13}{3} + 4(x - \frac{4}{3}) + (x - \frac{4}{3})^2)$ it is clear that $f(\frac{4}{3}) = \frac{1}{9}$. A first approximation is $\frac{4}{3}$. One gets a better approximation x_2 by solving the equation $0 = \frac{1}{9} + (x_2 - \frac{4}{3})(\frac{13}{3})$ for $x_2 = \frac{51}{39}$. For an efficient continuation see p. 379, Ex. 4.

Page 380

4b. It is clear that if f'' is positive (or negative) on an open interval around c, then f' is increasing (or decreasing) on the interval, which should guarantee convergence. For a full discussion see Thomas E. Mott, "Newton's method and multiple roots." *Am. Math. Monthly* **64**:635–638 (1957).

Index